HYDRODYNAMICS OF SEMI-ENCLOSED SEAS

FURTHER TITLES IN THIS SERIES

Elsevier Oceanography Series, 34

HYDRODYNAMICS OF SEMI-ENCLOSED SEAS

PROCEEDINGS OF THE 13th INTERNATIONAL LIEGE COLLOQUIUM
ON OCEAN HYDRODYNAMICS

Edited by

JACQUES C.J. NIHOUL

*Professor of Ocean Hydrodynamics,
University of Liège
Liège, Belgium*

ELSEVIER SCIENTIFIC PUBLISHING COMPANY

Amsterdam — Oxford — New York   1982

ELSEVIER SCIENTIFIC PUBLISHING COMPANY
1, Molenwerf,
P.O. Box 211, 1000 AE Amsterdam, The Netherlands

Distribution for the United States and Canada:

ELSEVIER SCIENCE PUBLISHING COMPANY INC.
52, Vanderbilt Avenue
New York, N.Y. 10017

Library of Congress Cataloging in Publication Data

International Liège Colloquium on Ocean Hydrodynamics
   (13th : 1981)
   Hydrodynamics of semi-enclosed seas.

   (Elsevier oceanography series ; 34)
   Includes index.
   1. Oceanography--Congresses. 2. Hydrodynamics--
Congresses. I. Nihoul, Jacques C. J. II. Title.
III. Series.
GC200.I57 1981   551.47   82-2455
ISBN 0-444-42077-0 (U.S.)   AACR2

ISBN 0-444-42077-0 (Vol. 34)
ISBN 0-444-41623-4 (Series)

Printed in The Netherlands

FOREWORD

The International Liège Colloquia on Ocean Hydrodynamics are organized annually. Their topics differ from one year to another and try to address, as much as possible, recent problems and incentive new subjects in physical oceanography.

Assembling a group of active and eminent scientists from different countries and often different disciplines, they provide a forum for discussion and foster a mutually beneficial exchange of information opening on to a survey of major recent discoveries, essential mechanisms, impelling question-marks and valuable recommendations for future research.

Following a suggestion from the steering committee of the Medalpex Project (IOC), the thirteenth colloquium was devoted to the Hydrodynamics of Semi-enclosed Seas, with emphasis on the Mediterranean and the Baltic.

Essentially bounded by lands, semi-enclosed seas are threatened by increasing pollution resulting from man's activities. They constitute, on the other hand, quasi closed moderate scale systems for which general interdisciplinary models, integrating all aspects from hydrodynamics to chemistry and ecology, can be developed, calibrated and applied to the definition of control and management policies.

But, there is perhaps a more cogent reason for devoting a special research effort to the hydrodynamics of semi-enclosed seas : in many aspects they are reduced-scale models of the world oceans.

Gyres, synoptic eddies, meanders and fronts are often found in semi-enclosed seas at relatively much smaller scales, easier to observe and to represent in mathematical models.

The papers presented at the Thirteenth International Liège Colloquium on Ocean Hydrodynamics, not only constitute a necessary state of the art review preparing the Medalpex experiment, they also contribute to a better understanding of Ocean Hydrodynamics.

Jacques C.J. NIHOUL.

The Scientific Organizing Committee of the Thirteenth International Liège Colloquium on Ocean Hydrodynamics and all the participants wish to express their gratitude to the Belgian Minister of Education, the National Science Foundation of Belgium, the University of Liège, the Intergovernmental Oceanographic Commission and the Division of Marine Sciences (UNESCO) and the Office of Naval Research for their most valuable support.

LIST OF PARTICIPANTS

AITSAM, A., Prof., Dr., Department of the Baltic Sea, Academy of Sciences Estonian SSR, Tallinn, USSR.

ALENIUS, P., Mr., Institute of Marine Research, Helsinki, Finland.

AMBROSIUS, V., Dr., Department of the Baltic Sea, Academy of Sciences Estonian SSR, Tallinn, USSR.

BADAN-DANGON, A., Dr., CICESE, Ensenada, B.C. Mexico.

BAH, A., Dr., Ecole Polytechnique de Conakry, Guinea.

BERGAMASCO, A., Dr., C.N.R., Venice, Italy.

BETHOUX, J.P., Dr., Laboratoire de Physique et Chimie Marines, Villefranche s/mer, France.

BOUKARI, S., Mr., University of Niamey, Niger.

BOWMAN, M.J., Prof., Dr., State University of New York at Stony Brook, U.S.A.

CANDELA, J., Mr., CICESE, Ensenada, B.C., Mexico.

CLEMENT, F., Mr., Université de Liège, Belgium.

CREPON, M., Dr., Museum d'Histoire Naturelle, Laboratoire d'Océanographie Physique, Paris, France.

DISTECHE, A., Prof., Dr., Université de Liège, Belgium.

DJENIDI, S., Ir., 2, Rue BP, Cité Plaisance, Annaba, Algérie.

ELKEN, J., Mr., Department of the Baltic Sea, Academy of Sciences Estonian SSR, Tallinn, USSR.

FRACHON, B., Mr., Museum d'Histoire Naturelle, Laboratoire d'Océanographie Physique, Paris, France.

FRASSETTO, R., Dr., C.N.R., Venice, Italy.

GASCARD, J.C., Dr., Museum d'Histoire Naturelle, Laboratoire d'Océanographie Physique, Paris, France.

HAPPEL, J.J., Ir., Université de Liège, Belgium.

HECQ, J.H., Dr., Université de Liège, Belgium.

HEBURN, G.W., Dr., Science Applications Inc., Slidell, La., U.S.A.

HOWARTH, M.J., Mr., I.O.S., Bidston Observatory, Birkenhead, U.K.

HUA, B.L., Dr., Museum d'Histoire Naturelle, Laboratoire d'Océanographie Physique, Paris, France.

HURLBURT, H.E., Dr., NORDA, NSTL Station, Ms., U.S.A.

JACOBSEN, T., Dr., Marine Pollution Laboratory, Charlottenlund, Denmark.

JAMART, B.M., Dr., University of California, Santa Barbara, U.S.A.

KAHRU, M., Mr., Department of the Baltic Sea, Academy of Sciences Estonian SSR, Tallinn, USSR.

KAUP, E., Dr., Department of the Baltic Sea, Academy of Sciences Estonian SSR, Tallinn, USSR.

KRAAV, V., Dr., Department of the Baltic Sea, Academy of Sciences Estonian SSR, Tallinn, USSR.

KULLAS, T., Dr., Department of the Baltic Sea, Academy of Sciences Estonian SSR, Tallinn, USSR.

KULLENBERG, G., Prof., University of Copenhagen, Denmark.

KVASNOVSKY, G., Mr., SACLANT ASW Research Centre, La Spezia, Italy.

LACOME, H., Prof., Museum d'Histoire Naturelle, Laboratoire d'Océanographie Physique, Paris, France.

LEBON, G., Prof., Université de Liège, Belgium.

LEKIEN, B., Ir., Université de Liège, Belgium.

LILOVER, M.J., Department of the Baltic Sea, Academy of Sciences Estonian SSR, Tallinn, USSR.

LOFFET, A., Ir., Université de Liège, Belgium.

LOKK, J., Mr., Department of the Baltic Sea, Academy of Sciences Estonian SSR, Tallinn, USSR.

MANZELLA, G., Dr., C.N.R., Lerici, La Spezia, Italy.

MILLOT, C., Dr., Museum d'Histoire Naturelle, Laboratoire d'Océanographie Physique, Paris, France.

MOEN, J., Dr., SACLANT ASW Research Centre, La Spezia, Italy.

MOLINES, J.M., Mr., Institut de Mécanique de Grenoble, France.

MYUURISEPP, S., Mrs., Department of the Baltic Sea, Academy of Sciences Estonian SSR, Tallinn, USSR.

NADAILLAC De, G., Mr., Museum d'Histoire Naturelle, Laboratoire d'Océanographie Physique, Paris, France.

NGENDAKUMANA, P., Ir., B.P. 936, Bujumbura, Burundi.

NIEHAUS, M.C.W., Dr., University of Liverpool, Department of Oceanography, U.K.

NIHOUL, J.C.J., Prof., Dr., Université de Liège, Belgium.

PEDERSEN, F.B., Prof., Dr., Technical University of Denmark, Institute of Hydrodynamics, Lyngby, Denmark.

PHILIPPE, M., Dr., Centre de Météorologie Spatiale, Lannion, France.

PODER, T., Dr., Department of the Baltic Sea, Academy of Sciences Estonian SSR, Tallinn, USSR.

PORTSMUTH, P., Mr., Department of the Baltic Sea, Academy of Sciences Estonian SSR, Tallinn, USSR.

PRELLER, R., Miss, JAYCOR, NORDA, NSTL Station, Ms., U.S.A.

RENOUARD, D., Dr., Institut de Mécanique de Grenoble, France.

RICHEZ, C., Mrs, Museum d'Histoire Naturelle, Laboratoire d'Océanographie Physique, Paris, France.

RONDAY, F.C., Dr., Université de Liège, Belgium.

RUNFOLA, Y., Mr., Université de Liège, Belgium.

SAINT GUILY B., Prof., Museum d'Histoire Naturelle, Laboratoire d'Océanographie Physique, Paris, France.

SCHAUER, U., Miss, Institut für Meereskunde, Universität Kiel, W. Germany.

SMITZ, J., Ir., Université de Liège, Belgium.

TANG, C., Dr., Bedford Institute of Oceanography, Dartmouth, N.S., Canada.

THOMASSET, F., Ir., INRIA, Le Chesnay, France.

TOOMPUU, A., Mr., Department of the Baltic Sea, Academy of Sciences Estonian SSR, Tallinn, USSR.

VAULOT, D., Mr., Université de Montpellier, France.

WACONGNE, S., Miss, Museum d'Histoire Naturelle, Laboratoire d'Océanographie Physique, Paris, France.

CONTENTS

XIV

OCEANOGRAPHY OF SEMI-ENCLOSED SEAS

Medalpex : an international field experiment in the Western Mediterranean

by

Jacques C.J. NIHOUL *

Mécanique des Fluides Géophysiques - Université de Liège

INTRODUCTION

There is no clear-cut definition of a semi-enclosed sea. A continental sea which, like the Baltic and the Mediterranean, is essentially bounded by land is called an "enclosed sea" or a "semi-enclosed sea". The characteristic of semi-enclosed seas is the limited communication with adjacent seas or oceans, contrary to "semi-open seas" like the North Sea or the China Sea or "open seas" with a long indefinite boundary with the ocean like the Sea of Andaman.

At the Nato Conference on Modelling of Marine Systems (OFIR, Portugal, June 1973) a special working group was set up on enclosed seas. It is illuminating to recall the main conclusions of this working group (Nihoul, 1975)

"Enclosed seas lend themselves particularly well to the study of the whole unit as an ecosystem, for the following reasons :

(1) Boundary conditions are usually relatively well defined.

(2) Nutrient, salt and water budgets can often be framed with more precision than elsewhere.

(3) Small basins lend themselves to whole-system field experiments.

Moreover, from the practical viewpoint, enclosed seas often serve as waste sinks and give rise to serious management problems, such as conflict of interest between waste disposal and recreation or aquaculture.

A fundamental component of a good model of an aquatic ecosystem is the hydrodynamic structure. We recommend that support be given to continued development and refinement of fundamental hydrodynamics.

Outputs of the hydrodynamic models will be specification of flow patterns under varying conditions of forcing particularly by forces of meteorological origin. These flow fields will include circulation patterns, upwelling phenomena, long surface and internal waves, and the formation, movement and dissipation of ice. These outputs provide the basis for enhanced understanding of the physics of the

* Also at the "Institut d'Astronomie et de Géophysique" Université de Louvain.

system, and serve as the essential framework for an integrated model of an ecosystem

Progress in modelling must proceed hand-in-hand with experiments and field verification, through collection of relevant physical, chemical and biological data
observed as nearly simultaneously as possible. For many such field operations, large
coordinated programmes will be required. The design of such programmes should depend
on the results of preliminary modelling and the results of the programmes should
be used to modify and improve the models.

Planning and implementation of a collaborative programme should include the following stages :

(1) A review of existing data and an initial attempt at modelling, leading to

(2) Optimization of field programmes with respect to improved data coverage,
coordinated collections, standardized and automated methods.

(3) Experiments in laboratory and field to elucidate mechanisms not sufficiently understood.

(4) As a consequence and parallel development, successive improvements in modelling.

Equipment needed for such a programme should include ships and aircrafts, instruments for automated data collection (e.g. moored buoys) and access to the largest
available computers."

Two of the main reasons to devote a special research effort to the study of
semi-enclosed seas are stressed in the recommendations. Essentially bounded by
lands, semi-enclosed seas are threatened by increasing pollution resulting from
man's activities. They constitute, on the other hand, quasi-closed moderate scale
systems for which general interdisciplinary models, integrating all aspects from
hydrodynamics to chemistry and ecology, can be developed, calibrated and applied to
the definition of control and management policies.

One point that the working group did not raise , though, - because, in 1973,
the question was much less evident - is that semi-enclosed seas are, in many aspects,
reduced-scale models of the world oceans.

Gyres, synoptic eddies, meanders and fronts are often found in semi-enclosed
seas at relatively much smaller scales, easier to observe and to represent in mathematical models. The title of this paper "Oceanography of semi-enclosed seas"
has been chosen to emphasize this important feature.

The Working Group's recommendations on the planning and implementation of large
scale international programs include , in priority

(i) a review of existing data and models

(ii) an optimization of field programmes with respect to important data coverage,
coordinated collections, standardized and automatic methods.

The first point is the objective of the 13th International Liege Colloquium
(with emphasis on the Baltic and the Mediterranean).

The second recommendation is adressed - with an exceptional deployment of technical and human means - by the Medalpex experiment in the Mediterranean, in 1981-1982 [*].

THE ALPEX-MEDALPEX EXPERIMENT

Recognizing the global importance of the influence of mountain complexes on the atmospheric circulation and weather developments, the Joint Organizing Committee (WMO, ICSU) for the Global Atmospheric Research Programme (GARP) recommended the establishment of a sub-programme on "Air Flow over and around Mountains".
As a first step, a field experiment, "ALPEX" was planned in the region of the Alps (fig. 1) for a period of 13 months from September 1, 1981, to September 30, 1982, with an intensive special period of observations from February 15 to April 30, 1982.

The Executive Council of the International Oceanographic Commission (IOC) decided to support the development, during the same period, of an oceanographic programme in the Mediterranean Sea, and in particular the Liguro-Provençal Basin and the Adriatic Sea : "MEDALPEX".

The mobilization of several vessels to provide the required sea-air interaction data for Alpex, the intense coverage of meteorological observations in the area, (fig. 2, table 1) offers a unique opportunity to study oceanographic processes which strongly depend on atmospheric forcing (heat and momentum fluxes).

In the Liguro-Provençal Basin, in the summer, a marked seasonal thermocline is formed and, when the wind is blowing, a well-defined mixed layer develops. In the winter, under the action of cold, dry continental winds (Tramontane, Mistral), the stratification wears off, but the center is affected earlier than the periphery : fairly deep convection takes place first in the central area, while outside the usual three-layer system of "bottom", "intermediate" and "surface" waters remains. A front is thus created (analogous to the polar front, with a scaling factor of the order of 1/100).

As a result of baroclinic instability, the front meanders and generates couples of eddies in the vicinity of the convective region. Vertical motions associated with the instability may produce patches of nutrient enriched waters with intense primary production and may result, in the center region, in the intermediate warm water coming to the surface. Thus, the water temperature of the surface layer increases in the central area with subsequent heat loss through evaporation and increase of density. The position of this excess heat in the central area presumably plays a role in the atmosphere's behaviour.

---

[*] The material presented in the following is partly borrowed from successive reports written, under the auspices of IOC, by a working group of expert of which the author was a member.

4

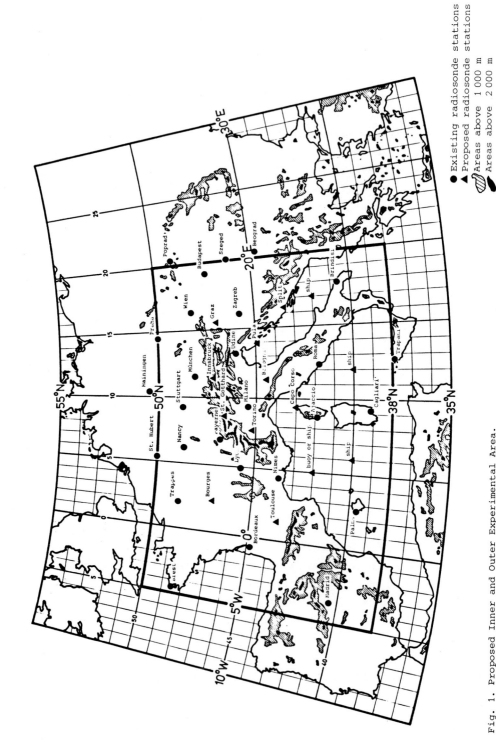

Fig. 1. Proposed Inner and Outer Experimental Area.

● Existing radiosonde stations
▲ Proposed radiosonde stations
▨ Areas above 1 000 m
◼ Areas above 2 000 m

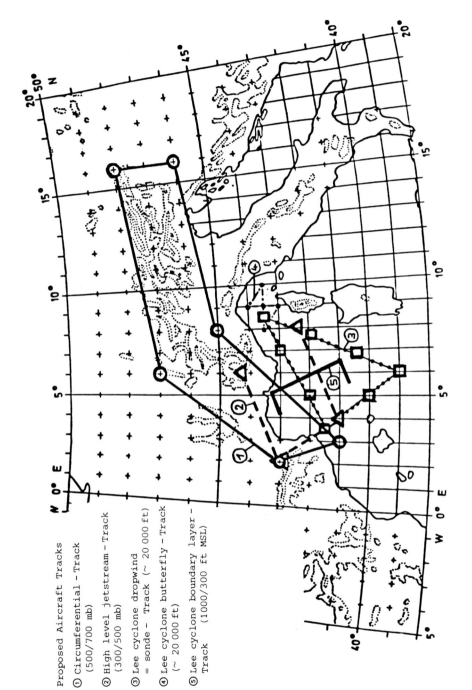

Proposed Aircraft Tracks

① Circumferential – Track
   (500/700 mb)

② High level jetstream – Track
   (300/500 mb)

③ Lee cyclone dropwind
   = sonde – Track (~ 20 000 ft)

④ Lee cyclone butterfly – Track
   (~ 20 000 ft)

⑤ Lee cyclone boundary layer –
   Track   (1000/300 ft MSL)

Fig. 2.

TABLE 1

ALPEX data requirements

SCIENTIFIC OBJECTIVES	PARAMETERS	RESOLUTION			ACCURACY		REMARKS
		Vertical	Horizontal	Time scale	Absolute	Relative	
1) Airflow and mass field (a) scales 1 + 2	u , v	1.0 km	50 km	6 h	2 ms^{-1}	—	to be computed
	w	1.0 km	50 km	6 h	10^{-2}ms^{-1}	—	
	T	0.2 km	50 km	6 h	1 K	0.5 K	
	p	0.2 km	50 km	6 h	1 mb	0.5 mb	for the detection
	q (mixing ratio)	0.2 km	50 km	6 h	> - 10 °C *	—	of inversions
					< - 10 °C **	—	* 5 %
							** 10 %
	precipitation	—	50 km	6 h	standard	as available	
	clouds	1.0 km	10 km	0.5 h	—	—	for satellite movie loops
	trajectories	1.0 km	50 km	0.5 h	5 km	—	
(b) scale 3	(tracer studies) u,v,w,T,p,q	0.2 km	5 km	3 h	see (a)	see (a)	
2) Formation and development of lee side cyclogenesis (scale 1)	u , v w T p	standard levels and significant points	150 km	3 h	see (1)	see (1)	
	q						
	precipitation	—	150 km	3 h	20 %	—	
	sea surface temperature	—	150 km	24 h	0.5 K	—	
	satellite – pictures (cloudiness)	—	10 km	5 h	standard	—	METEOSAT + TIROS-N
	– soundings	150 mb	100 km	12 h	—	—	TIROS-N
3) (a) Total drag and (b) Momentum transport (scales 2 + 3) – wave drag and surface stress	$p\,\overline{u'w'}$	2-3 km	⩽10 km	6 h	1 dyn cm^{-2}	—	
– form drag	p	0.5 km	—	continuous	0.5 mb	0.1 mb	by microbarograph
(c) Energy dissipation	$\overline{u\,u'w'}\;\;\overline{w'p'}$ $\overline{w'p}$	2-3 km	10 km	6 h	5 km^{-2}	—	
4) Sensible and latent heat flux (scales 1 + 2)	$c_p.\overline{w'T'}$	—	150 km	6 h	5 Wm^{-2}	—	
	$L.\overline{w'q'}$	—	150 km	6 h	10 Wm^{-2}	—	
	Sea surface temperature	—	150 km	24 h	0.5 K	—	
5) Radiation	$\phi_s^{\downarrow}\quad\phi_s^{\uparrow}$	1.5 km	50 km	6 h	} 5- 10 Wm^{-2}	—	ϕ : fluxes from air-craft s : short wave l : long wave
	albedo $\phi_l^{\downarrow}\quad\phi_l^{\uparrow}$	1.5 km	50 km	6 h		—	
	T_0 (surface)	—	50 km	6 h	1 K	—	
	N (cloud coverage)	1.5 km	50 km	6 h	10 %	—	
6) Precipitation	Objective can be met by using data specified for objective (1).						
7) Floods, surges and wind storms (scales 1 + 2)	Objective can be met by using data specified for objectives (1) and (2) plus :						
	Sea surface temperature	—	10 km	3 h	—	0.5 K	NOAA Satellite
	Sea level	—	100 km	—	—	20 cm	buoys, tide gauges
	Sea roughness	—	20 km	—	—	—	wave gauges, ships, advanced satellites
	River run off	—	standard			standard	

Relevant scales :
(1) = 1 000 km
(2) = 200 km
(3) = 20-30 km

Processes in the Western Mediterranean are reminiscent of what happens in the Labrador Sea or the Antarctic, leading to the formation of deep oceanic waters. However observations needed to validate models are more easily collected in the Mediterranean.

Strong upwellings are generated in the Gulf of Lion when the Mistral or the Tramontane is blowing.

Internal waves, generated at the shore, propagate to the deep sea.

All these phenomena are directly related to the conditions of the atmosphere and, especially, to their spatial pattern.

The absence of significant tides in the Mediterranean makes it possible to observe the effects of meteorological forcing without bias. Remote sensing techniques are easily applicable to the Mediterranean sea as the sky, when the Mistral or the Tramontane blows, is relatively free of clouds.

In the relatively shallow Adriatic Sea, in addition to the seasonal cycle of stratified water in the summer and mixed water in the winter, tides and seiches are significant. During some winters, under the influence of Bora, a strong dry northeasterly wind, very dense water is formed in the Northern part. This water flows down to the South and contributes to the formation of deep mediterranean water.

Under the action of strong winds coming from the South with some 500 km fetch, intense storm surges can occur in the North and deeply affect Venice. From an economic point of view, forecasting this phenomenon is essential and Medalpex is a unique opportunity to gather the necessary information for better understanding and more accurate modelling.

SPECIFIC CASE STUDIES IN THE SCOPE OF MEDALPEX

(i)   Offshore dynamic response under severe weather conditions

Although Mediterranean hydrodynamics has been investigated by scientists of several countries for many years, one must admit that very limited information is available on the behaviour of the Mediterranean sea in severe weather conditions when oceanographic vessels cannot operate.

During the Special Period of intensive observations of the GARP Alpine Experiment, time series of classical oceanographic observations may occasionally be interrupted by bad weather but they will be complemented by information from remote sensing surveys, moored laboratory buoys and fixed platforms, drifting buoys, sea-level gauges and near-shore investigations. It is thus reasonable to expect that the importance of the unique experimental network (part of which will be serviced, if only for the meteorological experiment) will provide enough data to gain, with the help of specially devised mathematical models, a fairly good and new understanding of the response of the sea to atmospheric forcing.

This understanding will include the effects of the passing storms

8

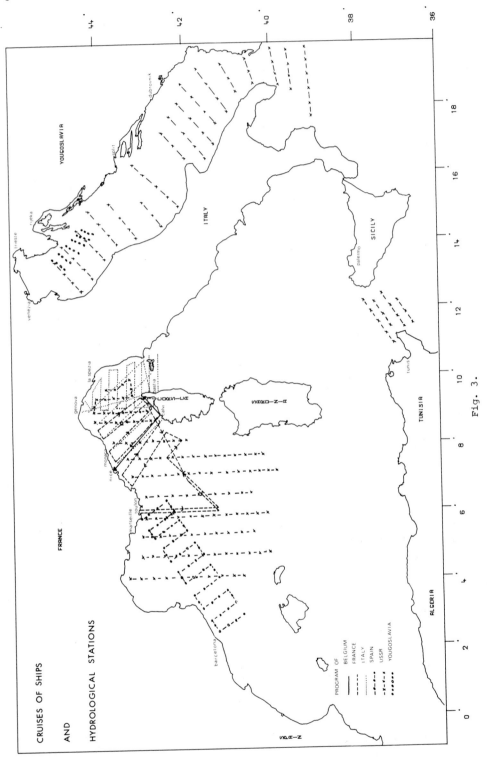

CRUISES OF SHIPS

AND

HYDROLOGICAL STATIONS

Fig. 3.

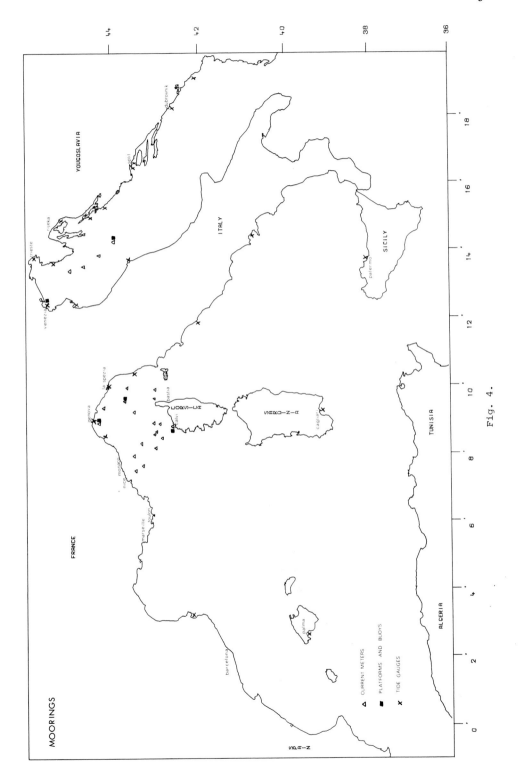

Fig. 4.

(i) on the general circulation – the general features of which are reasonably well-known in moderate weather conditions, (ii) on vertical motions, (iii) on the conditions of barotropic and baroclinic instabilities with increased current shears, (iv) on the response of oceanic fronts to modified hydrological conditions during storms, (v) on the generation of mesoscale eddies (which, in Mediterranean feature at smaller – easier to observe – scales the synoptic eddies of the ocean), and (vi) on the identification of periods of intense turbulent mixing and dissipation leading to a reassessment of the turbulent dissipation rate in the ocean, taking time intermittency into account.

Such an intensive investigation of the response of the sea to severe weather conditions will be new in the sense that for the first time a limited but representative area will be adequately covered both from the meteorolgical and the oceanographic point of view (fig. 3).

(ii) Storm surges and coastal piling-up

For the Adriatic Sea, the verification of storm surge prediction models which are now based on sea level observations along the Venetian coastline and on wind stress over the Adriatic derived from the atmospheric pressure gradient using data of the synoptic network, can be improved with a more detailed information on the wind field (speed and direction) over the sea.

The Ligurian Sea has practically no tides but the sea level and the coastal waves during cyclogenesis, mistral gusts and libeccio (SW wind with 500 n.m. fetch) produce damage on the coastline. So far no model has been developed to simulate storm surges or coastal water piling-up in semi-enclosed basins such as the Liguro-Provençal and the Tyrrhenian Basins.

With a good determination of the wind field, with its time and space variation, and wave and sea level data, such a model can be developed and verified. The envisaged model can be improved further if sea level observations along the African coastline as well as the entire Algero-Provençal and Spanish Basin can be included, thus forming a closed boundary model for the entire Western Mediterranean.

For such studies, a network of tide and wave gauges separated by 200 or 300 km will be installed, implementing the existing sea level and wave observing system along the coast of the Western Mediterranean. The network will work over the entire ALPEX period and will also be of great interest to test, later on, climate related studies on mean sea level variations (fig. 4).

(iii) Air-sea boundary-layer studies

The importance of sea-air interactions has been stressed in the Alpex Design Proposal. Fluxes of momentum, energy, sensible and latent heat and radiation budgets, as listed in table 1 must be measured near the sea surface from fixed platforms in shallow water, and from moored laboratory buoys as well as from ships recording data from auxiliary buoys in deep water.

An effort must be made to increase the accuracy by using simultaneously different methods for the calculation of turbulent fluxes (correlation analysis from direct measurement of turbulent fluctuations, fitting of mean profiles, etc.) and to correlate observations in the atmospheric boundary layer with observations in the upper layer of the sea.

These measurements are indispensable for the study of air-sea interactions and such problems as mixed-layer deepening with its implications in primary production.

(iv) Upwelling

Transient upwellings have been observed in the Adriatic Sea and in the Gulf of Lion. They are easily observed in the summer when the thermal gradients are important.

Their offshore length scale is roughly of the order of the internal radius of deformation and their spin-up time of some hours.

Their shape is linked to the shore geometry and the space variability of the wind as it can be seen from infra-red satellite thermography.

Numerical models have been developed. They often succeed in reproducing the complicated upwelling patterns but they have been sofar limited by an approximate knowledge of the wind field.

The data provided by Medalpex will contribute to a better calibration of the models.

(v)   Marine ecosystems and pollution

Different conditions of water quality and of water dynamics in shallow water (Adriatic) with intense run-off from seven rivers, one of which - the Po - is one of the major rivers of the Mediterranean and in deep water (Liguro-Provençal area) with rivers more spaced (Arno, Rhone) can be better studied when the meteorological and particularly wind patterns are known, during on-going measurements.

Marine ecological and pollution models cannot provide realistic results without the correct values of wind, waves, evaporation, depth of mixed layer and of the thermocline, and current patterns in space and time.

Medalpex will provide a unique set of data for these models.

(vi) Climate modelling

Direct measurements of fluxes at the air-sea interface and energy budget determination will provide useful observations for climate studies.

The size of the Mediterranean and the subsequent possibility of monitoring it with relatively modest facilities (which were never implemented systematically, except in limited areas), tend to prove that this sea may be a good field for studying the ways in which the sea responds to atmospheric and energy exchange forcing.

The fact, also recognized, that the long-term (century) evolution of the sea-surface temperature in the Mediterranean is identical with that recorded for all studied areas of the Northern hemisphere demonstrates that this sea may be a "pilot" basin for that time scale.

REFERENCES

Alpex Experiment Design Proposal, (revised February 1980). Report of the International Study Conference on Airflow Over and Around Mountains held in Sveti Stefan, Yugoslavia and Venice, Italy, May 1976.

Coastal Ecosystems of the Southern Mediterranean : Lagoons, Deltas and Salt Marshes - Report of a Meeting of Experts, Tunis, September 1978. Unesco reports in marine science No. 7 (Unesco 1979).

Lacombe, H., Gascard, J.C., Gonella, J., Bethoux, J.P., 1979. Response of the Mediterranean to the water and energy fluxes across its surface, on seasonal interannual and climatic scales (paper presented at the General Assembly of International Union of Geodesy and Geophysics, Camberra, Australia, December 1979 Symposium "Ocean and atmospheric boundary layers".

Marine Ecosystem Modelling in the Mediterranean - Report of the Second Unesco Workshop on Marine Ecosystem Modelling, Dubrovnik, Yugoslavia, October 1976, Unesco reports in marine science No. 2 (Unesco 1977).

Nihoul, J.C.J., 1975. Modelling of Marine Systems, Elsevier Publ., Amsterdam, 272 pp.

Oceanographic Aspects of the First GARP Global Experiment (Prepared jointly by IOC and GAO/WMO), IOC/INF-351 (Unesco, November 1978).

Rapports et Procès-Verbaux des Réunions - Commission Internationale pour l'Exploration Scientifique de la Mer Méditerranée - Vol. 25/26, Fasc. 7 (Monaco 1979). Rapport concernant l'activité du Comité d'Océanographie physique durant le XXVIe Congrès-Assemblée plénière (Antalya, November 1978).

Report of the IOC/GFCM/ICSEM International Workshop on Marine Pollution in the Mediterranean. IOC Workshop Report No. 3 (Unesco 1975).

THE REGIME OF THE STRAIT OF GIBRALTAR

H. LACOMBE[1] and C. RICHEZ[1]

1. Laboratoire d'Océanographie Physique du Muséum National d'Histoire Naturelle
43-45, rue Cuvier 75231 PARIS Cédex 05   FRANCE

ABSTRACT

The strait of Gibraltar, and the associated sill (about 300 m deep) is a remarkable model for the study of the regime of a strait connecting the ocean with a "concentration basin", i.e. a basin which, through its surface and from its watershed, receives less water than it loses by evaporation.

In the long run, the resulting water deficit is compensated by important exchanges through the strait. The conservation of the water volume in the sea and of its salt content makes it possible to expect the presence, in the strait, of two opposite movements : the first entering near the surface, carrying a flux of relatively small salinity (Atlantic water) ; the second, outflowing at depth (for it is denser), carrying a somewhat smaller flux (about - 4 %) but saltier (about + 4 %), so that it carries the same amout of salt than the inflowing flux.

In the strait, these two mean fluxes (which can be evaluated from current measurements of sufficient duration) are separated by an "interface", or transition layer of high vertical salinity gradient. Its mean depth decreases from West (180 m) to East (100 m) within the strait itself. The shape of the strait sections in the West (where it is "triangular" and widens out at the surface) and in the East (where it has a deep "U" shape) governs in the West a surface current which is much smaller than in the East : while in the East there exists a strong (and rather shallow) surface easterly set and a very slow deep westerly flow.

To this mean regime, whose characteristics are relatively well known, complex phenomena are superimposed which result :
- either from the action of processes generated in the ocean (the tides which are periodic) and of aperiodic atmospheric factors (local winds and field of pressure over the Mediterranean). The former generates strong tidal streams in the strait and tidal internal waves which are propagated on the interface between the Atlantic and Mediterranean waters. These waves have a greater amplitude on the southern side of the strait. The latter induce variations of the mean daily fluxes of water exchanged through the strait ;
- or from the effects, on the resulting current (mean value, tidal part, aperiodic part due to atmospheric conditions), of complex non-linear phenomena, which are generated in the strait and which introduce drastic modifications of the instantaneous flow regime, specially in the surface Atlantic layer, East of the sill. In particular, an "internal front" on the interface and an associated current front are generated near the sill at about the time of high water and are propagated towards the East at a velocity of 3-4 knots, into the western Alboran Sea.

Lastly, the strait regime has a great influence on the surface currents in the Alboran Sea (to the East) and on the near-bottom currents on the Atlantic slope.

INTRODUCTION

The information contained in the present paper results mainly from field measurements taken during the 60' (1960-1967), part of which has not yet been published systematically; however, the renewed interest in the Mediterranean, which the present Liège XIIIth Symposium on Hydrodynamics of the ocean illustrates, is an opportunity to present a number of results on this very interesting area.

Throwing a glance on the Mediterranean suffices to demonstrate that this "semi-enclosed" sea is a succession of basins and sills, among which the strait of Gibraltar is merely one : its interest lies in the fact that it is a typical model of "strait and sill" system in which a number of phenomena occur with so great clarity that they are "exemplary" of the other strait-and-sill-systems in the Mediterranean, a concentration basin communicating finally with the ocean. In addition, the Strait of Gibraltar is a relatively well known area, due, in particular, to the fact that the NATO subcommittee on Oceanic Research, from 1960 to 1965, under the Chairmanship of Prof. Häkon HOSBY, from Norway, organised a number of cruises in the area (see charts A and B).

As presented in NATO Technical Report (T.R.) n° 2 (see bibliography), the NATO subcommittee on Oceanographic Research, following the preceding work by the Spanish and the French during 1957-58 (IGY) and during september 1960, decided to organize in may-june 1961 a multi-ship survey of the strait of Gibraltar. A working group, which one of us had the honour to chair, was set up to prepare the program. Its aim was essentially :

   - to continuously monitor during the period may 15-june 15, 1961, the hydrological regime as well as the current regime in a central point considered as representative (Point A.4, - see chart A - 5 miles North of Cape Spartel) ;

   - to study the hydrology by <u>simultaneous</u> measurements made in principle every two hours for 24 hours, during spring and neap tides, at hydro-stations distributed on one longitudinal section of the strait and on five transverse sections.

The the East and to the West of the strait, measurements of hydrology and current should be made to relate the regimes of the strait to those present to the East and to the West. Tidal records and meteorological observations were to be made to try to correlate the sea regime in the strait and the meteorological regime.

The ships involved in the concerted work were :
- "Aragonese" from Saclantcen (H. CHARNOCK)
- "Calypso" France (H. LACOMBE)
- "Eupen" Belgium (A. CAPART)

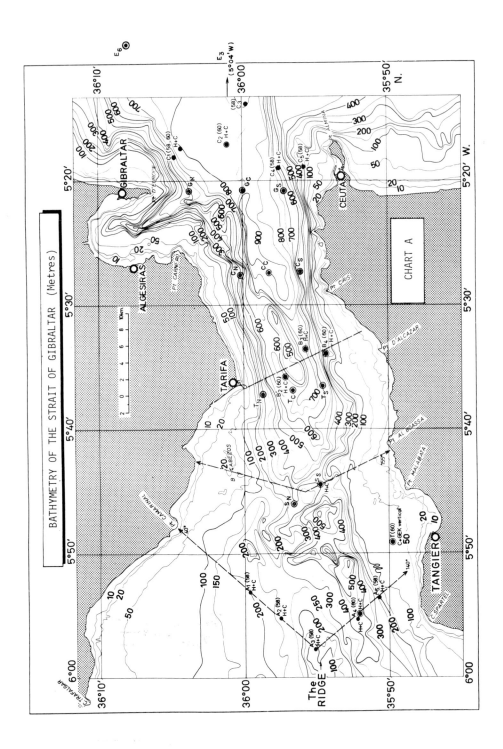

BATHYMETRY OF THE STRAIT OF GIBRALTAR (Metres)

CHART A

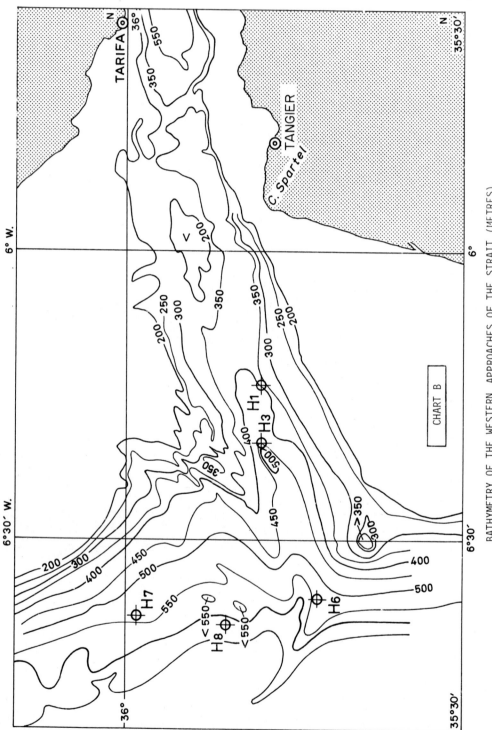

BATHYMETRY OF THE WESTERN APPROACHES OF THE STRAIT (METRES).

- "Helland-Hansen" Norway (H. MOSBY, then G. BOYUM)
- "Origny" France (G. PELUCHON)
- "Staffetta" Italy (M. CANO)

In addition, two ships has an action coordinated with the main programme :
- "Amiral-Mouchez" France (G. BRIE) Echo-sounding and GEK in the Alboran Sea
- "Xauen" Spain (N. MENENDEZ)

A great part of the information presented in this paper results from the multiple ship survey. However some additional data result from cruises made by the French, CALYPSO (H. LACOMBE) and ESPADON (P. TCHERNIA) in 1960, from the NATO "Mediterranean Outflow project" of 1965 (cf T.R. n° 34, 35, 36 - G. BOYUM) and, finally, from the CHARCOT cruise of 1967 (H. LACOMBE and al-1968 - F. MADELAIN 1970).

Most of the Mediterranean Straits, such as the Gibraltar one, are places where very varied hydrodynamical phenomena occur, which result from exchanges of water between basins and from the effects, on their regime, of phenomena gene-rated outside the strait area such as the tides or the meteorological conditions. These, in turn, may start complex phenomena of waves and instabilities which are generated by non linear flows. It seems appropriate to begin with the "mean regime" in the Strait of Gibraltar, then, having in mind the factors which maintain it, to deal with phenomena of smaller time scale.

This paper will be mainly descriptive and relate the results of observations and we shall not give any dynamical considerations.

We must add, however, that the various small scale motions which are kwown to exist in the Strait, generate mixing between adjacent layers which have an incidence on the "mean regime" or, at least, on the way in which this regime is evaluated. In addition, what occurs in the Strait have an important effect on the hydrography of adjacent areas, like the Alboran Sea, on one side, on the Gulf of Cadix on the other. We shall give few indications on this point.

I. THE MEAN REGIME

This regime is governed by the climatic conditions prevailing over the Medi-terranean basin and its watershed : in fact this sea forms a system which trans-forms the Atlantic water flowing into the sea (S $\simeq$ 36,15 ‰) into an outflowing water which becomes typically mediterranean under the effect of the climate over the sea area.

The climate of the sea itself and of its watershed is characterized by a great diversity : desertic lands occupy a great part on the East of its southern shore. Instead, the watershed which feeds it in the NW is woody and humid, particularly in winter : the flow of rivers into the sea is mainly important on the Northern shore and into the Black Sea ; the only important river of the Southern shore is the Nile. If the flows from the Rhône, the Pô, the Danube and the Nile are relatively regular, those from the Russian rivers to the Black Sea exhibit a maximum volume at the end of spring and at the beginning of summer.

For the watershed, the summer is dry, the winter humid. In summer the Azores anticyclone proceeds over Western Europe ; the solar heating over great continental areas on the East and South of the sea generates rather low pressure there, so that there is a tendency of an anticyclonic wind , blowing from North over the Eastern sea and from East over the North African area. In winter, meteorological lows coming from the Atlantic sweep over the basin from West to East ; however they often tend to remain and to become deeper in certain areas like the Gulf of Genova, the Adriatic, Cyprus. As a consequence, the winds tend to be cyclonic and to generate precipitations which are particularly important on coasts facing West. Behind the lows, strong winds from NW to N blow over the Northern shores, which are particularly violent in the Gulf of Lions (Tramontane, Mistral), over the North Adriatic (Bora). In winter also, the Northern parts of the sea may be submitted to bursts of polar continental air - cold and dry - when the Southern slopes of anticyclones situated over Central and Eastern Europe direct Easterly winds over the Northern areas of the Mediterranean.

A particular meteorological character is the presence of transient phenomena, of small scale, but very violent, for the winds as well as for the precipitations : these may be torrential and generate very strong floods of coastal rivers, which may play an important role on the dispersion of sediments.

I.A <u>The mean regime of the strait as inferred from the balances of water and salt in the sea</u>

The Mediterranean (including the Black Sea), being closed in the East, the mass of salt and the volume of water it contains are invariable (at a time scale of human life), since its level and its salinity remain invariable in time, (the salinity since the "THOR" cruise in 1907-1910). On the other hand, the evaporation E exceeds the water gains P resulting from the precipitations and the river flow. BETHOUX (1980) presents the water budget across the sea surface in various Mediterranean areas. Everywhere (except the Black Sea and the Northern Adriatic), there is water deficit across the sea surface. In the Gulf of Lions the budget is nil. It results that the Mediterranean is a <u>concentration basin</u> : the typical

Mediterranean outflowing water (S $\cong$ 38 $\permil$) is denser than the entering Atlantic water and flows near the bottom of the strait of Gibraltar.

If the water deficit was compensated only by entering Atlantic water, the salt brought in by the latter would continuously increase the amount of salt within the sea, contrary to what occurs. Then, in the strait there take place an inflow of Atlantic water (near the surface) and, below, over the bottom, an outflow of saltier (+ 4 %) and denser Mediterranean water which, under a some-what smaller volume (- 4 %), carries the same quantity of salt as the entering Atlantic water.

Expressing - the conservation of <u>salt</u> in the Mediterranean, we have
$\rho i.Vi.Si = \rho o.Vo.So$ (ρ density, V volume, S salinity ; index <u>i</u> refers to the inflow, index <u>o</u> to the outflow). As $\rho i \cong \rho o$ since $\rho o - \rho i = 2.10^{-3}$, we may write :
$Vi.Si = Vo.So$

- the conservation of <u>water</u> in the sea :
$Vi + P = Vo + E$
(P precipitation over the sea + river discharge to the sea, E = evaporation from the sea).
Combining the two relations :
$Vi/So = Vo/Si = (Vi - Vo)/(So - Si) = (E - P)(So - Si) = \Delta V/ \Delta S$ (1)
and $Vi = VoSo/Si$

All the factors entering equation 1 can be measured in the strait or eva-luated for the sea, but not with the same degree of simplicity or accuracy.

I.A.1 <u>The exchanges of water from measurements in the strait</u> : Among them, the most accessible are the local values which have to be measured only <u>in</u> the strait : Vi, Vo, Si, So ; but we must have access to their <u>mean local</u> value. However the elimination of the effects of tides, meteorological conditions, of fluctuations due to many factors requires, in difficult marine conditions (great depth, strong currents, high vertical shear, intense navigation, frequent fog, E or W winds...) measurements of <u>long duration</u>. The presence of important mixing between the superimposed water masses requires that all factors to be measured in the same representative point.

The hydrology is given by hydrocasts made at the same place during, at least, one tidal cycle (fig. 1). Our measurements of 1960 at point A.4 (see chart. A) lead us to Si $\cong$ 36,15 $\permil$ and So $\cong$ 37,9 $\permil$. This evaluation is delicate because of the changing depth of the transitional layer between the Atlantic and Medi-terranean waters, whose thickness depends on the intensity of mixing and on the velocity shear and, of course, on the position. ΔS is then about 1,75 $\permil$.

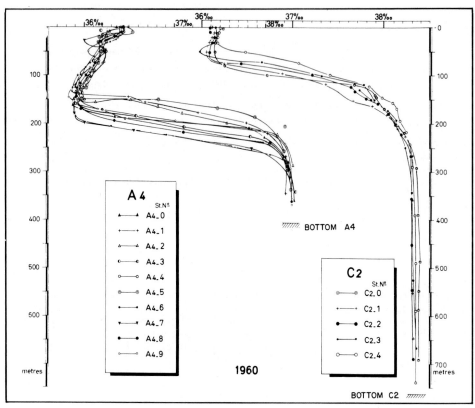

FIG.1 Vertical profiles of salinity : in the West (A4) and
in the East (C2) of the strait.

The evaluation of Vi, Vo is more difficult : the values found are presented
(Table I, fig. 2) for point A.4 also, where Si and So have been determined. It
is seen that there are very large fluctuations of the mean flux for 12 h and
24 h (100 %). Besides the diurnal tidal component is not negligible.

The accuracy with which these fluxes are obtained is difficult to evaluate :
however, the deep section being much smaller than the upper section through
which Vi goes, the deep flux Vo is, probably, more accurate : its mean value as
found by the direct measurements (1960, 1961) is Vo = 1,15 10^6 m3/s at point A.4
or about 36.10^{12} m3/year. The incoming flux Vi measured is 1,26.10^6 m3/s and somewhat exceeds by 5 % what would be determined by the relative excess of So.
However, Vo being more accurate we shall take (from equation 1) Vi = So Vo/Si
1,20 10^6 m3/s = 37.7 10^{12}m3/y.

The net gain of water through the strait is about 1,7.10^{12} m3/y ; as the net
gain through the Dardanelles is 0,2.10^{12} m3/y (TIXERONT, 1970). The total deficit

TABLE I

STRAIT OF GIBRALTAR (Sept. 1960- May-June 1961)

Mean flux averaged over 12h and 24h, in 10^6 m^3/s. Western Section through A4

	Inflow Vi		Outflow Vo	
	aver. over 12h	aver. over 24h	aver. over 12h	aver. over 24h
Sept. 1960 (Point A4)	0.60		1.11	
	1.37	0.98	0.85	0.98
	0.53	0.95	1.38	1.11
	1.15	0.84	0.94	1.16
	0.95	1.05	0.99	0.96
	1.68	1.31	0.66	0.82
	1.33	1.50	0.88	0.77
	—		—	
	1.05		0.42	
May June 1961 (Point A4) Recalculated values	1.67		0.46	
	—		—	
	1.87	1.06	0.59	1.01
	0.25		1.42	
	—		—	
	1.05	1.77	0.89	0.63
	2.49	1.84	0.37	0.82
	1.19	1.82	1.26	0.92
	2.45		0.58	
	—		—	
	0.99	1.61	1.35	1.03
	2.24	1.55	0.72	1.07
	0.86	1.22	1.43	1.08
	1.58	1.27	0.73	0.94
	0.96	1.14	1.15	1.11
	1.32		1.07	
	—		—	
	0.97	1.27	1.71	1.30
	1.57	1.20	0.90	1.59
	0.83		2.28	
	—		—	
	1.50	1.18	0.98	1.58
	0.86	1.44	2.17	1.48
	2.02	1.64	0.78	1.23
	1.26	1.57	1.67	1.24
	1.89	1.30	0.80	0.97
	0.72	0.96	1.13	1.22
	1.21	1.26	1.31	1.56
	1.31	1.08	1.81	1.52
	0.85	0.69	1.22	1.37
	0.53	0.45	1.51	1.45
	0.38		1.39	

FLUXES IN A4

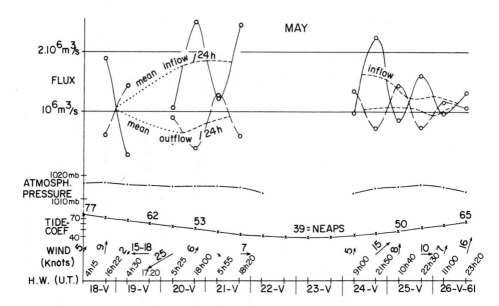

FIG. 2 Mean inflow and outflow - fluxes averaged over 12h and 24h
in A4 (Western entrance). May-june 1961.

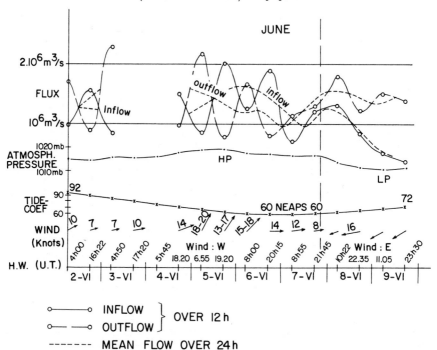

INFLOW } OVER 12h
OUTFLOW
------- MEAN FLOW OVER 24h

for the Mediterranean proper (excluding the Black Sea) is $1,9 \times 10^{12}$ m3/y. As the surface of the Mediterranean proper is $2,53 \times 10^{12}$m3, the mean water deficit across the surface is $\frac{1,9 \times 10^{12} \text{ m3/y}}{2,53 \times 10^{12} \text{m2}} \cong 0,75$ m/y. With the value of P admitted by TIXE-RONT (1970), i.e. 0,55 m/y, the mean evaporation over the Mediterranean proper is 1,30 m/y.

On the other end, the total flux $\underline{\text{entering}}$ the Mediterranean proper is $37,7 \times 10^{12}$ m3/y (through Gibraltar) + $0,4 \times 10^{12}$ m3/y (through Dardanelles) = $38,1 \times 10^{12}$ m3/y ; this gives the renewal time of the Mediterranean water $= \frac{3,71 \times 10^{15} \text{ m3}}{38,1 \times 10^{12} \text{ m3/y}} = 98$ years, ratio of the total volume of the sea to the incoming flux.

I.A.2 $\underline{\text{The exchanges of water from evaluations over the whole sea combined}}$ $\underline{\text{with measurements in the strait}}$. BETHOUX (1978,79) had the idea of evaluating E, the evaporation,using the heat budget of the sea : the heat loss by evaporation is the difference between the heating processes (solar radiations received + the weak advections through the strait) and cooling processes (infra-red radiations, loss of sensible heat). On the other hand, he evaluates P. From there he deduces E - P = Vi -Vo. The mean unit area value of E - P is thus found to be about 1m/year. Taking the values of Si and So, given above in I.A.1, he obtains Vi and Vo by eq. (1). He finds Vi = 53×10^{12} m3/y ; Vo = $50,5 \times 10^{12}$ m3/y. In addition, neglecting the inflow by the Black Sea he finds a renewal time of :

$\frac{3,71 \times 10^5}{53 \times 10^{12}}$ = 70 years. These fluxes exceed by about 30 % those obtained from direct measurements in the strait. Given the incertainty - difficult to evaluate - of elements involved in the two methods of estimation, this discrepancy is not surprising.

I.B Characters of the mean regime in various places in the strait

I.B.1 Vertical profile of mean velocity and longitudinal slope of the mean interface. One of the important characters of the mean regime is the vertical mean velocity profile in various places. The width of the channel for various depths on different cross-sections, as well as the depth of the "interface" between the two superimposed waters,play a considerable role on the vertical mean current profile (fig. 3, 4, 5).

In the Western part of the strait, in A.4 (see chart. A), the sea depth does not exceed 400-450 m and the section offered to the deep outflow is much smaller than that offered to the inflow : the section is more or less triangular (fig. 3). On the contrary, on sections more to the East (Tarifa, Gibraltar) the section offered to the outflow is much greater than that offered to the inflow, the

24

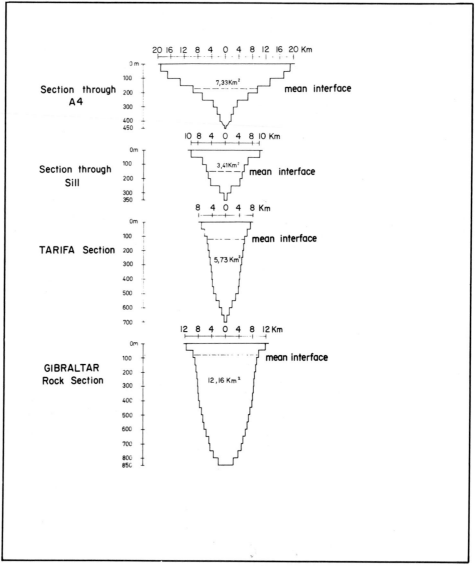

FIG. 3 Cross channel area of different sections of the strait
(see chart A : The positions of the sections).

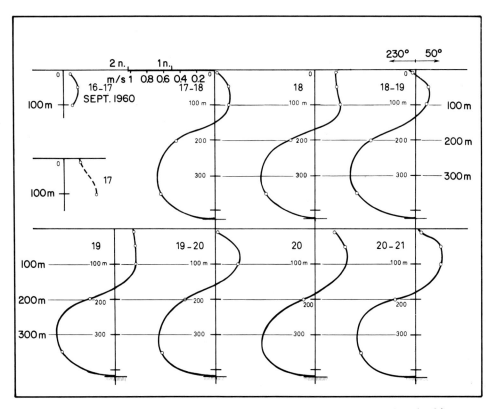

FIG. 4 Mean velocity profiles for nine successive tidal cycles in A4.

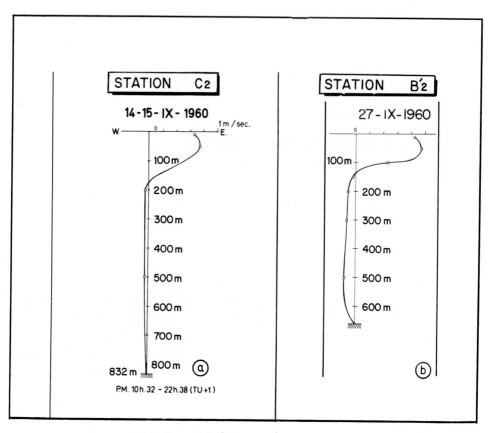

FIG. 5 Mean velocity profiles in C2 (a) and B'2 (b).

27

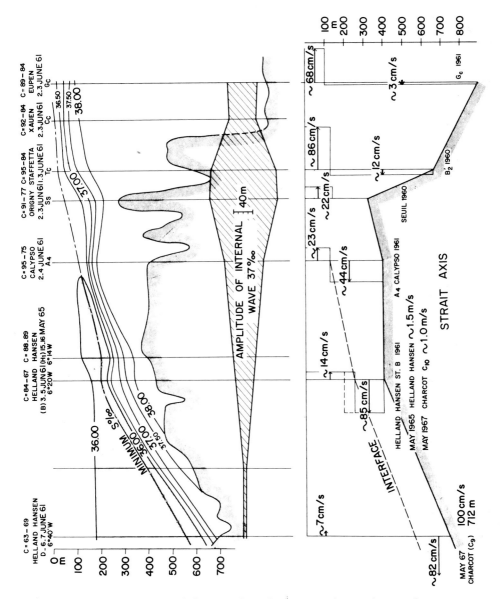

FIG. 6 Longitudinal mean salinity section along the axis of the strait from 6°40' W to the meridian of Gibraltar. Amplitude of the internal wave for a salinity 37 ‰. Mean current in the two layers.

more as (fig 1, 6) the internal interface is ascending from West to East, thus reducing the water thickness for the inflow.

In the Western approaches, the Mediterranean deep outflow is guided by a deep valley which prolongs to the West the valley South of Spartel bank ("the Ridge") till about 6°25' W ; more to the West the deep valley widens (see chart B). Thus the deep outflow is concentrated in the valley while the inflow takes place in a very large section.

Fig. 6 represents a section of the mean longitudinal salinity from 6°40' W (in the West) to the meridian of Gibraltar Rock (5°20'W) for spring tides. It is seen that the mean longitudinal slope of the isohaline 37,0 ‰ (which may be considered as the interface) increases toward the West and is close to the bottom slope between meridians 6°14' W and 6°40' W. As the widening of the channel is relatively small till 6°25'W, this implies that the velocity of the outflow in these deeper layers increases, despite the mixing with overlying waters. In fact, according to our Norwegian colleagues' measurements on board of the "HELLAND-HANSEN" in may 1965 (TR 34, 35, 36 G. BOYUM 1967), in longitudes about 6°14' and 6°20' W, the mean current down to about the interface is weak to the East (about 20 cm/s or .4 kn) The situation is quite different in the deeper layer of "Mediterranean water". In longitude 6°14' W near the southern flank of the valley, where the interface is deeper, the mean velocity between 250 and the bottom at 430 m is about 140 cm/s ; while in longitude 6°20' W, deeper than 250 m, the mean velocity may exceed 150 cm/s (3 kn). It is in this area that our colleagues have measured a record velocity of 245 cm/s (almost 5 kn) in 6°14', and others exceeding 200 cm/s near 6°20' W. On the contrary, in 6°47' W, after the widening of the valley the mean deep velocities decrease to about 80 to 100 cm/s (1,6 to 2 kn) ("Campagne GIBRALTAR UN", 1970),10 m above the bottom (705 m) in 35°48' N - 6°44'W.

In addition it is seen on figure 6 (middle) that the vertical displacement of the interface at springs is also maximum in the vicinity of the sill.

In the Western entrance of the strait, point A.4, fig. 4, the mean current in the surface layer is weak, while it is strong in the deeper ones.

Near the meridians of Tarifa (fig 5b) and Gibraltar (fig 5a) the mean current is conversely, high in the surface layers and small in the deeper one.

I.B.2 Mean hydrological structure and mixing between layers. We have till now used the terms "inflowing Atlantic water", "outflowing Mediterranean water" to designate the waters affected by opposite mean movements. It is useful to better define their characteristics and to evaluate the effect of mixing between them on the local T and S of the water present.

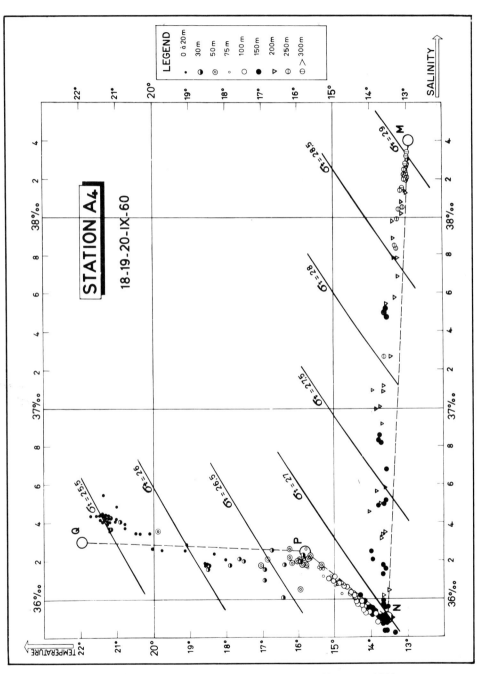

FIG. 7 T.S. diagrams for stations A4, 18-20 sept. 1960.

The Mediterranean water which is present in the deeper layers at the Eastern end of the strait (section of Gibraltar rock) is nearly a "water type", whose T and S are very close to those of the Deep Water of the Western Mediterranean : $T \cong 12°9$, $S \cong 38.40$ ‰(In fact GASCARD recently showed that the deep water was able to creep towards the strait close to the ascending bottom). On all the following T.S. diagrams this water is represented by point M.

On the Atlantic side, the situation is more complex and we have to deal, not with a water-type, but with a "water-mass", the "North Atlantic Central Water" (NACW) defined by SVERDRUP (1942) ; near the Western entrance of the strait (Point A4) the T and S fall on a line between T = 16°C, S = 36.2 ‰ and T = 13.5 °C, S =35.9 ‰. This is segment PN on the T.S diagrams. Above (ie from 0 to 50 m in summer) the T and S present do not fall on this line (due to the solar heating) but on a segment noted QP.

When, under the effect of tide, the interface between the Atlantic and Mediterranean waters is deeper, the T and S of the NACW at its lower level are smaller than when the instantaneous interface is higher. In point A4 (Cape of Spartel meridian),the lower values found were T = 13.3°C ; S = 35.84 ‰.

The characteristics present within the transition layer between the two waters result from the mixing between them, which is increased by the current shear present at that level at certain moments of the tide (fig. 7). The fact that the T. S points intermediate between N and M are above line NM shows that the water present at the corresponding levels result from mixing of water M (Mediterranean water-type) with less deep Atlantic water : this may be due to the fact that, when the mixing responsible of these points took place, the lower layer of the NACW present was somewhat shallower (different state of the tide and shallower interface with higher T and S) or may be due to ascending motions having taken place at other places in the strait and "building up" the mixing elsewhere in the strait (in the sill area ?) : the current present may subsequently have advected this water to them.

The densities in the lower layers of NACW are smaller by about 0.002 than those of the Mediterranean water. This density shift, apparently very small, is sufficient to act as a shield for the exchange of properties and movements of the water above and below : the transition layer is, at least in A4, relatively thin (50 m) ; the kinetic energy must feed the layers with the potential energy needed to build the transition layer .

More to the East, near the meridian of the Rock, (Point C2), the T.S diagram (fig. 8) shows that the NACW is only present on a small range of depth near the surface (30-50 m) ; the vertical profile of salinity (fig. 1 right) also shows that the transition layer reaches about 100 m in thickness.

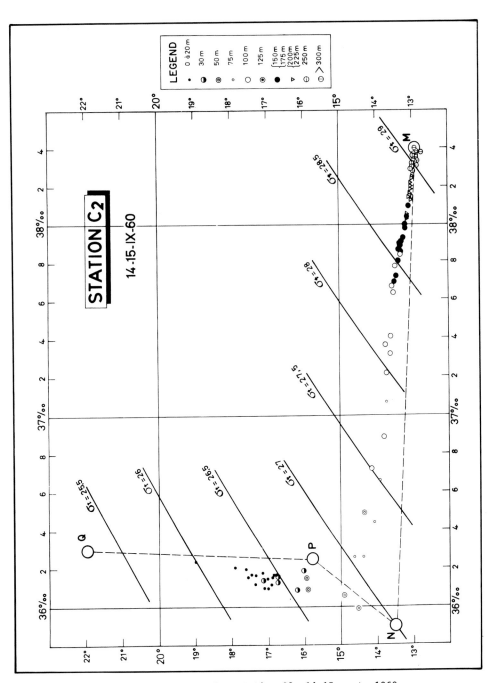

FIG.8 T.S. diagrams for station C2, 14-15 sept. 1960.

32

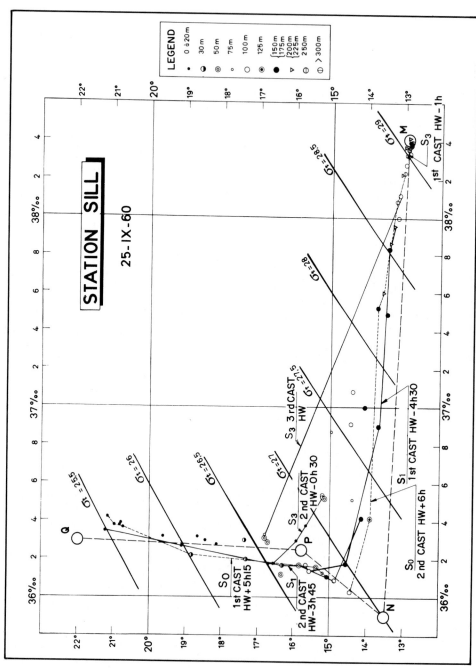

FIG. 9 T.S. diagrams for stations Ss, 25 sept. 1960.

The T and S conditions present on the sill (point S₅on chart A, fig. 9) are
subject to drastic variations during the tidal cycle and according to the time
with respect to High water, one finds either conditions similar to those found
in the West (A4) when the interface is deep in the sill or a mixed layer coming
up to the surface, in particular near the time of High Water, when the salinity
minimum ascends near the surface, during the phase of violent accelerating
tidal surface current (see below II.C).

Due to Coriolis' force, the existence of opposite mean flows on the vertical
generates a mean transverse slope of the interface, which is deeper on the Southern
side (while the sea surface is higher) than on the Northern side ; this slope is
important, since for a relative density of 0.002 between layers, and for latitude
36°, it reaches 4.3 m/1 km for a relative current of 1m/s : one must expect depths
of the interface to be greater on the Southern side by an order of 50 m : as a
consequence, the interface may reach the surface itself near the Northern coast
of the strait (see fig.36). Of course in addition we shall see (II.E) that the
tidal streams in such a "channel" induces additional more or less geostrophic
transverse slope of the interface.

II FLUCTUATION OF THE MEAN REGIME FORCED BY THE TIDE

The difference of the characters of the tide in the Gulf of Cadix, to the West,
and in the Alboran Sea, to the East, generates in the strait important periodic
modifications of the local hydrology and of the currents.

The tide in the area is essentially semi-diurnal ; its amplitude is much greater
at the Western entrance to the strait (about 2 m) that in the center (1.3 m in
Tarifa) and at the Eastern end (0.8 to 1 m).

The tidal wave of the Atlantic reaches the Western approaches to the strait
about two hours after the (lower or upper) moon transit of Greenwich meridian ;
it reaches Tangier somewhat earlier than Cadix. But, in the area between
the sill and Gibraltar, the High Water takes place almost at the same time, which
is about 2 hours before the time of the corresponding high water in Brest.

The tide affects the regime of the strait as well as that of its Western and
Eastern approches, by the tidal streams and by the tidal effects on the hydrological structure. We shall rapidly survey these effects in the surface and deep
layers where sufficient processed data are available.

We shall follow the evolution of phenomena from West (about 6°40' W) to East
(about 5°20' W). We shall see that the phenomena suffer drastic changes on the
sill and Eastward, so as to deeply influence the whole regime to the East.

We also give (II.E) simultaneous internal tidal wave profiles on a number of transverse sections (on the basis of the multi-ship measurements of 1961, see the introduction) so as to put in evidence indications of the transverse slope of the interface and its variation with tide. Finally we also present simultaneous T.S. diagram for 5 stations along the central axis of the strait, from A4 to Gc, at springs and neaps for a number of tidal hours.

II.A Tidal forcing in the Western approaches

We shall limit ourselves here to the vicinity of meridian 6°40' W. Fig. 10, 11 show (TR 34 35 36 G. BOYUM 1967) the results of our Norwegian colleagues on the basis of data collected in may 1965 under the NATO project "Mediterranean Ourflow". Near 6°38' W (fig. 10) it is seen, within of layer of about 40-50 m above the bottom, an individualised deep Mediterranean density flow is present with little depth variation under the effect of tide. Also, it seems that little current variation with tide takes place. In 6°20'W and 6°14 (fig. 11), within the deep valley, the deeper salinities are much greater and close to those of the Mediterranean. A clear tidal internal wave is apparent, the mean interface being about 100-150 m above the bottom. The "High Water" of the internal wave , in 6°14 'W, takes place near the time of the surface "High Water"[*]. As indicated above in I.B.1 the mean current is very strong only in the deep layer. It seems to be stronger between HW-5h and HW-1h (i.e. between 5 hours and 1 hour before the surface High Water in Tarifa).

II.B Tidal forcing in the valley north of Cape Spartel (point A4)

We have indicated earlier (I.B.1) that the variation with depth of the width of the channel (cf fig. 4) imposed to the mean current weak values near the surface, but high values in the deeper layers.

---

[*]On a number of figures the letter C (for "coefficient" of the tide) appears. Let us recall that the "coefficient" is directly proportional to the amplitude of one definite tide, provided the phenomenon is essentially semi-diurnal : it is then valid for all places. The Coefficient is expressed in "centièmes" ("hundredths").

As a comparison : the mean spring tide range corresponds to C = 95
the mean tide range corresponds to   C = 70
the mean neap tide range corresponds to   C = 45
The highest possible tide range is characterized by C = 120
The lowest possible tide range is characterized by C = 20
The mean equinoxial spring tide range corresponds to C = 100

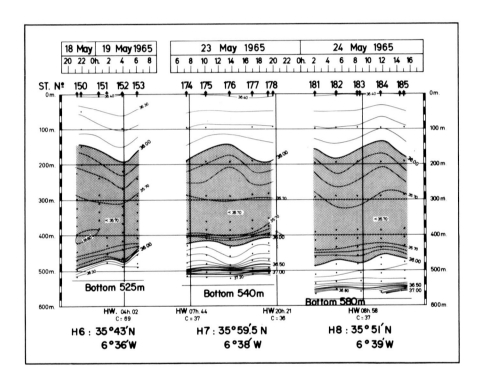

FIG. 10 : Salinity structure in the Western approaches to the strait ("HELLAND-HANSEN" ; may 1965), near longitude 6°38'W.

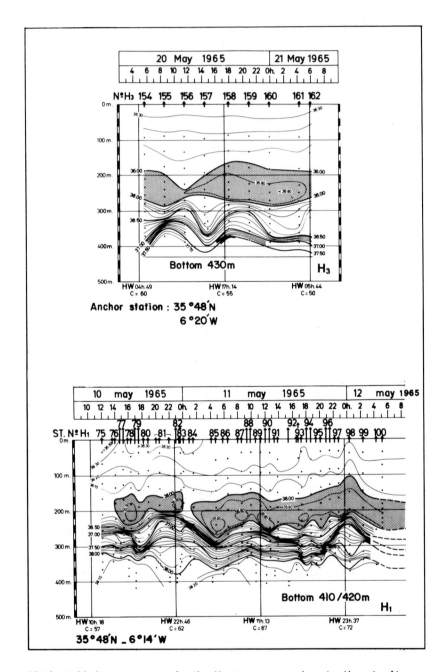

FIG. 11 Salinity structure in the Western approaches to the strait. ("HELLAND-HANSEN"; May 1965), near longitudes 6°20'W (úp) and 6°14'W (Below).

A tidal current, with a dominating semi-diurnal component (12h,4 .hours) and
a weak diurnal one, is superimposed to the mean regime. The corresponding periodic current constituents reverse with tide, but the amplitude of the tidal
current is greater than the mean current in the surface layer (above the interface) but weaker than the mean current in the deeper layer (beyond 250 m). It
results that the total current (mean + tidal) reverse during a semi diurnal tidal
cycle in the surface layer while it is always outflowing in the deeper ones, thus
keeping a constant direction there (fig. 12). On this figure, hours before and
after the local high water (Tarifa) are along the vertical (from - 7 hours to
+ 7 hours), while in abscissa the instantaneous total current is along ox
(positive when inflowing, negative when outflowing). The currents at 5 depths
are plotted.

The total current, as well as its alternative components, have their maximum
values (in and out)at about the same moment at all depths : 3 to 4 hours before
High Water (HW - 3 to HW - 4) for the maximum outflow ; 3 hours after HW for
the inflow current (or the minimum of outflow in the deeper layers). In the
upper layers, the inflow current begins about 1 hour before HW (HW - 1h) and
the outflow about HW + 6 h.

The mean maximum values reached in A4, according to our measurements of 1960
are :

depth	to the East	to the West
10 m	1.8 kn	1.4 kn
50	2.1	1.2
100	1.8	1.1
200	1.8	2.3
	to the West	
350	0.5	2.25

(N.B. 100 cm/s = 1,94 kn)

But there are appreciable fluctuations of current from one semi-diurnal tide
to the following one (Table I, fig. 2). One will note the fast evolution of the
global current at 200 m near HW + 1h, which coincides with the maximum descent
rate of the interface : before this hour, at 200 m, Mediterranean water is
present (S $\cong$ 37.5 %o) ; after Atlantic water is met (S $\cong$ 36.5 %o) (see fig. 12).

The IOS Wormley (Dr THORPE, personal communication) carried out in 1974
(july-september) a very nice current record near point A4 about 60 m above the
bottom. The record shows the invariance of the mean current and, in spring
tide, during a few tidal cycle, short inversions (inflows) of the global current.

38

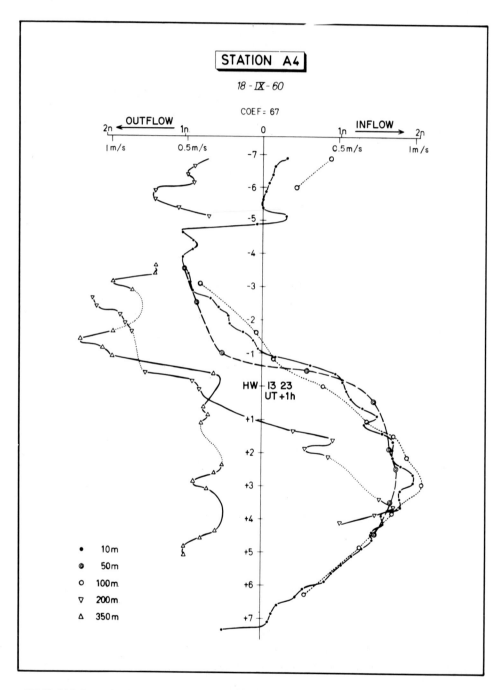

FIG. 12 Tidal variation of the longitudinal component of the global current in A4, for different depths.

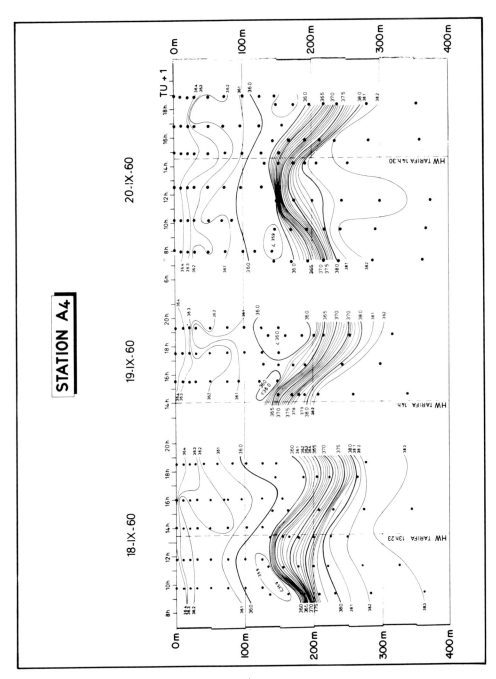

FIG. 13   Internal wave of salinity in A4. 18-20 sept. 1960.

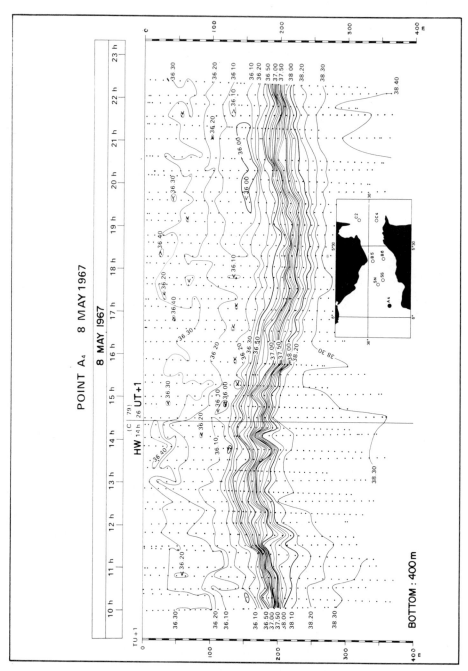

FIG.14   Internal wave of salinity in A4. 8 may 1967.
Bathysonde yoyo-ing (N/O "Jean Charcot").

The hydrological   regime is also subject to important tidal effects; a determined isotherm, or isohaline,changes its depth with time (fig. 13 and 14). Fig. 14 is resulting from the use of a yo-yoing bathysonde every 15 mn. Internal waves are present; their amplitude is 50 to 60 m ; the "high water" of the internal tide is about one hour in advance with respect to the surface tide, and coincides in time with the beginning of the global inflow - current at the surface. The "low water" of the internal tide, on the contrary, coincides with the moment when the outflow-current begins at the surface. The salinity is relatively homogeneous beyond 300 m : it is almost "pure" Mediterranean water.

II.C Tidal forcing in the central sections of the strait, between the sill and the section of point Ciris (5° 90' W)

Clearly there is a rapid evolution in that central sector.

II.C.A1 The sill. As regards currents and their evolution during a tidal cycle, fig. 15 shows that, in the surface layers, as well as in the deeper ones, the phase of the alternative component of the current with respect to the sur-face tide is similar to the phase in A4 : the current sets East at about - 1 h (Tarifa). One notes, however, that in the upper 100 m the velocities are much higher (about 3.5 kn (180 cm/s) to the East and 2 kn (100 cm/s) to the West) after a sudden reversal about - 0h 30 (Tarifa) : the variation is about 3 kn in half an hour (between - 1h and -0h30 Tarifa). On the sill itself, the phase of outflowing current (- 5h 30 to -0h 30 Tarifa) is accompanied in the surface by quasi permanent line of eddies,a feature which must be linked to the hydrological structure during that phase. The available deep current measurements are however scarce.

As for the hydrology (fig. 16, 17 for the South sill Ss) and fig. 18 (for the North sill Sn) the hydro-stations made during the current measurements of fig. 15 exhibit very complex variations in depth, for the isotherms as for the isoha-lines (fig. 16). In 1967, on the basis of measurements by a yo-yoing bathysonde (fig. 17 for Ss and 18 for Sn), the shape of the internal wave is different. In addition, in the same place, Ss, it is different for two successive semi-diurnal tides. It must be noted however, that these measurements were made from a drifting ship, manoeuvering to keep the same position...

Instead of exhibiting, as in the case in A4 (fig. 14),a regular sinusoidal profile, here the interface is subject to irregular motions and, sometimes, occupy two levels only, one around 150 m between the time of low water and HW-4h Tarifa ; then another one around 80 m, between HW - 4 and HW + 0h 30 (Tarifa), followed by a fast deepening of the interface (fig. 16). It is probable that such a behaviour does not occur for all tides (cf. BOCKEL NATO, TR n°2 oct. 2 1962 p. 325).

42

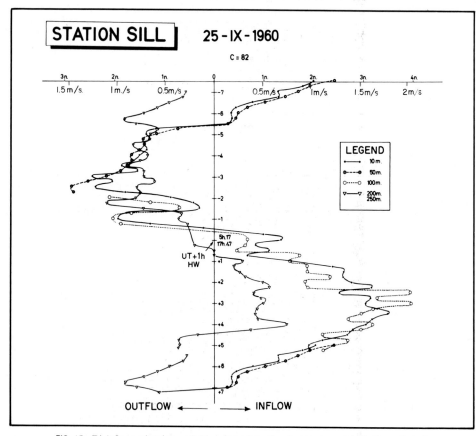

FIG. 15 Tidal variation of the longitudinal component of the global current on the sill (point Ss). 25 sept. 1960.

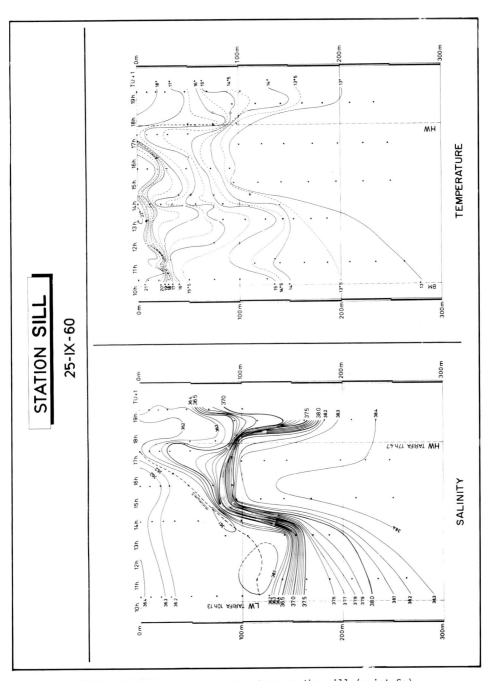

FIG. 16 Simultaneous water structure on the sill (point Ss).
25 sept. 1960.

44

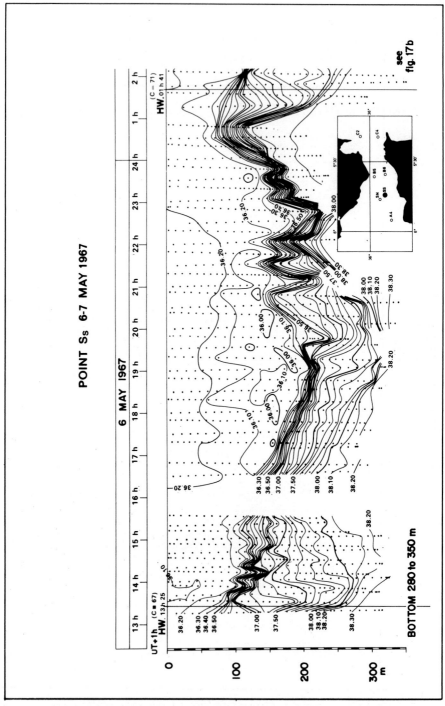

FIG. 17 a   Internal wave of salinity during a diurnal cycle in Ss.
6-7 may 1967. Bathysonde yoyo-ing (N/O "Jean Charcot").

45

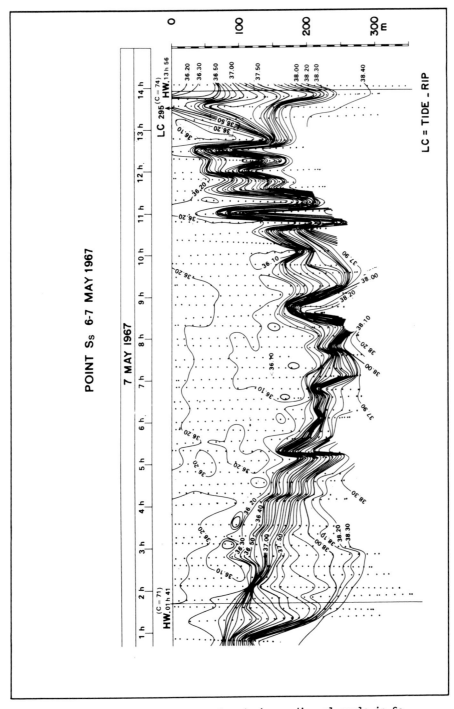

FIG. 17 b Internal wave of salinity during a diurnal cycle in Ss.
6-7 may 1967. Bathysonde yoyo-ing (N/O "Jean Charcot")

46

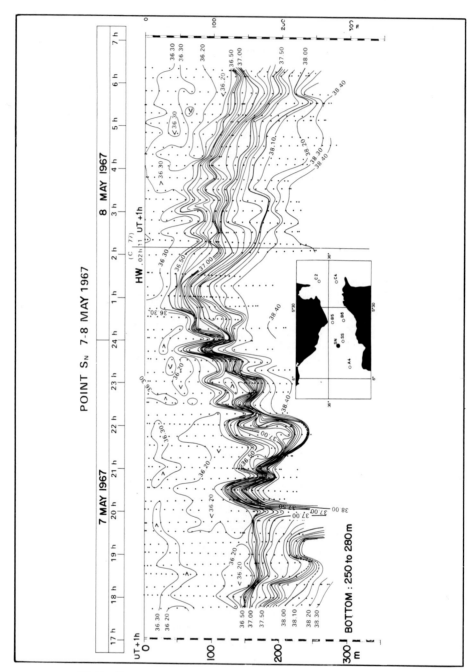

FIG. 18 Internal wave of salinity on the sill (Point Sn) 7-8 may 1967. Bathysonde yoyo-ing (N/O Jean Charcot).

Before trying to explain such a variability, we shall compare the evolution in time of currents (fig. 15) and the internal wave (fig. 16), observed the same day. From - 5 h to - 0h 30 (Tarifa), the current is outflowing in the 200 upper meters ; this is also the period when the isohalines and isotherms are shallower : the typically Mediterranean waters (S = 38.3 %$_o$) come close to the surface and, somewhat before HW (HW - 0h45), the surface temperature drops by more than 3 degrees C in 45 mn, while the salinity minimum reaches the surface. This shows that most of the water then present over the sill is directly influenced by Mediterranean water rapidly moving West and which has had to flow over the Mediterranean side of the sill and almost reaching the surface. The phenomenon is visible also on BOCKEL's curve (TR NATO n° 2 p. 326). This general ascending motion up to near the surface generates near the sill, during the period of outflow, very visible eddies already quoted.

It is at the end of that period that, on the sill (South sill Ss), the sudden reversal of current takes place in the surface layers at about HW-0h30 ; it affects at least the 100 upper meters and its phase is locked on the surface tide. A front is generated then, corresponding to a sudden inflow of Atlantic water which begins at the same time in A4. This sudden flow deeply modifies the local hydrographical structure and the interface sinks rapidly during a length of time of about 15 mn. The phenomenon is analogous to the bore, except that here, the bore is internal to the fluid. The front of the internal wave becomes steeper and tends to an "internal breaker" which is made of a front propagating East at a speed of 3 to 3.5 kn which can be followed to the East of the strait and even beyond. This kind of discontinuity appears when the wave amplitude is great with respect to the fluid depth.

II.C.2 On Tarifa section. What is particularly striking on Tarifa section is the fact that, within the 50 upper meters, the current has practically no important component to the West, contrary to what happens on the sill between - 5h 30 and - 0h 30 (Tarifa) ; instead, the inflowing component is submitted to a genuine discontinuity between + 1h 30 (Tarifa) in the center of the section and + 2h 30 (Tarifa) in the South, since (fig. 19, 20, 21) the current increases by about 3 kn in a length of time of about 30 mn.

The fact that the inflow current in the surface layers is weak between - 3 and - 1h 30 (Tarifa), that the outflowing deep current is strong between these hours, that, lastly, the maximum of outflow current is met when the interface on the sill is shallower lead to think that the deep Mediterranean outflow, creeping over the East side of the sill, reaches the surface there, as the hydrography suggested it, and brings in the necessary compensation of fluid which is necessary to fill in the divergent surface flow between the sill and Tarifa

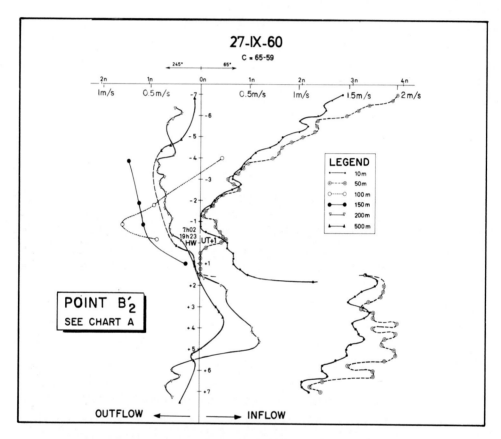

FIG. 19 Tidal variation of the longitudinal component of the global
current in B'2 (Tarifa section). 27 sept. 1960.

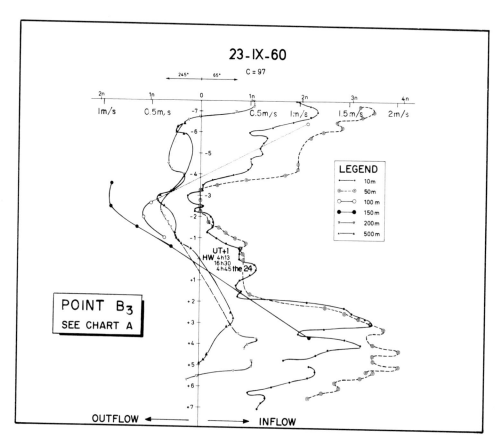

FIG. 20 Tidal variation of the longitudinal component of the global current in B3 (Tarifa section). 23 sept. 1960.

50

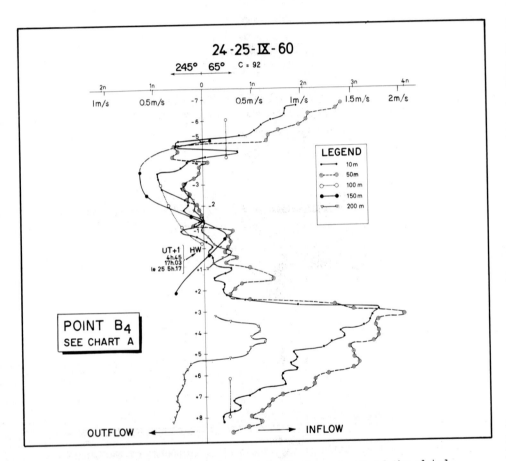

FIG. 21 Tidal variation of the longitudinal component of the global current in B4 (Tarifa section). 24-25 sept. 1960.

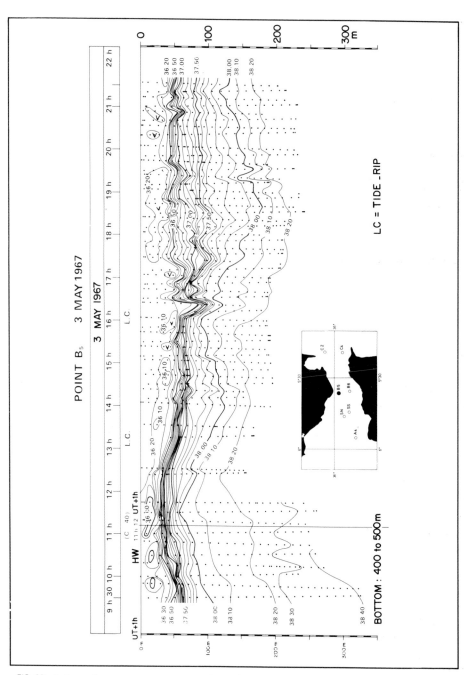

FIG. 22 Internal wave of salinity in the North of Tarifa section
(point B5). 3 may 1967. Bathysonde yoyo-ing (N/O "Jean Charcot").

52

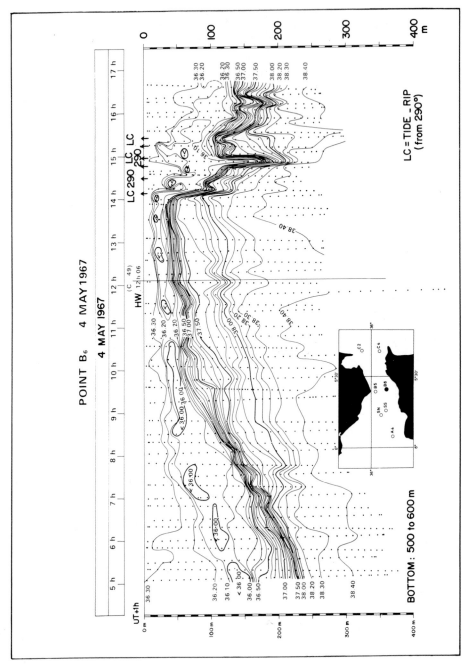

FIG. 23 Internal wave of salinity in the South of Tarifa section (point B6) 4 may 1967 (N/O "Jean Charcot").

section : as a matter of fact, the surface current is outflowing on the sill while it is inflowing on Tarifa section : it may be that, laterally, a surface flow along the North and South shores West of Tarifa section takes place also.

The current front is generated on the sill (Ss) slightly before HW and its passage coincides with the sudden deepening of the interface (fig. 15, 16), just after HW. It is propagated East and reaches Tarifa section at about + 1h 30 in mid channel and + 2h 30 (Tarifa) in the South (fig. 19, 20, 21). The passage of the front and the deepening of the interface coincide with the appearing, on the sea surface, of "slicks" which propagate locally to the ESE (from 290°) at about 3 kn.

In 1967, during the bathysonde yo-yoing in B6, slightly to the NW of B4, we observed half an dozen passages of those slicks (or tide-rips - L. C . on the figures) within 10 to 20 mn time differences between the successive ones ; the horizontal distance between them was about 1500 m. This also gives about 3 kn as the propagation speed. The passage of the front is very conspicuous in B6 (fig. 23). In the Northern part of the section, in B5, (fig. 22), the internal wave is much smaller and its profile is much more regular.

More to the East, near meridian 5° 30', the hydro-stations made on section Cn, Cc, Cs (chart A) (see fig. 35, later) display tidal internal waves more or less in phase with the surface tide, with an interface sloping down South. But no evidence of passage of the internal front visible in point B6 appears, perhaps due to an insufficient frequence of stations. However (fig. 24) the current measurements at 10 m (TR n° 30 M. CANO, 1966) show for Cc not only a rapid increase of the ever-inflowing current between HW + 0h 30 and HW + 2h, but mainly a very abrupt increase somewhat before HW + 4h 00. This corresponds probably with the passage of the front.

II.D Tidal forcing near the Eastern entrance (near meridian of Gibraltar).

The tidal effects are fairly different of those occurring on Cape Spartel meridian (A4) and in the central sector.

As regards the currents and particularly at point C2 (see chart A), strong currents are met only in the surface layer down to 80-100 m.Fig. 25, which presents the longitudinal currents at various depths as a function of the tidal hour shows that, contrary to what happens in the West, the global current does not reverse with tide in the surface layer but reverses in the deeper layers, in which the currents are weak, but with a small mean component to the West. The minimum of the inflow current in the upper layer occurs at about + 2h 30 (Tarifa : i.e. 2h 30 after the High Water at Tarifa), the maximum at about + 6 h (Tarifa) ; at depth, the phases of the alternating part of the current seem of opposite

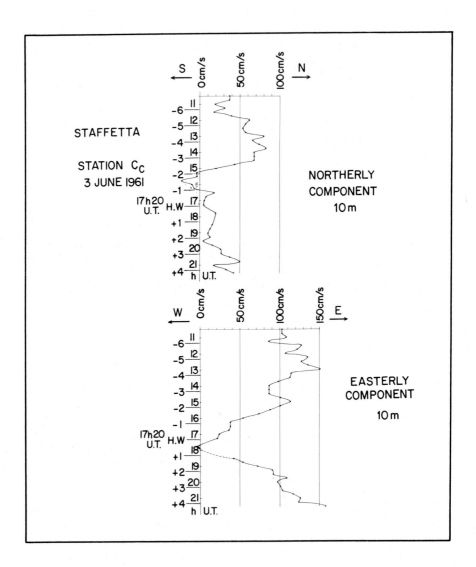

FIG. 24 Northerly and Easterly current components in Cc (meridian 5°30' W). June 3 1961.

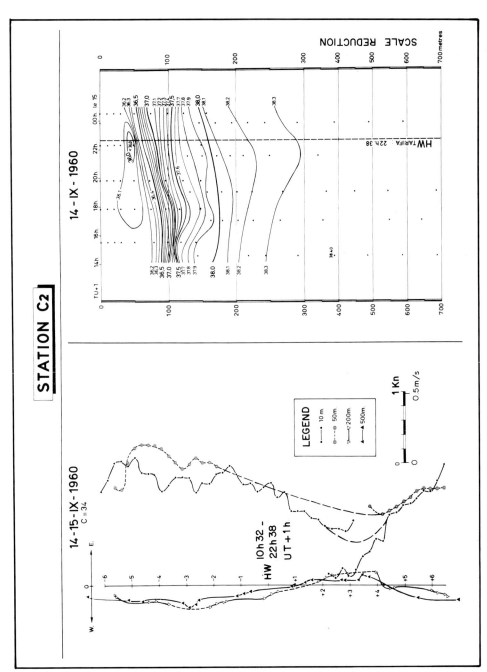

FIG. 25 Tidal variation of the longitudinal component of the global current in C2. 14-15 sept. 1960 (left) and salinity structure (right).

56

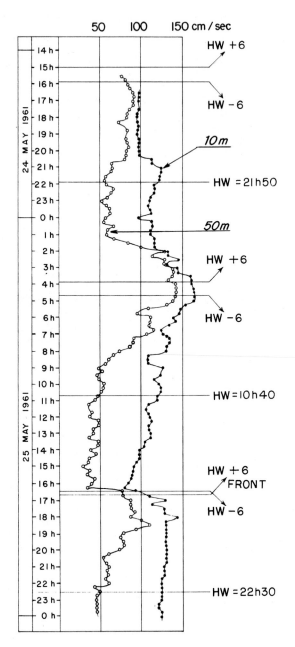

FIG. 26 Tidal variation of the longitudinal component of current (75-255°) in Gc, meridian of Gibraltar.

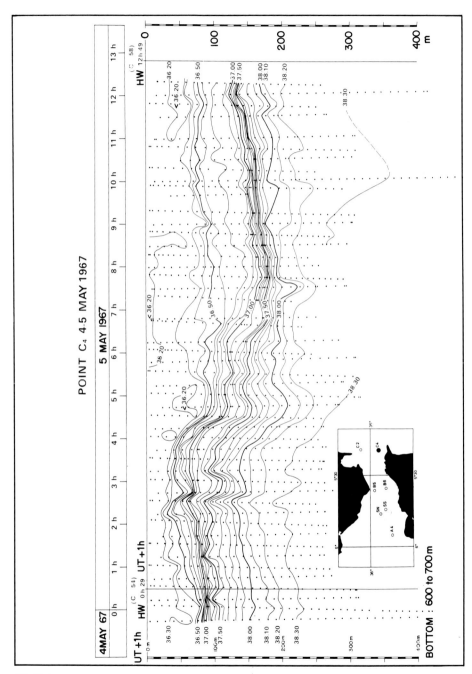

FIG. 27 Internal wave of salinity in the South of Gibraltar meridian (point C4). 4-5 may 1967. Bathysonde yoyo-ing (N/O "Jean Charcot").

58

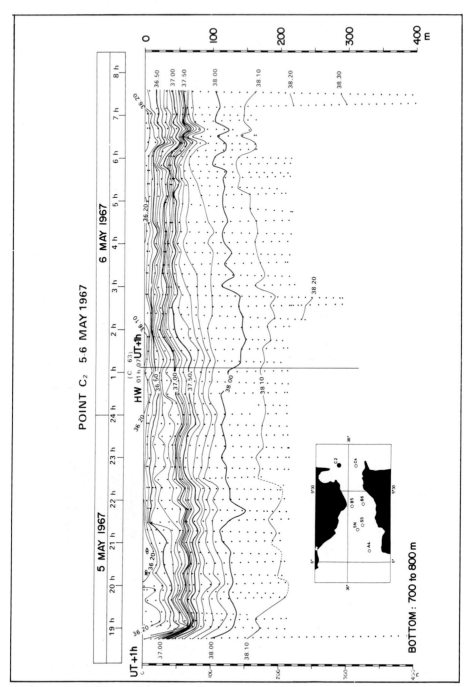

FIG. 28 Internal wave of salinity in the North of Gibraltar meridian (point C2) 5-6 may 1967. Bathysonde yoyo-ing (N/O "Jean Charcot").

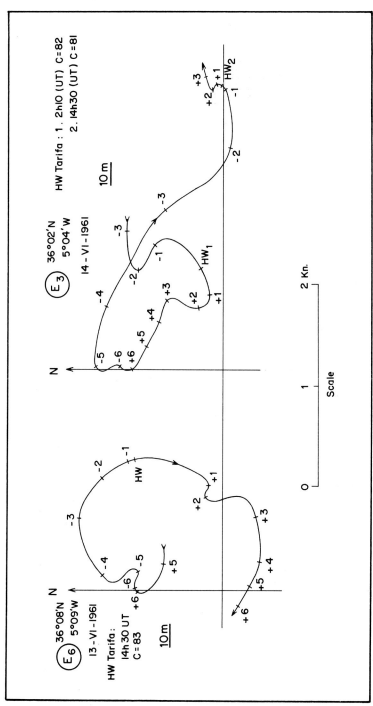

FIG. 29 Surface current roses off the Eastern entrance to the strait point E6 (13 june 1961) and E3 (14 june 1961).

phase : the maximum inflow part is about + 2 (Tarifa), the maximum outflow at about - 3 h. In the Southern part of the strait (C4, chart A), in great deapths, (latitude 35°57'6), the surface global inflow is minimum (1,2 kn) around + 5h and maximum (2,5 kn) around + 2h (Tarifa).

Coming back to the center of the waterway (point Gc) (TR n° 30. M. CANO, 1966) the maximum Eastward flow (fig. 26) is, as in C2, maximum around HW-6h 00, then decreasing slowly, at 10 m as well as 50 m. A remarkable fact (studied by CAVANIE 1973) is the <u>front</u> of current,which is stronger in 50 m (and 100 m according to CAVANIE's measurements) than in the surface ; but another curious fact is that, at least at neaps, the front takes place about HW + 3h for a tide and the next one at HW + 5h 30. This is an indication of an important effect of the diurnal tidal component on these non-linear discontinuities.

As for the hydrological regime, the internal waves have a smaller amplitude than in the West and, also, are shallower : however their amplitude is much greater near the Southern shore ; it is weak near the Northern one (fig. 27, 28).

Moreover,in the South at least (point C4 - fig. 27)the sudden increase of the depth of the isohalines about HW + 4h 00 is most probably to be connected with the passage of the front generated on the sill at HW - 0h 30, passing in point B3, B4, B6 between HW + 1h 30 and HW + 2h 30, passing through the point Ciris section slightly before HW + 4h and about the same time in C4 (or Gs in fig. 36). The front may be responsible of the small kink at HW + 5h 30 in C2 (fig. 28). Prof. FRASSETTO (1960) as well as ZIEGENBEIN (1969-70) have tracked it in the Alboran Sea. In addition CAVANIE (1972) observed them during a cruise under NATO aegis and was able to follow the movement of the front by the radar-sea return from the sill to meridian 5°10'W,in the Southern half of the strait.

Somewhat more to the East, measurements of current in CALYPSO Anchor stations E3 (36°02' N - 5° 04' W) and E6 (36°08' N - 5° 09' W), in addition to a probable large diurnal component (fig. 29), show, in the surface layer (10 m), an important component to the North specially notable about HW - 5h 00 corresponding to a clockwise rotation of the current. In the central waterway (E3) the maximum current exceeds 3 kn at springs. In the deeper layers the currents are much weaker with a mean component to the East deeper than 100 m.

The existence of an important northerly component for the mean current may be re-lated with the anticyclonic gyre in the Western Alboran sea.

II.E The synoptic hydrology

The multi-ship survey carried out in 1961 makes it possible to be informed on the water structure <u>at the same time</u> in different places;although we are far to have every two hours, as initially scheduled, hydrostations made on a longitudinal section and on five transverse sections, at springs and neaps, yet we are able to present here some indications which are probably unique.

Longitudinal_structure_on_the_line A4, Ss, Tc, Cc, Gc (fig. 30) the results are presented on a series of TS diagrams in neap tide (above) and spring tide (below) for two simultaneous hours (to within ± 0h 30) for HW + 0h 30 and HW + 6h 00 for neaps ; and for HW - 5h 00 and HW - 1 h 00 for springs. The evolution of the TS curves show that the effect of mixing is much stronger in spring tide (below) than in neap tide.

Transverse_structure_of_salinity

In the following figures(31 to 36) are shown the simultaneous evolution of the water structure in 2 or 3 points across the strait. The instantaneous transverse slope may be deduced from the graphs.

Sections_A2,_A4 (fig.31) in neap tide (Coefficient from 42 to 65). It is seen that depth of the interface is greater by about 30 to 40 m in A4 with respect to A2. The amplitude is smaller in A2.

Section_Sn_Ss (fig 32) in spring tide. As already seen on figures 18 and 19 (not simultaneous), here we have simultaneous, although much more sparse, measuments(classical hydrostations) ; the profile is bumpy and the shallow interface is found somewhat before HW. In general the interface is deeper to the South.

Section_Tn,_Tc,_Ts (fig 33) and Tn Ts (fig 34).The strong descent of the interface after HW is clear on fig. 33 for Tn and Tc ; and on fig. 34 in Ts.

Section_Cn,_Cc,Cs (fig. 35). The interface is very close to the surface in the North and the center of the section. No clear indication of the front passage appears.

Section_Gn,_Gc,_Gs (fig 36). The most remarkable fact is that the interface (37 ‰) practically reaches the surface in the North (Gn), while it is at least in 60 m in Gs.

This phenomenon which is regularly present may have a great influence in the generation of the instabilities of the internal waves and of the front which, according to CAVANIE (1972), is only visible on this Southern half of the strait. An important role of the earth's rotation is thus to be expected and should be included in dynamical models.

In conclusion to this chapter, one may say that, if, in this Western part of the strait (A4), the internal wave is "locked" on the surface tide phase and keeps a regular quasi-sinusoidal profile, an additional complex phenomenon is superimposed in this Eastern strait : this phenomenon generated on the sill

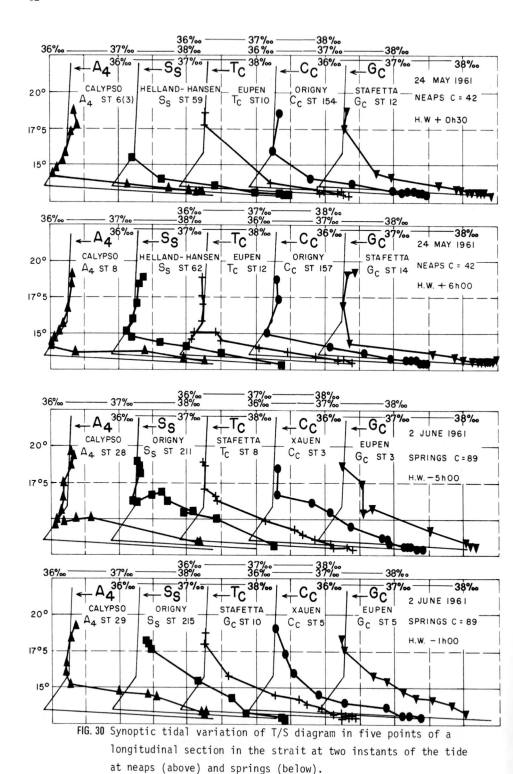

FIG. 30 Synoptic tidal variation of T/S diagram in five points of a longitudinal section in the strait at two instants of the tide at neaps (above) and springs (below).

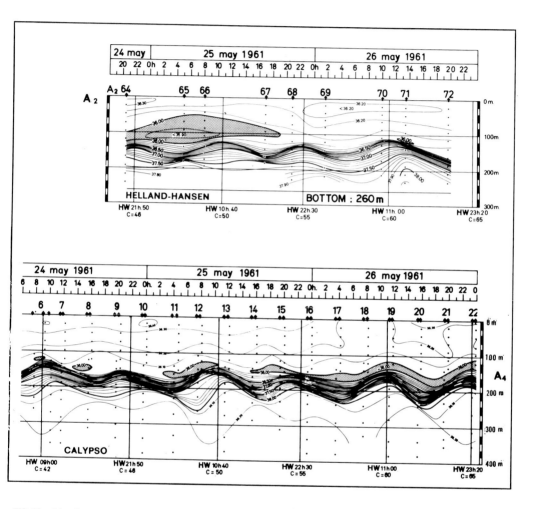

FIG. 31 Simultaneous internal wave of salinity on section A2 A4. (Western entrance) - neap tide.

64

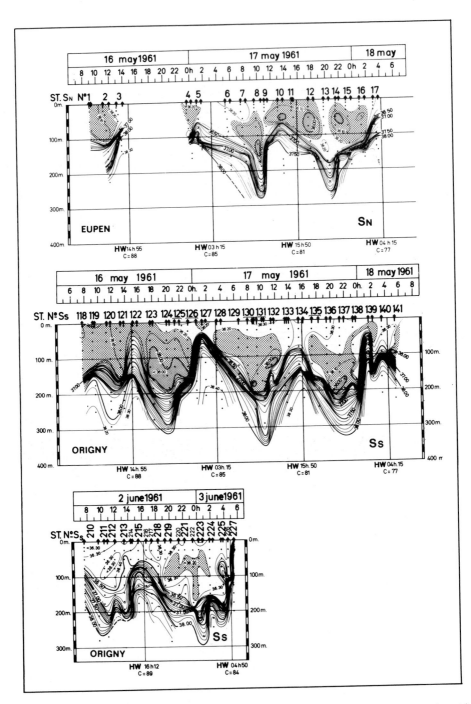

FIG. 32 Simultaneous internal wave of salinity on section SN SS (Sill) Spring tide

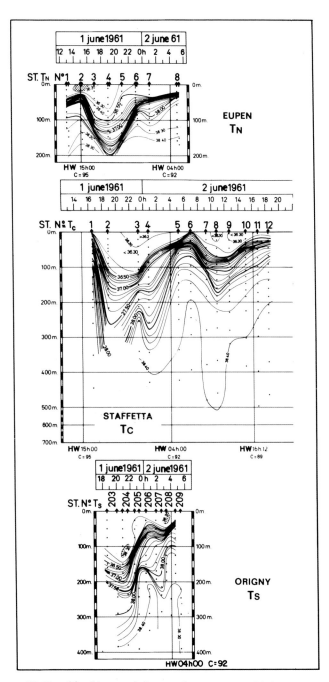

FIG. 33   Simultaneous internal wave of salinity on
          section Tn Tc Ts (Tarifa) - spring tide.

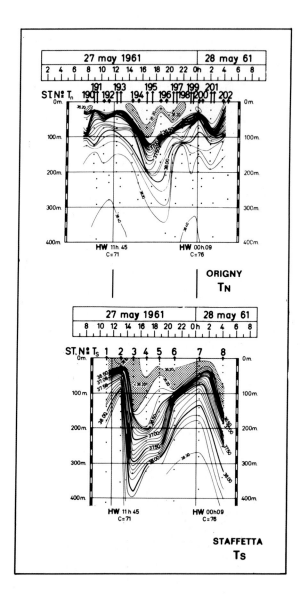

FIG. 34 Simultaneous internal wave of salinity
on section Tn Ts (Tarifa). Mean tide.

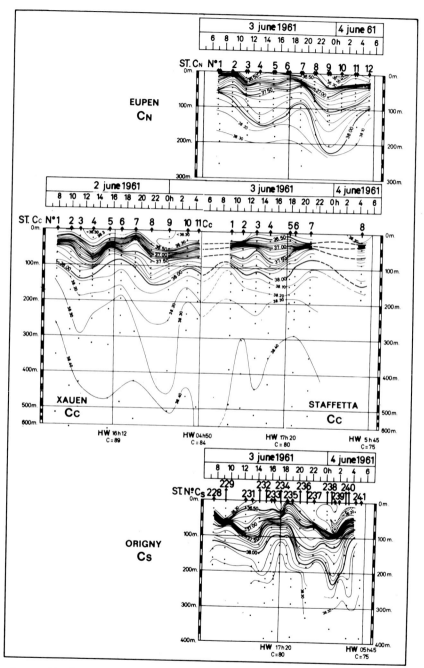

FIG. 35 Simultaneous internal wave of salinity on section Cn, Cc, Cs
(5°30'W). Spring tide.

68

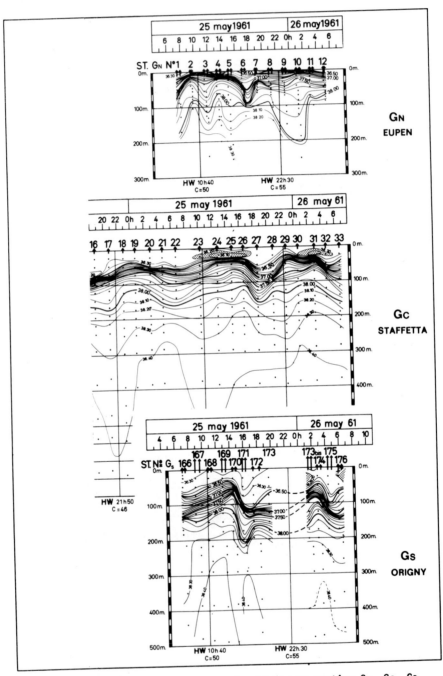

FIG. 36 Simultaneous internal wave of salinity on section Gn, Gc, Gs (Eastern entrance). Neap tide.

is very intense and made of an internal breaker which, more to the East, and particularly near the Southern shore of the stait, deeply modifies the internal wave profile and controls, in fact, the tidal part of the current.

III METEOROLOGICAL EFFECTS

But the tide is not the only phenomenon which induces, in the strait, important modifications of the regime ; if the tide was the only factor the values of the fluxes exchanged during a diurnal cycle should be the same. Clearly it is not the case.

Table I   listing the results based on direct measurements at point A4 in 1960 and 1971 shows that variations of at least 50 % are present for the diurnal fluxes.

Following our measurements of 1958 (LACOMBE 1961), we examined meteorological effects. These may act on two scales : 1 - the effects of local winds over the strait : 2 - the effects of "lows" on the Mediterranean and, more precisely, over the Western Mediterranean.

III.A Effects of the local meteorology

The wind regime, over the strait, is only longitudinal at sea level ; in autumn and winter the prevailing winds are from the West ; in summer from the East and and they may be strong 25-35 kn for over a week in August. The frictional force on the surface tends to increase the surface current in the direction of the wind ; to slacken or even reverse the current flowing upwind . The velocity modification of the current are mainly within the upper 20 m ; these may induce currents of .5 kn along the wind.

In A4, in the Western end of the stait, in may-june 1961, when the wind was strong from SSW, the incoming flux was particularly strong (5 june 1961), fig.2.

III.B The effects of the general distribution of atmospheric pressure over the Western Mediterranean have an incidence on a greater scale. It is well known that along many shores, there is a clear relationship between the evolution with time of the "daily mean sea level"(practically free from sea tidal effects) and of the local atmospheric pressure. Often the local sea level reacts as an "inverted barometer" : an increase of pressure of 1 mbar causes a decrease of about 1 cm of the sea level.

This "inverted barometer" reaction is fairly well verified in many Mediterranean harbors. Then, if we admit that this "law" can be applied in the open sea, it is seen that a drop of the mean pressure of 1 mbar in one day over the whole Medi-terranean corresponds to an increase of about 1 cm for the sea level. As the surface of the sea is 2.5 10^6 km^2 (excluding the Black Sea) the volume of water involved is 2.5 10^{10} m3/ day, ie about 2.9 10^5 m3/s : this is of the order of 1/4 of the mean fluxes in the strait. One can thus expect important effects on these fluxes.

Another approach may be made : in the presence of Coriolis force an increase of the incoming current at the surface will cause an elevation of the sea level on the Southern shore of the strait and/or a decrease on the Northern. In that line we tried to relate the variations of the daily mean sea level on the two shores of the strait to the mean atmospheric pressure over the Mediterranean. M. CREPON (1965) extended the study to a number of monthly periods during which the distribution of the atmospheric pressure over the Mediterranean showed large variation. Studying the relative mean sea level on the South shore (Ceuta) relatively to the North shore (Gibraltar)[*], he notes the frequent presence of fairly good correlation between the relative mean sea level and mean atmospheric pressure. As the surface flux is clearly related to the total incoming flux, it is apparent that low pressures tend to increase the incoming flux and conversely high pressures tend to decrease it.

This simple qualitative rule raises difficulties, in particular in relation with the equation of continuity (CREPON 1965), but it is a simple, approximate guide.

Of course, a relation often exists between the local wind regime and the general regime over the Mediterranean : the Westerlies blow over the strait when the pressure is low over the W. Mediterranean and the local effects may favour the increase of fluxes due to the inverted barometer reactions of the sea level in the Mediterranean.

IV RELATIONS OF THE REGIME OF THE STRAIT WITH PHENOMENA PRESENT IN THE ADJACENT SEAS EAST AND WEST

These are the Western Alboran Sea and the Bay of Cadix. The anticyclonic gyre of the Western Alboran Sea - a very conspicuous and permanent feature visible on satellite thermographs -which may be generated by the obliquity of the mean surface jet flowing to the East with respect to the E-W axis of the Western Alboran Sea - will be considered by other speakers in this colloquium (DONGUY (1962) NATO TR n° 2, oct 1962, GROUSSON and FAROUX (1963), LANOIX 1972, 1974 ; LACOMBE 1977, PETIT et al (1978) CHENEY and DOBLAR (1979).

---

[*]In the absence of any levelling network linking the two shores of the strait, the levels have to be referred to an arbitrary datum and, so, only the variations of their difference are accessible.

As for the existence of the "density current" of Mediterranean water flowing Westward in the thalweg of the submarine valley following the strait to the West, it is a remarkable example of the obstacle opposing to mixing between waters of small density differences, despite the presence of superimposed strong current (LACOMBE et al 1970, NATO TR n° 7 ₋ BOYUM G, MADELAIN 1970).

CONCLUSION

In the strait of Gibraltar a range of various phenomena occur which have a great interest for physical oceanography because they are typical examples for a number of them. It is a model strait. The relatively great length of the strait, about 100 km from 6°40' W to 5°20' W permit the full development of some processes which reach remarkable amplitude. Observation is still, for the time being, our main source of information, because purely dynamical modelling is inaccessible, due to the complexity of the events present. We know new programs are envisaged to be carried out in the area. This is very fortunate because, after the great effort during the 60', no important multiship work was made since then and we still need many informations to truly understand what happens. For instance sufficient current measurements are still lacking on the sill itself. We have very few information on the role which may have, for the regime of the Eastern half of the strait the flow taking place near the N and S shores W of Tarifa. We do not know with suffucent accuracy the fundamental data regarding the mean exchanged flows and their seasonal variations ; we have no clear idea of the large internal waves on the Southern shores, with respect to those on the Northern.

We hope that these questions will be elucidated by the planned future obser- vations, which may in turn permit the building of a good numerical model of the strait.

72

REFERENCES

Bethoux, J.P., 1980. Mean water fluxes across sections in the Mediterranean Sea, evaluated on the basis of water and salt budgets and of observed salinities. Oceanol. Acta, 3, 76-88.

Cavanie, A., 1972. Observations de fronts internes dans le détroit de Gibraltar pendant la campagne océanographique OTAN 1970 et interprétation des résultats par un modèle mathématique. Mém. Soc. Roy. Sci. Liège, 6ème série, II, 27-41.

Cavanie, A., 1973. Observations oceanographiques dans le détroit de Gibraltar pendant la campagne PHYGIB (sept.-oct. 1971). Ann. Hydrogr., 5ème série, Vol. 1, fasc. 1, 75-84.

Cheney R.E., R.A. Doblar, 1979. Alboran Sea 1977 : Physical characteristics and atmospherically induced variations of the oceanic frontal system, US Naval Oceanogr. Off., Techn. Note 3700-82-79, 24 p.

Crepon M., 1965. Influence de la pression atmosphérique sur le niveau moyen de la Méditerranée occidentale et sur le flux à travers le détroit de Gibraltar. Présentation d'observations. Cah. Océanogr., XVII, 15-32 and Nato T.R. n° 21 mars 1965.

Donguy, J.R., 1962. Hydrologie en Mer d'Alboran. Cah. Oceanogr. XIV.8 pp 573-578.

Frassetto, R., 1960. A preliminary survey of the thermal microstructure in the Strait of Gibraltar. Deep-sea res., 7, (3), 152-163.

Frassetto R., 1964. Short-period vertical displacements of the upper layer in the Strait of Gibraltar. Saclant ASW Res. Center, Tech. Rep. n° 30, part 1 text, part 2 diagrammes, Nov. 1964.

Grousson R. et J. Faroux, 1969. Measures des courants de surface en Mer d'Alboran. Cah. Océanogr. XV, 10 pp 716-721 and Nato T.R. n° 10 feb. 1964.

Lacombe H., 1961. Contribution à l'étude du détroit de Gibraltar, étude dynamique. Cah. Océanogr. XII, 2 pp 73-107.

Lacombe H. et C. Richez, 1961. Contribution à l'étude du détroit de Gibraltar II Etude hydrologique. Cah. Océanogr., XIII, 5 pp 276-291.

Lacombe H., P. Tchernia, C. Richez & L. Gamberoni, 1964. Deuxième contribution à l'étude du régime du détroit de Gibraltar (Travaux de 1960). Cah. Océanogr. Paris XVI, P. 283-327 and Nato T.R. n° 14 july 1964.

Lacombe H., F. Madelain, J.C. Gascard, 1968. Rapport sur la campagne "Gibraltar I" du N/O "Jean Charcot", 7 av.-12 mai 1967. Cah océanogr., XX, 102-107.

Lanoix F, 1972, 1974. Etude hydrologique et dynamique de la mer d'Alboran, thèse IIIème cycle Paris VI, 28.VI.72 et Rapp. Techn. OTAN n° 66 (mai 1974).

Madelain F., 1970. Influence de la topographie du fond sur l'écoulement méditerranéen entre le détroit de Gibraltar et le Cap Saint-Vincent. Cah. Océanogr. XXII, 43-61.

Peluchon G., M. Bockel, 1962. Travaux océanographiques de l'"Origny" dans le détroit de Gibraltar. 1ère partie : hydrologie dans le détroit. Cah. Oceanogr. XIV, 323-329.

Petit M., V. Klaus, R. Gelci, F.Fusey, J.J. Thery, P. Bouly, J.T. Gallagher, 1978. Etude d'un tourbillon océanique d'échelle moyenne en mer d'Alboran par emploi conjoint de techniques spatiales et océanographiques. CR. Acad. Sci. Paris, vol. 287 B, 215-218, 8 fig.

Tixeront J., 1970. Le bilan hydrologique de la Mer Noire et de la Méditerranée. Cah. Océanogr. 22, 227-237.

Zenk W., 1975. On the Mediterranean outflow West of Gibraltar. "Meteor" Forschungergebnisse n° 16 pp 23-34.

Ziegenbein J., 1969. Short internal waves in the Strait of Gibraltar. Deep Sea Res., vol. 16, 479-487.

Ziegenbein J., 1970. Spatial observations of short internal waves in the Strait of Gibraltar. Deep Sea Res., vol. 17, 867-875.

NATO Technical Reports (T.R.) du Sous-Comité océanographique

T.R. n° 2 - Projet Gibraltar. Résultats des observations océanographiques effectuées en mai et juin 1961 dans la région du détroit de Gibraltar.
Oct. 1962.

T.R. n° 3 - Mosby H., 1961-62. Hydrological observations of the M/S "Helland-
Hansen" near the Strait of Gibraltar. May-June 1961. Août 1962.

T.R. n° 4 - Current measurements, meteorological observations and soundings of
the M/S "Helland-Hansen" near the Strait of Gibraltar. May-June 1961.
Tables. Nov. 1962.

T.R. n° 7 - Boyum G., 1963. Hydrology and currents in the area West of Gibraltar.
Results from the "Helland-Hansen" Expedition May-June 1961. Mai 1963.

T.R. n° 10 - Projet Gibraltar. Résultats des observations effectuées en mai et
juin 1961 dans la région du détroit de Gibraltar. Février 1964.

T.R. n° 14 - Projet Gibraltar. Résultats des observations océanographiques effectuées dans la région du détroit de Gibraltar. Juill. 1964.

T.R. n° 21 - Projet Gibraltar. Résultats des observations océanographiques effectuées dans la région du détroit de Gibraltar. Mars 1965.

T.R. n° 30 - Cano M., 1966. Campagna oceanografica della nave "Staffetta" della
marina militare nelle stretto di Gibilterra (8 maggio - 19 giuno 1961).
Octobre 1966.

T.R. n° 31 - Projet Gibraltar. Résultats des observations effectuées à bord du
navire belge "Eupen" (mai-juin 1961). Décembre 1966.

T.R. n° 34 - Boyum G. Hydrological observations of the M/S "Helland-Hansen" in
the area West of Gibraltar. May 1965. Tables. Bergen. Feb. 1967.

T.R. n° 35 - Boyum G. Current measurements of the M/S "Helland-Hansen" in the
area West of Gibraltar. Tables. May 1965. Bergen march 1967.

T.R. n° 36 - Boyum G., 1967. Hydrology and currents in the West of Gibraltar.
Results from the "Helland-Hansen" expedition. May 1965. Bergen. April 1967.

A REDUCED GRAVITY NUMERICAL MODEL OF CIRCULATION IN THE ALBORAN SEA

RUTH PRELLER

JAYCOR, 205 South Whiting Street, Alexandria, VA 22304, USA

HARLEY E. HURLBURT

Environmental Simulation Branch (Code 322), Naval Ocean Research and Development
Activity, NSTL Station, MS 39529, USA

ABSTRACT

Oceanographic observations have shown the existence of a large anticyclonic
gyre in the western Alboran Sea. Satellite imagery demonstrates the persistence
of the Alboran Gyre and suggests that the direction of inflow through the Strait
of Gibraltar plays an important role in determining the size and location of
the gyre. Satellite data also reveals more time varying, smaller scale circulation patterns in the eastern Alboran Sea.

The reduced gravity model of Hurlburt and Thompson (1980, J. Phys. Oceanogr.
10: 1611-1651) has been adapted to the semi-enclosed basin of the Alboran Sea.
The model domain is a rectangle 600 km east-west by 160 km north-south. The
Strait of Gibraltar is modeled by a port in the western boundary and the eastern
boundary is entirely open. When the model is forced by a northeastward inflow
through the port in the western boundary, it evolves to a steady state which
exhibits a meandering eastward current. The first meander of this current forms
the northern boundary of a strong anticyclonic gyre in the western part of the
basin. The dimensions and location of the model gyre are consistent with the
persistent gyre observed to dominate the western Alboran Sea. A weaker cyclonic
circulation in the eastern Alboran is also predicted by the model. This model
solution closely resembles the observational data of Lanoix (1974, NATO Tech.
Report 66, Brussels). The solution was obtained without including bottom
topography, coastline features, or winds which have been suggested as important
factors in determining the size and location of the Alboran Gyre. A preliminary
investigation using the model indicates the importance of inflow angle, inflow
vorticity, and the location of the Strait of Gibraltar. This model does not
account for the variability observed in the circulation of the eastern Alboran
Sea.

1. INTRODUCTION

The Alboran Sea is an attractive semi-enclosed domain for the study of
hydrodynamic phenomena often observed in large oceans. These phenomena include
meandering currents, a persistent gyre, and transient eddies. Of particular
interest is a persistent and intense anticyclonic gyre which dominates the
circulation of the western Alboran Sea. A more complex time varying circulation
pattern exists in the eastern Alboran. This paper reports the preliminary stages
of an effort to model the circulation of the Alboran Sea. A highly idealized
numerical model has simulated the major features of the upper layer circulation,
particularly the anticyclonic gyre.

The circulation of the Alboran Sea is dependent on both Atlantic and
Mediterranean waters. Atlantic water flows through the narrow (20 km wide) and
shallow (300 m deep) Strait of Gibraltar into the Alboran Sea forming a 150-200 m
deep surface layer. (Ovchinnikov, 1966; Lanoix, 1974; Katz, 1972). Mediterranean
water enters the Alboran at its open eastern boundary and flows slowly westward
in the form of an intermediate and lower layer. It has been suggested that even
the deepest water can exit through the Strait (Stommel et al, 1973; Gascard, 1978).
The large volume transport of inflowing Atlantic water, 1 to 2 x 10^6 m^3/sec,
(Lacombe, 1971; Bethoux, 1979; Lacombe, 1982) retains its   as a narrow
(30 km wide) jet with initial speeds of 100 cm/sec near the Strait (Lacombe,
1961; Peluchon and Donguy, 1962; Grousson and Faroux, 1963; Lanoix, 1974; Cheney,
1977; Petit et al, 1978; and Wannamaker, 1979). The jet enters the basin and
flows northeast to approximately $4^{\circ}W$, curves southward and then splits (Fig. 1).
Part of the jet flows to the west and is incorporated in an anticyclonic gyre,
while the remainder flows southeast to Cape Tres Forcas and then along the African
coast forming the southern periphery of a cyclonic circulation.

Satellite infrared imagery (Fig. 2) indicates variations in the shape,
location and intensity of the persistent anticyclonic gyre which dominates the
western Alboran Sea. Figure 2a shows the gyre occupying the majority of the
western Alboran basin as in Fig. 1. Figure 2b shows the gyre with a smaller
north-south extent and indicates a jet through the Strait of Gibraltar which
flows almost due east. Hydrographic data and satellite infrared images support
the year-round persistence of the gyre, although its size and location varies
(Stevenson, 1977; Cheney, 1978; Wannamaker, 1979; Burkov et al, 1979; Gallagher
et al, 1981). In the eastern portion of the Alboran Sea a general pattern of
alternating cyclonic and anticyclonic circulations has been observed (Cheney,
1978; Lanoix, 1974). Satellite imagery shows that, compared to the western
Alboran, this circulation pattern is far more variable and of smaller scale.

The purpose of this project is to simulate observed circulation patterns
in the Alboran Sea and to investigate their dynamics. In this paper we report

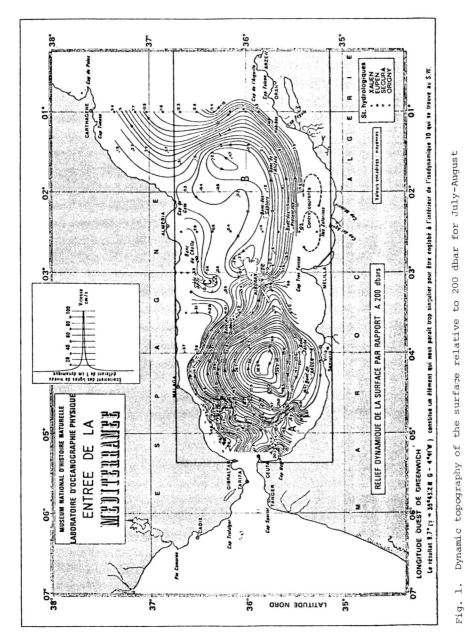

Fig. 1. Dynamic topography of the surface relative to 200 dbar for July-August 1962. Overlaid rectangle is the model Alboran Sea geometry. (Lanoix, 1974)

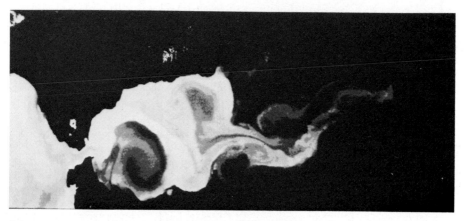

(a)

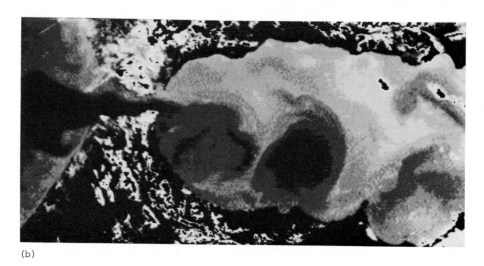

(b)

Fig. 2. NOAA 6 infrared satellite imagery view of the Strait of Gibraltar and Alboran Sea. Lighter shades indicate colder surface temperatures. a) June 25, 1980; b) December 14, 1979.

on preliminary results from the simplest model capable of simulating major features of the circulation. This is a reduced gravity model in a semi-enclosed, rectangular domain. It is essentially a model of the first baroclinic mode and does not permit baroclinic instability or the inclusion of bottom topography.

The model formulation and parameters are discussed in Section 2. In Section 3 the model results are presented in terms of a pivotal experiment and some deviations from it. Section 3.1 discusses the pivotal experiment. The subsections which follow investigate the influences of (3.2) inflow angle, (3.3) port location, (3.4) boundary effects, and (3.5) inflow vorticity.

2. THE MODEL

A nonlinear reduced gravity model, developed for the Gulf of Mexico by Hurlburt and Thompson (1980), has been adapted for the Alboran Sea. The model equations are solved numerically using an economical semi-implicit scheme. The model consists of an active upper layer and a lower layer which is infinitely deep and at rest. It is stably stratified and has a fixed density constrast between two immiscible layers. The model assumes a hydrostatic, Boussinesq fluid in a rotating right-handed coordinate system on a β-plane. The vertically integrated model equations are

$$\frac{\partial \vec{V}_1}{\partial t} + (\nabla \cdot \vec{V}_1 + \vec{V}_1 \cdot \nabla)\vec{v}_1 + \hat{k} \times f\vec{V}_1$$

$$= -g'h_1 \nabla h_1 + (\vec{\tau}_1 - \vec{\tau}_2)/\rho + A\nabla^2 \vec{V}_1$$

$$\frac{\partial h_1}{\partial t} + \nabla \cdot \vec{V}_1 = 0$$

where

$$\nabla = \frac{\partial}{\partial x} \hat{i} + \frac{\partial}{\partial y} \hat{j}$$

$$\vec{V}_1 = h_1 \vec{v}_1 = h_1 (u_1 \hat{i} + v_1 \hat{j})$$

$$g' = g(\rho_2 - \rho_1)/\rho$$

$$f = f_o + \beta(y - y_o)$$

$$\underset{i}{} = \frac{x}{i} \hat{i} + \frac{y}{i} \hat{j}$$

and x and y are tangent-plane Cartesian coordinates with x directed eastward
and y northward, u_1 and v_1 are the eastward and northward velocity components
in the upper layer, h_1 is the upper layer thickness, t is time, g is the acceleration due to gravity, ρ_i is the density of seawater in layer i, f_o and y_o are
the values of the Coriolis parameter and the y-coordinate at the southern
boundary, $\vec{\tau}_1$ is the wind stress, and $\vec{\tau}_2$ is the interfacial stress. The
remaining parameters are defined in Table 1.

TABLE 1

Model parameters for the pivotal experiment

Parameter	Definition	Value
A	eddy viscosity	$250 \text{ m}^2 \text{sec}^{-1}$
β	(df/dy)	$2 \times 10^{-11} \text{m}^{-1} \text{sec}^{-1}$
f_o	Coriolis parameter	$8 \times 10^{-5} \text{sec}^{-1}$
g'	reduced gravity due to stratification	$.02 \text{ m sec}^{-2}$
H_1	undisturbed upper layer depth	200 m
H_2	undisturbed lower layer depth	∞
$L_x \times L_y$	horizontal dimensions of the model domain	600 km x 160 km
$\Delta x \times \Delta y$	horizontal grid spacing for each dependent variable	10 km x 5 km
Δt	time step	1 hr.
$\vec{v}_{1 in}$	inflow velocity	100 cm/sec
α	angle of inflow	21° north of east
t_s	inflow spin up time constant	30 days

   Figure 1 shows the model domain superimposed on a map of the Alboran Sea.
This domain is 600 km x 160 km with 10 km x 5 km grid resolution for each
dependent variable. Forcing is due solely to prescribed inflow through the
western port (Strait of Gibraltar). Inflow is exactly compensated by outflow
through an open eastern boundary. This is accomplished by allowing normal flow
at the eastern boundary to be self-determined and by imposing an integral
constraint on total mass outflow (Hurlburt and Thompson, 1980). Except at the
inflow and outflow ports, the boundaries are rigid and a no-slip condition is
prescribed on the tangential flow. Along the eastern boundary the tangential
component is set to zero one-half grid distance outside the physical domain.
   The model parameters for the pivotal experiment are given in Table 1.
In this experiment the western (inflow) port is centered 102 km from the southern
boundary and is 15 km wide, a width appropriate for the Strait of Gibraltar

at a depth of 100 m. The specification of the model forcing is accomplished
in either of two ways. 1) by prescribing velocity ($\vec{v}_{lin}$) or 2) by prescribing
transport ($\vec{V}_{lin}$) and allowing the model to determine the inflow velocities. The
former is used in the pivotal experiment. The total inflow transport used in
the model (2.5×10^6 m^3/sec) is higher than observed. This value is necessary
to drive a uniform inflow profile for $\vec{v}_1$ or $\vec{V}_1$ with speeds of $\sim$ 100 cm/sec,
given the port width and upper layer depth in Table 1. The inflow is spun up
with a time constant of 30 days to minimize the excitation of high frequency
waves. The angle of inflow was varied based on direct observations (Lacombe,
1961) and on inferences from satellite imagery. The standard inflow angle was
chosen to be 21° north of east based on the geometric orientation of the Strait
of Gibraltar. Possibly important wind forcing (Ovchinnikov et al, 1976; Mommsen,
1978) is neglected to allow focus on the circulation driven by flow through the
Strait of Gibraltar.

Substantial effort was made to assure that unphysical aspects of the model
such as the grid resolution and the time step did not significantly influence
the model solution. The open eastern boundary condition was a special concern
and one important test of its influence is discussed in Section 3.4. The integral
constraint on the total mass flux through the eastern boundary resulted in plane
wave reflection of sufficient amplitude to pose a significant problem. The eddy
viscosity (A) chosen for the model is the minimum value which prevents any
visible oscillation in the solution due to this reflection. An eddy viscosity
$2\frac{1}{2}$ times smaller yielded nearly the same solution except for some unphysical
oscillations. A viscous boundary layer using a linear interfacial stress was
also applied near the open eastern boundary in an effort to damp the oscillations
due to the integral constraint. The maximum value for the drag coefficient was
10^{-3} sec^{-1} at the eastern boundary. It decreased exponentially away from the
boundary with an e-folding width of 50 km. This aided only slightly in damping
the reflection from the integral constraint. Except for the viscous boundary
layer, the interfacial stress was zero.

3. MODEL RESULTS

Over 40 numerical experiments were performed for the Alboran Sea. Some
preliminary results will be presented in terms of a pivotal experiment and
selected variations from it. Most of the numerical solutions evolved to a
steady state in about one year.

3.1 The pivotal experiment

The pivotal experiment uses the parameters in Table 1. Figure 3 shows the
steady state model solution (day 500) in terms of the pycnocline anomaly (PA).

The PA is the deviation of the interface between the upper and lower layers
from its initial flat position at 200 m depth. Downward deviations are positive
(upper layer thicker than initially). The most striking features are 1) a
meandering current which traverses the model domain from west to east, 2) a
strong anticyclonic gyre in the western 240 km of the basin, and 3) a weak
cyclonic circulation to the east. This pattern is very similar to the temperature field shown in a satellite image (Fig. 2a) and to Lanoix's dynamic topography (Fig. 1).

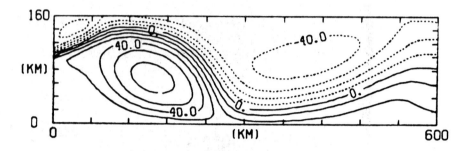

Fig. 3. PA (pynocline anomaly) of the pivotal case solution at day 500. Inflow
angle is 21° north of east. Solid contours are positive (downward) deviations.
Dashed contours are negative (upward) deviations. Contour interval is 10 m.

In rotating tank experiment, Whitehead and Miller (1979) attempted to simulate the Alboran Gyre using a density driven current. They suggest that the
dimensions of the gyre depend on a coastline feature, Cape Tres Forcas. It has
also been suggested by Porter (1976) that the dimensions of the gyre are directly
related to the bottom topography with Alboran Island acting as the eastern
boundary of the gyre. Yet the reduced gravity model is able to simulate an
Alboran Gyre with realistic dimensions, while including neither coastline
irregularities nor bottom topography. The model gyre is also a persistent
rather than a transient feature of the flow, again in accord with observations
noted earlier.

3.2 The effect of inflow angle
     The circulation pattern in the pivotal experiment (Fig. 3) and satellite
imagery (Fig. 2) suggest that the inflow angle may exert an important influence
on the meandering current and the Alboran Gyre. Thus, a number of experiments
were carried out varying the inflow angle. One experiment used the standard
parameters from Table 1 except that the inflow entered the model domain normal
to the western boundary. In the steady state solution for this case (Fig. 4),
the jet enters the basin flowing due east, but quickly veers southward. The

anticyclonic gyre in the western part of the basin is restricted to a much smaller north-south extent than in the standard case. The cyclonic circulation to the east is intensified and a new anticyclonic flow appears in the eastern 200 km. This circulation pattern is similar to that of the sea surface temperature seen in the satellite infrared imagery of Fig. 2b.

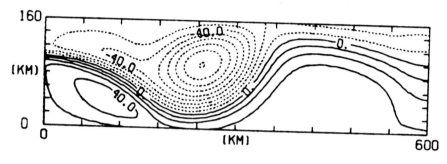

Fig. 4. PA of the pivotal case at day 500 but with due east inflow. Contour interval is 10 m.

3.3 Port location

The next set of experiments was designed to observe the importance of the north-south location of the inflow port. If the Strait of Gibraltar was located south of the basin center, how would the circulation pattern be affected? Two such experiments used the standard parameters of Table 1 except that the port was centered 7 km south of the center of the western boundary and the inflow angles were those of Fig. 3 (standard 21° north of east) and Fig. 4 (0°). The steady state solutions are presented in Fig. 5. Figure 5a, with the angled inflow of the standard case, shows 1) an anticyclonic gyre smaller than that of the standard case in the western part of the basin, 2) a strong cyclonic circulation in the central part, and 3) a weak anticyclonic circulation in the eastern part. When the inflow enters flowing due east (Fig. 5b) the western gyre is even smaller than in Fig. 5a and the two gyres to the east are slightly stronger. Clearly, the entrance of the Atlantic water in the northern half of the Alboran Sea facilitates the development of an Alboran Gyre of large north-south extent.

3.4 Boundary effects

The influence of the domain size and the open eastern boundary were also investigated. As described in Section 2, the pivotal experiment includes a viscous boundary layer near the open eastern boundary. One test compared the pivotal experiment with this boundary layer (Fig. 3) to an identical experiment without it (not shown). Except in the region of the viscous boundary layer, the results were almost identical. In the experiment without the boundary layer,

84

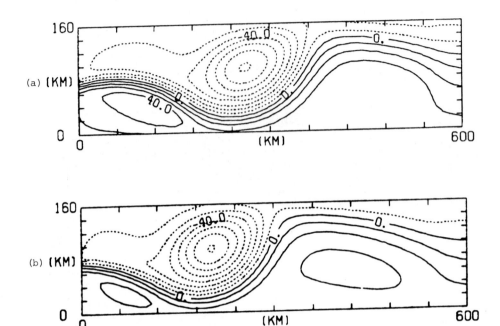

Fig. 5. PA of the pivotal case at day 500 but with the port centered 7 km south of the center of the western boundary. a) inflow angled 21° north of east; b) due east inflow. Contour interval is 10 m.

the current maintained its cross-sectional structure as it approached and passed through the open eastern boundary. When it was included, the PA contours spread out in the viscous boundary layer and the jet structure disintegrated to a more uniform flow (see Fig. 3).

Numerical experiments were also performed to determine if the open eastern boundary was seriously distorting the solution. Fig. 6 shows the results of a critical test. It compares two solutions which differ only in the east-west extent of the model domain. In each case there is a viscous boundary layer near the open eastern boundary. In this test, changing the location of the open eastern boundary caused only minor changes in the solution in the western 400 km of the model domain. The eastern 100 km in Fig. 6b differs from the same region in Fig. 6a, due mostly to the viscous boundary layer in the vicinity of the open boundary.

The effect of the north-south extent of the basin was examined by doubling the y-dimension of the standard experiment (Fig. 3) and keeping the port location slightly north of the basin center. Figure 7 shows the flow entering the basin

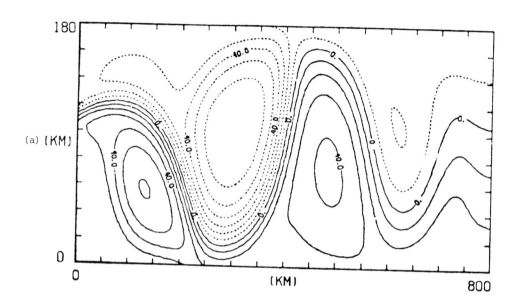

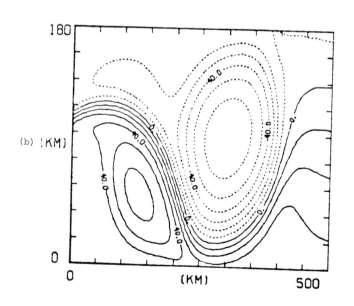

Fig. 6. PA of the pivotal case at day 190 but with different dimensions a) 180 km x 800 km basin; b) 180 km x 500 km basin. Scale factor for these figures x:y is 1:2.5. Contour interval is 10 m.

at the standard angle of 21° and then curving southward in a manner similar to Fig. 5a. Even though the north-south extent of the basin has been doubled, the northern and southern boundaries of the domain still limit the north-south scale of the current meanders. Despite a large increase in the amplitude of the meanders in Fig. 7, the wavelengths in Fig. 5a and Fig. 7 are almost the same. A striking feature in Fig. 7 is the downstream amplification of the current meanders. Less dramatic examples of this appear in some of the other figures. It should be noted that this and all the other solutions are steady and not unstable.

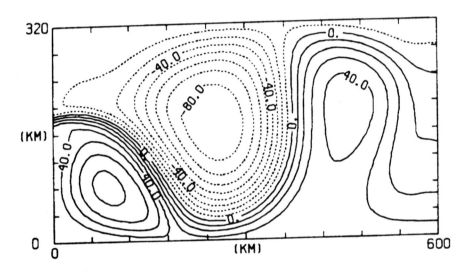

Fig. 7. PA at day 600 of an experiment where the north-south dimension of the basin has been extended to 320 km, contour interval is 10 m.

3.5 Shear at inflow

In all the experiments discussed so far, the inflow has been prescribed as a velocity profile $(\vec{v}_1)$. However, in this model the inflow may also be prescribed in terms of transport $(\vec{V}_1)$. In the latter case, the model partially controls the inflow velocity profile through the geostrophic tilt in the interface. Fig. 8 shows a steady state solution for an experiment similar to that shown in Fig. 5b, except that $\vec{V}_1$ is prescribed instead of $\vec{v}_1$. In both cases the inflow is eastward. In Fig. 8 the prescribed inflow transport is 2.5×10^6 m^3/sec. This yields inflow velocities similar to Fig. 5b, but the geostrophic tilt in the interface introduces a shear $(\partial u/\partial y)$ of 1.54×10^{-5} sec^{-1} at inflow. Without the shear (Fig. 5b) the current turns southward after inflow, but with the shear (Fig. 8) the current turns northward. In addition, Fig. 8 shows a larger Alboran

Gyre which is further to the east and a small cyclonic gyre in the northwest corner. The possibility that vorticity at inflow turns the incoming Atlantic water northward has been suggested by Nof (1978).

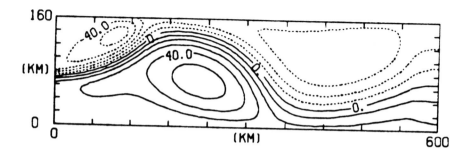

Fig. 8. PA at day 500 of a case identical to the case represented in Fig. 5b except that the model is forced with a prescribed transport. Contour interval is 10 m.

4. SUMMARY AND FUTURE WORK

A nonlinear, semi-implicit, reduced gravity numerical model (Hurlburt and Thompson, 1980) has been adapted to study the circulation in the Alboran Sea. Both hydrographic data and satellite imagery indicate the existence of a permanent anticyclonic gyre in the western Alboran. This circulation appears to be driven by a jet of Atlantic water which enters through the Strait of Gibraltar. In the model the Strait was represented by a port in the western boundary and the eastern boundary was entirely open. Model results using an idealized rectangular geometry (600 km x 160 km), no topography and a northeastward inflow through the Strait of Gibraltar show an anticyclonic gyre similar in size, shape and location to the Alboran Gyre (Fig. 3). These results closely resemble the dynamic height contours of Lanoix (Fig. 1) and suggest that topography and particular coastline features are not necessary to create a gyre with realistic dimensions and location. However, model results for the eastern Alboran show a series of cyclonic and anticyclonic circulations of much larger scale and smaller variability than observed. Additional numerical experiments showed the importance of the inflow angle and inflow vorticity in determining the size and location of the Alboran Gyre.

This paper has presented preliminary results of an attempt to model the Alboran Sea. Future work will include an investigation of the model dynamics, more realistic models, and interaction with a field experiment. The meandering current observed in the model solutions might be considered a standing Rossby wave with a highly distorted conservation of absolute vorticity trajectory (e.g. see Haltiner and Martin, 1957). The flow trajectory is strongly influenced by the proximity of the northern and southern boundaries, the large amplitude variations in the upper layer depth, cross-isobaric inertial effects, and possibly by frictional effects. Planned model refinements include more realistic coastline geometry, an additional active layer, bottom topography, and winds. The influence of each of these features on the Alboran Gyre will be tested, but they will also be used in an attempt to obtain a more realistic simulation of the circulation in the eastern Alboran Sea. We have already begun to use the model results in the design of a NORDA (Naval Ocean Research and Development Activity) field experiment. The intended result is a cooperative interaction in which the models aid in the interpretation of the observations and the observations lead to more realistic model simulations.

ACKNOWLEDGEMENTS

We wish to thank Dr. J. Dana Thompson, George Heburn, and Thomas Kinder for their helpful comments. The fast, vectorized Helmholtz solver for the semi-implicit model was provided by Dr. Daniel Moore of Imperial College, London. Some of the graphics software was provided by the National Center for Atmospheric Research which is sponsored by the National Science Foundation. Computations were performed on the two-pipeline Texas Instruments Advanced Scientific Computer at the Naval Research Laboratory in Washington, D.C. Partial funding was provided by the ONR Coastal Science Program contract N00014-81-AB-11-12.

REFERENCES

Bethoux, J. P., 1979. Budgets of the Mediterranean Sea. Their dependence on the local climate and on characteristics of the Atlantic waters. Oceanol. Acta. 2, 2: 137-163.

Burkov, V. A., Krivosheya, V. G., Ovchinnikov, I. M. and Savin, M. T., 1979. Eddies in the current system of the western Mediterranean Basin. Oceanology, 19: 9-13.

Cheney, R. E., 1977. Recent observations of the Alboran Sea front. NAVOCEANO Technical Note 370-73-77, 24 pp.

Cheney, R. E., 1978. Recent observations of the Alboran Sea frontal system. J. Geophys. Res., 83: 4593-4597.

Gallagher, J. J., Fecher, M. and Gorman, J., 1981. Project HUELVA oceanographic/acoustic investigation of the western Alboran Sea. NUSC Technical Report 6023, 106 pp.

Gascard, J. C., 1978. Mediterranean deep water formation. Baroclinic instability and oceanic eddies. Oceanologica Acta 1,3: 315-330.

Grousson, R. and Faroux, J. 1963. Measure de courants de surface en Mer d'Alboran. Cah. Oceanogr., 15: 716-721.

Haltiner, G. J. and Martin, F. L., 1957. Dynamical and Physical Meteorology. McGraw-Hill, pp. 470.

Hurlburt, H. E. and Thompson, J. D., 1980. A numerical study of Loop Current intrusions and eddy shedding. J. Phys. Oceanogr., 10: 1611-1651.

Katz, E. J., 1972. The Levantine intermediate water between the Strait of Sicily and the Strait of Gibraltar. Deep Sea Res., 19: 507-520.

Lacombe, H., 1961. Contribution A L'Etude du Regime du Detroit de Gibraltar. Cah. Oceanogr., XIII: 74-107.

Lacombe, H., 1971. Le Detroit de Gibraltar. Note et Memoires de Service Geologique du Maroc., No. 222 bis, 111-146.

Lacombe, H., 1982. Regime of the Strait of Gibraltar and of its east and west approaches. In: J. C. J. Nihoul (Editor), Hydrodynamics of semi-enclosed seas. Elsevier, Amsterdam, pp. 13-73.

Lanoix, F., 1974. Project Alboran Etude Hydrologique Dynamique de la Mer d'Alboran. Tech. report 66, N. Atl. Treaty Org. Brussels, pp. 39.

Mommsen, D. B., Jr., 1978. The effect of wind on sea surface temperature gradients in the Strait of Gibraltar and Alboran Sea. Report from Fleet Weather Central, Rota, Spain, 18 pp.

Nof, D., 1978. On geostrophic adjustment in Sea straits and estuaries: theory and laboratory experiments. Part II: Two-layer system. J. Phys. Oceanogr., 8: 861-872.

Ovchinnikov, I. M., 1966. Circulation in the surface and intermediate layers of the Mediterranean. Oceanology, 6: 48-59.

Ovchinnikov, I. M., Krivosheya, V. G. and Maskalenko, L. V., 1976. Anomalous features of the water circulation of the Alboran Sea during the summer of 1962. Oceanology, 15: 31-35.

Peluchon, G. and Donguy, J. R., 1962. Travaux Oceanographiques d "l'Origny" dans le Detroit de Gibraltar. Compaigne internationale - 15 mpi, 15 Juin 1961. Zemi partie. Hydrologie en Mer d'Alboran. Cah. Oceanogr., 14: 573-578.

Petit, M., Klaus, V. Gelci, R., Fusey, F., Thery, J. J. and Bouly, P., 1978. Etude d'un tourbillon oceanique d'echelle moyenne en mer d'Alboran par emploi conjoint techniques spatiales et oceanographiques. C.R. Acad. Sci. 287: 215-218.

Porter, D. L., 1976. The anticyclonic gyre of the Alboran Sea. Independent research report from M.I.T.-WHOI joint program, Woods Hole, Ma, pp. 29.

Stevenson, R. W., 1977. Huelva Front and Malaga, Spain eddy chains as defined by satellite and oceanographic data. Deut. Hydrogr. A. 30, 2: 51-53.

Stommel, H., Bryder, H. and Magelsdorf, P., 1973. Does some of the Mediterranean outflow come from great depth? Pure and Appl. Geophysics. 105: 879-889.

Wannamaker, B., 1979. The Alboran Sea Gyre: Ship satellite and historical data. SACLANT ASW Research Centre Report SR-30, La Spezia, Italy, 27 pp.

Whitehead, J. A. and Miller, A. R., 1979. Laboratory simulation of the gyre in the Alboran Sea. J. Geophys. Res. 84: 3733-3742.

SURFACE TEMPERATURE FRONTS IN THE MEDITERRANEAN SEA FROM INFRARED SATELLITE IMAGERY.

Michèle PHILIPPE, Loïc HARANG.

1 - INTRODUCTION

In the Mediterranean Sea, thermal fronts which outcrop at the sea surface can be easily observed using radiometric satellite measurements in the infrared wavelength.

Up to now, especially the Navies have been interested in them, because of the possible implications of such fronts in the propagation of submarine acoustic waves.

Navy Studies about Mediterranean fronts had been achieved by the US Naval Oceanographic Office (Cheney, 1977), (Cheney, 1978), and by the SACLANT ASW Research Center (Briscoe et al., 1974), (Johannessen and Smallenburger, 1977), (Wannamaker, 1979) and by the US Naval Underwater System Center (Gallagher et al., 1981).

In France, the monitoring of fronts in the Mediterranean Sea has been achieved since 1978 at the Centre de Météorologie Spatiale (C.M.S.) with the participation of French Navy meteorologists. The data come from the polar orbiting satellites (TIROS N and NOAA 6), operated by the National Oceanic and Atmospheric Administration (U.S.A.) and received at the C.M.S.

Seasonal changes of surface fronts were derived and discussed from satellite data collected over one year (April 1979-March 1980). These changes were inferred from charts of fronts, drawn for each month of this period. These charts display the major fronts observed over each month and the oceanic features associated with them : currents, eddies, convergence and divergence areas, upwellings.

A few characteristics of the interannual front variability were also obtained by comparing the contours of the surface fronts for the same months of two consecutive years (April 1979 to March 1981).

2 - DATA

2.1 DATA PROCESSING

Data are recorded by AVHRR (Advanced Very High Resolution Radiometer) in the 10.5 to 11.5 μm wavelength range. Data from both TIROS N and NOAA 6 satellites were used, when available. The AVHRR scanner has a spatial resolution of 1.1 km at the satellite subpoint and a temperature sensitivity of less than 0.2°K at 300°K. Raw data are processed to allow the optimum detection of oceanic temperature fronts and the results are stored on negative films. This computing process leads to adjust the available discrete shades of grey within the range of sea temperatures. The principle of the enhancement processing is given in figure 1. Warm waters are represented using the darker tones of grey and colder waters using ligther ones.

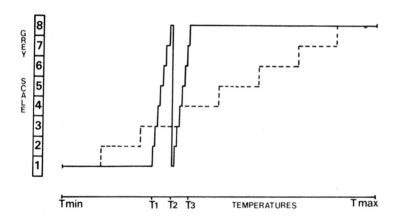

Fig. 1.a Contrast enhancement curves. Example with 8 shades of grey (1=white color, 8=black color).
---- = without contrast enhancement - see Fig. 1b.
____ = with contrast enhancement. Curve between T3 and T2 is used for sea surface temperatures and curve between T2 and T1 for coldest waters and some low level clouds - see Fig. 1c.

However, especially in summer and autumn, when the pictures show very high temperature contrasts, the grey scale (16 shades each covering a temperature interval of 0.5°C) is not wide enough to cover the whole temperature range of the sea surface. Then temperature gradients inside the coldest water masses are displayed

Fig. 1b TIROS N image of the Ligurian sea (September, 7th, 1980) visualized without contrast enhancement.
Fig. 1c Same scene as in figure 1b but visualized with contrast enhancement. As in all the images presented below 16 shades of grey are used. The center of the Ligurian divergence (cold waters) is represented in black which is the first shade of the second curve of enhancement.

using the grey scale for a second time (again from black to white tones). Low level clouds are also displayed using this second scale due to their temperature which is very close to the temperature of the coldest waters (see Fig. 1c). The images presented in this text were realized using a grey scale of 16 shades, each shade covering a temperature interval of 0.5°C.

From the analysis of negative films, using a densitometer, temperature gradients between any couple of sea points can be evaluated, at least in a first order approximation, since atmospheric absorption effects are neglected.

2.2 VOLUME OF DATA

The radiometer swaths obtained for two consecutive satellite passes are represented in figure 2. Examining this figure shows that two or three consecutive passes (depending on their ascending nodes) are necessary for the total survey of the Mediterranean Sea, from West to East. Each day the best orbits with regard to the

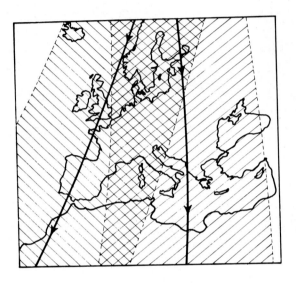

Fig. 2 AVHRR swaths obtained after two consecutive passes of a TIROS N satellite over the Mediterranean Sea.

cloud cover over the sea, are selected and processed. From April 1979 to March 1981, more than 1200 images were produced. Figure 3 shows the monthly distribution of the images. In a given restricted area located between the Alboran Sea and the Ionian Sea, a cloudfree scene can be obtained on average every 3 days, on an annual basis.

For the most eastern areas the amount of available data decreases because these areas are located near or outside the TIROS N acquisition circle at Lannion (see Fig. 4).

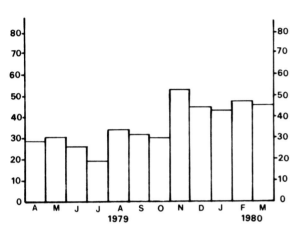

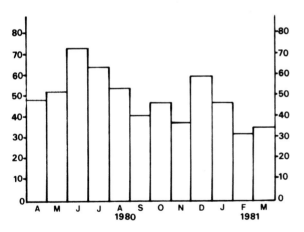

Fig. 3 Monthly distribution of thermal images of the Mediterranean
Sea from April 1979 to March 1981.

96

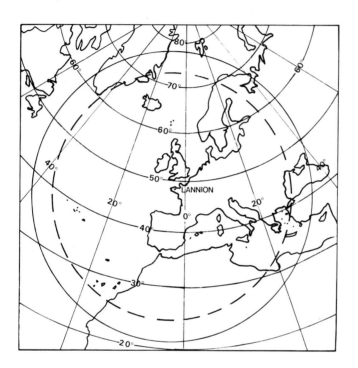

Fig. 4. TIROS N acquisition circle at C.M.S.
—— 0° elevation ; --- 5° elevation.

2.3 METHOD OF FRONT ANALYSIS

The following definition of fronts was used : a surface temperature front occurs in areas where gradients are equal to or greater than 1°C within a distance of about 5km. This is a rather limitative definition in view of the values given by other authors (Johannessen 1975). But the aim of the study concerning the whole Mediterranean Sea is only to detect and monitor the main fronts.

Figure 5 shows a thermal image of the Liguro-Provençal basin (see figure 8 for geographical locations). On this image, the arrows point out the fronts detected according to the above definition.

The images are not geographically corrected. The locations of fronts are retrieved using 0.5° x 0.5°.latitude-longitude grids.

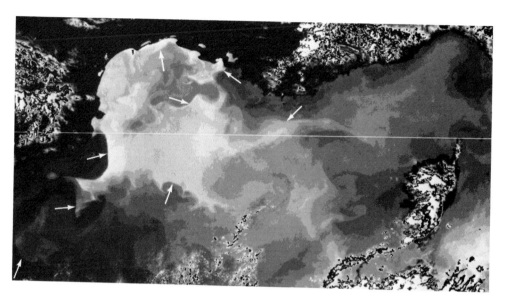

Fig. 5. TIROS N image of the Liguro-Provençal basin. The arrows
indicate the fronts, according to the definition given in section
2.3 : gradients > 1°C/5km.

These grids are computed from the average orbital parameters of
the satellites. The accuracy of the location retrievals reaches
about 3 nautical miles near the satellite subtrack.

3 - SEASONAL CHANGES OF FRONTS

To study the seasonal changes of fronts, the results of the
analyses of all the images produced, between April 1979 and March
1980, were used to draw monthly charts of fronts. On such charts
(see Fig. 7, 12, 16 and 21) the general contours of areas where
fronts were detected during the month are filled in black. Other
indications are also given on the charts : the maximum gradient
measured during the month in each frontal area, the oceanic features associated with fronts (divergences, convergences, upwellings).
Significant areas of cold or warm waters are also indicated. The
arrows give an idea of the assumed surface currents near frontal
areas. Because no in situ simultaneous current measurements were
made, these arrows must only be considered as indications.

Fronts in the Mediterranean Sea are linked up with surface
water circulation. Figure 6 gives a surface current chart calculated
by Ovchinnikov (1966) using the geostrophic method. The main

98

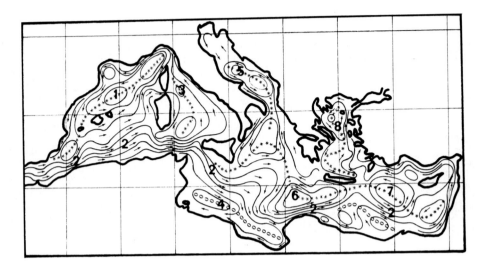

Fig. 6. Winter chart of geostrophic surface current (Ovchinnikov)
xxxx divergence line ; °°°° convergence line ; 1 : cyclonic circulation of the Liguro-Provençal basin ; 2 : African current ;
3 : Divergence of the straits of Bonifacio ; 4 : Anticyclonic
circulation of the Syrta gulf ; 5 : Cyclonic circulation of the
Adriatic Sea ; 6 : Divergence southwest of Creta ; 7 : Divergence
southeast of Rhoda ; 8 : Cyclonic circulation of the Aegean Sea.

Mediterranean surface current is the African current which runs
along the African coast and carries "Atlantic" waters from the
straits of Gibraltar to the Levantin basin. On the North of the
African current develop large cyclonic circulations. In the chart
of figure 6, these cyclonic circulations exist in all the basins
located on the North of the African current. On the contrary, on
the South of the African current, anticyclonic eddies and circulations appear. The chart in figure 6 was computed for the winter
period. According to its author (Ovchinnikov, 1966), the summer
chart of surface currents could be very similar to the winter one,
unless for the rate of circulation which should be divided by two.

Interpretations of oceanic phenomena, given here under, will be
founded on the Ovchinnikov chart but also on the global knowledge
existing about the Mediterranean oceanography. And, we have to quote
some of the most important papers written till now about the Mediterranean Sea : its general hydrology (Lacombe and Tchernia, 1960),
its regional oceanography : in the Alboran Sea (Lanoix, 1974), in
western Mediterranean (Furnestin, 1960), in the Levantin basin
(Ozturgut, 1976).

It is not possible to describe the evolution of the fronts month by month in this paper. But the seasonal changes in their surface patterns can be illustrated by four charts, each one being representative of one season.

3.1 SPRING : APRIL, MAY, JUNE 1979

In spring, as a result of cooling and wind mixing which has occurred during the winter, temperature gradients at the sea surface are weak (maximum gradients reach 1 to 1.5°C/5km). Figure 7 shows the front chart of May 1979. May is the month during which the minimum amount of fronts can be detected. Fronts only appear in the South of the straits of Messina and in the Alboran Sea. The image in figure 9a is typical of the end of spring. This image covers the Aegean Sea and parts of the Ionian Sea and of the Levantin basin. According to the above definition, fronts cannot be detected on this image outside very restricted areas where they are associated with coastal upwellings. However, numerous eddies and wave-like features appear on the image, probably due to the strong vertical temperature gradient which occurs directly below the sea surface. In figure 9b these thermal features are better enhanced using a 0.25°C temperature interval instead of a 0.50°C one.

In figure 9b, the major part of mesoscale eddies (with diameters of about 50 nautical miles) are anticyclonic. Smaller scale wave-like features (with a wavelength of about 8 nautical miles), encountered North of the Cyrenaïcan coast, have a lifetime of about one or two days.

Such thermal features are sometimes emphasized by filament-like patterns. Since good images of such filament-like patterns could not be obtained during spring 1979, the example given in figure 10 was processed from NOAA6 data taken in June 1980.

On this image, filament-like patterns appear in the East of the Tyrrhenian Sea and if the Afro-Sicilian basin (name given to the area spreading between Sicily, Tunisia, and Western Lybia, see Fig. 8).

Such a phenomenon may perhaps be linked up with diurnal heating or more precisely with the dissipation of diurnal heating effects because it mainly appears on late afternoon images.

But the most important phenomenon induced by diurnal heating can be detected on early afternoon images.

It consists of warm patches of water which appear in black on

100

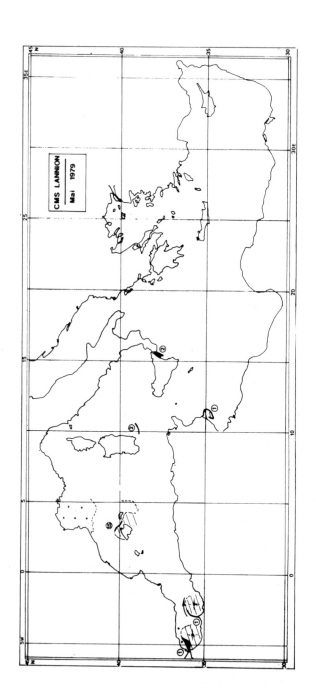

Fig. 7. ▮ spatial envelope shape of frontal feature   ┼ cold core eddy or circulation

        ▨ warm water   ┿ warm core eddy

        ⊡ cold water   ▲ supposed direction of the surface current

        ③ maximum gradient in °C/5km measured accross the front.

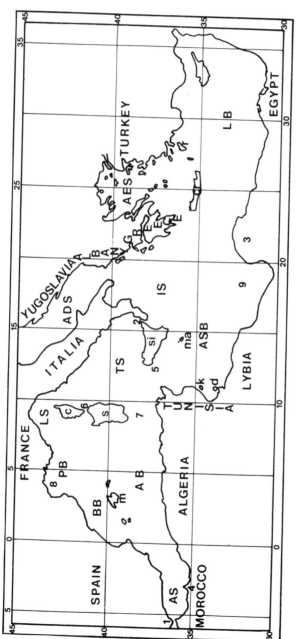

Fig. 8. AS : Alboran Sea ; AB : Algerian basin ; BB : Balearic basin ; PB : Provençal basin ;
LS : Ligurian Sea ; TS : Tyrrhenian Sea ; ASB : Afro-Sicillian basin ; IS : Ionian sea ; ADS :
Adriatic Sea ; LB : Levantin basin ; AES : Aegean Sea ; m : Majorca ; c : Corsica ; s : Sardinia
si : Sicily ; m : Malta ; k : Kerkennah ; d : Djerba ; cr : Creta ; r : Rhoda ; l : Gibraltar ;
2 : straits of Messina ; 3 : Cyrenaïca ; 4 : Tres Forca cape ; 5 : Adventure bank ; 6 : Bonifacio straits; 7 : Sardinia straits ; 8 : gulf of Lion ; 9 : gulf of Syrta.

Fig. 9a. TIROS N image of the eastern Mediterranean sea obtained on
June 28th, 1979.

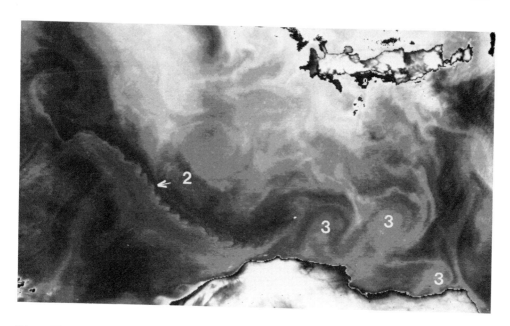

Fig. 9b. Part of the same scene visualized using 0.25°C per shade of grey instead of 0.50°C. 1 : upwellings ; 2 : wave-like features ; 3 : eddies.

the images. Temperature gradients on the boundaries of such patches are high but not enough to build fronts according to the above definition. An example of such warm patches is given in figure 11 (obtained on May 18th, 1979 on the Ionian sea). Such warm patches are induced by strong diurnal heating occuring at the sea surface in calm wind areas. Their geographical positions change from day to day following the centers of sunny windless areas. These warm patches obscure the underlying temperature structure which is representative of surface water dynamics. Images with warm patches cannot be used in front analysis.

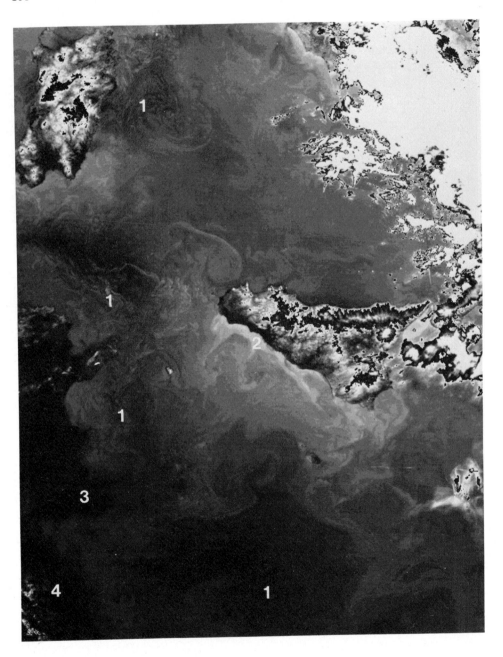

Fig. 10. Image NOAA6 4892 obtained on June 5th, 1980. 1 : filament-like features ; 2 : upwellings ; 3 : Kerkennah shallows ; 4 : Djerba shallows.

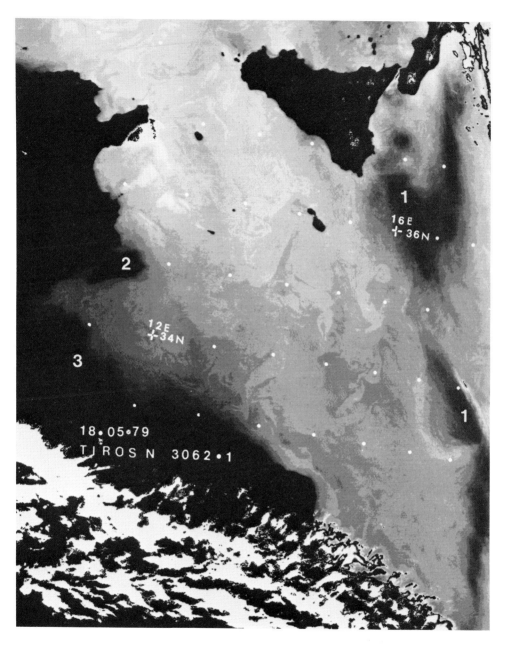

Fig. 11. TIROS N image of the Afro-Sicilian basin obtained on May 18th, 1979. 1 : warm patches ; 2 : Kerkennah shallows ; 3 : Djerba shallows.

3.2 SUMMER: JULY, AUGUST, SEPTEMBER 1979

The front chart chosen to illustrate the summer period is the August chart (see figure 12).

The vertical summer temperature stratification of the water masses is now well formed and most of the fronts detected are associated with horizontal and vertical water circulations.

Movements of water modify the slopes of the isothermal layers. Therefore, horizontal temperature gradients appear, which may out-crop on the sea surface and create surface temperature fronts.

Other fronts could be induced by turbulence effects occuring in straits or above shallows. These turbulence effects mix the waters and weaken the seasonal thermocline.

The fronts shown in figure 12 are firstly created by the African current. Such fronts are observed in the Alboran Sea, where two anticyclonic gyres appeared in August 1979. The most important of them is observed West of the Tres Forca cape and the second one East of this cape. The gyre diameters reach about 150 km. Fronts are detected on both sides of the cold tongues which encircle their warm cores.

Figure 13 shows an image of the Alboran Sea obtained on August 20th, 1979. The above mentioned gyres appear clearly on this image. On August 20th and during the previous days, the wind was blowing from the East in the Alboran Sea.

Consequently, upwellings can be noticed off the African coast and a warm counter current runs along the Spanish coasts.

Fronts due to the African current are also detected South of Sicily, especially above the Adventure Bank and above the Eastern slope of the Sicilo-Maltese continental shelf (Malta front).

But, in this area, the African current interacts with coastal upwellings and continental shelf effects.

Consequently, the fronts in this area result from several effects including current, mixing and upwellings.

Other major fronts are linked up with cyclonic circulations.

These fronts appear at the limit between the cold cores of these circulations (divergences) and the warm waters running round them. The most important fronts are found in the Liguro-Provençal

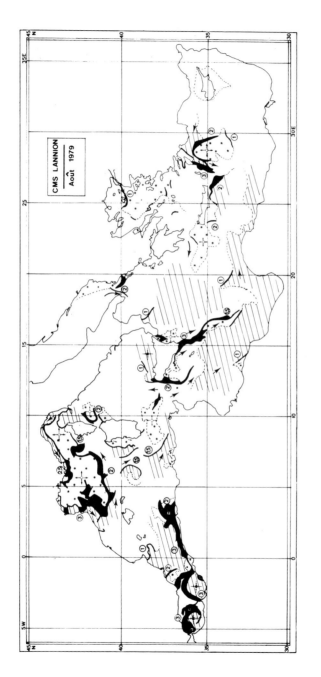
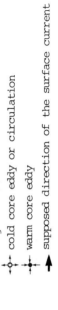

Fig. 12. Monthly chart of surface thermal fronts – August 1979

■ spatial envelope shape of frontal feature

⊕ cold core eddy or circulation

◪ warm water

⊕ warm core eddy

⋯ cold water

↑ supposed direction of the surface current

③ maximum gradient in °C/5km measured accross the front.

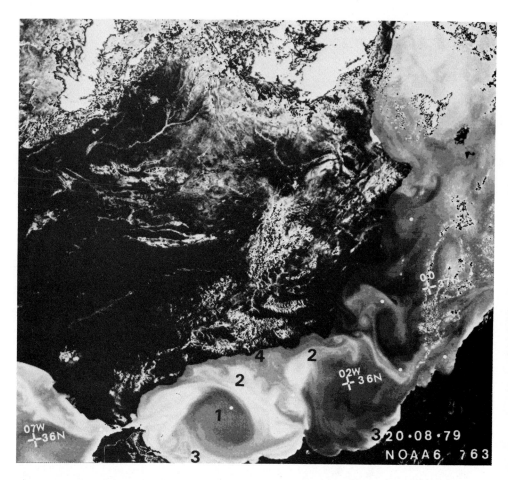

Fig. 13. NOAA6 image of the Alboran Sea obtained on August 20th,
1979. 1 : warm core of the anticyclonic eddy ; 2 : cold boundaries
of anticyclonic eddies ; 3 : upwellings ; 4 : warm coastal countercurrent.

basin (figure 14) and South-East of Rhoda (figure 15). A smaller,
but equally active divergence is detected East of the Bonifacio
straits (figure 14). Other circulations are intermittently observed
in the Sardinia straits (figure 14) and West of Creta (figure 15).

A third type of fronts is induced by upwellings. Fronts mark
the offshore limits of cold upwelled waters. Throughout summer,
upwellings can be detected in the East of Aegean Sea (see figure 15).
The upwellings are caused by strong north winds, called Etesian
winds or Meltemi.

Fig. 14. TIROS N image of the central Mediterranean Sea obtained on August 22th, 1979. 1 : Liguro-Provençal divergence ; 2 : warm current ; 3 : upwellings ; 4 : secondary cyclonic divergences ; 5 : warm patches due to strong diurnal heating ; 6 : mesoscale eddy.

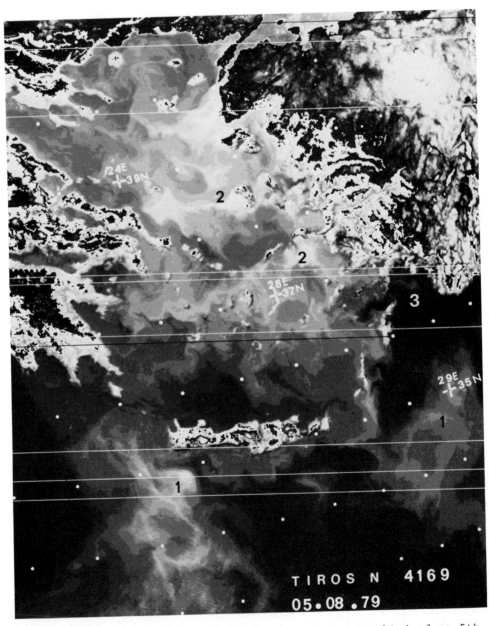

Fig. 15. TIROS N image of the Eastern Mediterranean obtained on 5th, August 1979. 1 : cyclonic divergences ; 2 : upwellings due to etesian winds ; 3 : warm current.

Upwellings along the coast of Albany are also caused by northerly winds similar to the etesian winds.

Along the African and Lybian coasts, winds often blow from the
East in summer and upwellings also appear.

More intermittent upwellings develop in the gulf of Lions.

In summer, fronts cause gradients which may reach 3 or 4°C
within a distance of about 5 km. Such values are reached in August
and September in the Alboran Sea, the South of the Provençal basin
and the Malta front.

3.3 AUTUMN : OCTOBER, NOVEMBER, DECEMBER 1979

The autumn front chart presented here is the November chart
(figure 16).

The distribution of sea surface temperatures in autumn is representative of a transitional period.

Some summer fronts persist on the autumn infrared images. Other
fronts appear, which will also be observed during the winter months.
The remaining fronts are typical of the autumn period. Consequently
autumn is the season during which the greatest amount of fronts can
be detected on the infrared images.

Major fronts are still linked up with disturbances of the summer
thermocline.

Cyclonic divergences and associated fronts are observed during
the autumn. In November (see figure 16), they appear in the liguro-
Provençal basin (figure 17), East of the straits of Bonifacio and
Southeast of Rhoda (figure 20).

Fronts at the limit of their cold cores seem to become more
instable during the autumn (see figure 17).

At the beginning of autumn, the temperature structure of the
Alboran Sea is disturbed by the changes occuring in the wind
fluxes.

In summer, prevailing winds blow from the East, whereas, they
come from the West in winter.

Such changes in the main wind direction occured in 1979 during
late September and October.

During these months periods of easterly winds alternated with
periods of westerly ones.

In November, westerly winds are well established in the Alboran
Sea and along the coast of Algeria, hence the gyres of the Alboran
Sea become clearly visible again. The path of the African current

112

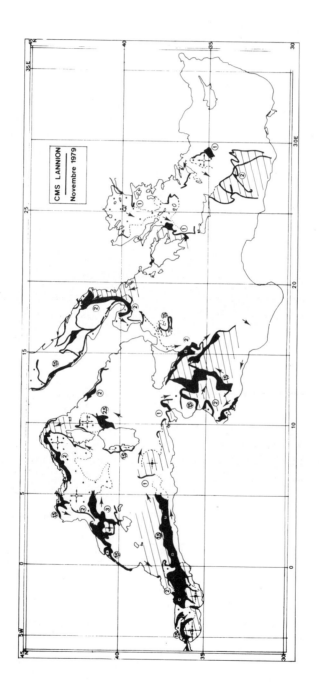

Fig. 16. Monthly chart of surface temperature fronts. November 1979.
spatial envelope shape of frontal feature

⊕ cold core eddy or circulation

warm water

⊕ warm core eddy

cold water

▲ supposed direction of the surface current

③ maximum gradient in °C/5km measured accross the front.

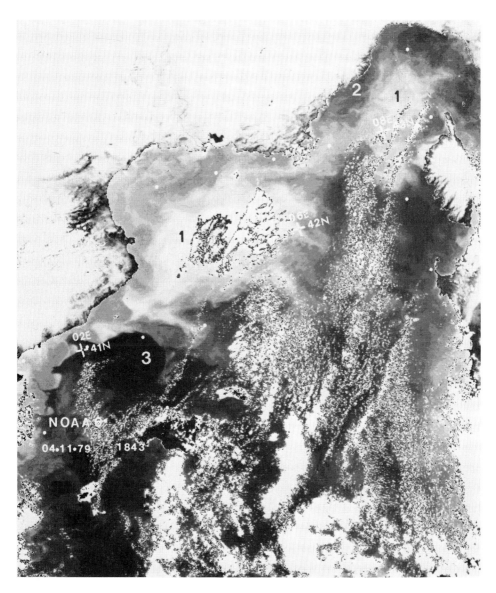

Fig. 17. NOAA6 Image of the Liguro-Provençal basin and the balearic basin obtained on 4th, November 1979. 1 : cold divergences of the Liguro-Provençal cyclonic circulation ; 2 : warm coastal current ; 3 : warm water inclusion.

off the African coast is underlined by an irregular cold tongue.

The image of figure 18 obtained on November 28th, 1979 shows that this cold tongue follows the Northern boundary of series of small anticyclonic eddies (about 25 to 30 nautical miles in diameter). These eddies develop between the main current and the African coast.

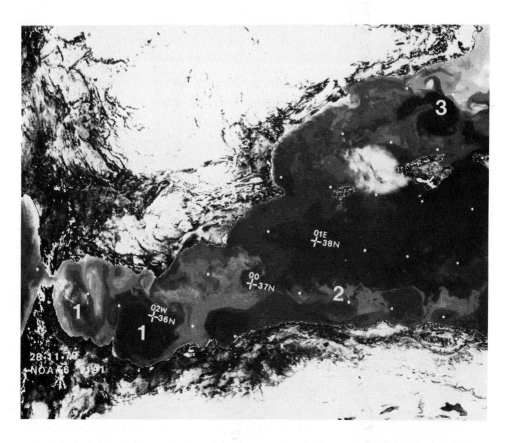

Fi. 18. NOAA6 image of the western Mediterranean obtained on 28th, November 1979. 1 : eddies of the Alboran Sea ; 2 : path of the African current ; 3 : warm water inclusion.

In the Aegean Sea and in the South of the Adriatic Sea, the northwesterly winds (etesian winds) stop blowing at the beginning of autumn. Wind fluxes become more irregular. But in autumn, the prevailing winds seem to blow from the South (Sirocco). Warm water intrusions take the place of summer upwellings in the East of the

Aegean Sea (see figure 19). A similar phenomenon occur in the
Adriatic Sea where a warm current can be observed in the place of
the summer upwellings off the coasts of Yugoslavia and Albany. This
warm current underlines the eastern northward branch of the general
cyclonic circulation in the Adriatic Sea. The western southward
branch is emphasized by a narrow strip of cold coastal waters. These
cold waters may originate in the north of the Adriatic Sea where
shallow waters undergo a strong winter cooling (effect of Bora
wind). Fronts are detected along the western side of the warm water
intrusion and along the offshore limit of coastal waters (see
figure 20). This latter type of fronts will persist in winter.
Similar fronts typical of the winter period appear in some places

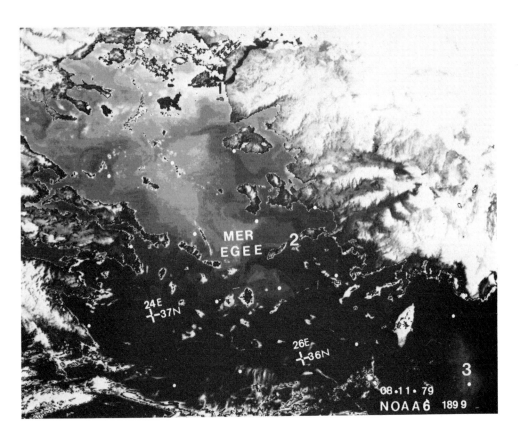

Fig. 19. NOAA6 image of the Aegean Sea obtained on 8th, November
1979. 1 : cold waters from the Black Sea ; 2 : warm water intrusion
3 : cyclonic divergence.

where cold coastal waters can be observed, due to wind mixing over
continental shelves and to river outflows (gulf of Lions with the
Rhône river for instance).

Fig. 20. NOAA6 image of the Adriatic Sea obtained on 5th, December
1979. 1 : cold coastal waters ; 2 : warm water intrusion ; 3 :
center of one of the Adriatic cyclonic circulation cell; 4 : runoff of river ?

Upwellings induced mainly by northly to northwesterly winds are
still visible on the infrared images. In November 1979, upwellings
were observed west of Sardinia and south of Sicily.

In the Afro-Sicilian basin the temperature structure of the
surface is very intricated and a great number of fronts can be
detected : upwelling fronts, fronts associated with the African
current, fronts due to winter cooling of shallow waters (around the

the islands of Djerba and Kerkennah, for instance).

An interesting phenomenon can be observed in autumn. It consists of warm nearly circular patches (about 40 nautical miles in diameter) of warm waters embedded in colder circulations. On the image of figure 18, such warm inclusions can be seen north of Majorca (Balearic basin). Figure 17 was obtained on November 4th, 1979. The image of figure 18, obtained more than three weeks later, shows the same warm pattern in the same place. Its boundary has become irregular. Strong gradients (> 4°C/5km) can be measured at the limit between these warm waters and the cyclonic circulation of the provençal basin.

But outside this area gradients in fronts are weaker than in summer. They vary from 1 to 2.5°C/5km. Warm inclusions may be due to changes occuring during autumn in the general water circulation (influence of wind fluxes).

3.4. WINTER : JANUARY, FEBRUARY, MARCH 1980

The summer thermocline has been destroyed by the winter cooling and fronts associated with the dynamic disturbances of subsurface isothermal layers have almost completely disappeared (see the February front chart in figure 21).

An exception can however be found in the Levantin basin where the divergence observed southeast of Rhoda persists till February 1980. Fronts detected on the thermal images are now mainly linked up with cold water masses which may be caused by the cooling of shallow coastal waters, river run-offs or Black Sea outflow (in the Aegean Sea).

Some of these fronts were already observed in autumn, such as for instance, fronts at the offshore limit of Italian coastal waters(see figure 24), in the gulf of Lions (see figure 23) or around the Djerba and Kerkennah shallows.

In the Afro-Sicilian basin, fronts develop in the North of the Syrta anticyclonic circulation. In this area, the African current and, possibly waters from the North of the Ionian Sea, contrast with the warm center of the anticyclonic circulation (convergence area), (see figure 24).

In the Aegean Sea (see figure 25), waters from the Black Sea are cold but lighter than the surrounding Aegean waters. Therefore these cold waters spread over the northwestern part of the Aegean Sea due to the Coriolis effect. The temperature of waters in this

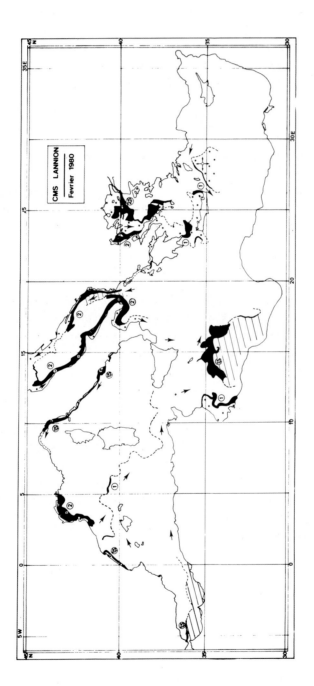

Fig. 21. Monthly chart of surface temperature fronts. February 1980.

spatial envelope shape of frontal feature

warm water

cold water

maximum gradient in °C/5km mearused accross the front.

cold core eddy or circulation

warm core eddy

supposed direction of the surface current

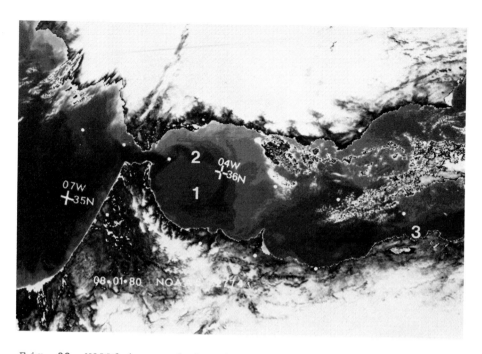

F ig. 22. NOAA6 image of the Alboran Sea obtained on 8th, January 1980. 1 : anticyclonic eddy ; 2 : warm surface inflow of Atlantic waters ; 3 : path of the African current.

part of the Aegean Sea is also lowered by the cold northerly wind, which often blows in this area in winter (Vardar wind), and also by river run-offs. Fronts appear at the limit between cold waters in the northwest of the sea and warmer waters in the southeast.

Outside the Mediterranean areas where fronts can be detected, the thermal sea surface structure is smooth (see figure 23). In the Alboran Sea an interesting feature can sometimes be observed : the waters carried by the African current may be warmer, near the surface than the surrounding Mediterranean waters. These warmer waters appear as a warm tongue on the satellite images (see figure 22). In winter, gradients in front areas are of the same order of magnitude as in autumn : 1 to 2.5°C/5km.

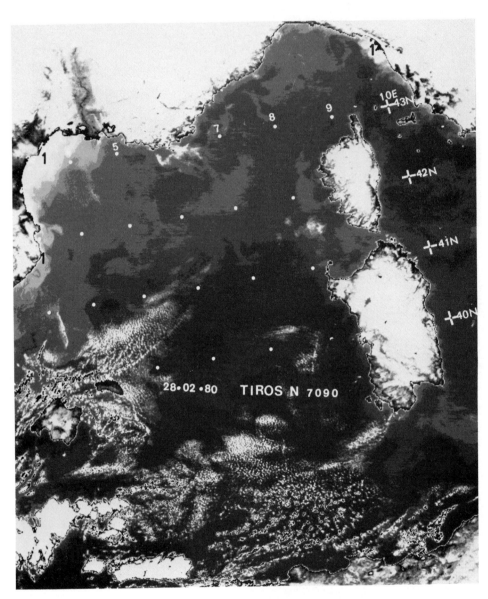

Fig. 23. TIROS N Image of the Liguro-Provençal basin obtained on 28th, February. 1 : cold coastal waters.

Fig. 24. TIROS N image of Ionian Sea obtained on 3rd, February 1980.
1 : Syrta anticyclonic circulation center ; 2 : cold coastal waters.

Fig. 25. TIROS N image of the Aegean Sea obtained on 7th, February 1980. 1 : cold water inflow from the Black Sea.

4. INTER ANNUAL VARIABILITY

To emphasize the inter annual variability of Mediterranean surface temperature fronts, charts were drawn by superimposing the frontal envelope shapes for the same months of two consecutive years.

From the analysis of the twelve monthly charts, a significant similarity can generally be observed between the locations of frontal areas during both years. Figure 26 which shows the chart of November 1979 and November 1980, gives an example of such a similarity. During both months major fronts first appeared in the Alboran Sea (eddies) and along the path of the African current. In the latter area frontal envelop shapes were almost coïncident. Fronts

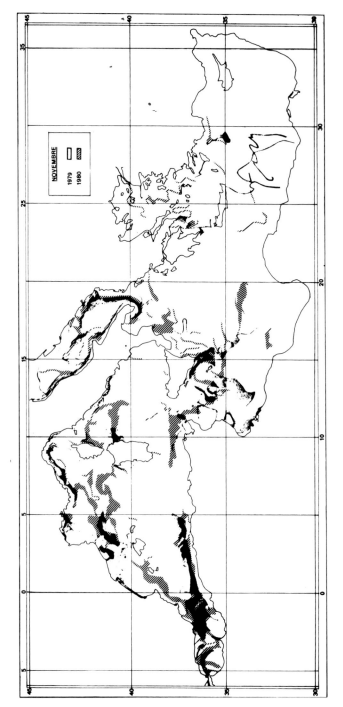

Fig. 26. Superimposition of frontal envelope shapes. November 1979–November 1980.

associated with cyclonic circulations were also found during both
months : Liguro-Provençal basin, East of the Straits of Bonifacio,
and South-East of Rhoda. Here the locations and extensions of
frontal contours changed between 1979 and 1980, probably due to
changes in general wind conditions. For instance, the cold center
of the Bonifacio divergence was more extended in November 1980 than
in November 1979.

In the South of the Liguro-Provençal basin, a greater number of
frontal areas were detected during the second year of measurements.
On the contrary, fronts of both years are nearly superimposed in the
Adriatic Sea.

In the Straits of Sardinia and in the Afro-Sicilian basin, fronts
are complex during both months. If they are always related to the
same oceanic features (African current, upwellings, Syrta circulation, topography of continental shelves), their contours are not
well coïncident outside the area of the Malta front.

The image of figure 27 shows a scene taken above the central
Mediterranean in November 1980. By comparing this image with the
monthly chart of fronts of November 1979 (see figure 28), the similarities and differences described above appear clearly.

The comparison between fronts observed in the Levantin basin
and in the Aegean Sea, in 1979 and in 1980, shows a greater dispersion in the front distribution, perhaps because autumn is a transition period in the Aegean Sea (see section 3.3 above).

The season during which the best coïncidence between front areas
observed during two consecutive years can be observed is winter.
It is especially true for the fronts appearing at the offshore
limits of coastal waters because they seem to be linked up with the
bottom topography.

The chart of figure 27 points out this fact for the months of
February 1980-February 1981.

5. DISCUSSION

Most of the phenomena observed on the thermal images above have
been interpreted according to the general knowledge we have on the
Mediterranean oceanography. The source of information was a bibliography which was mainly constituted from historical in situ measurements (see section 3 above). Other phenomena on which no bibliography was available were interpreted taking into account their analogies with the previously identified phenomena. A few phenomena
such as warm water intrusions in autumn and filament-like features

Fig. 27. NOAA6 image nr. 7210 obtained on November 15th, 1980. 1 : Liguro-Provençal cyclonic divergence ; 2 : divergence west of the straits of Bonifacio ; 3 : divergence of the straits of Sardinia ; 4 : cold coastal waters ; 5 : warm intrusion.

126

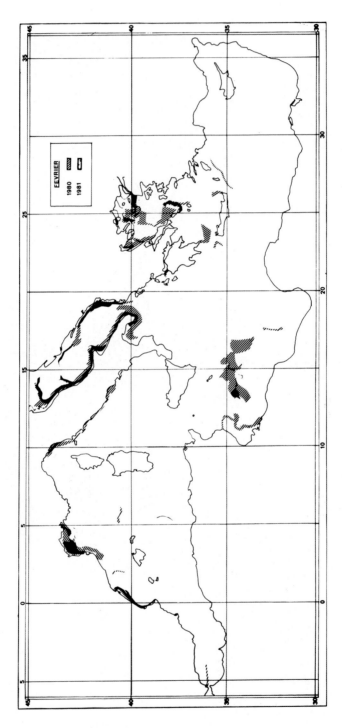

Fig. 28. Superimposition of front envelope shapes. February 1980–February 1979.

in spring are not yet fully understood. Taking these facts into
account and considering that very few in situ measurements, obtained
simultaneously with satellites images, are available, it is likely
that some interpretations of phenomenon given in this text are wrong.

But, though results are imperfect, they, however, improve the
general knowledge of fronts in the Mediterranean Sea.

Some of the results presented in section 3 indicate that the
winter chart of surface currents given by Ovchinnikov (see figure 5)
is not everywhere representative of the summer circulation. For
instance, upwellings which appear in summer in the eastern Aegean
Sea and off the coasts of Albany and Algeria seem to stop or even to
reverse the surface currents.

Such changes in the surface circulation are not surprising however
because surface currents in the Mediterranean Sea are mainly induced
by winds and winds undergo important seasonal changes in the areas
concerned.

Another fact has to be pointed out : fronts in the Mediterranean
Sea may be strong. Surface gradients of 3 to 4°C/5km are often
encountered in summer and autumn in certain areas such as the
Alboran Sea and the Provençal basin.

6. CONCLUSION

From two years of satellite infrared data over the Mediterranean
Sea, it was possible to study the surface temperature fronts, their
seasonal changes and some characteristics of their interannual variability.

Surface temperature fronts in the Mediterranean Sea are seasonal.
Their distribution follows the annual cycle, summer heating - winter
cooling. In spring, the surface waters are well mixed and only a
few fronts appear. In summer numerous fronts are detected, associated
with dynamic disturbances of the summer thermocline. Autumn is a
transition period during which summer fronts can be observed together
with winter ones. In certain areas, such as the Alboran Sea in
October, the Afro-Sicilian basin and the Aegean Sea, fronts seem to
be dizorganised. In winter fronts appear at the limit of waters of
different origins. They are mainly detected on the offshore limits
of cold coastal waters, except in the northeast of the Aegean Sea
where other fronts occur, linked up with the cold inflow of Black
Sea waters.

From one year to another the same seasonal evolution of fronts
can be observed on the infrared images. Major seasonal fronts are

detected, associated with the same oceanic features but their precise locations and their extensions may have changed.

Associated with surface temperature fronts a great number of oceanic phenomena were detected and analysed. Some of them are not yet fully understood. Satellite teledetection gives numerous informations about the Mediterranean oceanography but raises an equally important number of new questions about this oceanography.

This study shows the interest of using infrared imagery from meteorological satellites for the monitoring of wide oceanic areas, specially in areas where the cloud cover is not important, such as over the Mediterranean Sea. Such satellite data are very useful for the study of mesoscale oceanic phenomena which induce temperature gradients at the sea surface. But it can be assumed that the simultaneous use of in situ measurements, of infrared satellite data and also of data from other satellite sensors such as altimeters or synthetic aperture radars will improve such studies and enlarge it to phenomena with no temperature signature.

REFERENCES

Briscoe, M.G., Johannessen, O.M. and Vicenzi, S., 1974. The Maltese oceanic front : a surface description by ship and aircraft. Deep Sea Research, 21(4): 247-262;

Cheney,R.E., 1977. Aerial observations of oceanic fronts in the western Mediterranean Sea. Technical Note, 3700-69-77. US Naval Oceanographic Office, Washington, DC.

Cheney, R.E., 1978. Recent observations of the Alboran Sea frontal system. Journal of Geophysical Research, 83(C9):4593-4597.

Furnestin, J., 1960. Hydrologie de la Méditerranée occidentale (golfe du Lion, mer Catalane, mer d'Alboran, Corse orientale). Revue des Travaux de l'Institut des Pêches Maritimes. 24(1):5-98.

Gallagher, J.J., Fecher, M., Gorman,J., 1981. Project HUELVA. Oceanographic/Acoustic investigation of the western Alboran Sea. NUSC Technical Report 6023A. Naval Underwater Systems Center.

Johannessen, O.M., 1975. A review of oceanic fronts. In Proceedings Conference SACLANTCEN on Oceanic Acoustic Modelling, 17(5).

Johannessen, O.M., and Smallenburger, C., 1977. Observation of an oceanic front in the Ionian Sea during early winter in 1970. Journal of Geophysical Research, 82(9):1381-1391.

Lacombe, H., and Tchernia, P., 1960. Quelques traits généraux de l'hydrologie méditerranéenne. Cahiers Océanographiques, 12(8): 527-547.

Lanoix, R., 1974. Projet Alboran : étude hydrologique et dynamique de la mer d'Alboran. Technical Report 66, NATO, Brussels, Belgium.

Ovchinnikov, I.M., 1966. Circulation in the surface and intermediate layers of the Mediterranean.Oceanology, 6(1):48-58.

Ozturgut, E., 1976. The sources and spreading of the Levantine intermediate water in the eastern Mediterranean. SACLANTCEN Memorandum, SM-92.

Wannamaker, B., 1979. The Alboran Sea gyre : ship, satellite and historical data. SACLANTCEN Report, SR-30.

THE WATER CIRCULATION IN THE NORTH-WESTERN MEDITERRANEAN SEA,
ITS RELATIONS WITH WIND AND ATMOSPHERIC PRESSURE

J.P. Bethoux[x], L. Prieur[x], F. Nyffeler[xx]

ABSTRACT

Mean values of hydrological data (relating to the period 1950-1973)
are used to evaluate the cyclonic fluxes in the Ligurian Sea, i.e.,
through the Nice-Calvi section and the Corsican channel. A marked
seasonal cycle appears off Nice and also through the Corsican channel
where are confirmed some previous direct measurements of the flow.
The study of wind and atmospheric pressure shows that these external
forces only exert a moderate effect on the water circulation which
therefore should be chiefly thermohaline.

1   INTRODUCTION

The different basins of the North-Western Mediterranean, the Tyrrhenian Sea, the Ligurian Sea, the Gulf of Lions and the Catalan Sea are
the site of great cyclonic circuits whose general outline was suggested
by Nielsen in 1912. Most studies of the marine environment and the
modelling of observed phenomena require a quantitative knowledge of
water circulation. The water flow of the Ligurian Sea forms an important link in the circulation of the Western basin, since it con-
nects the Tyrrhenian Sea, the Algero-provençal basin and the Gulf
of Lions. In this study, we present first a dynamical evaluation of
the water fluxes in the Ligurian Sea and of their seasonal variations.
But the dynamical method does not give any information upon the external or internal forces which create the measured density gradients.
So, after, we examine what may be the respective effects of the external forces, wind and atmospheric pressure, on the different
calculated fluxes.

[x] Laboratoire de Physique et Chimie Marines, Era CNRS, Station
   Marine, BP 8, 06230 Villefranche sur Mer, France.
[xx] Université de Neuchatel, Institut de Géologie, 11 rue E. Argaud,
   CH 2000 Neuchatel, Suisse.

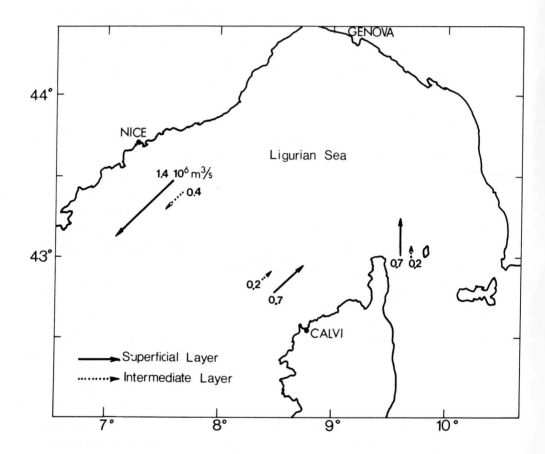

Fig. 1. Mean values of fluxes (in $10^6 m^3$/sec, or Sv) in the superficial (0-200m) and intermediate (200-800m) layers, through the Nice-Calvi section and the Corsican channel.

2   FLUXES AND THEIR SEASONAL VARIATIONS

The presence of a Marine Station at Villefranche sur Mer has allowed
the frequent taking of measurements off Nice and along the Nice-Calvi
section, through the permanent cyclonic circulation. This circulation
concerns the superficial water (about 0-200m) and intermediate water
(200-800m). Two streams of meridional waters flow up both sides of Corsica, join at the North of Cap Corse and form the Ligurian current
which laps the shores of the Italian Riviera and the French Côte d'Azur.
In the case of lack of direct measurements, the knowledge of the circulation is based on the calculation of the geostrophic current across
the Nice-Calvi section. During the past years, a growing number of
hydrological data have been exploited, and recently hydrological averages have been calculated, based on the complete measurements carried
out during the period of 1950-1973 and stored in the archives of the
data bank of the BNDO-COB in Brest (Nyffeler et al., 1980). Among 2200
hydrological stations in the Ligurian Sea, more than 900, on the Nice-
Calvi section, were thus used. The average annual flows on this section have been calculated and, taking into account the water budget
of the basin, the fluxes through the Corsican channel have been deduc-
ted and compared to previous estimations (Bethoux et al.,1980). In
figure 1 and in table 1 are presented the mean flows relating to the
superficial (SL) and intermediate (IL) layers, the + sign indicates
a SW/NE flow (off Calvi) or a S/N flow (Corsican channel), and the -
sign indicates a flow in a NE/SW direction (1 Sv = $10^6 m^3$/sec).

TABLE 1

Mean flows in the superficial (SL) and intermediate (IL) layers in
the Ligurian Sea

	Nice side	Calvi side	Corsican channel
SL	- 1.4 Sv	+ 0.7 Sv	+ 0.7 Sv
IL	- 0.4	+ 0.2	+ 0.2

These flows are large, especially off Nice, where the strongest
currents stay channelled into a coastal band 20 to 30 miles wide.
The surface speeds are between 20 to 30 cm/sec and are below 5 cm/sec
from 250m downwards (see Fig.2). In the central zone the average geostrophic flows are almost null.The flows on both sides of Cap Corse
are, on an average, equal, which shows the importance of the Tyrrhenian Sea outflow, perhaps underestimated up to now.

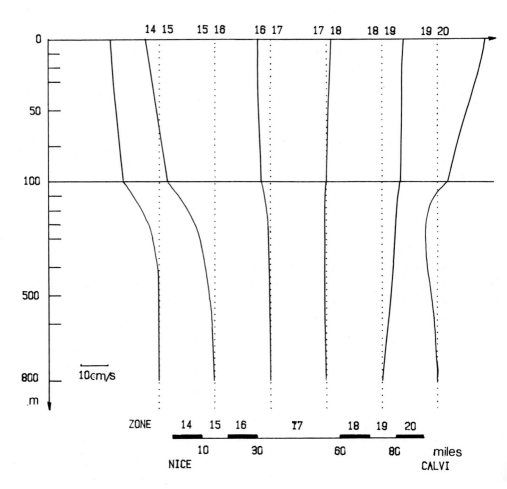

Fig. 2. Vertical profiles of currents through the Nice-Calvi section (90 miles, divided into 7 zones numbered 14 to 20).

For the study of the seasonal cycles, based on hydrological criteria and taking into account the number of hydrological stations available each month, the year has been divided into 7 periods which correspond to the months:

```
period : 1   2    3     4      5       6          7
month  : I   II   III   IV,V   VI,VII  VIII,IX,X  XI,XII
```

The seasonal cycles of the water flows off Nice and Calvi, and, for
comparison, through the Corsican channel, are shown in figure 3, for
both water layers examined. The flow on the half section on the Nice
side shows a very marked cycle, with a noticeably high rise between
periods 6 (August, September and October) and 7 (November and December)
from 1.4 to 2.3 Sv. Near Calvi, the seasonal cycle of flow is less
marked and seems more irregular. In comparison with the two preceding
cycles, a cycle comparable to that found off Nice is found in the Corsican channel, with a very marked flux increase between periods 6 and
7, when the total flow (0-400m) goes from 0.2 to 1.8 Sv. On this
graph concerning the flow through the Corsican channel, the direct
measurements of Stocchino and Testoni (1969) carried out in June-July
1966 (0.7 Sv) are shown together with those of LeFloch (1963) performed
in February and in August 1960 (1.5 and 0.4 Sv, respectively). These
direct flow measurements agree with our calculated cycle and the geostrophic calculations. They also confirm the clear decline of the flow
between periods 2 and 6.

During period 7, up to about 30 miles off Nice, the average speed
calculated is 28 cm/sec on the surface and 3 cm/sec at 300m depth.
With regard to period 6, the speeds increase on average by 5 cm/sec
between the surface and 150m depth. Moreover, off Nice, a decrease
appears in the salinity of the surface up to 300m, on average equal
to 0.07°/₀₀ (see figure 4). Such a variation in the salinity cannot
be a result of the surface water budget (the months of November and
December are relatively rainy, but at that time heavy evaporation also
occurs) and therefore it leads to the hypothesis of the influx of less
saline water, originating from the South. This decrease in salinity,
in effect, between periods 6 and 7, can be equally observed, in the
0-100m layer, on both sides of Cap Corse and even between period 5
and 6 off Calvi.

Different authors have studied the external forces effects (wind,
atmospheric pressure, tide) upon the superficial fluxes in the Mediterranean. Among them, Crepon (1965) examined the effects of the atmospheric pressure variations on the sea level, and Elliott (1979) studied

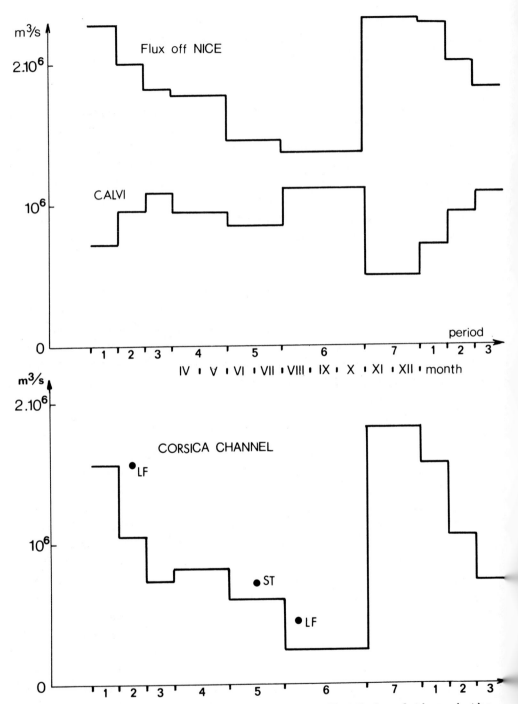

Fig. 3. Seasonal cycles of fluxes off Nice, off Calvi and through the Corsican channel. Direct measurements of LeFloch (LF) and those of Stocchino and Testoni (ST) through the Corsican channel.

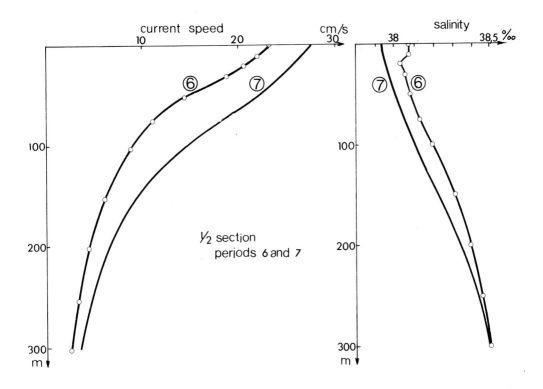

Fig. 4. Vertical profiles of currents and salinities, off Nice, at a period 6 (August, September and October) and 7 (November and December).

the wind effect on the sea level and currents in the Gulf of Genova, whereas Laevastu (1972) shown that about 1/4 of the inflowing Atlantic waters result from the tidal effects (amplitude difference at opposite ends of the straits) through the Strait of Gibraltar. Since Villain (1949,1952) very few studies about Mediterranean tides have been carried out. So it is not possible to estimate tide effects upon the circulation inside the Mediterranean. However, owing to Purga et al. (1979), tide is synchronous in the Tyrrhenian Sea, and so, it may have a static effect (such as atmospheric pressure) on the sea level and on the superficial circulation.

We have looked for the possible climatic external causes of the important mean calculated fluxes first, and then of the seasonal cycle, by examining the effects of wind and of atmospheric pressure variations on the water circulation, on a monthly scale.

3   WINDS IN THE NORTH-WESTERN MEDITERRANEAN SEA

In order to make a comparison with hydrological averages(referring to the years 1953-1973) we have used the wind averages relative to the period 1951-1960, obtained from the meteorological stations of Cap Béar, Sète, Pomègues, Cap Camarat, Cap Ferrat and Cap Corse (Darchen and DeBlock, 1968), which give the speed, the origin and the frequency of wind for each month. It is possible to evaluate the consequent drift flux, F, at 90° to the wind, linked to the square of the wind speed, V, by the empirical equation:

$$F = \frac{K \rho a \, V^2}{2 \, \omega \, \sin\phi \, \rho w}$$

where ρa and ρw are air and water densities. If we assume the adimensional friction coefficient, K, be equal to $2 \, 10^{-3}$, the equation is:

$$F_{m3/sec/m} = 2.7 \, 10^{-2} \, V^2 \; m/sec$$

3.1 Wind at Nice (Cap Ferrat)

The average speed of wind at Cap Ferrat, from all directions, is 2.7 m/sec. However, as a result of different sectors, frequencies and speeds of wind, the resulting average wind speed, V, favourable to the flow (NE/SW) is only about 1 m/sec (see Fig.5). On a half section 45 miles off Nice, the average flow resulting from the wind is about $2.2 \, 10^3 m^3/sec$, that is around one thousandth of the calculated geostrophic flow. In addition, the seasonal wind cycle explains neither qualitatively nor quantitatively the flow cycle off Nice.

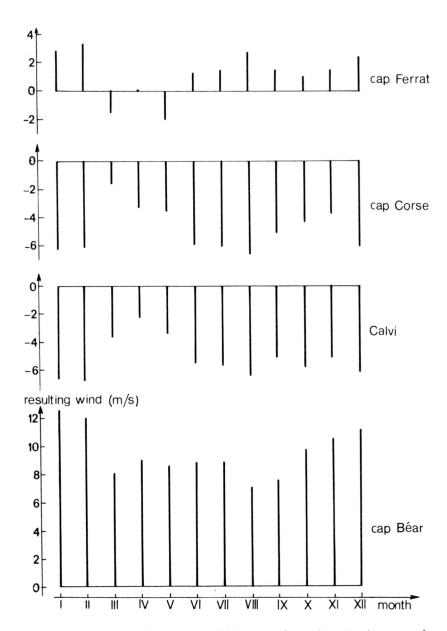

Fig. 5. Seasonal cycle of mean resulting wind, owing to its speed, frequency, origin and to the mean local water circulation.

3.2 Wind on either side of Cap Corse

The consequent average wind at Cap Corse is always from the North
or West sectors, and it is therefore always unfavourable to the SW/NE
circulation off Calvi, as well as to the S/N circulation through the
Corsican channel. Its resulting annual average is -4.8 m/sec for the
flow off Calvi, and -4.6 m/sec for the flow coming from the Tyrrhenia
Sea. In addition, the seasonal wind cycle has no apparent connection
with that of the flows.

3.3 Wind in the Gulf of Lions

In order to study a possible effect of the wind downstream of the
currents, we examined the data on wind relating to the stations of
the Gulf of Lions. At Cap Béar, Sète and Pomègues the dominant wind,
a northwesterly wind, is therefore favourable to the circulation in
the open sea (NE/SW). The resulting average wind speeds are 6 m/sec
at Pomègues, 1.9 m/sec at Sète and 9 m/sec at Cap Béar. For the latte
station, which corresponds to the most favourable case (see figure 5)
the NE/SW flow generated by the wind along a width of 45 miles is
about 0.2 Sv, which still only represents nearly a tenth of the geostrophic water flow calculated off Nice.Furthermore again, the seasona
wind cycle does not seem to account for the water flow cycle.

Gales play an important role as much on the surface flow (advection
phenomena) as on the ocean-atmosphere interchanges,particularly in
the Gulf of Lions. But with regards to the average circulation of a
cyclonic type in the North-Western Mediterranean, winds can only gene
rate about a tenth of the calculated flows, in the most favourable
case, i.e. in the Gulf of Lions. In the Cap Corse sector, wind is
countrary to the circulation, while off Nice, it is only slightly
favourable. Therefore there is definitely no direct relation between
the water fluxes and the winds, on a monthly or seasonal scale, in
the North-Western Mediterranean.

4   ATMOSPHERIC PRESSURE IN THE WESTERN MEDITERRANEAN

The atmospheric disturbances above the Mediterranean have been
studied in particular by Berenger (1955). One peculiarity, due to
the geographic position and the mountainous surroundings, is that
73% of the depressions in the Mediterranean are formed above this
sea, chiefly in the Western basin. In this basin, the most frequent
are the Gulf of Genova (50%), the Balearic (25%) and the Saharan depressions. These disturbances occur principally in autumn, winter

and spring. There is therefore a marked contrast between summer and the other seasons.

Various authors have dealt with the qualitative linkage between atmospheric pressure and sea level in the Mediterranean. Lisitzin (1954) studied the seasonal variations in the sea level in differents ports, where the sea level undergoes a great increase in October and November before decreasing at the beginning of the year. This cycle therefore presents remarkable analogies with the current wariations off Nice, but, according to Pattullo et al. (1955), a high sea level during the fall (a low sea level during spring) is associated with temperature and salinity fluctuations in the upper 100m (specific volume fluctuations). However, at Monaco, Marseille and Porto-Maurizio, Lisitzin found quite a good correlation between the monthly variations in the sea level and those of the atmospheric pressure. According to Crepon (1965), the variations in atmospheric pressure, in effect, are the essentiel cause of the variations in the average level of various ports in the Western basin. On the other hand, according to Lacombe (1960), a lowering of the atmospheric pressure upon the Mediterranean involves an increase of the inflow (0-200m) through the Straits of Gibraltar, in counterpart, a rise of the outflow (at more than 180m depth) will accompany a rise of the atmospheric pressure.

In order to estimate the fluxes due to the atmospheric variations of sea level, we studied the Mediterranean atmospheric pressure variations as a function of the seasons, whose examples are given in figure 6.

- The Gulf of Genova being a low pressure center all along the year, a horizontal gradient of pressure exists from Gibraltar to Genova.The seasonal cycle of the figure 6a, estimated from the data in 'Weather in the Mediterranean' (1962), shows a jump between period 6 and 7.
- The figure 6b is a reproduction of the average seasonal cycle of the atmospheric pressure at Nice, for the years 1951-1960 (Garnier, 1966). The average pressure is maximum during period 6 and minimum in February or March.
- The local atmospheric pressure shows a marked semi-diurnal cycle, whose amplitude at Nice (figure 6c) varies from 0.7mb in period 6 to about 0.9mb in period 7.

Owing to the seasonal cycles of the atmospheric pressure (figures 6 a, b and c) it is possible to find qualitative correlations between fluxes and atmospheric pressure variations off Nice. However, only the semi-diurnal atmospheric pressure variation (Fig.6c) can produce

140

more or less permanent fluxes, on a monthly or seasonal scale.

For the whole Mediterranean (area about 2.5 $10^{12} m^2$), a semi-diurnal amplitude of the atmospheric pressure of about 0.8mb involves a maximum in-or-out flowing fluxes of 0.46 Sv, that is about 30% of the est mated fluxes through the Straits of Gibraltar (Bethoux,1979).
The fluxes off Nice forming an important branch of the circulation in the Western basin, it is difficult to know the influence area of the atmospheric pressure variations. As a rough estimate, if we suppose that the static variations of the sea level of about half of the Western basin ($0.4 10^{12} m^2$) act on the fluxes off Nice, the atmospheric semi-diurnal variations may produce about 10% of the calculated fluxe Semi-diurnal variations of the atmospheric pressure may be an importa cause of the Mediterranean circulation, specialy through the Straits of Gibraltar (and Sicily). But, in the Ligurian Sea, they do not seem to involve more than 10% of the fluxes, and do not explain the increa of the fluxes between period 6 and 7.

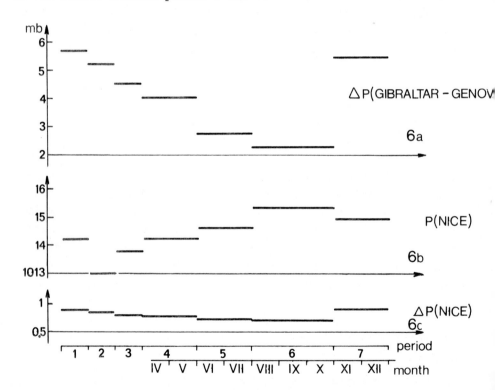

Fig. 6. Seasonal cycle of atmospheric pressure differences between Gibraltar and Genova (6a), of mean atmospheric pressure in Nice (6b) and of its semi-diurnal variations (6c).

5   CONCLUSION

The use of averages, calculated from a great number of hydrological stations between Nice and Calvi, allows not only the average annual value of the flows but also their seasonal variations to be obtained. These results should be useful in different studies in dynamics, chemistry or marine biology.

The Ligurian Sea is an important link in the circulation of water in the North Western Mediterranean, and it seems to be necessary to prove the calculated flows by direct measurements on the sections of the Riviera-Corsica and Elba-Corsica. The Corsican channel appears to be one of the key points in the understanding of the dynamics of the Mediterranean.

The study of meteorological data obtained on the North-West coasts lead to attribute a reduced effect on the average water flows and on their seasonal variations by the mechanical action of wind. On the other hand, the semi-diurnal variation of atmospheric pressure may only produce about 10% of the fluxes, and cannot explain the annual cycle of the circulation off Nice.

Since these two external forces, wind and atmospheric pressure, exert moderate effects, the circulation should be chiefly thermohaline. The initial cyclonic gyre, certainly produced by the water deficit (Bethoux,1980), is amplified by the arrival at the periphery of the basin of waters coming from the southern regions. These waters are relatively warmer and less saline than those of the central area. Such a thermal advection by the surface waters issued from the Tyrrhenian Sea is clearly visible on the infra-red satellite pictures (Bethoux et al.,1979). The increase of the circulation between period 6 and 7 is due to the density contrast between the coastal and central waters. In the central area, the sea undergoes the effects of the negative heat and water budgets with the atmosphere, while, in the periphery area, such effects are lowered by thermal advection of southern waters and by coastal runoff.

Acknowledgements- This work was supported by CNEXO (contract 79/2084) CNRS (GRECO 34) and Fonds National Suisse de la Recherche Scientifique (project 2.280.079).Thanks are due to F. Louis, who drafted the figures.

142

REFERENCES

Berenger, M.,1955. Essai d'étude météorologique du bassin méditerranéen. Mémorial de la Météorologie Nationale, 40, 42pp.
Bethoux , J.P.,1979. Budgets of the Mediterranean Sea. Their dependan
on the local climate and on the characteristics of the Atlantic
waters. Oceanol. Acta,2,2,157-163.
Bethoux ,J.P.,1980. Mean water fluxes across sections in the Mediterr
nean Sea, evaluated on the basis of water and salt budgets and of
observed salinities. Oceanol. Acta,3,1,79-88.
Bethoux, J.P., Prieur, L. and Albuisson, M.,1979. Apports de la télé-
détection infra-rouge à la connaissance de la circulation superficielle dans la partie Nord-Est du bassin Occidental. Rapp.Comm.int
Mer Médit., 25-26.
Bethoux, J.P., Nyffeler, F. and Prieur, L.,1980. Utilisation de moyen
nes hydrologiques pour le calcul des flux d'eau dans le bassin Liguro-provençal, XXVII Congrés CIESM,Cagliari,9-18 octobre 1980,4pp
Crépon, M.,1965. Influence de la pression atmosphérique sur le niveau
moyen de la Méditerranée Occidentale et sur le flux à travers le
détroit de Gibraltar. Cahiers Océanographiques, XVII,1,15-32.
Darchen, J. and deBlock, A.,1968. Le vent sur les côtes de la France
Métropolitaine, Méditerranée. Monographies de la Météorologie Nati
nale,62,2,97pp.
Elliott, A.J.,1979. The effect of low frequency winds on sea level an
currents in the Gulf of Genova. Oceanol. Acta,2,4,429-433.
Garnier, M.,1966. Climatologie de la France, Eléments de la variation
diurne. Mémorial de la Météorologie Nationale,51,148pp.
Lacombe, H.,1960. Note sur le régime du détroit de Gibraltar. Mémoire
et Travaux de la S.H.F.,II,136-143.
Laevastu, T.,1972. Reproduction of currents and water exchange in the
Strait of Gibraltar with hydrodynamical numerical model of Walter
Hansen. In: Studies in Physical Oceanography. Arnold L.Gordon,edi-
tor, Gordon and Breach,2,219-232.
LeFloch, J.,1963. Sur les variations saisonnières de la circulation
superficielle dans le secteur Nord-Est de la Méditerranée Occidentale. CREO,5,1,5-10.
Lisitzin, E.,1954. Les variations du niveau de la mer à Monaco,Compa-
raison avec quelques autres stations marégraphiques de la côte fra
çaise et italienne. Bull.Inst.Océan.Monaco,1040,24pp.
Nielsen, J.N.,1912. Hydrography of the Mediterranean and adjacent waters. Danish Oceanog.Exp.1908-1910,Rep.VI,77-191.
Nyffeler, F., Raillard, J. and Prieur, L.,1980. Le bassin Liguro-provençal, Etude statistique des données hydrologiques 1950-1973. Rap
ports scientifiques et techniques CNEXO,42,163pp.
Pattullo, J.,Munk, W., Revelle, R. and Strong, E.,1955. The seasonal
oscillations in sea level. J.of Marine Research,14,1,88-123.
Purga, N.,Mosetti,F. and Accerboni, E.,1979. Tidal harmonic constants
for some Mediterranean harbours. Bolletino Di Geofisica Teorica Ed
Applicata, XXI,81,72-81.
Stocchino, C. and Testoni, A.,1969. Le correnti nel canale di Corsica
e nell'archipelago Toscano,C.N.R.,Ser.A,19,26pp.
Villain,M.C., 1949. Sur la marée à Alger et en Méditerranée Occiden-
tale. COEC,9,16-19.
Villain, M.C.,1952. Les marées de la Méditerranée Orientale. COEC,
IV,3,92-103.
Weather in the Mediterranean,Meteorological office,1962.Her Majesty's
Stationery Office,London,362pp.

ANALYSIS OF UPWELLING IN THE GULF OF LIONS

MILLOT Claude[x]

ABSTRACT

The salient features of the upwelling phenomenon, already presented in a reference paper (Millot, 1979), are first described with infrared thermographies. Some hypothesis about the dynamics of the surface layer, supported by the sea surface temperature distribution, have been verified and completed by numerous in situ measurements. Numerical and analytical models have been performed, and it has been possible to evaluate the effects of some parameters on both the localisation of the cool water source points, and the structure of horizontal circulations. The dynamics of upwelling in the Gulf of Lions seems to be now correctly understood (a much more detailed and complete analysis is presented in Millot (1981)).

1-THE THERMOGRAPHIES

The Mistral and the Tramontane are strong north-westerlies (fig 1); the view in fig 2 has been obtained about one day after the onset of these winds. At a large scale, the sea surface temperatures off the Roussillon coast and off the Languedoc and Provence coasts are very different. Although the Roussillon is the most windy region, the coastal waters have nearly the same temperature as the open sea. Due to the Coriolis force, surface waters are drifted to the south-west ; they are accumulated along the Roussillon coasts (downwelling) when upwelling is observed along the coasts of Languedoc and Provence.

x : Antenne du Laboratoire d'Océanographie Physique du Muséum
    BP 2, 83501 La Seyne, France.

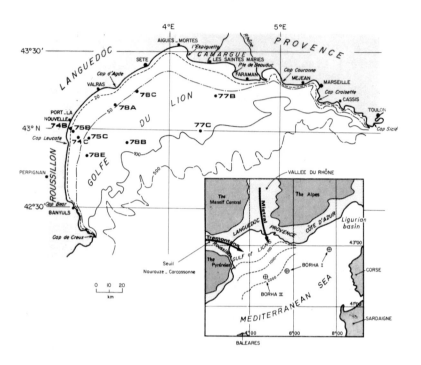

Fig 1 : The studied area.

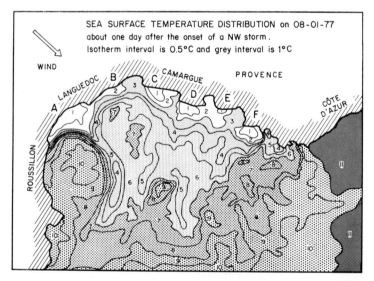

Fig 2 : The infrared thermography obtained on the 1st of August 1977, at about 09 00 TU.

At a smaller scale, the upwelling is discontinuous (zones A-F in fig 2). The bathymetry is rather smooth and the windfield is rather homogeneous in the Camargue coastal area ; consequently, this discontinuity is an interesting observation. Cool surface tongues extend from some upwelling zones. The tongue associated with zone A suggests a cool seaward current turning to the right ; correlatively, the isotherms in the south-western part of the gulf reveal an eddy structure. In some coastal areas, on the edge of the upwelling zones, large alongshore temperature gradients ($\sim 1°C/$ some km) are observed.

The north-westerly wind is not always blowing over the entire gulf, but when observed, the upwelled waters are located in the zones A,...,F. The characteristics of the upwelling zones (intensity, dimension,...) vary from one view to the other. In order to estimate the sea surface temperature map observed during north-westerly wind events, we have summed 15 photos. From the mean map (fig 3), it appears that the characteristics of the upwelling already described are very significant.

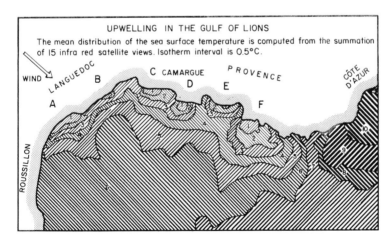

Fig 3 : The mean distribution of the sea surface temperature obtained by summation of 15 photos.

2.- THE IN SITU MEASUREMENTS

The data obtained in 1974, 1975, and 1977 have been presented in the reference paper ; we will now discuss those obtained in 1978 (fig 4 for instance).

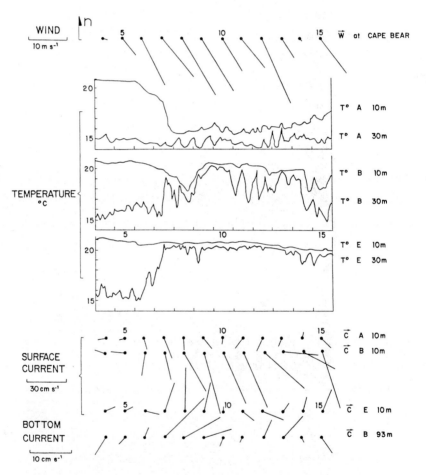

Fig 4 : The daily winds and currents and some temperature records from September 4 to 15, 1978. Vectors are plotted in such a way that the vertical axis is north-south.

2.1- The temperature data

During the gusts of wind, these data show that the stratification
is much more disturbed by advection, up and downwelling, internal
waves at the inertial frequency (Millot and Crépon, 1981) than by
mixing. The temperature records at 10 and 30 m (fig 4) clearly show
an upwelling at 78-A and a downwelling at 78-E. At 78-B near the
surface, the temperature is decreasing and then increasing up to the
values observed before the wind event : this is clearly due to advection of cool water (revealed by the tongue) in the surface layer
only. The main temperatures over the whole experiment at 78-B and
78-E are nearly the same.

2.2 The surface current data

These data are instructive if we separate the wind induced circulation from the general one. The features suggested in fig 4 are
supported by a statistical analysis over the whole experiment
(Millot and Wald, 1980). Fig 5 shows that during the wind events,
the mean surface current at 78-B is to the SSE (21 cm/s) when it is
to the N (11 cm/s) at 78-E. At 78-E, the observed wind induced
surface current is roughly opposed to the theoretical drift current.

When comparing the current and temperature data at 78-B and 78-E,
it appears that the 2 points are concerned with an anticyclonic
circulation induced by the wind in the surface layer. Let us mention
that the characteristics of this northward current are different from
those of the coastal current presented in a preceding paper (Millot,
1976), although both are induced by the wind. The circulation over
the whole continental shelf is described with much more details in
Millot (1981).

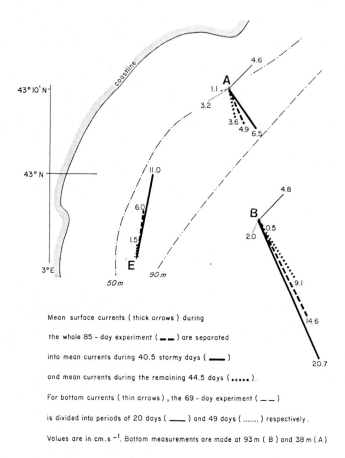

Mean surface currents (thick arrows) during

the whole 85 - day experiment (▬ ▬) are separated

into mean currents during 40.5 stormy days (▬▬)

and mean currents during the remaining 44.5 days (•••••).

For bottom currents (thin arrows) , the 69 - day experiment (▬ ▬)

is divided into periods of 20 days (▬▬) and 49 days (.......) respectively .

Values are in cm.s $^{-1}$. Bottom measurements are made at 93 m (B) and 38 m (A)

Fig 5 : Dependence of mean surface and bottom currents upon the occurrence of north-west storms.

2.3 The bottom current data

These data (fig 4 and 5) reveal more homogeneous features. At 78-A (50 m) and at 78-B (100 m), the mean speed induced by the wind is 5 cm/s to the NE along the isobaths (Millot and Wald, 1980). Similar values are observed at 77-C (fig 1) on the edge of the shelf (Millot, 1979). Then, the whole bottom layer is advected by the north-westerli from the downwelling zone to the NE, and locally to the upwelling zones (A,...,F).

3-INTERPRETATION AND MODELISATION

3.1 The discontinuity and the localisation of upwelling

The non-influence of the spatial variability of both the bathymetry and the wind stress applyes only to zones A,...,E (in zone F, the wind tends to be parallel to the coast, and the continental shelf is reduced). Some hours after the onset of the wind, actual cool water source points appear at the surface, along straight coastal segments some ten-twenty nautical miles long. These cool areas then spread out, while warm waters remain in the vicinity of capes and small bays.

In fact, the upwelling phenomenon is linked to an offshore drift of surface water. This seaward drift has a large spatial extension off a regular coastline well oriented with respect to the wind, because the drifting of all the particles results in the same phenomenon, i.e. the upwelling. This is not the case in the vicinity of an irregular coast, where different phenomena (for example up and downwelling) are induced in adjacent places. Due to large horizontal gradients, local circulations reducing the extension of each phenomenon probably occur.

It is difficult to model such an effect because of the small scale of the coastline features. Nevertheless, Saint-Guily (1980), Crépon and Richez (1981) and Hua (1981) have elaborated more or less simple models which confirm our interpretation : the spatial variability of the upwelling in the coastal zone is mainly dependent on the coastline drawing.

3.2 The tongues of cool water

These features reveal that the water upwelled near the coast is then drifted seaward, roughly in the wind direction. But if we consider the records at 78-B (fig 4), it is clear that large speeds at a 10 m depth are associated with both cool and warm surface water. The tongue reveals the direction of the drift current on a thermography, but this current is wider than the tongue. The tongue is a permanent feature of an upwelling zone, but its position is not well defined and so (as in fig 4), it may sweep across a mooring point.

3.3 The anticyclonic circulation

One week after the onset of the wind, we noticed (fig 4) that warm surface waters were still drifted seaward. If we consider the current speed which is of the order of some tens cm/s, the warm water now observed cannot come from the coastal zone.

As suggested by the isotherm structure in fig 2 and by the mean temperature values in the surface layer at 78-B and 78-E which are nearly the same, there is a continuity between the northward current at 78-E and the south-south eastward current at 78-B. The flows observed at the 2 points are parts of an anticyclonic circulation, centered off the Roussillon coasts and which does not concern the point 78-A. Let us mention that very similar features have been observed in the southern part of Lake Michigan (Bellaire and Ayers, 1967).

Among the mechanisms by which the wind induces such an eddy, only the effect of the spatial and temporal variability of the wind speed has been studied (Hua, 1981). It has been shown that the anticyclonic circulation only develops with specific meteorological conditions : the speed must be stronger and/or the onset must be earlier in the central part of the gulf. We have not modeled the spreading of the wind in the vicinity of zone A (Millot, 1979), though this spatial variability of the wind direction is probably important.

Whatever the most important meteorological parameters are, a large seaward current is drifted from the upwelling zone A . As shown with observations (Lamy, Millot and Molines, 1981) and computations (Hua, 1981), the deficit of surface water is not entirely compensated by the upwelled water. Due to the strong stratification remaining outside the upwelling zone during a wind event (fig 4), the condition of continuity in each layer requires the drift current from zone A to be compensated by currents originated from the edges of zone A. This dynamical process explains both the continuity of the surface currents measured at 78-E and 78-B, and the fact that wind induced currents can be opposed to the local wind.

4-SYNTHESIS OF THE MAIN RESULTS

The upwelling phenomenon induced by north-westerly winds in the Gulf of Lions has the following specific features.

The observations and the models show that the vertical mixing is clearly discernible in a few km near the coast only : anywhere else, the dynamics of the shelf waters during summer is those of a two-layer system with a coupling between the two layers only due to pressure forces.

At a large scale, the surface waters are drifted to the right of the wind. The compensating flow in the bottom layer is to the left of the wind, and it is discernible near the bottom as far as the shelf break area. Upwelling spreads out over the 2/3 part of the gulf (in the NE), and downwelling over the 1/3 part (in the SW).

At a smaller scale, actual source points of cool water are systema-tically observed : they are located in the center of straight coastal segments some 20-40 km in length. Upwelling zones are limited by capes and small bays in the vicinity of which large alongshore temperature gradients are observed. The spatial variability of upwelling is mainly dependent on the coastline drawing.

Strong drift currents issued from the upwelling zones are visualized by tongues of cool surface waters, but they carry away a large amount of warm water. In the vicinity of the upwelling zones, the bottom currents are directed to the source points of cool water.

Off the coast of Roussillon, an anticyclonic eddy is induced by the wind from a rather complex mechanism. First, the spatial and temporal variability of the wind stress defines the main characteristics of the upwelling zone A and the associated drift current. Outside the upwelling zone the stratification remains strong, and by continuity the drift current is associated with compensating flows in the surface layer. Due to the semi circular shape of the Gulf of Lions, a down-welling phenomenon occurs in the south-western part of the gulf ; in this area, the dynamical sea level is higher than it is in the upwelling zone. Consequently, compensating flows opposed to the theoretical drift current develop and create the anticyclonic eddy.

REFERENCES

Bellaire, F.R., Ayers, J.C., 1967 . Current patterns and lake slope. Proc. 10th Conference Great Lakes Res., pp. 251-263.

Crépon, M., Richez, C., 1981. Transient upwelling generated by two-dimensional atmospheric forcing and variability in the coast-line. This issue of the Mem. Soc. Roy. Sc. Liège.

Hua, B.L., 1981. A non-linear numerical model of upwelling in the Gulf of Lions. This issue of the Mem. Soc. Roy. Sc. Liège.

Lamy, A., Millot, C., Molines, J.M., 1981. Bottom pressure and sea level measurements in the Gulf of Lions.J. Phys. Ocean., 11, 3, pp. 394-410.

Millot, C., 1976. Specific features of the sea-shore circulation near Cape Leucate. Mem. Soc. Roy. Sc. Liège, 6, 10, pp. 227-245.

Millot, C., Crépon, M., 1981. Inertial oscillations on the continental shelf of the Gulf of Lions. Observations and theory. J. Phys.

Ocean., 11, 5, pp. 639-657.

Millot, C., Wald, L., 1980 : Upwelling in the Gulf of Lions. CUEA
    Volume on "Coastal Upwelling Research, 1980". To be published.

Millot, C., 1981. La dynamique marine sur le plateau continental
    du Golfe du Lion en été. Thèse d'Etat, Paris VI-Muséum.

Saint-Guily, B., 1980 . Note sur la structure discontinue des upwel-
    lings. XXVII Congrès-Assemblée Plénière de la CIESM, Cagliari.

DISCONTINUOUS UPWELLING ALONG A RECTILINEAR COAST WITH A SERIES OF SMALL CAPES

by

Bernard SAINT-GUILY

Muséum National d'Histoire Naturelle, Paris, and

Laboratoire Arago, Banyuls sur Mer, France

Introduction

Summer upwellings which occur in the Gulf of Lions, in the Mediterranean Sea, have a discontinuous shape. They are composed of several cold water sources fixed on certain places along the coast (Millot, 1979, 1981). The positions of these source seem to be imposed by the coastal geometry. In addition the circulation in the surface layer is mainly advective with quasi slab motions. In the following pages the wind induced circulation along a rectilinear coast with small spitlike irregularities is studied. The theory shows that the presence of small capes gives necessarily birth to singular points, which are vortex points for a wind normal to the coast, and source or sink points for a wind parallel to the coast. This problem is examined by regarding the superficial currents as irrotational and confined in a thin layer of constant depth. Afterwards a solution is obtained when currents are considered as linear in a baroclinic layer (reduced gravity layer).

Inertial and steady flow

In the superficial (mixed) layer of constant depth h, the currents are considered as two-dimensional and irrotational. The circulation induced by a uniform wind stress is described by a stream function ψ or a potential function φ, which are solutions of the Laplace equations :

$$\Delta \psi = 0 \quad , \qquad \Delta \varphi = 0 \ . \tag{1}$$

The components of the velocity u, v, are given by

$$u = \frac{\partial \psi}{\partial y} = \frac{\partial \varphi}{\partial x} \quad , \qquad v = -\frac{\partial \psi}{\partial x} = \frac{\partial \varphi}{\partial y} \quad ; \tag{2}$$

and the pressure is obtained from the Bernoulli's equation

$$p + \frac{\rho}{2} (u^2 + v^2) + \rho f \psi - \frac{1}{h} (x\tau_0 + y\tau_*) = C \quad , \tag{3}$$

where $f = 2\omega \text{Sin } l$ (ω angular velocity of the earth, l latitude), and τ_0, τ_* are the wind stress components respectively normal and parallel to the coast.

Far from the rectilinear coast which is taken as oy axis, that is when $x \to \infty$, the circulation tends to an Ekman drift. Then we have the condition

$$\psi \to \frac{1}{\rho fh} \ (x\tau_0 + y\tau_*) \quad \text{for} \quad x \to \infty \ . \tag{4}$$

If there exists on the coast a series of small spitlike capes, regularly distributed at the points $x = 0$, $y = \pm (2n-1)\pi a$ ($n=1,2...$), the boundary conditions for the normal and the tangential velocity are given by

$$u = 0 , \quad \text{for} \quad x = 0 ,$$
$$v = 0 , \quad \text{for} \quad x = 0 \quad \text{and} \quad y = \pm (2n-1)\pi a \ . \tag{5}$$

The stream function is the sum of two terms ψ_0, ψ_*, corresponding to wind stress components respectively normal and parallel to the coast. Taking $\tilde{x} = x/2a$, $\tilde{y} = y/2a$ as non-dimensional coordinates, and leaving out the tildes, the solution takes the following form :

$$\psi = \psi_0 + \psi_* \ ,$$

$$\psi_0 = \frac{2a\tau_0}{\rho fh} \left[x - \frac{(1 + tg^2 y)thx}{tg^2 y + th^2 x} \right] \ , \tag{6}$$

$$\psi_* = \frac{2a\tau_*}{\rho fh} \ \text{arctg} \left[\frac{tgy}{thx} \right] \ .$$

In these two terms, systems of singularities for the velocity appear between the capes at the points $x = 0$, $y = \pm n\pi$, $n = 0, 1, 2...$, (Betz, 1964). These singularities are vortices (here anticyclonic) in the first term, for a wind normal to the coast (figure 1), and sources in the second term, for a wind parallel to the coast (figure 2). If the wind is making an angle of 45° with the coast, the singular points are composite (figure 3), and the circulation shows an anticyclonic curvature. The potential function corresponding to (6) is given by

$$\varphi = \varphi_0 + \varphi_* \ ,$$

$$\varphi_0 = - \frac{2a\tau_0}{\rho fh} \left[y + \frac{(1 - th^2 x)tgy}{tg^2 y + th^2 x} \right] \ , \tag{7}$$

$$\varphi_* = \frac{2a\tau_*}{\rho fh} \ \log \left[2 (Sin^2 y + Sh^2 x) \right] \ .$$

Inertial flow dependent on time

If the motion in the superficial layer of constant depth h is dependent on time, two-dimensional and irrotational, there are still stream and potential functions which are solutions of Laplace equations.

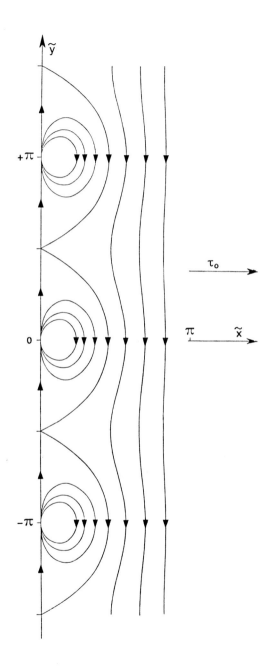

Fig.1. Stream lines of the superficial circulation for a wind normal to the coast.

158

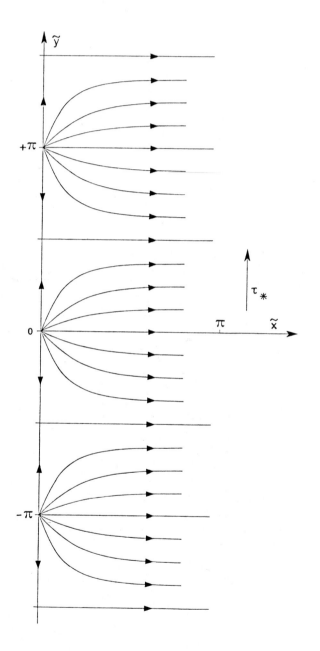

Fig.2. Stream lines of the superficial circulation for a wind parallel to the coast

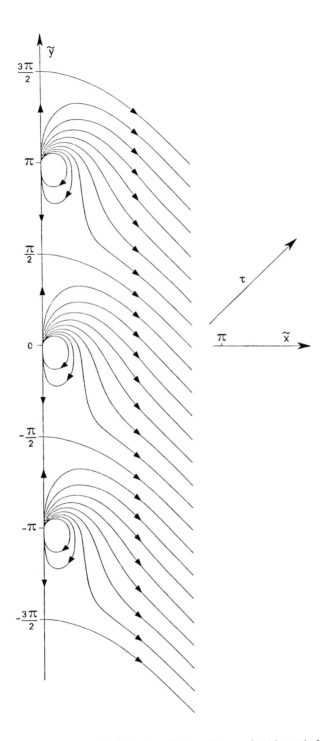

Fig.3. Stream lines of the superficial circulation for a slanting wind.

But the Bernoulli's equation is now

$$p + \frac{\rho}{2} (u^2 + v^2) + \rho f \Psi + \rho \frac{\partial \Phi}{\partial t} - \frac{1}{h} (x\tau_0 + y\tau_*) = C(t) , \qquad (8)$$

where the wind stress τ_0, τ_*, depends on time. Far from the coast we must have an Ekman regime. So we have the condition

$$\text{for} \quad x \to \infty, \quad \Psi \to \frac{1}{\rho f h} \left[x (T_0 - S_*) + y (S_0 + T_*) \right] , \qquad (9)$$

where

$$S_{0,*} = f \int_0^t \tau_{0,*} (t') \, \text{Cosf}(t-t') dt' ,$$
$$T_{0,*} = f \int_0^t \tau_{0,*} (t') \, \text{Sinf}(t-t') dt' . \qquad (10)$$

If the wind stress is constant after the initial instant ($t = o$) we have simply inertial oscillations with the period $2\pi/f$:

$$S_{0,*} = \tau_{0,*} \, \text{Sinft} , \quad T_{0,*} = \tau_{0,*} (1 - \text{Cosft}) . \qquad (11)$$

the boundary conditions are not modified ; and the stream function takes the following form :

$$\Psi = \Psi_0 + \Psi_* ,$$
$$\Psi_0 = S_0 \frac{\psi_*}{\tau_*} + T_0 \frac{\psi_0}{\tau_0} , \qquad (12)$$
$$\Psi_* = T_* \frac{\psi_*}{\tau_*} - S_* \frac{\psi_0}{\tau_0} ,$$

where ψ_0, ψ_* are the solutions (6).
In the same manner the potential function is found to be

$$\Phi = \Phi_0 + \Phi_* ,$$
$$\Phi_0 = S_0 \frac{\varphi_*}{\tau_*} + T_0 \frac{\varphi_0}{\tau_0} , \qquad (13)$$
$$\Phi_* = T_* \frac{\varphi_*}{\tau_*} - S_* \frac{\varphi_0}{\tau_0} ,$$

where φ_0 , φ_* are the solutions (7).

Linear baroclinic flow dependent on time

We regard now the superficial layer as baroclinic with a variable depth h ; and we suppose the flow linear, and the wind stress uniform and parallel to the coast. Then we have the following equations :

$$\frac{\partial u}{\partial t} - fv = - \delta g \frac{\partial h}{\partial x} \quad,$$

$$\frac{\partial v}{\partial t} + fu = - \delta g \frac{\partial h}{\partial y} \quad, \tag{14}$$

$$\frac{\partial h}{\partial t} + h_o \left[\frac{\partial u}{\partial x} + \frac{\partial v}{\partial y} \right] = 0 \quad,$$

where $\delta = (\rho' - \rho)/\rho'$ is the relative density difference, and h_o is the initial depth (at $t = o$). Eliminating successively h and v we obtain first a system of equations for u and v

$$\left[\frac{\partial^2}{\partial t^2} - \delta g h_o \frac{\partial^2}{\partial x^2} \right] u - \left[f \frac{\partial}{\partial t} + \delta g h_o \frac{\partial^2}{\partial x \partial y} \right] v = 0 \quad,$$

$$\left[\frac{\partial^2}{\partial t^2} - \delta g h_o \frac{\partial^2}{\partial y^2} \right] v + \left[f \frac{\partial}{\partial t} - \delta g h_o \frac{\partial^2}{\partial x \partial y} \right] u = \frac{1}{\rho h_o} \frac{\partial \tau}{\partial t} \quad, \tag{15}$$

and then a wave equation for u

$$\frac{\partial^2}{\partial t^2} \left\{ \left[\frac{\partial^2}{\partial t^2} + f^2 \right] u - \delta g h_o \left[\frac{\partial^2 u}{\partial x^2} + \frac{\partial^2 v}{\partial y^2} \right] - \frac{f}{\rho h_o} \tau \right\} = 0 \quad. \tag{16}$$

Let the axis oy be taken still along the rectilinear coast ; supposing that there is only one small spitlike cape at the point $x = 0$, $y = a$, the boundary conditions are

$$u = 0 \quad, \quad \text{for} \quad x = 0 \quad, \quad v = 0 \quad, \quad \text{for} \quad x = 0 \quad \text{and} \quad y = a \quad. \tag{17}$$

Let the velocity be the sum of two terms

$$u = u_0 + u_* \quad, \qquad v = v_0 + v_* \quad, \tag{18}$$

where u_0, v_0 represents the solution of the complete equations (15) which satisfies the first boundary condition (17), and u_*, v_*, the solution of the homogeneous equations (15) which satisfies the complementary conditions

$$u_* = 0 \quad, \quad \text{for} \quad x = 0 \quad, \quad v_* + v_0 = 0 \quad, \quad \text{for} \quad x = 0 \quad \text{and} \quad y = a \quad. \tag{19}$$

We consider first the case of a periodic wind stress

$$\tau = \tau_0 \sin \sigma t \tag{20}$$

with a low frequency ($\sigma < f$). The expressions of u_0 and v_0 are given by

$$u_0 = \frac{f\tau_0}{(\rho h_0(f^2-\sigma^2))} (1-e^{-kx})\sin\sigma t \quad ,$$

$$v_0 = -\frac{\tau_0}{(\rho h_0 \sigma(f^2-\sigma^2))} (f^2 e^{-kx}-\sigma^2)\cos\sigma t \quad , \qquad (21)$$

$$k = \left[\frac{f^2-\sigma^2}{\delta g h_0}\right]^{1/2} .$$

We know that the terms u_* and v_* must vanish far from the coast and be finite along the coast, except possibly at certain singular points. These terms are obtained in the following way. We note that if φ is a solution of the homogeneous wave equation (16), the expressions of u_* and v_* take the form

$$u_* = \frac{\partial^2 \varphi}{\partial t^2} - \delta g h_0 \frac{\partial^2 \varphi}{\partial y^2} \quad ,$$

$$v_* = -f \frac{\partial \varphi}{\partial t} + \delta g h_0 \frac{\partial^2 \varphi}{\partial x \partial y} \quad . \qquad (22)$$

The appropriate solution φ has a singularity at the origin :

$$\varphi = -\frac{A}{\delta g h_0} \frac{x}{r} K_1 \cos\sigma t \quad ; \qquad (23)$$

Where $K_1 = K_1(kr)$ is the modified Bessel function of the first species, and $r^2 = x^2 + y^2$. Making use of the Bessel functions properties (Abramowitz and Stagun, 1964), the following expressions for u_* and v_* are obtained

$$u_* = A \frac{x}{r} \left\{ \left[\frac{\sigma^2}{\delta g h_0} + \frac{k^2 y^2}{r^2}\right] K_1 - \frac{(x^2-3y^2)}{r^4} (2K_1 + krK_0) \right\} \cos\sigma t \qquad (24)$$

$$v_* = Af \frac{\sigma}{\delta g h_0} \frac{x}{r} K_1 \sin\sigma t + A \frac{y}{r} \left[\frac{(y^2-3x^2)}{r^4} (2K_1 + krK_0) - \frac{k^2 x^2}{r^2} K_1\right] \cos\sigma t \qquad (25)$$

When $K_1 = K_1(kr)$, $K_0 = K_0(kr)$.

The first boundary condition (19) is satisfied, and the second one gives the constant A ; we have

$$A = -\frac{\tau_0 a^2}{\rho h_0 \sigma \llbracket 2K_1(ka) + kaK_0(ka)\rrbracket} \qquad (26)$$

This result shows clearly that singularities are necessary to fulfil the boundary conditions on small capes. In general, the wind stress is not periodic and we must have recourse to the Laplace transformation. Let $\bar{w}(s)$ be the transform of the function $w(t)$:

$$\bar{w}(s) = \int_0^t e^{-st} w(t) dt \quad .$$

The expressions of $\bar{u}_0$, $\bar{v}_0$ are easily found. Then the second terms $\bar{u}_*$, $\bar{v}_*$ must vanish far from the coast and be finite along the coast except possibly at certain singular points. The solution is constructed from the transform $\bar{\varphi}$ of a solution φ of the homogeneous wave equation (16) :

$$\bar{\varphi} = \frac{\bar{A}}{\delta g h_0} \frac{x}{r} K_1 (kr) \; ; \tag{27}$$

the expressions of $\bar{u}_*$, $\bar{v}_*$ are then given by (22). It is easy to write the explicit forms of $\bar{u}_*$ and $\bar{v}_*$, to verify that the first boundary condition (19) is satisfied and that $\bar{A}$ is determined by the second one. It is not necessary to proced further, to study the case of a row of small capes, and to engage into the problem of obtaining the original functions u_* , v_* . It appears clearly that the addition of small capes on a rectilinear coast entails the production of singularities in the resulting flow.

Conclusion

We may observe that, in the first model, the flow is irrotational and non linear, and that the superficial layer is "rigid" the depth h being maintained constant. This advective and irrotational flow represents the main part of the superficial motion. And the source points appear between the capes, in agreement with the observations. But the slightly rotational motions associated with barotropic and baroclinic waves are obviously left out. This restraint is relaxed in the second model where the motion is linear. Nevertheless both these analyses lead to solutions with singularities. We must also note that in the first model, with a wind parallel to the coast, even in the absence of capes source points are necessarily present. The role of the coastal singularities is only to fix their distribution. Along a perfectly rectilinear coast the distance between the sources must depend on a characteristic length ; and the most eligible one is the internal radius of deformation. In the Gulf of Lions the distance $2\pi a$ between the upwelling sources is about 37 km. And a = 6 km, a value which is equal to the local internal radius of deformation. In any case these theoretical considerations, with a permanent rigid layer and with a transient reduced gravity layer, plead in favour of a strong influence of coastal geometry on the sources distribution in the upwellings.

References

Abramowitz, M. and Stegun, I.A., 1964. Handbook of Mathematical Functions. National Bureau of Standards, 1046 pp.
Betz, A., 1964. Konforme Abbildung. Springer. 407 pp.
Millot, C., 1979. Wind induced upwellings in the Gulf of Lions. Oceanologica Acta, 2 (3): 261-274.
Millot, C., 1981. La dynamique marine sur le plateau continental du golfe du Lion en été. Thèse Muséum National d'Histoire Naturelle, Paris.

DEVIATION WITH RESPECT TO CORIOLIS PERIOD FOR GRAVITY-INERTIAL INTERNAL WAVES GENERATED IN AN OCEAN BASIN BY AN IMPULSIONAL WIND

Dominique P. RENOUARD

Institut de Mécanique de Grenoble

B.P. 53 X

F-38041 GRENOBLE-CEDEX

France

ABSTRACT

Our aim is to study large amplitude oscillations of the season of thermocline of period close to that of the Coriolis period. In some respect, they are the measurable translation of a geostrophic adjustment occurring at the onset of, or immediately after, a rapid varying wind or storm. Consequently, this phenomenon is observed only during some pendular period, although a few observations made in the Mediterranean Sea have shown that they may exist for almost two weeks (cf. Perkins, 1972). As for the period, it is 3 to 20 % shorter than the Coriolis period (cf. Day and Webster, 1965; Gonella, 1971; Perkins, 1972; Fomin, 1975; Kundu, 1976). These thermocline oscillations are associated with currents of maximum speeds of of 10 to 20 cm/s, rotating clockwise with time in the northern hemisphere. These currents have exactly the Coriolis period, and appear immediately after the onset of the wind. This indicates a propagative phenomenon (cf. Crépon et al., 1972; Millot, 1981).

As just indicated, these baroclinic movements are the ocean's response to a modification in the geostrophic equilibrium. This phenomenon has been the subject of numerous studies reviewed, for instance, in Blumen (1972), or, more recently, Thorpe (1975) or Briscoe (1975).

1 ANALYTICAL AND EXPERIMENTAL FOREGROUND

1.1 Among the numerous studies devoted to that subject, we have chosen that of Crépon (1969), for whom the near Coriolis oscillations of the seasonal thermocline first appear at the coast, at the onset of a gust of wind, and then propagate towards the open sea. The conclusions of this model seem to be in good agreement with observations made in the Gulf of Lions (Mediterranean Sea) (cf. Millot, 1981) both for the gravity-inertial waves and for the upwelling generated by the conjunction of a local stationary wind perturbation and a coast (cf. Crépon and Richez, 1981).

From the hypothesis first adopted by Crépon (1969) -long wave approximation ; momentum and mass conservation equations linearized and integrated along a verti- cal in each layer - we have developed a model, which is an approximate solution of the problem of the generation of such wave by an impulsional wind, blowing over a rectangular ocean. Our main result is that the periods found for the gravity-inerti oscillations linked to the geostrophic adjustment, are constant with time, in- dependent from the observation point, depending on the dimensions of the basin and of the parameters characterizing the stratification. They are given by:

$$T_2(m,n) = 2\pi/\beta_2(m,n)$$

with

$$\beta_2(m,n) = f^2 + \pi^2 c_2^2 \left[(2n + 1)^2/a^2 + (2m + 1)^2/b^2\right]$$

where : f is the Coriolis parameter, $c_2^2 = g.h_1 h_2/(h_1 + h_2).\Delta\rho/\rho$ is the baroclinic phase speed (h_i being the thickness of the upper ($i = 1$) and lower ($i = 2$) layers, $\Delta\rho/\rho$ the buoyancy), a and b the dimensions of the basin.

All these periods tend towards the inertial period when the two horizontal dimensions of the basin become large. It may be noted that, from the same equa- tions, but using an other way to solve them, Csanady (1973) had proposed, and verified by measurements, a solution next of ours, for oblong lakes. Though, for its calculations, this author considered the lake as infinitely long.

Our solution does not satisfy the condition of null mass transport across every side of the basin. However, at least for the beginning of the movement, for a sufficiently large basin, thus mass transport will be weak, and we will consider our solution as an approximate one, and the experiments will have to verify the legitimity of this point of view.

1.2   In order to study the internal waves generated by the wind in a rectangu- lar tank in rotating axis we have built, on the large rotating platform, 14 cm diameter, of the Grenoble's University, a channel (8 x 2 x 0,6 m) fitted with a wind-tunnel.

We are able to obtain winds reaching their equilibrium value, at every point in the air test section, in less than 1.2 s, which is a time shorter than all the characteristic periods of the observed phenomena. So that we can say that we have a wind quasi-impulsional with time. In practice, a wind-speed of V = 5.5 m/ is used in quite all our experiments.

In order to record interface height variations with time, at any given point, so-called "interface followers" are used. There consist of conductivity meters equipped with a sensor slaved to follow a layer of given resistivity. It has been verified that, during an experiment the thickness of the interface is

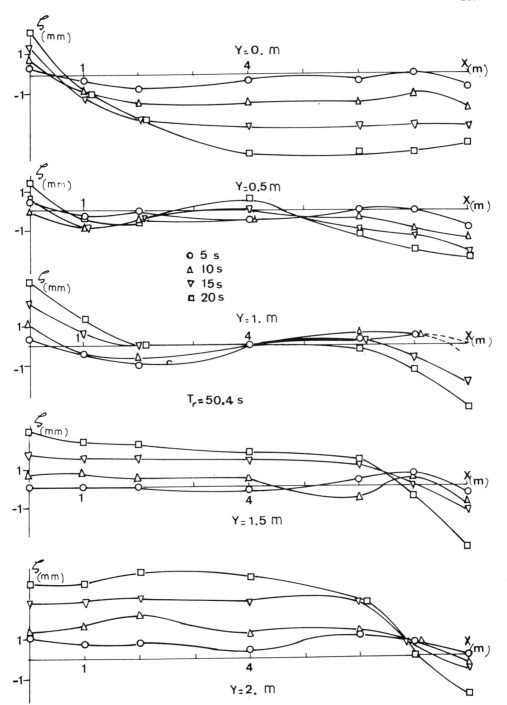

Fig. 1. Interface height variations, along five longitudinal lines at different times, after the onset of the wind. In this experiment $h_1 = h_2 = 26$ cm ; $\rho_1 = 0,9987$; $\rho_2 = 1,0168$; $T_{rot} = 50.4$ s.

spatially uniform and does not vary two much with time. Thus we can say that, as a first approximation, the successive recordings obtained during an experiment, are representative of these which would have been obtained in a single gust of wind.

2   GENERAL DESCRIPTION OF THE PHENOMENA OCCURRING IN THE TANK AS THE WIND BLOWS

If the variations in the interface height with time are considered at a given point, the following movements will be observed starting from rest :

a   The variation in the mean level of the interface, from a static equilibrium level corresponding to the interface at rest (σ_2^S) to a dynamic equilibrium level, with wind (σ_2^D). This variation can be broken down into two parts : the first, and most important, is due to the slope that the wind gives to the free surface ; this exists independently of the rotation. The second part of this variation results from the rotation : this can be called a geostrophic adjustment in the channel due to the currents generated by the wind. It is this part of the mean level variation of the interface which is accompanied by the gravity-inertial waves looked for. But, the experiments have pointed out that if the latter part of this variation of the mean level first appear along all the sides of the tank, and then propagates towards the inside of it, the former first appear at the upstream and downstream[x]ends of the basin, as Kelvin-type upwelling or downwelling then propagating along the sides of the tank they leave at the right of their direction of propagation (sense of f) (cf. fig. 1).

b   An oscillation of period close to :

$$T_2 = 2a/c_2$$

which is the natural longitudinal baroclinic oscillation of the tank (order of magnitude 120 s). This also exists without rotation which only affects its shape : without rotation, this oscillation is a plane swash whereas, with rotation, it becomes a Poincaré-Kelvin amphidromy, but with this difference that the denivellations are to be measured from (σ_2^D) and not from the plane $z = -h_1$ (cf. fig. 2). So it seems preferable to speak of a "pseudo-Poincaré-Kelvin amphidromy".

c   An oscillation of period close to :

$$T_1 = 2a/c_1 \qquad (c_1 = g(h_1 + h_2))$$

which is the natural longitudinal barotropic oscillation of the tank (order of magnitude 7 s). This oscillation has the same shape as the baroclinic one.

It is obvious that because the tank is on the rotating platform, the phase speed of the baroclinic and barotropic modes are modified ; and as the tank is a closed basin, the phase speeds are, in fact, weaker than c_i so that the natural periods are longer than T_i by some percent ($\sim$5%).

---

[x] Upstream and downstream with respect to the wind flow.

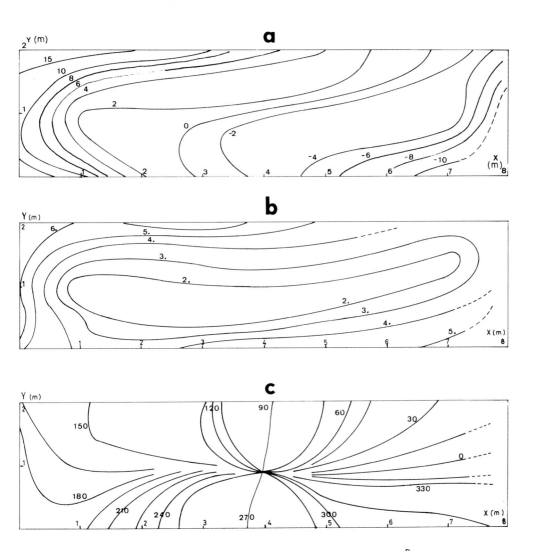

Fig. 2. Level lines of the dynamic equilibrium level, with wind (σ_2^D) of the interface (a), and lines of equal amplitude (b), and equal phase (c) of the pseudo-Poincaré-Kelvin amphydromy. The experimental conditions are those given in fig. 1 ; heights are in mm, phases in degrees.

3   ESTABLISHMENT OF THE GRAVITY INERTIAL WAVE LINKED TO THE IMPULSIONAL
    CHARACTER OF THE WIND

For an experiment, i.e. for a given total depth, thickness and density of each
layer, and rotation speed, several wind gusts were made, each corresponding to
what will be called a test. For each of these tests, a recording of interface
height variations is obtained at five different points. A spectral analysis has
been carried out on each of these points, after having eliminated the variations
in mean level of the interface.

The spectra obtained show peaks corresponding to the longitudinal baroclinic
and barotropic periods ; in these experiments, the harmonics of these periods,
like the periods of the transverse baroclinic and barotropic oscillations, do
not generally appear.

However, the spectral analysis always shows the existence of a significant
peak at a period shorter than the Coriolis period of 8 to 21 %. The difference
between the observed and the Coriolis frequency is always greater than at least
two frequency spectrum calculation steps. This difference appears systematically
when the wind blows suddenly.

In order to check that this difference between the Coriolis period and the
observed period is due to the suddenly applied wind, the wind establishment time
is gradually increased and it is found that when this time is greater than approximately half the Coriolis period, then the difference disappears.

In order to gain a clearer understanding of this difference, the two types
of mean spectra were computed, each spectrum corresponding to a given experiment.

In the first, the mean of the spectra obtained in the various tests was computed, the interface followers having been in various places in the channel during
the experiment. The results of a number of experiments are given in table 1.
It is noticeable that these mean spectra always show only one significant peak
for a given value lower than the Coriolis period.

In the second computation, for each experiment, the interface followers were
not moved and several gusts of wind were simulated (several tests). The mean
spectrum was then computed for the experiment for each interface follower, and
for the experiment as a whole considering all the sensors together, as in the
first mean type.

The following observations were made regarding the last two types of mean
spectra :

a   The significant peak nearest the Coriolis period corresponds to a period
that is clearly different from, and always shorter than, the Coriolis period.

b   This peak corresponds to the same period for all the interface followers
then this period appears to be independent of the observation point, a fact that
was to be expected because the first type of mean spectra also shows only one
significant peak for these periods.

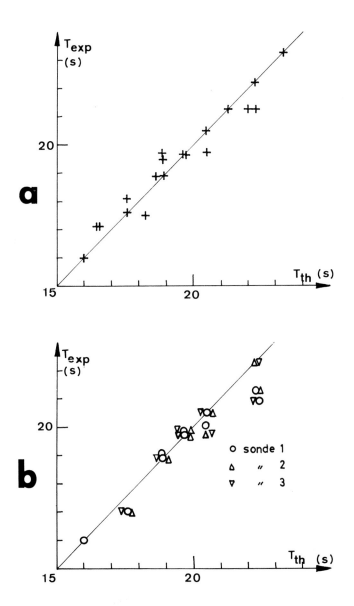

Fig. 3. Comparison between the experimentally measured period, and the period calculated by the "chequerboard" model, (a) for the mean spectra corresponding to each experiment, (b) for the mean spectra corresponding to each interface-followers, for the experiments in which they were at a fixed point throughout the experiment.

If the relative difference between this period and the Coriolis period is plotted
on log-log paper against the internal radius of deformation (R_D = C_2/f) which is
a parameter integrating the physical characteristics of the experiment, it can be
seen that the points are located on a straight line of slope equal to two.

If the experimentally found period is compared with the period computed using
the "chequerboard" model, i.e., T_{TH} = $2\pi/\beta_2$ (m = 0, n = 0) very good agreement
is found between them (cf. fig. 3). Moreover, the differences found between the
observed and predicted periods, for some experiments, can be very well explained
by experimental measurement errors, for example, in the determination of thicknesses (h = $\pm$ 3 mm) which leads to an error in the predicted period. Nevertheless,
it is to be noted that this difference between the observed and predicted frequency is never greater than one frequency spectrum calculation step.

The same comparison was made between the period corresponding to a significant
peak in the experimental spectrum immediately shorter than the gravity inertial
wave period, and the period given by the "chequerboard" model for T_{TH} = $2\pi/\beta_2$
(m = 0, n = 1). The results are not in such good agreement as previously, corresponding to very small amplitudes, but the agreement nevertheless seems significant
It should be noted that the "chequerboard" model predicted that the periods do
not depend on the position of the measurement point, and this has been verified
in the tank experiments.

In order to see whether the period found experimentally changes with time,
each recording was cut into two or four equal parts and the spectrum of each of
these parts was calculated successively (by partial spectral analysis). In all
the spectra calculated, the significant peak nearest to the Coriolis period was
either exactly in the same place or at the computation point of the part spectrum nearest the point found for the significant peak on the spectrum of the
whole recording. No change in peak position was noted as time increases and it therefore seems reasonable to say that the period found for the gravity inertial wave linked to the impulsional wind is constant with time. It should
be added that, in real life, such a change in period of the gravity inertial
wave has never been evidenced, at least to the author's knowledge. This last
point is in agreement with the "chequerboard" model conclusion.

As already demonstrated in the "chequerboard" model, the period depends on
the tank dimensions. Experiments have been made with different tank lengths, and
it has been found that the agreement between the observed and predicted periods
is good as long as the length of the tank is larger than the width of the channel.
If these two dimensions are equal, the predicted difference between the "chequerboard" model and the Coriolis period is greater than the experimental difference.

If consideration is now given to the cross-section of the tank, it is found
that at mid-length (x = 4 m) (cf. fig. 4) a) there is a time interval of about
7 s near the sides, between the onset of the wind and the time at which the

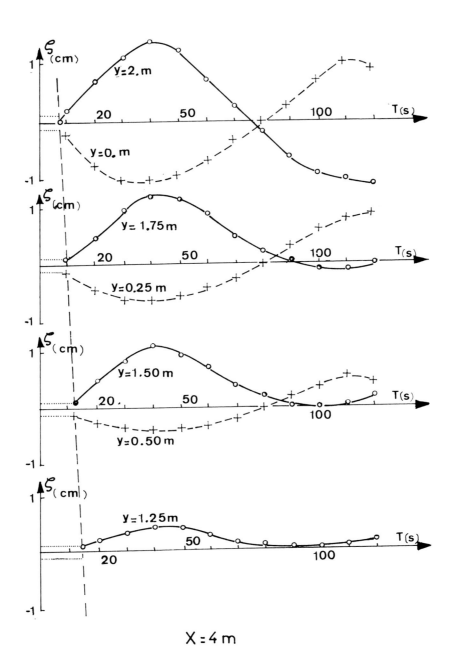

X = 4 m

Fig. 4. Interface height variation, with time, for different points of the transversal section, in the middle of the channel (X = 4 m) from top to bottom, close to the sides, and at distances of 25 cm, 50 cm, and 75 cm from the sides. The dotted lines indicate heights ± 0,1 cm. The propagation time corresponding to a velocity of about 10 cm/s, which is the order of magnitude of the baroclinic phase speed for this experiment, is indicated by the dashed line.

interface height variations reach an amplitude of 1 mm, and b) above all, as
regards the time required to obtain a height variation of 1 mm, there is an interface height variation propagation time from the sides to the centre of the channel.
This corresponds to a propagation velocity of the same order of magnitude as the
baroclinic wave phase speed for the experiment considered. As previously said
(cf. fig. 3) the longitudinal baroclinic oscillations first appear in only two
particular points, namely, the right upstream ($x = 0$, $y = 0$) and left downstream
($x = 8$ m, $y = 2$ m) corners and then propagate from there along the longitudinal
sides. The time required for such baroclinic oscillations to reach the central
section of the tank is greater than that measured for the interface height variation to become greater than 1 mm at $x = 4$ m, $y = 1.25$ m. Consequently, the propagation noted in figure 8 is that of the geostrophic adjustment in the channel and
of the gravity inertial waves accompanying it. These waves first appear near the
sides on their whole length and then propagate towards the axis of the channel.
This point also seems to be found in real life (cf. Kundu, 1976) and is also in
agreement with the "chequerboard" model.

Considering now the amplitude of this gravity inertial wave, computed by spectral analysis, it can be seen that for a given experiment, the amplitude reaches
its maximum value when the duration of the wind is half the period predicted for
this experiment by the "chequerboard" model.

The ratio between the amplitude of the gravity inertial wave and that of the
longitudinal baroclinic wave generated by the same gust of wind is at its maximum, and almost equal to one, for gusts of very short duration, then rapidly
decreases as this duration increases and remains at a value of about 0.1 as soon
as the duration is equal to or greater than the Coriolis period.

As regards the interface height variations at different times after the onset
of the wind along the longitudinal channel, it was found that, immediately after
the wind starts to blow, the variation is quite independent of the measurement
point, except near the two previously mentioned corners. It can thus be deduced
that, as soon as the wind starts blowing, the geostrophic adjustment appears and
the amplitude of the mean variation in interface level resulting from this adjustment is independent of the x-axis, as calculated in the "chequerboard" model
(cf. fig. 1).

If one looks at the currents generated by the wind, in the upper layer, immediately after it starts to blow, it can be noticed that, in a thin layer, near
the free surface, it appears an oscillation at exactly the Coriolis period ($2\pi/f$)
and that, under this layer and above the interface, two oscillations of the
current are to be distinguished : one at the Coriolis period, and one at the gravity inertial one $[2\pi/\beta_2(0.0)]$. This last one being more and more important as
we are nearer the interface meanwhile the first one disappears at 3 or 4 cm from
the free surface. In the lower layer the velocities are too weak to be measured.

CONCLUSION

So, evidence seems to have been clearly given of the existence of a gravity inertial wave linked to the impulsional character of the wind in the experimental channel fitted with a wind tunnel, and this for various experimental conditions.

It has a period constant with time and given, with a very good approximation, by the model we have imagined. This wave accompanies the variation in mean level of the interface resulting of the geostrophic adjustment in the channel. It is a progressive wave, first appearing along the sides and then propagating towards the inside of the channel. Its amplitude depends on the wind speed, and, for a given wind of its deviation ; it is independent of the x-axis along the longitudinal sides.

In addition, it is shown that two privileged corners exist for the appearance of Kelvin-type perturbations of the interface which then give place to the mean level variation of the interface due to the slope imposed by the wind at the free surface, and to the longitudinal baroclinic oscillation (pseudo-Poincaré-Kelvin amphidromy) which is linked to this variation.

These two results are in good agreement with the analytical developments obtained from the hypothesis first adopted by Crépon (1969) and thus justify then a posteriori. And they show the importance and usefulness of a physical model to study natural phenomena which would otherwise be difficult to understand, and to check theoretical hypothesis more easily than by sea-measurements.

REFERENCES

Blumen, W., 1972. Geostrophic adjustment. Rev. Geophys. Space Phys., 10: 435-528.
Briscoe, M.G., 1975. Internal wave in the ocean. Rev. Geophys. Space Phys., 13: 591-598.
Crépon, M., 1969a. Hydrodynamique marine en régime impulsionnel. Cah. Océanogr. 21: 333-358.
Crépon, M., 1969b. Hydrodynamique marine en régime impulsionnel. Cah. Océanogr. 21: 863-877.
Crépon, M., Gonella, J., Lacombe, H. and Stanislas, G., 1972. Participation française à la campagne COFRASOV I, Rpt. CNEXO No. 04, 156 pp.
Crépon, M. and Richez, C., 1981. Transient upwelling generated by two dimensional atmospheric forcing and by shore variability. Part I. Analytical model (in press).
Csanady, G.T., 1973. Transverse internal seiches in large oblong lakes and marginal seas. J. Phys. Oceanogr., 3: 439-447.
Day, G.G. and Webster, F., 1965. Some current measurements in the Sargano Sea. Deep-Sea Res., 12: 805-814.
Fomin, L.M., 1975. Inertial oscillation in a horizontally un-homogeneous current velocity field. Izv. Atm. Oceanic Phys., 9: 37-40.
Gonella, J., 1971. A local study of inertial oscillations in the upper layer of the ocean. Deep-Sea Res., 18: 775-788.
Kundu, P.K., 1976. An analysis of inertial oscilliations observed near Oregon coast. J. Phys. Oceanogr., 6: 879-893.
Thorpe, S.A., 1975. The excitation, dissipation and interaction of internal waves in the deep ocean. J. Geophys. Res., 80: 328-338.

HYDRODYNAMICS OF THE ADRIATIC SEA

P. MALANOTTE RIZZOLI[1] and A. BERGAMASCO[2]

[1] Istituto per lo Studio della Dinamica delle Grandi Masse, C.N.R., Venezia (Italy)

[2] Scientific Collaborator, ISDGM-CNR, Venezia (Italy)

ABSTRACT

   Two extreme average situations characterize the Adriatic Sea. The first one, typical of seasonal conditions of autumn-winter, with a complete homogeneity of the vertical distribution of the water physical properties (temperature,salinity, hence density); the second one, relative to the seasonal conditions of spring-summer, with a very strong vertical stratification. The relevant models of the Adriatic Sea circulation so far constructed are summarized. The first one has been developed to study the relative importance of air-sea thermal and evaporative fluxes, wind stress, horizontal advection and diffusion and the dense,deep water formation process. The second, a multilevel model, satisfies two basic flexibility criteria of being applicable to basins of quite different geometries and capable of describing quite different phenomenological situations. Results are shown and discussed.

1   PHENOMENOLOGY

   From the phenomenological point of view, two extreme average situations can be distinguished in the Northern Adriatic. The first one, typical of the seasonal conditions of late autumn-winter, is characterized by essentially complete homogeneity of the vertical distribution of the water physical properties (temperature, salinity, hence density) north of the sill of Pelagosa, with the exclusion of the only southernmost, deepest part in communication with the Ionian Sea (Cruises Najade-Ciclope 1911-1914; Trotti, 1966; Franco, 1970, 1972 a,b; Malanotte Rizzoli, 1977). This vertical homogeneity is complete down to depths of about 200 m, characteristic of the mid-Adriatic (Jabuka) pit, at the breaking point of the continental shelf, which constitutes all the northern half of the basin.

   As well-known, the Northern Adriatic Sea is one of the three Mediterranean sites of dense deep water formation. This mechanism, lasting from 10 to 20 days, occurs in wintertime, at the outbreaks of cold, dry air of Euro-Asiatic origin blowing directly onto the Northern Adriatic. The evaporation fluxes at the air-sea interface are then so intense as to produce a quick overturning of the water column, with vertical mixing down to the bottom of the basin, accompanied by the formation of a mass of water of remarkably high density ($\sigma_t > 29.4$) in the interior region (Trotti, 1970; Hendershott and Rizzoli, 1976, Figs. 1,2).

Fig. 1. Surface distribution of density anomaly for the period January-February 1972 (from Malanotte Rizzoli, 1977).

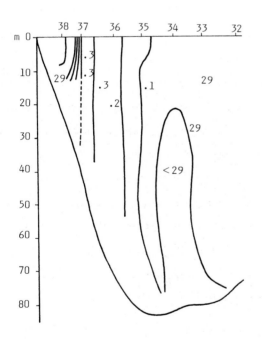

Fig. 2. Vertical distribution of density anomaly Winter 1972 cross-section from Porto Civitanova to Isola Grossa (from Malanotte Rizzoli, 1977).

The second average situation is the one relative to the seasonal conditions of late spring-summer, characterized by a very strong vertical stratification, with pycnoclines rising to the very surface in the northernmost, shallowest part of the basin.

A further fundamental characteristic of the Adriatic Sea is the major outflow of fresh, light water along the northwestern Italian side, due to the runoff of the rivers, the most important of which is the Po. This river runoff constitutes one of the basic driving forces of the horizontal circulation, producing very intense horizontal density gradients with the salty water mass of the interior of Ionian origin. This river outflow forms a narrow boundary region elongated along the Italian (western) coastline, colder in winter, warmer in summer relative to the interior mass.

2   THE MODELS

We summarize now the relevant models of the Adriatic Sea circulation so far constructed.

For the late autumn-winter condition, a numerical model has been developed to study the relative importance of some of the physical processes (such as river inflow, air-sea thermal and evaporative fluxes, wind stress, horizontal advection and diffusion, exchange with the Southern Adriatic) in determining the winter fields of density and horizontal transport (Hendershott and Rizzoli, 1976). The basic conservation equations are adimensionalized using the characteristic length scales of the Northern Adriatic Sea, typical values for its average velocities and values for the eddy viscosity and eddy diffusivity used in the literature for basins of its size. The model's primary idealization, corresponding to the above discussed phenomenological evidence, is that vertical mixing of heat and salt is always complete, the density field depending essentially only upon horizontal variables. The model is constituted by a geostrophic interior and two top and bottom, Ekman layers of small thickness relative to the total depth. Considering average, seasonal evolutions, one does not allow for sea level variations, but rather impose a rigid lid on the sea surface. Thus, both the momentum and the density equations are vertically integrated to obtain two coupled equations in the density field and the transport streamfunction, with complex interactions with the bottom topography.

A series of numerical experiments was performed solving the model equations for two winter situations (1966-1972) and the theoretical predictions were found to be in good agreement with experimental results for the main interior part of the Adriatic basin (Hendershott and Rizzoli, 1976; Malanotte Rizzoli and Dell'Orto, 1981).

In Fig. 3, the evolution of the transport streamfunction and density fields are shown at successive steps of the time integration. The formation process is

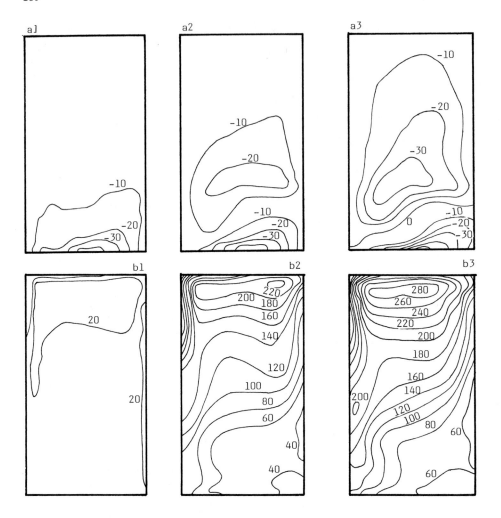

Fig. 3. Time evolution of transport streamfunction (a1,a2,a3) and density (b1, b2,b3) both in dimensionless units, multiplied by 100: streamfunction contours may be interpreted as dimensional transports in units of 10^{-4} m^2/s while density contours are increments of $2\sigma_t$ in units of 10^{-2}.
a1,b1 = time step   5, corresponding to 3,46 days
a2,b2 = time step 25,   "   "   " 17,38   "
a3,b3 = time step 45,   "   "   " 31,14   "

quite well reproduced of the dense water pool centered in the northern part of the basin stretching southward in a characteristic tail which follows isobath contours. The transport streamfunction shows a typical circulation gyre of thermohaline origin, determined by the strong gradients between light water of river runoff along the boundaries and the dense water of the interior. The gyre is completely disconnected from the forcing condition given at the southern, open boundary.

The model cannot describe the flow near the Italian coastline due to its basic assumption of complete vertical mixing. In fact, near this coastline, river
induced vertical stratification is observed to persist very intensely all the
year long. An analytical treatment has been developed for this density boundary
layer adjacent to the Italian coastline, in which the vertical density stratification is maintained. This treatment is based upon boundary layer analysis, em-
phasizing therefore the importance of cross-boundary density gradients and diffusion processes in determining the nearcoastal circulation (Malanotte Rizzoli and
Gazzillo, 1976; Malanotte Rizzoli and Dell'Orto, 1981).

The previous models describe and reproduce the wintertime seasonal evolution
of the circulation and density field. A much more flexible model is necessary
for the Adriatic Sea if one wants to satisfy the following requirements:

1) Capability to reproduce, describe and predict phenomenological situations as
   widely different as late autumn-winter and spring-summer seasons. In these
   last ones a very strong pycnocline is present throughout the basin under average meteorological conditions.

2) Capability to represent phenomena with time scales ranging from the seasonal
   one down to the time scales typical of the tidal circulation (about 1 day).

3) Capability to be applied to the whole Adriatic Sea or to subportions of it.

4) Capability to include all necessary driving forces for the circulation (thermohaline and wind driven). The wind can be an important driving force for
   the Adriatic Sea, for instance scirocco inhibits Adriatic outflow along the
   western coast (Italy) and forces inflow along the eastern one (Yugoslavia),
   on the time scales typical of storm surges.

Such a model has been constructed (Malanotte Rizzoli and Bergamasco, 1981). Fig.
4 shows its schematic representation.

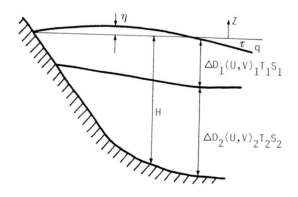

Fig. 4. Schematic representation of model.

The model gives the space-time evolution of sea level; total mass transport (integrated over the total depth); mass transport in each layer (integrated over the layer thickness); vertical velocities at the layer interfaces; horizontal distributions of temperature, salinity, density anomaly for each layer.

The model accepts as input the wind stress field τ and the thermal-evaporation fluxes q at the air-sea interface; the coastal river runoff at coastal boundaries.

The model equations can be sythesized as follows:

$$A(U_k) = f\,V_k - \frac{\Delta D_k}{\bar{\varrho}}\,\frac{\partial \psi}{\partial x} - \int_{\Delta D_k} \frac{\partial}{\partial x}\,\frac{\chi}{\varrho}\,dz + D(U_k) + \tau_x^{k+1} - \tau_x^k$$

$$A(V_k) = -f\,U_k - \frac{\Delta D_k}{\bar{\varrho}}\,\frac{\partial \psi}{\partial y} - \int_{\Delta D_k} \frac{\partial}{\partial y}\,\frac{\chi}{\varrho}\,dz + D(V_k) + \tau_y^{k+1} - \tau_y^k$$

the horizontal momentum equations for each layer k, integrated over the layer depth.

$$A\begin{pmatrix} T \\ S \end{pmatrix}_k = D\begin{pmatrix} T \\ S \end{pmatrix}_k + \begin{pmatrix} q_T \\ q_S \end{pmatrix}_k$$

the thermodynamical equations for the temperature T and salinity S of each layer k.

$$\varrho_k = \bar{\varrho} + \sigma_t(T,S)_k$$

is the equation of state for the density in each layer k.

Where

ΔD_k is the k-layer thickness

f is Coriolis parameter, considered constant

$(U,V)_k = \int_{\Delta D_k} (u,v)dz$ horizontal transport components for each layer k

$\psi = p_{sur} + \bar{\varrho}g\eta$ barotropic pressure, with p_{sur} the surface pressure and the mean density

$\chi = \int_{\Delta D_k} \varrho_k\,dz$ baroclinic pressure

η is the surface sea level

τ^{k+1} is the tangential stress at the (k+1) upper interface of the k-layer

$\tau^{k+1} = \tau^W$ the wind stress, at the free surface

τ^k is the stress at the k-layer lower interface of the k-layer

$\tau^k = \tau^B$ the bottom stress at the bottom.

$$A(\Phi) = \int_{\Delta D_k} \mathcal{Q}(\Phi)\,dz \quad \text{with} \quad \mathcal{Q}(\Phi) = \Phi_t + \frac{\partial}{\partial x}\,u\Phi + \frac{\partial}{\partial y}\,v\Phi + \frac{\partial}{\partial z}\,w\Phi \quad \text{the advection operator}$$

$$D(\Phi) = \int_{\Delta D_k} \mathcal{D}(\Phi)\,dz \quad \text{with} \quad \mathcal{D}(\Phi) = c_H \nabla^2 \Phi + c_V \Phi_{zz} \quad \text{the diffusion operator.}$$

w is the vertical velocity for each layer k.

$\begin{pmatrix} q_T \\ q_S \end{pmatrix}_k$ are the source functions of heat and salt in each layer k, that is the vertical fluxes at the k-layer interfaces.

As an application of the model, a numerical simulation has been carried out for the nearcoastal strip along the Italian littoral in the period September 15-October 16, 1978. For this period a set of data exists, namely time series of current records at a current site 6 km from the coast and vertical sections of temperature, salinity and density along two transepts, extending 20 km into the sea, measured every week, northern and southern boundaries of the test area. These data have been used for comparison and calibration of the model. The model was considered in its two-layer version (surface layer 7 m thickness). A realistic bottom topography distribution with 1 km^2 space resolution was given as input. Other inputs were time series of the sea level at the boundaries; surface wind stress and air-sea interface thermal evaporation fluxes, as computed by meteorological data recorded at coastal stations.

Comparing the Figures 5 and 6 we can see the cooling occurred at the air-sea interface during the simulation period. In fact the temperature in front of the Po River delta decreases from 22°-23°C to 18°-19°C. We can see moreover the trend of the undercoastal river water (Brenta, Adige, Po) to extend southward along the coast in a tongue-like movement.

This trend is shown even better in the surface salinity distributions of Figures 7 and 8. In these last maps it is also clear the intrusion of the salty water mass of southern origin protruding northward in the interior of the basin.

184

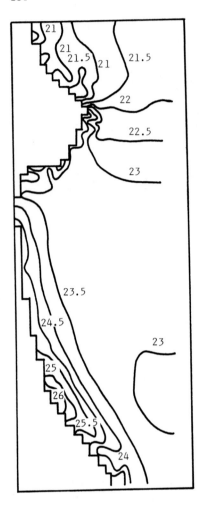

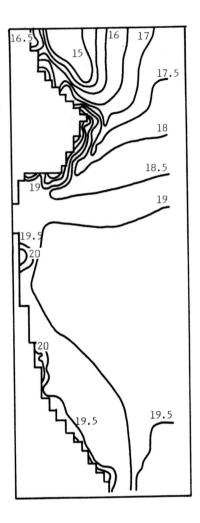

Fig. 5. Surface temperature distribution on Sept. 15, 1978, 12:00
hours.

Fig. 6. Surface temperature distribution on Oct. 16, 1978, 12:00
hours.

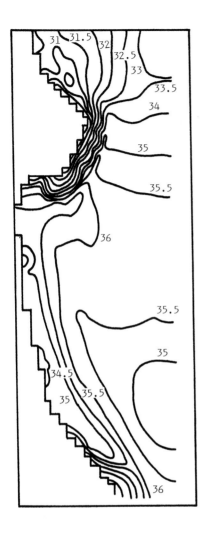

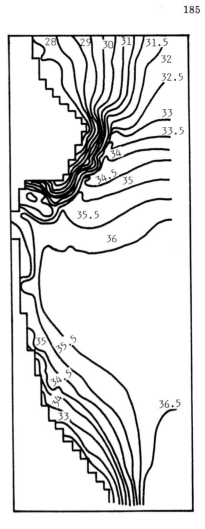

Fig. 7. Surface salinity distribution as in Fig. 5.

Fig. 8. Surface salinity distribution as in Fig. 6.

186

Figure 9 shows the density distribution in the surface layer. This is essentially determined by the salinity distribution, as evident from the strong correlation of the corresponding maps. The numerical predictions are given every 2 hours. Subsequently, they are averaged over 24 hours, to eliminate the tidal component and obtain the average daily evolution. The maps shown in Figures 5 to 9 are in very good agreement with the corresponding experimental distributions relative to the same period.

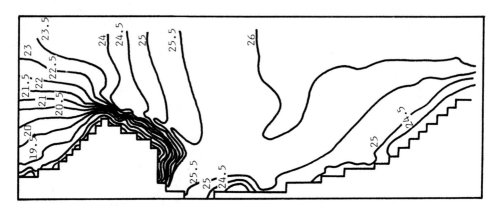

Fig. 9. Density distribution as in Fig. 8.

REFERENCES

Franco, P., 1970. Oceanography of Northern Adriatic Sea. 1. Hydrologic features: cruises July-August and October-November 1965. Arch. Oceanogr. Limnol., Suppl. 16: 1-93.

Franco, P., 1972 a. Oceanography of Northern Adriatic Sea. 2. Hydrologic features: cruises January-February and April-May 1966. Arch. Oceanogr. Limnol., Suppl. 17: 1-97.

Franco, P., 1972 b. Oceanography of Northern Adriatic Sea. 3. Distribution of the water transparency: cruises July-August and October-November 1965, January-February and April-May 1966. Arch. Oceanogr. Limnol., Suppl. 17: 1-14.

Hendershott, M.C. and Rizzoli, P., 1976. The winter circulation of the Adriatic Sea. Deep Sea Res., 23: 353-370.

Malanotte Rizzoli, P. and Gazzillo, D., 1976. On the influence of the vertical density structure on the dynamics of small basins, with specific application to the Adriatic Sea. Ann. Geofis., XXIX, 4: 247-275.

Malanotte Rizzoli, P., 1977. Winter oceanographic properties of Northern Adriatic Sea. Cruise January-February 1972. Arch. Oceanogr. Limnol., 19, 1: 1-45.

Malanotte Rizzoli, P. and Dell'Orto, F., 1981. Coastal boundary layers in ocean modelling: an application to the Adriatic Sea. Il Nuovo Cimento, Marzo-Aprile, Serie 1, 4C: 173-220.

Malanotte Rizzoli, P. and Bergamasco A., 1981. A multilayer model of the circulation in small basins. In preparation.

Mosetti, F. and Lavenia, A., 1969. Ricerche oceanografiche in Adriatico nel periodo 1966-1968. Boll. Geofis. Teor. Appl., XI, 43: 191-218.

Trotti, L., 1970. Crociere Mare Adriatico. CNR, Raccolta dati Oceanografici, Serie A, No. 29.

Zoré-Armanda, M., 1963. Les masses d'eau de la mer Adriatique. Acta Adriatica, 10: 5-88.

Zoré-Armanda, M., 1968. The system of currents in the Adriatic Sea. Etud. Rev., 34: 1-42.

CURRENT CIRCULATION IN THE LIGURIAN SEA

A. ESPOSITO

C.N.E.N. Laboratorio per lo Studio dell'Ambiente Marino, Fiascherino (La Spezia), Italy

G. MANZELLA

C.N.R. Istituto per lo Studio della Dinamica delle Grandi Masse, Stazione Oceanografica, San Terenzo (La Spezia), Italy

ABSTRACT

Observation of the circulation in the Ligurian Sea have generally been inferred indirectly from the field of mass, while few observational data gathered by
moored currentmeters can be found in the literature. The cyclonic circulation
seems to be forced by the wind stress that imparts vorticity (curl of the wind
stress) to the sea. In particular, a southerly wind seems to cause a coastal
countercurrent in the Gulf of Genova. A special attention deserves the interaction between the Ligurian Sea and the Tyrrhenian Sea, since the data collected on the shelf during Spring 1979 showed a significant coherence of the alongshore current only at about 1 cpd.

INTRODUCTION

The Ligurian Sea is an abyssal depression delimited by the shallow water
shelf of the Tuscan Archipelago toward the south-east and largely open toward
the Western Mediterranean. The continental shelf is narrow and steeps deeply
(see Fig. 1).

It is well known that the Ligurian Sea is a cyclogenetic area and that the
cyclogenetic activity is more frequent from October to May (Gleeson, 1954).The
seasonal variations of the atmospheric motions influence the dynamics of the
basin. A statistical analysis of the wind measured at Genoa shows that in
winter the winds are generally north or north-westerly, so that they reinforce

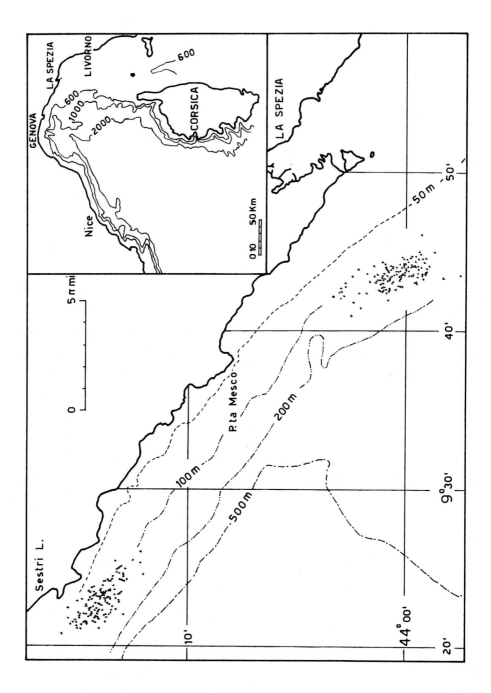

Fig. 1 The Ligurian Sea. The scatter plots show the difference between the currents.

the general cyclonic circulation of the Ligurian Sea. In summer the prevailing winds are southerly and tend to modify the general cyclonic circulation in the Gulf of Genoa.

The Ligurian Sea circulation has been inferred indirectly from the field of mass (Stocchino and Testoni, 1977), while few observational data from moored currentmeters were gathered in the deep basin. They do not constitute sufficiently long-term time series in order to attain a significant statistical analysis.

Analyzing the Genoa and Leghorn sea-levels Elliott (1978) found that the coherent motions in the Ligurian Sea are at 33, 3.6 and 1-2 hours. The oscillations at 3.6 and 1-2 hours were studied by Papa (1977) and are associated with the seiche motions, while the origin of the 33 hours oscillation is not really known.

About the lower frequency motions the circulation patterns given by climatological averages, several synoptic studies and a great number of satellite images suggest an annual cycle of the horizontal dynamics.

The observations of the low-frequency motions were limited to some restricted areas, so that it is not known over what alongshore distance is the flow coherent.

In order to study the annual evolution of the shelf circulation a long term current observation was programmed. It consisted in the mooring of three Aanderaa RCM-4 currentmeters at 15, 50 and 95 m depth on the 100 m isobath in front of Sestri Levante. Because of the anticipated conclusion of the experiment, only circa 10 months (September 24, 1978 - July 12, 1979) long term current observations are available. The winds recorded at Genoa, Pisa, Civitavecchia (near Rome), Ponza island, Olbia (Sardinia), Calvi and Nice were provided. Since this paper is concerned with a particular study, only the Ligurian area wind data were examined and the current measured during April - May 1979 were analyzed. In this period a second array with a currentmeter at 50 m was moored in front of Portovenere (La Spezia) on the 100 m isobath.

THE ATMOSPHERIC MOTIONS

The importance of the wind as forcing was underlined by many authors but its effect on the circulation as well as the effect of the boundary conditions have yet to be quantified. An analysis of the winds measured at Genoa, Pisa, Calvi and Nice from September 1978 to March 1979 showed that they are influenced by the orography as can be seen in Figure 2. Therefore the coherence analysis of the principal components showed that all the winds were coherent at 14-18 days and at 42 days. Peaks at 6, 8 and 17 days were present in the wind spectra. The first two values are close to the cyclogenetic characteristic time scale.

The atmospheric pressure presented some typical patterns. The spectra at Genoa, Calvi and Nice has the same peaks at 5 and 14 days, furthermore the coherence between the pressure measured at these stations was very high for periods greater than 2 days. The pressure peak at 5 days can be related to the same periodicity oscillation affecting the Mediterranean region (Gupta and Sing, 1977).

THE GENERAL CIRCULATION

The measurements described by De Maio et al. (1977) showed that the cyclonic circulation affects the water mass from the surface to 1000 m depth. The analysis of currentmeter data gathered at location 44°11'80''N - 8°59'00''E on the 1000 m isobath showed that the EW component decreased reaching a value close to zero at a 600 m depth. The counterclockwise current veering was fitted by the empirical formula $\theta=363.58 - 0.15xZ$ (θ in degrees and Z in meters, positive downward - Stocchino private communication). But the veering was probably related to the particular morphology of the area, that is the presence of two deep canyons in front of Genoa.

A coastal countercurrent is present during summer in the Gulf of Genoa, the inner part of the Ligurian Sea. It is associated to a southerly wind and can be explained as a drift current whose characteristic depends on the coastal curvature. This countercurrent was predicted by Bossolasco and Dagnino (1957); a numerical model was constructed by Papa (1980).

The coherence analysis of wind stress and sea level at Genova showed that for periods greater than 10 days they are out of phase, i.e. at a wind blowing toward the coast corresponded a lowering of the sea level. This phenomenon was modelled by Elliott (1980) who showed that it was related to a flow going from the Ligurian Sea to the Tyrrhenian Sea. From the observational data, Elliott estimated that a 16 m/s wind should cause a reduction of the sea level of circa 20 cm in the Gulf of Genoa. Continuity reasons required a return flow of the surface water near Corsica. From this model one should expect at lower fre-

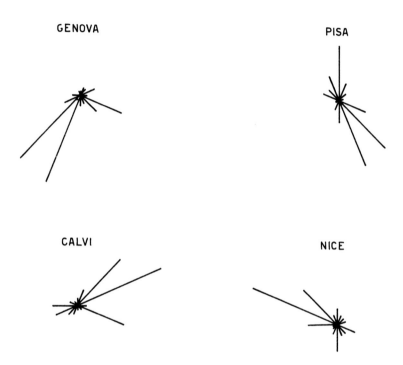

Fig. 2 The wind roses at Genoa, Pisa, Nice and Calvi.
It is possible to see the orographical orientation.

quencies a coherent response of the coastal current along the eastern Ligurian
continental shelf. One month-long observational data of April - May 1979 showed that the interaction between the Ligurian and Tyrrhenian Seas is very complicated since a front and meanders were present just north of the Elba Island
(See Figs. 3a,b).

THE INTERACTION BETWEEN THE LIGURIAN AND TYRRHENIAN SEAS

The analysis of current data gathered on the 100 m isobath in front of Sestri Levante from September 1978 to July 1979 (Bruschi and Manzella, 1980; Esposito and Manzella, 1981) dealt with conclusions different from Elliott's
(1981). The non local winds seemed to play a non relevant role on the continental shelf circulation, that seemed forced by the circulation in the interior.
The different conclusions can be better evidenced by examining the data both at
Sestri Levante and Portovenere. The hodograph ellipses were calculated and the
results are presented in Table 1 (see also Figs. 1 and 4).

TABLE 1

The hodograph ellipse parameters

	u′	v′	$\frac{u'v'}{u'+v'}$	θ	A	B	A/B	u′v′
Sestri	3.16	8.21	0.02	0.93	134.74	19.93	6.76	1.25
Portov.	3.58	8.52	0.09	5.02	147.03	23.80	6.18	7.56

The mean values indicated the presence of a more energetic current in front
of Sestri Levante (the mean alongshore components were V=29 cm/s at Sestri and
V=20 cm/s at Portovenere). It is very surprising to see that at the two sites,
whose distance is circa 20 mni, the alongshore currents were neither correlated
(r=0.12 while the 95% significant level is 0.14) nor coherent at lower frequencies (see Fig. 5). Only for periods of about 1 day there was a significant
coherence. This could be caused by the thermal front shown in Figures 3a, b,
due to the meeting of the Tyrrhenian and Ligurian Seas. Large meanders could
indicate an inflow of vorticity producing a local upwelling activity. In some
sense one can think that the Ligurian water was funnelled approximately by the

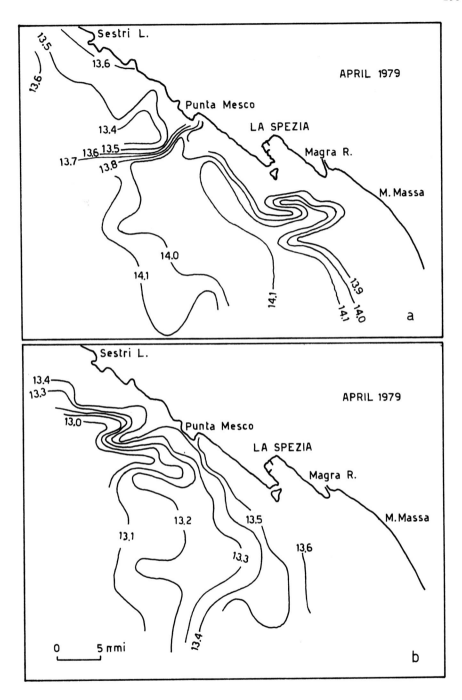

Fig. 3 The temperature pattern observed during April 1979.
Integral between 5-20 m depth (a) and between 40-60 m depth (b).

194

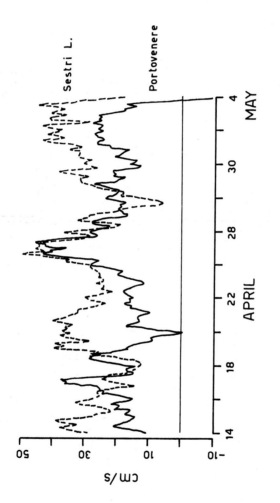

Fig. 4 The alongshore currents measured at 50 m depth. The currents were measured with Aanderaa RCM-4 moored on the 100 m isobath.

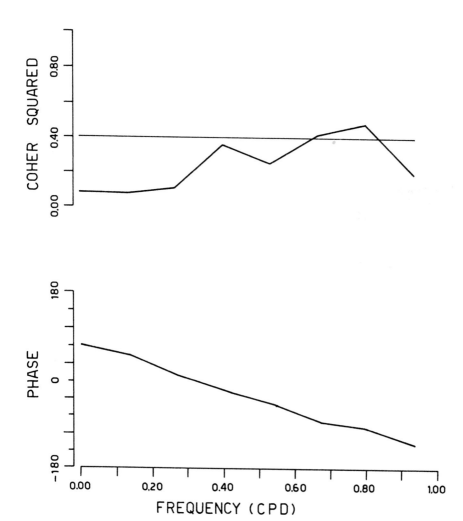

Fig. 5 The coherence squared between the alongshore currents
measured at Sestri Levante and Portovenere.

500 m isobath. In the existing literature this phenomenon is found in Trotti (1954).

In order to study the influence of the wind on the coastal circulation the variance at various frequencies was found by performing a Fourie r analysis on 300 hours overlapping blocks data. This method causes a loss of data (150 hours) at the beginning and at the end of the records. This analysis was performed after applying a 30 hours lowpass filter to the records. In this way the tidal and strong breeze signals were removed. From Figure 6a one can see that the large amount of Sestri current variance was after April 26 for periodicities comprised between 8-11 days. The Portovenere current had the maximum variance at lower frequencies from April 22 to 25. About the winds one can see in Figure 6b the variance patterns of Genoa, Pisa and Ponza; the last one was used in order to verify Elliott's (1981) conclusions on the coastal circulation forcings. In effect at lower frequencies the pattern was similar for the Portovenere alongshore current and the Ponza wind if one considers a delay of more than one day between the two time series. Unfortunately the cuts due to either the filtering or the Fourier decomposition reduced enormously the time series.

A MODEL

It can be said that the lack of a clear forcing action of the winds on the Ligurian shelf circulation was due to the effect of the motion in the deep basin. In order to approach the problem, we modified Allen's model (Allen, 1976) considering its application to the Ligurian Sea. Other authors (Buchwald and Adams, 1968; Adams and Buchwald, 1969; Gill and Schumann, 1974) previously studied the shelf waves but one of their fundamental hypothesis was the condition V=0 for the alongshore velocity at the shelf-interior junction. This is correct for free shelf waves, but needs modification for forced shelf waves. On the other hand the above hypothesis is very useful because it permits to uncouple the motion in the shelf from that in the interior. Allen corrected the hypothesis and dealth with the problem by using a perturbative method. This only requires that the width of the shelf W and the length of the whole basin offshore satisfy the condition W/L$\ll$1, in the present case W = 20 km and L = 150 km. Allen used the hypothesis $\frac{\partial P}{\partial z} = 0$ but this restrictive imposition is not necessary. The hydrostatic hypothesis is more realistic and does not

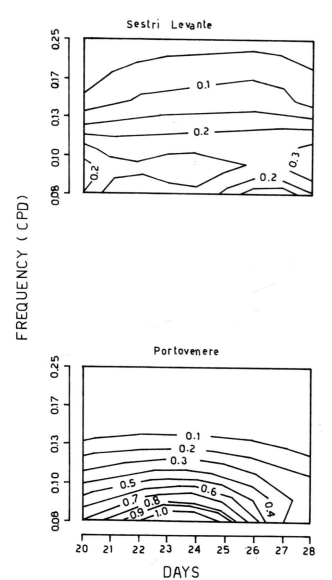

Fig.6a The variance at various frequencies vs. the time for the alongshore currents.

198

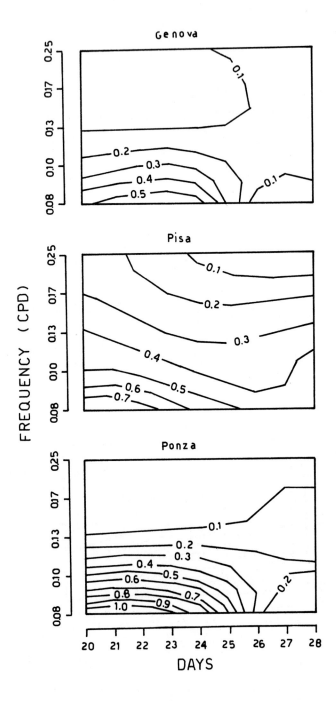

Fig. 6b As in Figure 6a for the winds resolved in
the alongshore direction.

modify the calculations, so that it can be maintained. By neglecting the non linear terms one obtains for the stream function the equation

$$\nabla(\tfrac{1}{D}\nabla\tfrac{\partial\Psi}{\partial t}) + f\underline{k}(\nabla\Psi \times \nabla\tfrac{1}{D}) = -\underline{k}(\nabla\times\tfrac{\underline{\tau}}{D})$$

where

$$\nabla \equiv (\tfrac{\partial}{\partial x} ; \tfrac{\partial}{\partial y}) \qquad\qquad \underline{k} \equiv (0;0;1)$$

The above equation can be better treated in non dimensional form. The fluid is contained in a rectangular basin X=0,1 and Y=0,L. We also assume that the wind stress component variations on the X,Y scales are O(1). The depth has an exponential behaviour on the shelf and is constant in the interior:

$$D = D(x) = \begin{cases} \exp(\tfrac{X-W}{Wd}) & 0 < X < W \\ \\ 1 & W < X < 1 \end{cases}$$

The equation requires a different treatment in the interior and in the shelf regions. A particular attention needs the condition at the junction.

$$\frac{\partial\Psi_i}{\partial y} = \frac{\partial\Psi_s}{\partial y} \qquad\qquad \text{continuity of the flux across the junction}$$

$$\frac{\partial^2\Psi_i}{\partial x\partial t} = \frac{\partial^2\Psi_s}{\partial x\partial t} \qquad\qquad \text{continuity of the pressure along the junction}$$

where i stands for interior and s stands for shelf.
At lowest order the equations on the interior and on the shelf are:

$$\frac{\partial}{\partial t}(\frac{\partial^2\Psi_i}{\partial x\partial x} + \frac{\partial^2\Psi_s}{\partial y\partial y}) = \frac{\partial\tau^x}{\partial y} - \frac{\partial\tau^y}{\partial x}$$

$$\frac{\partial}{\partial \tau}(\, \partial \frac{\partial^2 \psi_{os}}{\partial \zeta \partial \zeta} - \frac{\partial \psi_{os}}{\partial \zeta}) + \frac{\partial \psi_{os}}{\partial y} = \tau^y + \frac{\partial^2 \psi_{oi}}{\partial \zeta \partial \tau}\bigg|_{x=0} - \zeta \frac{\partial^2 \psi_{oi}}{\partial x \partial y}\bigg|_{x=0}$$

where $\tau = tW$; $\zeta = x/W$ and $\psi_{os} = \psi_{bs} - \zeta \frac{\partial \psi_{oi}}{\partial x}\big|_o$ (see Allen, 1976). The equation for ψ can be solved in terms of the eigenfunction expansion

$$\psi = \sum \varphi_n(x,t) \, F_n(\zeta)$$

where the F_n are the free shelf waves eigenfunctions (Gill and Schumann, 1974; Gill and Clark, 1974, Sect. 10). The streamfunction φ_n can be expanded in sine and cosine time series. The resulting equation is an ordinary differential equation in the Y variable whose solution is obtained numerically. We regarded only the first mode and investigated the solution for atmospheric motions having at all frequencies a magnitude given by the mean values of the observed data. The wind stress curl acting on the deep basin was computed using the Genoa, Calvi and Nice wind data, the mean value was $0.3 \times 10^{-5} \text{dyn/cm}^3$. On the shelf an alongshore wind stress with a mean value of $-4.8 \times 10^{-2} \text{dyn/cm}^2$ was applied (the minus means a northward wind stress). In Table 2 the results in terms of sine and cosine are shown for some periodicities. The comparison is made with the weighted means obtained from the seasonal data, the weight is given by the length of the record in each season.

TABLE 2

Comparison between the model and the observations

PERIODICITY (days)	MODEL cos	MODEL sin	OBSERVATIONS cos	OBSERVATIONS sin
20.0	-16.8	6.5	-0.72	2.27
10.0	- 4.9	4.8	-3.09	1.20
5.0	- 2.4	2.4	-3.62	1.37
2.5	- 1.1	1.1	-3.34	2.58

The model tends to overestimate the current at lower frequencies and to underestimate the current at higher frequencies, the best result being at 5 days.

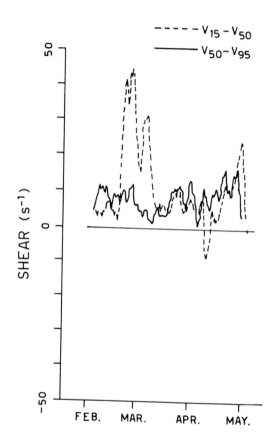

Fig. 7 The shear computed by using the data
gathered in front of Sestri Levante
from February 12 to May 30, 1979.

DISCUSSION

The analysis of the data suggest that the circulation of the Ligurian Sea depends on the atmospheric motions and on the unknown boundary conditions. In particular the shelf circulation seems forced by the deep basin circulation and a local wind. The interaction with the Tyrrhenian Sea is not clear. It can be seen from Trotti (1954) that there is a strong seasonal variation of the physical structure in the area just north of the Tuscan Archipelago.

An attempt to investigate the wind forced motion was made by using a forced shelf wave model. This was applied with a very crude approximation, since we disregarded the advective terms. The importance of the advective terms can be qualitatively appreciated by analysing the data gathered in front of Sestri Levante during the winter season. The vertical shear of the current was computed by filtering the data by means of a 80 hours lowpass filter. The values of the shear evaluated from the difference between the 15 m and 50 m currents and that of the 50 m and 95 m is shown in Figure 7. The shear was sometimes uniform indicating advective processes. A large value of the surface shear points out the importance of local forcing affecting the surface water motion.

REFERENCES

Adams, J.K., and Buchwald, V.T., 1969. The generation of continental shelf waves. J. Fluid Mech., 35: 815-826.

Allen, J.S., 1976. On forced, long continental shelf waves on f-plane. J. Phys. Ocean., 6: 426-431.

Bossolasco, M. and Dagnino, I., 1957. Sulle correnti costiere nel Golfo di Genova. Geofis. Pura Appl., 30: 123-140.

Bruschi, A. and Manzella, G., 1980. Wind and current autumnal data series analysis on the Ligurian continental shelf. Il Nuovo Cimento,3C: 151-164.

Buchwald, V.T. and Adams, J.K., 1968. The propagation of continental shelf waves. Proc. Roy. Soc. London, A305: 235-250.

De Maio, A., Moretti, M., Sansone, E., Spezie, G. and Vultaggio, M., 1975. Su la circolazione superficiale e profonda nel Golfo di Genova. Ist. Univ. Nav. Napoli, Vol. XLIII-XLIV: 97-112.

Elliott, A.J., 1978. The response of the coastal waters of Northwest Italy. Saclantcent Memo. SM 117, La Spezia, 14 pp.

Elliott, A.J., 1980. The effect of low frequency winds on sea level and currents in the Gulf of Genova. Oceanol. Acta, 2: 429-433.

Elliott, A.J., 1981. Low frequency current variability off the west coast of Italy. Oceanl. Acta, 4: 47-55.

Esposito, A. and Manzella, G., 1981. An analysis of the Ligurian shelf circulation. Tech. Rep. CNEN RT/FI(81)3, 101 pp.

Gill, A.E. and Clark, A.J., 1974. Wind induced upwelling, coastal current and sea level changes. Deep Sea Res., 21: 325-345.

Gill, A.E. and Schumann, E.H., 1974. The generation of long shelf waves by wind. J. Phys. Ocean., 4: 83-90.

Gleeson, T.A., 1954. Cyclogenesis in the Mediterranean region. Arch. Meteo. Geo. Bio., A6(2): 153-171.

Gupta, B.R. and Sing, G., 1977. A power spectrum analysis of the mean daily pressure over the Mediterranean and neighborhood during November 1967 to April 1968. Tellus, 29: 382-384.

Papa, L., 1977. The free oscillation of the Ligurian Sea computed by the H-N method. Deutsche Hydrograf. Zeit., 30: 82-90.

Papa, L., 1980. A numerical verification of a clockwise circulation in the Gulf of Genoa. App. Math. Model. 4: 313-315.

Stocchino, C. and Testoni, A., 1977. Nuove osservazioni sulla circolazione delle correnti nel Mar Ligure. Ist. Idrogr. Mar. Militare, Genova, 39 pp.

Trotti, L., 1954. Report on the oceanographic investigations in the Ligurian and North Tyrrhenian Seas. Cent. Talassograf. Tirren., Genova, 21 pp.

NON-TIDAL FLOW IN THE NORTH CHANNEL OF THE IRISH SEA

M.J. HOWARTH

Institute of Oceanographic Sciences, Bidston Observatory,
Birkenhead, Merseyside, England

ABSTRACT

    The entrance to a semi-enclosed sea forms a constricted
connection between two different water masses and so processes
there will significantly affect the dynamics of the sea.
Across the entrance there are likely to be large density and
elevation gradients which will drive easily measurable currents.
Measurements have been recorded in the North Channel, the
narrower of two entrances to the Irish Sea. For a year coastal
elevations and voltages induced in a cross-channel telephone
cable were recorded and, as well, for 45 days in summer, currents
and off-shore sea bed pressures. The flows were dominated by
strong tidal currents (in excess of 1 m/s) which caused strong
mixing. During the 45 day experiment the current and CTD
observations showed a well defined circulation pattern which
had large spatial gradients and with currents in excess of
0.05 m/s. There were also wind driven events which caused
uniform currents along the channel with a magnitude comparable
to that of the circulation. The 45 days experiment has enabled
the physics of the low frequency flows in the channel to be
investigated in detail and an indication of their variability
has been gained from the year long measurements.

INTRODUCTION

    In studies of the dynamics of semi-enclosed seas it is often
convenient to isolate the sea by making an entrance a boundary
where conditions are measured or assumed to be known, for example
in tide and surge numerical models or when estimating the flushing
or residence time of the sea. Further understanding of the sea's
response can often be gained by considering the shelf sea combined
with the adjacent ocean. Since the entrance is a constriction
between the two water masses any exchange between them should
generate there large current or pressure gradient signals which
can be easily measured either directly by deploying instruments
in the sea or remotely from the land or sky. The first approach

is expensive both because the equipment has to be robust and reliable in a hostile environment and also because a ship is needed for deployment and recovery. In addition, the equipment is vulnerable and data losses can be significant and are of unknown extent until recovery is attempted. These measurements are usually local so that, in order to gain an adequate spatial coverage, many instruments must be deployed. The second, remote, approach is often cheaper since the equipment is less vulnerable, easier to install and cheaper to check and repair if faulty. In general, the measurements are integrated. However, calibration of the system is often unsure, particularly for zero flow conditions, and the measurements can be susceptible to instrumental drift.

The approaches can be combined by deploying current meters and pressure recorders in the sea for one month to provide the data to calibrate and validate the shore based measurements which are then recorded for longer. This was the design of an experiment to study a semi-diurnal tidal amphidrome in the North Channel of the Irish Sea and the region's low frequency (less than 1 cpd) dynamics. The offshore current and sea bed pressure measurements were made in August and September 1979 whilst onshore elevation and telephone cable measurements were recorded from July 1979 to July 1980. This paper contains a brief description of the physical oceanography of the area and of the experiment followed by a preliminary discussion of the low frequency results looking at both the measuring systems and the dynamics of the North Channel, Irish Sea and Malin Shelf Sea.

DESCRIPTION OF THE NORTH CHANNEL

A region of inter-connected seas which loop from the Atlantic Ocean through the Irish Sea back to the Atlantic Ocean exists off the west coast of Britain. The southern arm of the loop is formed by the Celtic Sea (which is also the entrance to the English and Bristol Channels) and the St. George's Channel; the northern arm by the North Channel and the Malin Shelf Sea, Figure 1a.

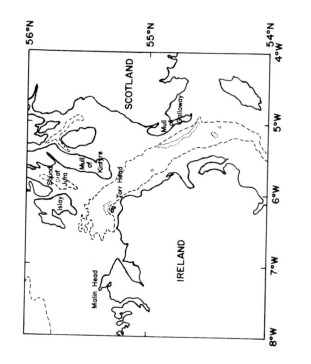

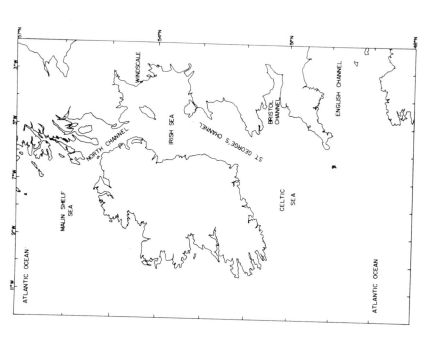

Figure 1. a) Map of west coast of Britain   b) Bathymetric map of North Channel
---- 100 m : .... 200 m contours

Depths in the loop slope gently from 200m at the Celtic Sea shelf edge to about 100m in the St. George's Channel and western Irish Sea (the eastern Irish Sea is shallower, less than 55m). The greatest depths in the loop occur in localized depressions in the North Channel - the deepest being 280m in a narrow trough off the Mull of Galloway, Figure 1b. The average depth of the North Channel is between 120m and 140m but there is a sill of depth 40m between Islay and Malin Head followed by a gentle slope down to the shelf edge. The narrowest part of the loop occurs in the North Channel (20km between Torr Head and the Mull of Kintyre) and also the smallest cross-sectional area (about 4×10^6 m^3 compared with 6×10^6 m^3 for the narrowest part of the St. George's Channel.

The dominant physical process in the area is the semi-diurnal tide which propagates from the Atlantic Ocean into the Irish Sea through both arms of the loop and is reflected by the English coast, forming a standing wave in the Irish Sea (Doodson and Corkan, 1932). In the North Channel the incident and reflected waves combine to make an amphidrome in the region between the Mull of Kintyre, Islay and Torr Head. The net flux of semi-diurnal tidal energy through the North Channel is small (Taylor, 1919; Robinson, 1979), implying near perfect reflection for the northern arm. Because of the amphidrome tidal elevations are small in the North Channel but currents (and hence tidal mixing) are large - the M_2 amplitude between the Mull of Kintyre and Torr Head exceeds 1 m/s - and the phase of the current varies little throughout the North Channel.

For average conditions at any time the surface water in the southern part of the North Channel is the freshest and coolest in the whole loop, ignoring regions close to the shores and in the eastern Irish Sea. Throughout the year there is a salinity difference of approximately 1.3×10^{-3} between the surface water of the Atlantic Ocean and the North Channel (ICES, 1962). The corresponding temperature difference varies between $2^\circ C$, for most of the year, and $0^\circ C$, in October and November. Hence the density difference for the surface water is small (about 0.8 Kg/m^3) with the North Channel water lighter than the Atlantic water. Because of strong tidal mixing the water in the North Channel is vertically homogeneous throughout the year. However, tidal current amplitudes decrease rapidly away from the North

Channel and a seasonal pycnocline occurs in the Malin Shelf Sea. In the region between the homogeneous and stratified waters (between Malin Head and Islay) a front is formed which is visible in summer in satellite infra-red photographs (Pingree et al., 1978, Simpson et al., 1979).

The overall circulation of the North Channel region is weak but well defined, according to previous measurements by drifters (Barnes and Godley, 1961) and by tracers such as salinity (Bowden, 1950) and Caesium 137 (Wilson, 1974; McKinley et al. 1981a). Both Bowden and Wilson calculated from the distribution of their tracers a net northward flow between Dublin and Holyhead of 0.0035 m/s - equivalent, by continuity, to 0.01 m/s through the narrowest part of the North Channel. This northward flow is clearly shown in the distribution of the waste output from the nuclear re-processing plant at Windscale. The waste includes radio-active Tritium and Caesium 134 and 137, each of which appears to remain in the water column. The usefulness of Tritium as a tracer is reduced because of a large atmospheric input but monitoring of Caesium 137, in particular, has shown that the flow from Windscale extends to the North Channel (time taken to reach it about 6 months), northward around Scotland and into the North Sea (McKinley et al., 1981b; Kautsky et al., 1980).

The salinity distribution (Craig, 1959; Lee, 1960; Slinn, 1974) and plankton distributions (Williamson, 1956) show that the northward flow is not uniform across the North Channel but that there is a flow of Atlantic water into the Irish Sea close to the Irish coast, which is probably intermittent. This flow was also observed in current meter records from the Skulmartin Lightvessel (at the southern end of the North Channel close to the Irish shore) which lasted 13 months and had an overall mean of 0.008 m/s towards the south-east (Proudman, 1939).

Superimposed on this circulation pattern are more energetic higher frequency (0.1 to 1 cpd) currents driven by storms. In the North Channel area these have been studied in two ways - by numerical models and by the voltages induced in a cross channel telephone cable. Heaps and Jones (1975 and 1979) have used two- and three-dimensional numerical models to study storm surges within the Irish Sea, taking the North Channel as a boundary. They have shown that the external surge propagating through the

North Channel is, for most areas of the Irish Sea, more important
than the locally generated surge. A two-dimensional numerical
model of the shelf seas around the British Isles by Pingree and
Griffiths (1980) predicts that uniform winds will not generate
appreciable elevation gradients, either along or across the North
Channel, and that the maximum flow through the North Channel will
be generated by winds blowing along it.

The latter prediction is supported by the cable measurements
of Bowden and Hughes (1961) and Prandle (1976). Since sea water
is an electrical conductor which moves through the Earth's
magnetic field an e.m.f. is generated. For flow through a
channel the e.m.f. becomes a potential difference between the
two sides of the channel which can be measured via a conducting
cable across the channel. The relationship between cable
voltage and flow varies according to the flow pattern (Robinson,
1976) so that a calibration made with tidal current measurements
will not necessarily hold for circulation. Another problem,
especially for circulation estimates, is that the cable has an
unknown constant potential difference, arising from its
properties and its earthing arrangement. The measurements
showed a good correlation between the wind resolved along the
channel and cable voltage (coefficient of 0.7 for the whole year,
smaller in summer, larger in winter) and that the voltage lagged
the wind by about 2 hours. Therefore water flows through the
North Channel into or out of the Irish Sea in response to winds
from the north-west or south-east with very little delay.

MEASUREMENTS AND COMPARISONS

The topography of the North Channel is relatively simple
and some of the dynamics at frequencies less than 1 c.p.d. -
storm driven and circulation - broadly known, as indicated above.
The purpose of the experiment was to see if these dynamics could
be quantified in agreement with the equations of motion by means
of accurate offshore and shore based observations, to measure
the response in more detail and to determine the driving forces
for elevations and currents. The measurements would also enable
the calibration of the cable at both tidal and, for the first
time, low frequencies.

211

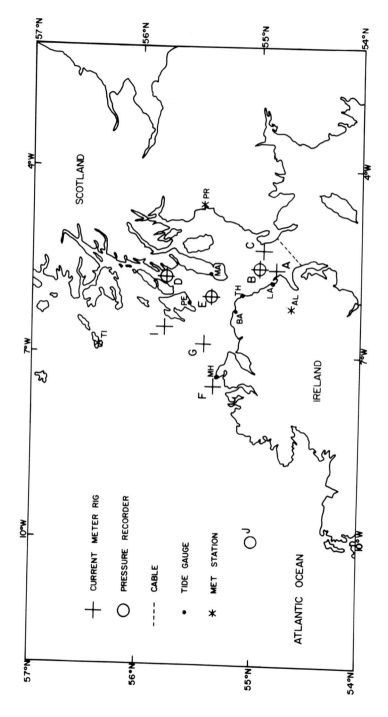

Figure 2. Map of station positions. Tide gauges at BA-Ballycastle, LA-Larne, MA-Machrihanish, MH-Malin Head, PE-Port Ellen, TH-Torr Head, Met. stations at AL-Aldergrove, PR-Prestwick, TI-Tiree.

The observations were shore based measurements lasting 13
months, from July 1979 to July 1980 (sea surface elevation,
voltage in a cross channel cable, atmospheric pressure, wind
speed and direction) and offshore measurements lasting 45 days,
from August to September 1979 (sea bed pressure, current and sea
water density), see Figure 2 for a map.

The results discussed in this paper have all been low pass
filtered, unless otherwise stated, by a Butterworth squared
filter with half power point at 0.7164 cpd and N=9 (see for
instance Hamming 1977, pp 189-195 or Thomson and Chow, 1980).
Its response, Figure 3, is monotonic, at 0.6 cpd is 0.96 and
at 0.9 cpd is 0.01, so that all diurnal and semi-diurnal tides,
as well as inertial currents, have been completely suppressed.
The Butterworth filter is recursive and was applied twice
(forwards then backwards) so that no phase lags were introduced.
The data were re-sampled every 3 hours and to reduce ringing 1½
days were deleted from the beginning and end of each record.

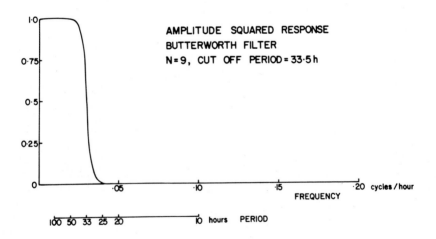

Figure 3. Response of low pass filter.

Shore based measurements

Sea surface elevation Pneumatic tide gauges were installed at
Machrihanish, Port Ellen, Ballycastle and Torr Head. The
difference between the pressure at a point fixed below lowest
sea level and atmospheric pressure was measured by a Digiquartz
(quartz crystal) pressure transducer and recorded by an Aanderaa
logger (Browell and Pugh, 1977). The pressure transducer
stability was good - it was checked every 4 months and found to
be within 100 Pa. The records from Port Ellen and Torr Head
were complete but at Machrihanish the air pipe was cut and 30
days lost between 17 December 1979 and 15 January 1980. At
Ballycastle the pressure point was not stable for the period of
offshore measurements so its record has not been considered
further. Measurements from stilling well tide gauges at Larne
and Malin Head were obtained from the appropriate authorities.
That from Larne contained 5 gaps totalling 35 days during the
13 months, whilst that from Malin Head was good for the period
of offshore measurements but after that the gauge silted up.

The hydrostatic equation is assumed to hold so that the sea
bed pressure p is given by

$$p = \rho g \ (h + \zeta) + (P - \bar{P})$$

were ρ is the sea water density, g the acceleration due to
gravity, ζ the sea surface elevation, h the mean water depth,
P the atmospheric pressure and $\bar{P}$ the mean atmospheric pressure,
taken to be 1.012×10^5 Pa. The atmospheric pressure at each
tide gauge site was calculated by linear interpolation from
three sets of observations, see below. The pneumatic tide
gauges recorded differential pressure $(p - \bar{P})$ and so the sea
surface elevation was easily calculated. The sea bed pressure,
p, is a more useful parameter when considering the dynamics of
the sea and this, too, was calculated for each site.

To investigate whether the observations conformed to an
'inverted barometer', where an increase in atmospheric pressure
of 100 Pa causes a decrease in elevation of 0.0099 m, the
elevations multiplied by ρg were correlated with the atmospheric
pressure at each site, Table 1. The correlations are highly
significant and the magnitudes of the slopes of the least squares
linear fits are slightly greater than the expected value of 1.

This is common for the west coast of the British Isles, whereas
for the east coast the magnitude of the slope is normally less
than 1 (Thompson, 1980). The differences are presumably because
of wind stress set up/set down associated with atmospheric
pressure systems. Two common weather patterns for the British
Isles are first a depression moving eastward to the north of
Scotland accompanied by winds veering from southerly to north-
westerly and second a stationary high pressure over Scandanavia
accompanied by winds from the east. In both patterns the wind
set up/set down against the west coast of Britain will re-inforce
the adjustment of the sea surface to the atmospheric pressure.
The standard deviations of the elevation records were
approximately 1700 Pa and for the sea bed pressure records
were 1150 Pa, a reduction in variance by 54%.

TABLE 1

Least squares linear fit between sea surface elevation and
atmospheric pressure.

Site	Correlation coefficient	Slope of fit
Torr Head	-0.74	-1.11
Port Ellen	-0.77	-1.17
Machrihanish	-0.76	-1.11
Larne	-0.71	-1.06
Malin Head	-0.77	-1.04

Telephone cable voltage   The voltage induced by the flow of water
through the southern part of the North Channel was recorded on a
data logger between July 1979 and July 1980 using the Portpatrick
to Donaghadee telephone cable, which is approximately 35 Km long.
Maximum recorded voltages were ± 1 volt. Two gaps, one of 12 hours
and one of 2 days, both at the beginning of August 1979, were
interpolated by synthesizing the tides from a harmonic analysis
of the rest of the record and making an allowance for the
residuals at the ends of the interpolations.
Meteorological   Hourly wind speed and direction and 3 hourly
atmospheric pressure readings from Tiree, Prestwick and
Aldergrove were obtained from the British Meteorological Office
and hourly wind speed and direction from Malin Head from the

Irish Meteorological Office. All data were low pass filtered.
From the atmospheric pressures a geostrophic wind was calculated
and compared with the observed winds, Table 2. The speed
correlation is highly significant at all sites, particularly for
the more exposed stations at Tireee and Malin Head. As expected,
the geostrophic wind was stronger than the observed and was
rotated clockwise relative to it. Also shown in Table 2 are
values obtained by Hasse and Wagner (1971) from light vessels in
the German Bight for neutral stability conditions. Their
observed surface wind speeds are slightly larger in comparison
with the geostrophic wind but the direction deviation is the
same. Since it was not known how representative the observations from the shore stations were for the estimation of wind
stress over the North Channel, the geostrophic wind calculated
from the observed pressures was used and converted to surface
wind with the values of Hasse and Wagner. The wind stress, τ,
is given by

$$\tau = C\rho U^2$$

where ρ is the density of the air, U the wind speed and C the
drag coefficient given by $C = 0.0015 (1 + \exp (-U+12.5)/1.56)^{-1}$
$+0.00104$ (Amorocho and De Vries, 1980). The wind stress time
series was then low pass filtered.

TABLE 2

Comparison between geostrophic and observed wind. Least squares
fit for wind speed in m/s is:- Observed = M x Geostrophic + c

Station	Correlation coefficient	Speed		Direction
		M	C	Observed-geostrophic
Tiree	0.80	0.42	2.4	−20
Prestwick	0.57	0.24	1.9	−16
Aldergrove	0.70	0.26	1.6	−26
Malin Head	0.74	0.40	3.2	−26
Hasse and Wagner		0.56	2.4	−20

Offshore measurements

The offshore measurements of sea bed pressure and current were
made by deploying internally recording instruments. The launch
and recovery cruises each lasted a fortnight (at the beginning
of August and end of September 1979, respectively) and were
separated by one month. During each cruise sea surface
temperature and conductivity were continuously monitored and
CTD profiles recorded.

Sea bed pressure Instruments were deployed at stations B, E, D
and J, Table 3 and Figure 2. Those at stations B and D were
fitted with Digiquartz quartz crystal pressure transducers and
at stations E and J with strain gauges. These pressure
transducers, whilst primarily designed to measure tides, are
reasonably stable so that low frequency pressures are also
measured. The agreement between the shore based and offshore
gauges for low frequency pressure is very good, for instance
Figure 4, but it will be shown that it is difficult to
differentiate between real gradients and instrumental problems
when considering pressure differences of less than 1000 Pa.

TABLE 3

Station positions

Station	Latitude N	Longitude W	Depth below lowest water level (m)
A	54° 49'	5° 38'	105
B	54° 58'	5° 36'	155
C	54° 58'	5° 14'	54
D	55° 52'	5° 45'	120
E	55° 28'	6° 10'	110
F	55° 25'	7° 31'	55
G	55° 31'	6° 51'	60
I	55° 53'	6° 33'	45
J	55° 00'	10° 00'	125

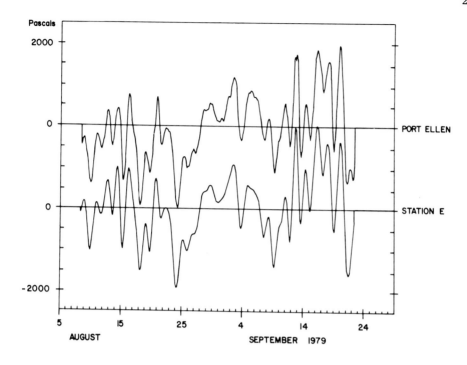

Figure 4.   Low frequency bottom pressure observations from
a shore based gauge (Port Ellen) and an offshore
gauge (station E), as recorded.

Currents   19 Aanderaa RCM4 current meters and 3 vector
averaging current meters manufactured by AMF (henceforward
referred to as AMF VACM) were deployed in 9 rigs at the
positions given in Table 3.   (There were two rigs at station D
where an Aanderaa was deployed in a bottom frame;   all the
other rigs were supported by sub-surface buoyancy about 5 m
above the top current meter.   No current measurements were
made at station J).   All the meters were recovered and record
lengths are given in Table 4.   77% of planned data was obtained;
two major failures were seaweed obstructed the rotor in the
bottom frame at station D and the tape head fell off the top
meter at station I during deployment.

TABLE 4

Current meter details. A - Aanderaa, V- AMF VACM

Station	Meter type	Meter height above sea floor (m)	Low pass filter record Start		End		Length (h)
A	A	70	0900	7/8	1800	20/9	1068
	A	45	0000	15/8	0600	8/9	585
	A	20	0900	7/8	1800	20/9	1068
B	A	110	0000	7/8	2100	20/9	1080
	A	60	0000	7/8	1200	2/9	639
	A	20	0000	7/8	0000	8/9	771
C	V	33	0600	7/8	1500	31/8	588
	A	31	0900	7/8	2100	19/8	303
	A	10	0600	7/8	0000	21/9	1077
D	A	81	0600	8/8	2100	21/9	1074
	A	41	0600	8/8	2100	21/9	1074
	A	1	-		-		-
E	A	6	1200	8/8	0300	22/9	1074
F	V	30	1200	9/8	1800	24/9	1113
	A	28	1200	9/8	0300	21/9	1026
	A	11	0900	9/8	1800	24/9	1116
G	V	39	0600	9/8	2100	26/9	1170
	A	37	0600	9/8	2100	26/9	1170
	A	27	0600	9/8	0000	5/9	645
	A	11	0600	9/8	2100	26/9	1170
I	A	26	-		-		-
	A	11	0000	13/8	0300	27/9	1086

Since intercomparisons have highlighted problems with Aanderaa
meters in shelf seas, particularly in the measurement of low
frequency currents (e.g. Beardsley et. al., 1977) AMF VACMs
were deployed close to the Aanderaa meters at the top of rigs
C, F and G as a check on their operation. The full account of
the comparison has been presented elsewhere (Howarth, 1981) but
the main conclusion was that there was no significant difference
between the low frequency records of the two meter types, see
Tables 5 and 6 for comparisons of the low pass filtered records
and overall means. This was probably because the meters were
not deployed close to the sea surface, because the tidal currents
were strong and because the records were obtained when wave

activity was likely to be low. These three factors combined so
that for only a small fraction of the record length was motion
with a period shorter than the sample interval, for instance
wave orbital motion, significant compared with the measured
velocity. The only major difference between the records
occurred for the overall means recorded at station C, where the
AMF VACM appeared to have a malfunction. Another conclusion was
that in fast tidal currents, at station G the M_2 amplitude was
1 m/s, meters which are moored directly into the meter wire will
experience problems caused by the inclination of the meter wire
and the meter due to the drag.

TABLE 5

Least squares fits for low pass filtered speeds.

$$AMF\ VACM\ =\ M\ x\ AANDERAA\ +\ c$$

Station	Slope-M	Intercept-C m/s	Correlation coefficient	Degrees of freedom
C	0.864 + 0.046	0.004 + 0.006	0.99	8
F	0.950 + 0.021	0.003 + 0.002	0.99	29
G	0.915 + 0.047	0.000 + 0.004	0.96	33

TABLE 6

Mean velocities recorded by Aanderaa (A) and AMF VACM (V) meters.
The directional stability is (Vector mean speed/scalar mean
speed) x 100.

Station	Record length(h)	Meter type	Speed (m/s) Mean	S.e.	Direction Mean	Stability
C	303	V	0.093	0.005	163	93
		A	0.105	0.005	198	95
F	1026	V	0.048	0.003	63	73
		A	0.048	0.003	64	72
G	1170	V	0.065	0.002	110	82
		A	0.071	0.002	101	82

Cable calibration

The voltage recorded via the cross channel telephone cable was calibrated against the observed currents at stations A, B and C for both tidal and low frequencies. Details will be presented elsewhere and only the conclusions described here. The cable voltages have been monitored intermittently since Bowden and Hughes (1961) started in 1955. Their paper contains the only previous calibration, 1 volt is equivalent to 1.35 m/s, based on several days of tidal stream observations. It also includes an estimate of the M_2 amplitude and phase from one month's harmonic analysis of voltages recorded in 1955 which has been compared with a similar estimate for the same month in 1979. The amplitude had changed by less than 1% and the phase by less than 1°, indicating that at tidal frequencies the cable observations had not changed significantly in 24 years. The current meter records and cable voltages were harmonically analysed for the same 29 day period to give a calibration of 1 volt is equivalent to 1.21 m/s at M_2, which also held for all tidal frequencies higher than and including diurnal.

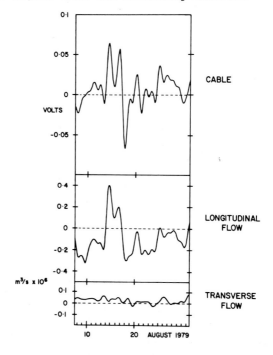

Figure 5. Comparison between low frequency cable voltage and observed flow.

The observed low frequency flow along the channel was calculated by resolving the current meter records in the direction of the M_2 currents at each station, which incidentally also minimized the variance in the calculated transverse flow, Figure 5. For the period when all the current meters functioned - 09.00 7 August to 15.00 31 August, 585 hours long - a least squares linear fit gave:-

Flow in m/s = (Cable voltage - 0.005 $\pm$ 0.004) x (2.259 $\pm$ 0.431)   (1)

There were 17 degrees of freedom and the correlation coefficient was 0.79. Hence the low frequency calibration is 1 volt is equivalent to 2.26 m/s, larger than for tidal currents and supported by comparisons at a fortnightly frequency, and at mean flows, assuming the above value of 0.005 V at zero flow. The calibrations for tidal and low frequencies are different presumably because their flow patterns are different (Robinson, 1976), see more below. Previous estimates for the cable voltage at zero flow have ranged from - 0.030 V to 0.019 V (Prandle, 1979) whilst the present estimate, 0.005 V, is not significantly different from zero. The mean voltage for the 13 month period was 0.010 V, equivalent to a northward flow 0.01 m/s by equation 1. This compares favourably, and fortuitously, with the estimates of the mean flow through the Irish Sea given by Bowden (1950) and Wilson (1974).

RESULTS

Low frequency dynamics

The vertically integrated equations of motion governing low frequency flow in a coastal sea whose dynamics are dominated by the tides are, assuming that the tidal elevation is small compared with the water depth, h :-

$$\frac{\partial}{\partial t}(hu) + K_x hu - fhv = -gh\frac{\partial}{\partial x}\left[\zeta - \bar{\zeta} + \frac{P}{\rho g}\right] + F_x + A\left[\frac{\partial^2}{\partial x^2}(uh) + \frac{\partial^2}{\partial y^2}(uh)\right]$$
$$+ \text{ non-linear tidal terms}\qquad(2)$$

$$\frac{\partial}{\partial t}(hv) + K_y hv + fhu = -gh\frac{\partial}{\partial y}\left[\zeta - \bar{\zeta} + \frac{P}{\rho g}\right] + F_y + A\left[\frac{\partial^2}{\partial x^2}(vh) + \frac{\partial^2}{\partial y^2}(vh)\right]$$
$$+ \text{ non linear tidal terms}\qquad(3)$$

$$\frac{\partial \zeta}{\partial t} + \frac{\partial}{\partial x}(hu) + \frac{\partial}{\partial y}(hv) = 0$$
$$(4)$$

where all variables have been low pass filtered and (u, v) is the depth mean current, K_x and K_g friction coefficients based on the tidal current and a square low for bottom friction, f the coriolis parameter, $\bar{\zeta}$ the law frequency equilibrium tide, (F_x, F_y) the wind stress and A the coefficient of horizontal eddy viscosity (Heaps, 1978, equations 85-87). The equations are linear in u, v and ζ since the convective acceleration terms are zero because the tidal elevation is small compared with the water depth. Equation 4 is the equation of continuity; equations 2 and 3 are the equations of motion in the x and y directions respectively with terms representing, from left to right, acceleration, bottom friction, Coriolis, pressure gradient, wind stress and horizontal friction.

Since the assumption that the tidal elevations are small compared with the water depth is valid for the North Channel and since the observed low frequency and mean currents were barotropic, these equations can be applied directly. All the variables were measured so the importance of the various terms in the equations can be calculated and the accuracy of the measurements assessed from discrepancies in balancing the equations. However, the absolute values of the cable voltage and the sea surface elevation were not known to sufficient accuracy so that, initially, each quantity was calculated relative to its mean.

The x axis was taken along the North Channel, positive towards the Atlantic Ocean, so that v, the transverse component, was small, Figure 5, and was taken to be zero. Since the sea area is small the low frequency equilibrium tide can be neglected as can the horizontal friction terms which are small compared with the bottom friction terms. The non-linear tidal terms in equations 2 and 3 were also small, approximately 0.8×10^{-4} m^2/s^2 compared with maxima greater than 10^{-3} m^2/s^2 for the other terms. The longitudinal speed, u, was calculated from the cable voltage since, as has been shown, it measured the low frequency flow well and since its record was longer than the current meter observations. The M_2 constituent dominates the tidal currents in the North Channel and is rectilinear parallel to the channel's axis. Hence the friction coefficients K_x and K_y are given by:-

$$K_x = \frac{4Ka}{\pi h} \qquad \text{and} \qquad K_y = 0.5 \, K_x$$

where a is the M_2 current amplitude and K the coefficient of bottom friction in a square law for tidal currents (taken as 0.0026, Heaps, 1978). For the North Channel a = 0.7 m/s and h = 120 m so that $K_x = 2 \times 10^{-5} \, s^{-1}$. Both the friction coefficient, K_x, and the non-linear tidal terms might be expected to vary with the spring-neap cycle; K_x by a factor of two and the non-linear tidal terms between approximately 0.4×10^{-4} and $1.5 \times 10^{-4} \, m^2/s^2$ but both have been taken to be constant.

Equation 2, the longitudinal momentum equation, has four major terms - acceleration, bottom friction, pressure gradient and wind stress (the Coriolis term is zero because v = o). The acceleration was calculated by subtracting low pass filtered currents 6 hours apart and the pressure gradient from the low pass filtered sea bed pressures from Malin Head and Larne (120 Km apart). Time series of the four terms from 5 August to 28 September 1979 are shown in Figure 6. This 55 day period is coincident with the period of offshore measurement and also enables the terms to be studied in detail. The amplitude of the variations in each of the terms is of a similar magnitude but the pressure gradient term has the largest variance - 6.2×10^{-8} m^4/s^4 compared with $2.3 \times 10^{-8} \, m^4/s^4$ for the wind stress and $1.5 \times 10^{-8} \, m^4/s^4$ for both the acceleration and friction terms.

The sum of the four terms (with due regard to sign) and the difference between the friction and wind stress terms are also shown in Figure 6. Equation 2 appears not to balance satisfactorily - there is a noise level of about $2 \times 10^{-4} \, m^2/s^2$ as well as periods of larger inbalance. However, for most of the time the friction and wind stress terms balance to within $\pm \, 10^{-4} \, m^2/s^2$. Moreover, when the wind stress and friction terms do differ, their difference is largely balanced by the pressure gradient term.

Previous studies of the cable voltages (Bowden and Hughes, 1961; Prandle, 1976 and 1979) also found a high correlation between the longitudinal wind stress and the cable voltages. For the present data set (3098 values, 1 July 1979 - 22 July 1980) the correlation coefficient between wind stress and cable voltage had a maximum value of 0.69 when the wind stress was resolved along 298° and the voltage lagged the wind stress by 2.4 hours. Then the least squares linear fit had a slope of 0.11 Vm^2/N which is of the same order as the theoretical value from equation 2 of 0.19 Vm^2/N. Possible causes for the difference, the theoretical value is larger, are that the wind stress was over-estimated or that the friction coefficient or cable calibration were too small. The difficulty in estimating the wind stress is the conversion from geostrophic to sea surface wind so the factor of 0.56 by Hasse and Wagner might be too large. This is corroborated by the comparisons in Table 2, although the shore based observations under-estimate the wind speed over the sea. The friction coefficient would be increased if a larger tidal current were representative - higher values than 0.7 m/s were recorded elsewhere in the North Channel.

The observations were split into two groups and correlation coefficients between wind stress and cable voltage calculated. When the wind was from the north-west, 1699 observations, the correlation coefficient was 0.69 whereas when the wind was from the south-west, 1399 observations, the coefficient was smaller, 0.51. These findings agree with those from the earlier studies in which the wind stress was calculated from observations at shore stations around the Irish Sea. The slopes of the least squares fits were larger in these cases (between 0.19 and 0.36 Vm^2/N) perhaps implying weaker calculated wind stresses. Also the wind stress directions for maximum correlation were more northerly, possibly because their wind stresses were calculated from winds within the Irish Sea whereas the winds covered the North Channel and its north-west approaches in the present study. However, the correlation coefficient showed only a weak dependence on wind stress direction - it was greater than 0.65 for wind stresses between 280° and 320°.

The longitudinal wind stress and cable voltage were correlated month by month. There was a small seasonal variation, the correlations being slightly weaker in summer when the wind stress was smaller, but all the values, except one, were between 0.55 and 0.85. The exception occurred for August 1979, part of the period of offshore measurement, when the correlation was very low, 0.24. During this month the winds were weak and on at least two occasions the wind stress differed significantly from the cable voltage, Figure 6.

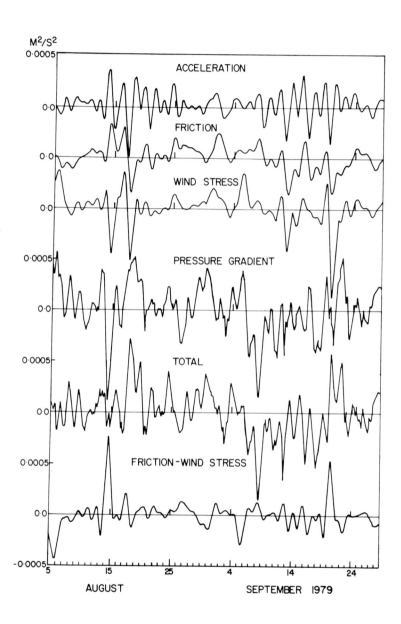

Figure 6. Time series of the four major terms in the low frequency longitudinal equation of motion from 5 August–28 September 1979.

One weather pattern caused most of the large wind stress events.
A depression moved eastward across the Atlantic passing to the
south of Iceland and to the north of Scotland accompanied by winds
which veered from southerly to north-westerly first driving water
out of the Irish Sea through the North Channel and then, as the
wind veered, into it. The depression usually covered a large
part of the Atlantic Ocean so that nearly uniform winds blew over
the area and generated an almost instanteneous current response
in the Irish Sea and North Channel with no elevation gradients
created within the North Channel. Winds blowing along the North
Channel appear not only to generate currents along the North
Channel (which is too narrow for the Earth's rotation to deflect
the currents) but are also in the right direction, in an Ekman
sense, to push water into or out of the Irish Sea through the
St. George's Channel giving the system a unified response. This
is supported by Pingree and Griffiths' (1980) numerical model
which predicted that the maximum flow through the St. George's
Channel would be generated by winds from $140^{\circ}/320^{\circ}$.

The paths of a few storms usually secondary depressions, were
more southerly, although they still travelled generally eastward,
and crossed Ireland and/or Scotland. These storms were smaller
in size and were accompanied by non-uniform winds over the region.
The response of the sea was not uniform and sea bed pressure
gradients were created in the North Channel. For instance, on
14 August 1979 a storm travelled north-eastward across southern
Ireland and the Irish Sea. Water flowed out of the Irish Sea
through the North Channel against the wind stress because a sea
bed pressure gradient had arisen with water in the Irish Sea higher
than that in the Malin Shelf Sea, Figure 6. Storms like this
occurred several times in August 1979 which led to the poor
correlation between the wind stress and the cable voltage.

Hence the response of the Irish Sea and North Channel area
subject to wind stress depends on whether the wind stress over
the area is spatially uniform. If it is, the wind stress along
the North Channel is balanced by linear friction whilst if it is
not, the wind stress is balanced by linear friction and a sea bed
pressure gradient. This is conjecture since the acceleration and,
to some extent, pressure gradient terms have been ignored. If the
acceleration term is included in the balance between wind stress
and friction the correlation is poorer and so the estimate for

this term is doubtful. Also, whilst the sea bed pressure gradient largely balances the gross differences between friction and wind stress when these occur, it is the noisiest term and at times is large when the wind stress and friction terms agree well.

The magnitude of the pressure gradient along the North Channel, both estimated from the difference between friction and wind stress and observed, varied between 10^{-3} and 10^{-2} Pa/m (equivalent to an elevation gradient of 0.01 to 0.1 m in 100 Km), Figure 6. The larger elevation differences should certainly have been measurable with well maintained conventional tide gauges - the noise level of the observed pressure gradient suggests that the low frequency records from the gauges at Malin Head and Larne had an uncertainty of about $\pm$ 0.02 m - so what are the possible causes for the larger discrepancies. First, one of the tide gauges could have been faulty; however nothing else indicates this. Second, local pressure gradients close to the tide gauge sites could have corrupted the measurements. This is unlikely because the local gradients would have to be very large, because of their small length scale, to generate elevations large enough to affect the measurements. No data supports this hypothesis. Third, other large scale sea bed pressure gradients could have been included in the measurements, generated by, for instance, the wind stress parallel to the west coasts of Ireland and Scotland, or the transverse Coriolis force from flow through the North Channel or the tides, particularly MS_f.

The sea bed pressures measured by all five shore based and three offshore gauges in the North Channel region were highly correlated (correlation coefficients between 0.91 and 0.99 for a common period of 37 days) indicating that the pressure field there was predominantly uniform. The pressure field was correlated with the north-east/south-west wind stress - the 13 month long records of wind stress and sea bed pressure at Port Ellen had a maximum correlation coefficient of 0.75 when the wind stress was resolved along $033^\circ/213^\circ$ and when the pressure lagged the wind by 6 hours. This suggests the following dynamics - the wind stress parallel to the Atlantic coasts of Ireland and Scotland generates a current parallel to the coast (by friction) which combines with the Earth's rotation to create a pressure gradient across the shelf. If the pressure variations are small at the shelf edge the pressures at the coast will be correlated with the alongshore wind stress.

A pressure recorder was deployed near the shelf edge at station J, Figure 2. Its record was correlated with those from the North Channel (correlation coefficient of 0.36, which is significant at the 95% level, with the pressure at Port Ellen and the latter lagging by about 1 hour) and had 10% of the variance.

The North Channel sea bed pressure records differed by up to 5×10^3 Pa from their mean during the 13 month period, which corresponds to a cross shelf gradient of 3×10^{-2} Pa/m and a long-shelf current of 0.3 m/s, according to the suggested dynamics. (For the period shown in Figure 6, the maximum gradient was 10^{-2} Pa/m). The slope of the least squares linear fit between the wind stress and sea bed pressure was used to estimate the friction coefficient $- 4 \times 10^{-5} s^{-1}$ - which whilst of the right order of magnitude is probably too large and suggests that as well as the frictional flow the wind stress is balanced by a longshore pressure gradient.

Secondly, a sea bed pressure gradient will balance the transverse (Coriolis) force from the flow through the North Channel. For the 55 day period of Figure 6 the largest flow recorded by the cable was 0.2 m/s leading to a gradient of 1.7×10^{-2} Pa/m and elevation differences of 0.1 m in 40 Km (the width of the channel at the cable). This is discussed in more detail below.

Thirdly, there are tidal sources. The gradients arising from the low frequency astronomic tides will be less than 10^{-4} Pa/m and can be ignored. However, non-linear interaction between the major tidal constituents can generate low frequency motion with shorter length scales and therefore larger gradients, the most significant being between M_2 and S_2 to generate MS_f which often occurs where there is a change in topography. Estimates for MS_f elevations are given in Table 7, showing that the largest amplitude occurs at Torr Head, where the North Channel changes direction. For the tide gauges listed in Table 7 the maximum elevation difference is 0.06 m and the maximum gradient 1.4×10^{-2} Pa/m. However, near Torr Head the gradients will be larger since the above gradients were calculated for tide gauges separated by more than 30 Km.

TABLE 7

Amplitude and phase of MS_f in the North Channel.

Tide gauge	Amplitude (m)	Phase
Malin Head	0.007	273
Port Ellen	0.017	205
Machrichanish	0.026	219
Torr Head	0.060	216
Larne	0.021	259

Hence pressure gradients of approximately equal magnitude arise in the North Channel from four different sources. The tidal, MS_f, contribution is easy to determine since it is periodic but it varies spatially within the North Channel. The others - the along channel gradient from equation 2, the across channel gradient balancing the Coriolis force and the across shelf generated by the along shelf wind stress, are approximately spatially uniform within the North Channel. Although the gradients from these three sources are of the same order, the across shelf gradient acts over the longest distance and so dominates the sea bed pressure records (producing elevations which vary between ± 0.2 m during 5 August - 28 September 1979, compared with ± 0.1 m for the other sources). This is one reason for the difficulty, referred to earlier, in measuring the pressure gradient term in equation 2 since we are trying to measure a signal in the presence of others of the same size or larger.

The pressure gradient was estimated from the records from Malin Head and Larne but other combinations were available - Port Ellen and Machrihanish, Malin Head and Torr Head, Torr Head and Larne and station E and station B. The various estimates do not agree well, see Figure 7 for three. The distance between Port Ellen and Machrihanish is 37 Km and between Torr Head and Larne is 39 Km so that the maximum elevation difference would be 0.03 m, near the limit the systems are capable of measuring so that neither estimate would be reliable. Although the drift in sea bed pressure records has greatly reduced recently so that both tides and low frequencies can be measured, it is highlighted by estimating the low frequency pressure gradient between two gauges.

230

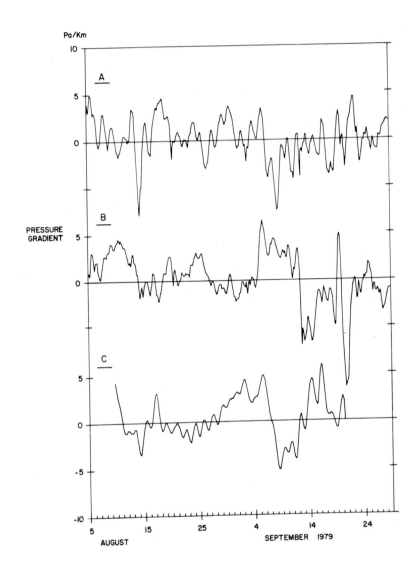

Figure 7. Time series of longitudinal sea bed pressure
gradient observations. a) Malin Head-Larne
b) Port Ellen-Machrihanish   c) Station E-
station B, with trend removed.

The gauges at stations E and B had overall drifts of approximately 0.06 m and 0.21 m respectively for their period of operation, both in the same sense, which dominated the pressure gradient signal. The drift, which can be discontinuous, has many possible sources, both from within the pressure sensor and from the relation of the frame to the sea floor. Hence it cannot be accurately removed although an attempt was made by fitting a straight line to the difference between the records from stations E and B. The problem at Torr Head is the large MS_f signal, which was removed, but cannot be accurately calculated even from a year's data. Hence, the Malin Head - Larne gradient was used since it should have been most accurately measurable because the gauges were furthest apart.

Figure 7 also shows that the background noise level was higher in the Malin Head - Larne signal, both stilling well tide gauges, compared with the Port Ellen - Machrihanish signal, pneumatic gauges one quarter the distance apart. The offshore measurement, station E - station B, had a lower noise level than either of these presumably since it was less affected by local nearshore gradients.

Much of this discussion of the longitudinal equation of motion for the North Channel (equation 2) is relevant to the transverse equation (equation 3). The three largest terms - Coriolis, pressure gradient and wind stress - and their sum have been plotted in Figure 8. The acceleration and friction terms are small since the transverse velocity, v, is small and the magnitude of the wind stress term is less than that of the Coriolis and pressure gradient terms which have the largest magnitude of any in the equations of motion. Their correlation coefficient is 0.50 and although this is significant at the 1% level it is not as high as might be expected. The variance of the Coriolis term is twice as large as that of the pressure gradient term and it is apparent in Figure 8 that the magnitude of the varitions in the Coriolis term are larger than those in the pressure gradient term.

Once again the equation has not balanced as well as antici-pated, either because an important factor has been omitted or because of errors in the flow or pressure measurements. There was no obvious problem with the flow measurement in the longi-tudinal equation and certainly no suggestion it had been over-

232

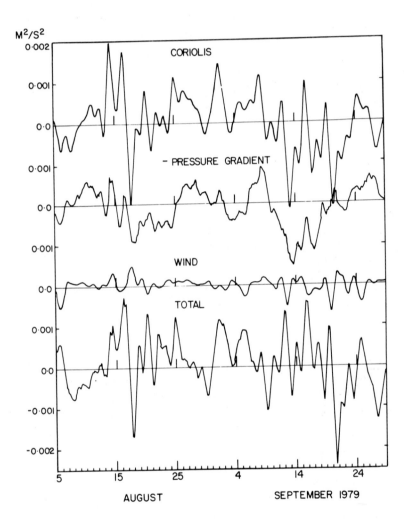

Figure 8.   Time series of the three major terms in the low
frequency transverse equation of motion for the
North Channel, 5 August–28 September 1979.

estimated. There are, however, at least two possible problems in measuring the pressure gradient signal both of which have already been mentioned. First, Torr Head and Machrihanish are separated by 33 Km so that the maximum expected level difference is only 0.06 m. However, the pneumatic pressure recorders installed at both sites should be capable of resolving differences of the order of $\pm$ 0.01 m and so should have measured at least the extreme events. Second, the MS_f signal at Torr Head is large and the attempt to remove it could also have affected the pressure gradient signal since the frequencies overlap.

To sum up, in the frequency range 0.5 to 0.1 cpd the wind stress is the major driving force for the dynamics of the North Channel. The longitudinal wind stress (along $118^o/298^o$) is immediately balanced by a frictional flow through the North Channel and Irish Sea whilst the transverse wind stress (along $033^o/213^o$) generates an along shore pressure gradient and current in the Malin Shelf Sea. The current creates a cross shelf (Coriolis) pressure gradient which dominates the sea bed pressure field in the North Channel and lags the wind stress by about 6 hours. The flow through the North Channel also sets up a transverse (Coriolis) pressure gradient there. In addition, if the scale of the weather pattern is small, a pressure gradient can be generated along the North Channel. For a depression moving eastward across the Atlantic Ocean this implies that water will first flow out of the Irish Sea through the North Channel and then reverse and flow into it as the depression passes, whilst elevations in the North Channel rise, both from the inverse barometer effect and the wind stress, and then fall after the depression has passed. This description is in accordance with the equations of motion but the measurements did not balance as well as had been hoped, in particular the acceleration and pressure gradient terms presented problems.

Mean currents

Of the three frequency bands commonly measured with recording current meters - inertial and tidal (12-1 c.p.d.), storm driven (1- 0.1 c.p.d.) and circulation (less than 0.1 c.p.d.) - the lowest is the most susceptible to errors. In continental shelf seas the circulation is usually weaker than the tidal and storm driven currents so that any faults in the meter's design, opera-tion or in its interaction with its **mooring** can alias energy to the lowest frequencies, swamping the signal and particularly causing erroneous directions. However, the mean recorded currents during August and September 1979 had high speeds (most between 0.05 and 0.125 m/s) and at most sites were barotropic (to within 15°), Table 8. Also Aanderaa and AMF VACM meters deployed close together recorded similar mean currents, as shown earlier. The currents formed an unusually coherent and stable pattern (small standard errors for the speeds and directional stability close to 100) which was largely supported by CTD observations and previous (Lagrangian) measurements. (In the North Channel Eulerian (current meter) and Lagrangian measurements should be comparable because the Stokes drift due to the semi-diurnal tide is small since the tide is a standing wave). All this suggests that the observations were a reliable estimate of the circulations for that period.

TABLE 8

Mean currents for the periods given in Table 4. Directional stability is (vector mean speed/scalar mean speed) x 100.

Station	Meter height above sea floor (m)	Vector mean Speed (m/s)	Direction	s.e. Speed (m/s)	Direction stability
A	70	0.123	134	0.002	99
	45	0.093	150	0.003	99
	20	0.080	141	0.002	95
B	110	0.041	215	0.002	63
	60	0.005	297	0.002	13
	20	0.012	222	0.002	31
C	33	0.091	172	0.002	94
	31	0.105	198	0.005	95
	10	0.052	173	0.002	82
D	81	0.079	89	0.002	94
	41	0.076	63	0.002	91
E	6	0.053	319	0.002	87
F	30	0.046	64	0.003	72
	28	0.048	66	0.003	73
	11	0.021	76	0.002	45
G	39	0.065	110	0.002	82
	37	0.071	101	0.002	82
	27	0.050	93	0.002	73
	11	0.067	116	0.002	85
I	11	0.050	351	0.002	80

The most obvious interpretation of the mean currents in Table 8 is that throughout the two months water flowed towards the Irish Sea both close to the Irish shore (at stations F, G and A) and also close to the Mull of Galloway (at station C) and flowed away from the Irish Sea close to Islay (at stations E and I). The strong southward flows near the shores at the southern end of the North Channel (at stations A and C) did not occur in the middle (at station B) where the top meter recorded a mean across the channel and the middle and bottom meters recorded weak means. At station F the mean currents were also weaker and more varied in direction, perhaps because it was the only station in stratified water and for part of the time was close to the front separating stratified and homogeneous water which appeared from the CTD observations and the satellite infra-red photographs to be advected towards the North Channel during August and September 1979.

A simple attempt to quantify the flow into and out of the North Channel based on this circulation pattern and the records from stations A, B, C, E, F and G failed since it showed a net loss of water which was not balanced by a change in sea level. 10 day averages of the low frequency currents were calculated which showed that the southward flow at stations A and C varied very little but that at stations B, E, F and G a change occurred about 5 September. Before then the flow at station B had a northward component so that the flow at stations F and G into the North Channel was balanced by a flow out of the North Channel at stations A, B and C ($\sim$ 0.8 x 10^5 m^3/). Hence the flow north-westward at station E ($\sim$ 1.3 x 10^5 m^3/s) represented a net loss to the region. After 5 September the flow at station B was southward, the flows at stations F and G increased and E (and I) decreased. However, the flow southward at stations A, B and C ($\sim$ 2.2 x 10^5 m^3/s) was now greater than the flow in at stations F and G by about 0.4 x 10^5 m^3/s and there was again a net loss of about 1.2 x 10^5 m^3/s . (The change in flow pattern was caused by the longitudinal wind stress which was stronger towards the Irish Sea after 5 September).

The attempted balance was very crude but the size of the disa-agreement implies that changing the cross-sectional area corresponding to each meter will not substantially improve the calculation. An alternative explanation for the imbalance is

that the mean current at station E instead of representing a flow
out of the North Channel was part of a clockwise gyre in the Sound
of Jura which included station D, where the mean current was large
and transverse to the sound. A similar, but oscillating, gyre in
the Sound of Jura would explain the quasi-fortnightly currents
recorded at stations D, E, F and G, Table 9, where the currents
at station E were 180° out of phase with those at stations D, F
and G. The mean gyre was stronger than the fortnightly gyre whose
driving forces include both wind and tidal, MS_f, so that the
combination always rotated clockwise but with a speed which varied
with fortnightly and monthly periods.

TABLE 9

Quasi-fortnightly current ellipses from a harmonic analysis of
a common 29 day period. Amplitudes are in m/s and the sense of
rotation is given by the sign of the minimum amplitude (+ ve
anti-clockwise).

Station	Meter height above the sea floor (m)	Maximum amplitude	Minimum amplitude	Phase	Direction
D	81	0.051	-0.015	41	56
	41	0.057	0.003	43	31
E	6	0.013	-0.001	213	132
F	30	0.020	0.007	90	107
	28	0.019	0.009	92	105
	11	0.013	-0.003	113	107
G	39	0.016	-0.003	81	141
	37	0.020	-0.003	72	139
	11	0.023	0.005	55	178

    On this interpretation the circulation of the North Channel for
August and September 1979 was:- constant flows towards the Irish
Sea both by the Mull of Galloway and by the Irish Coast from Malin
Head to Larne, a variable flow in the centre of the North Channel
depending on the longitudinal wind, a clockwise gyre in the Sound
of Jura and a northward flow in the Malin Shelf Sea bypassing
the entrance of the North Channel, schematically shown in Figure 9.
The flow through the southern end of the North Channel was always
towards the Irish Sea and was, therefore, atypical since Caesium

137 output from Windscale clearly shows a mean flow out of the Irish Sea through the North Channel (McKinley et al. 1981a, b).

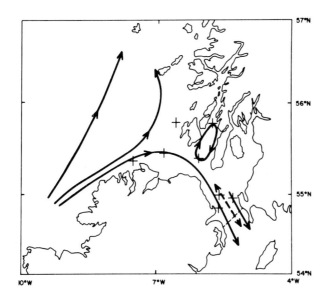

Figure 9. Scheme of mean flow as recorded by current meters during August and September 1979. The direction of the flow in the middle of the North Channel depends on the wind's direction.

This circulation pattern has a larger spatial variability than the tidal and storm driven currents, which were either uniformly towards or away from the Irish Sea. However, at most meters the mean speeds were so high that they dominated the low frequency records and storm driven flow reversals occurred only for short periods. Hence the cable calibration for low frequency flows reflects the circulation pattern and is different from the tidal calibration. If the circulation pattern changed so might the low frequency cable calibration (Robinson, 1976). Since the flow is not uniform across the North Channel and since the cable measures

the average flow through the channel, cable measurements on their
own will not determine the spatial variations in the circulation
pattern and so cannot be used to extend the current meter records.

From the previous section the wind stress is a major driving
force for the flows in the North Channel and the Malin Shelf Sea.
For both periods August to September 1979 and July 1979 to July
1980 the mean wind stress was approximately transverse to the
North Channel (0.105 N/m^2 towards 045° and 0.094 N/m^2 towards
018° respectively) suggesting that there was a mean current
northward through the Malin Shelf Sea, as observed previously by
McKinley et al (1981b). The component of the mean wind stress
along the North Channel ($118^{\circ}/298^{\circ}$) was 0.031 N/m^2 towards the
Irish Sea for August to September 1979 and 0.016 N/m^2 away from
the Irish Sea for July 1979 to July 1980. The mean cable
voltages for the corresponding periods were - 0.013V and 0.010 V
which correspond to mean currents of - 0.041 m/s and 0.011 m/s
respectively, assuming equation 1 is valid for mean currents.
The former value compares well with an estimate of - 0.035 m/s
from the current meter measurements. This suggests that the
wind stress is also important in determining the mean flow
through the North Channel.

CONCLUSIONS

The low frequency dynamics of the Irish Sea, North Channel
and Malin Shelf Sea are largely controlled by the wind. In the
storm driven frequency range, 1-0.1 c.p.d., the wind stress along
the North Channel is balanced by a frictional flow through the
Irish Sea and North Channel (and sometimes by a pressure
gradient along the North Channel if the storm's size is small).
The wind stress transverse to the North Channel, which is also
parallel to the west coasts of Ireland and Scotland, indirectly
forces the sea bed pressure field at the coast, with a lag of
6 hours. The mean wind stress is also important for the long
term flow along the Malin Shelf Sea and through the North Channel.
During the offshore measurements there was a well defined
circulation pattern within the North Sea, Figure 9.

The dynamics were observed by a 45 day long period of
offshore measurement and a 13 month long period of shore based
measurement. The combination enabled the calibration of the
cross channel telephone cable by comparison with three recording
current meter rigs which showed different calibrations for tidal

(1.21 Vs/m) and low frequency currents (2.26 Vs/m), the latter reflecting the circulation pattern. The voltage for zero flow (0.005V) was not significantly different from zero. There were difficulties in measuring the acceleration, pressure gradient and wind stress within the North Channel - the pressure gradient because the gradients were small and because of drift in the offshore measurements and the wind stress because no offshore measurements were available and so the geostrophic wind had to be converted to the surface wind. The extended shore based measurements of cable voltage elevation and atmospheric pressure enabled the monitoring of much of the dynamics - the storm driven flows in the North Channel and Malin Shelf Seas and also the spatially averaged mean flows but not the variations within this spatial average. Further and longer offshore measurements are required to study the latter and to confirm some of the above points.

REFERENCES

Amorocho, J. and De Vries, J.J., 1980. A new evaluation of the wind stress coefficient over water surfaces. Journal of Geophysical Research, 85 (cl) : 433-442.

Barnes, H. and Goodley, E.F.W., 1961. The general hydrography of the Clyde Sea area, Scotland. Part 1: description of the area; drift bottle and surface salinity data. Bulletins of Marine Ecology, 5 (43): 112-150.

Beardsley, R.C., Boicourt, W., Huff, L.C. and Scott, J., 1977 CMlCE 76: a current meter intercomparison experiment off Long Island in February-March, 1976. Woods Hole Oceanographic Institution, Technical Report, WHOI-77-62, 123 pp. (Unpublished manuscript).

Bowden, K.F., 1950. Processes affecting the salinity of the Irish Sea. Monthly notices of the Royal Astronomical Society, geophysical supplement 6(2) : 63-90.

Bowden, K.F. and Hughes, P., 1961. The flow of water through the Irish Sea and its relation to wind. Geophysical Journal of the Royal Astronomical Society, 5: 265-291.

Browell, A. and Pugh D.T., 1977. Field tests of the Aanderaa
pressure logger with pneumatic tide gauges, and
the design of associated pneumatic control
circuits . Institute of Oceanographic Sciences,
Report 37, 11 pp. (Unpublished manuscript).

Craig, R.E., 1959. Hydrography of Scottish Coastal waters.
Marine Research, 2: 1-30.

Doodson, A.T. and Corkan, R.H., 1932. The principal constituent
of the tides in the English and Irish Channels.
Philosophical transactions of the Royal Society
of London, A, 231: 29-53.

Hamming, R.W., 1977. Digital filters. Prentice Hall, New Jersey,
226 pp.

Hasse, L., and Wagner, V., 1971. On the relationship between
geostrophic and surface wind at sea. Monthly
weather review, 99 : 255-260.

Heaps, N.S. 1978. Linearized vertically-integrated equations
for residual circulation in coastal seas.
Deutsche Hydrographische Zeitschrift, 31(5):
147-169.

Heaps, N.S. and Jones, J.E., 1975. Storm surge computations for
the Irish Sea using a thre-dimensional numerical
model. Mémoires de la Société royale des Sciences
de Liège, 6 ser., 7 : 289-333.

Heaps, N.S. and Jones J.E., 1979. Recent storm surves in the Irish
Sea. In J.C.J. Nihoul (Editor), Marine forecasting.
Elsevior, Amsterdam, pp. 285-319.

Howarth, M.J., 1981. An intercomparison of AMF VACMs and Aanderaa
RCM4s in a tidally dominated continental shelf sea.
International council for the Exploration of the sea
c.m. 1981/c : 31 : pp. 12. (Unpublished manuscript).

I.C.E.S. 1962. Mean monthly temperature and salinity of the
surface layer of the North Sea and adjacent waters
from 1905-1954. Charlottenlund Slot, Denmark.

Kautsky, H., Jefferies, D.F. and Steele, A.K., 1980. Results of
the Radiological North Sea Programme RANOSP 1974 to
1976. Deutsche Hydrographische Zeitschrift, 33(4) :
152-157.

Lee, A.J., 1960. Hydrographical investigations in the Irish Sea,
January-March 1953. Fishery investigations, London,
2 Ser., 23(2) : 1-25.

McKinley, I.G., Baxter, M.S. and Jack, W., 1981a. A simple model
of radiocaesium transport from Windscale to the Clyde
Sea area. Estuarine, Coastal and Shelf Science, 13 :
59-67.

McKinley, I.G., Baxter, M.S., Ellett, D.J. and Jack, W., 1981b.
Tracer applications of radiocaesium in the Sea of the
Hebrides. Estuarine, Coastal and Shelf Science, 13 :
69-82.

Pingree, R.D.,Holligan, P.M. and Mardell, G.T., 1978. The effects of vertical stability on phytoplankton distributions in the summer on the northwest European Shelf. Deep-Sea Research, 25 : 1011-1028.

Pingree, R.D. and Griffiths, D.K., 1980. Currents driven by a steady uniform wind stress on the shelf seas around the British Isles. Oceanologica Acta, 3(2) : 227-236.

Prandle, D., 1976. Wind-induced flow through the North Channel of the Irish Sea. Geophysical Journal of the Royal Astronomical Society, 45(2) : 437-44.

Prandle, D. 1979. Recordings of potential difference across the Portpatrick-Donaghadee submarine cable (1977/78). Institute of Oceanographic Sciences, Report 83 : 9 pp. (Unpublished manuscript).

Proudman, J., 1939. On currents in the North Channel of the Irish Sea. Monthly notices of the Royal Astronomical Society, geophysical supplement, 4 : 387-403.

Robinson, I.S., 1976. A theoretical analysis of the use of sub-marine cables as electromagnetic oceanographic flowmeters. Philosophical Transactions of the Royal Society of London, A, 280(1297) : 355-396.

Robinson, I.S. 1979. The tidal dynamics of the Irish and Celtic Sea. Geophysical Journal of the Royal Astronomical Society, 56 (1) : 159-197.

Simpson, J.H., Edelsten, D.J., Edwards, A., Morriss, N.C.G. and Tett, P.B., 1979. The Islay front: physical structure and phytoplankton distribution. Estuarine and coastal Marine Science, 9 : 713-726.

Slinn, D.J., 1974. Water circulation and nutrients in the north-west Irish Sea. Estuarine and Coastal Marine Science, 2 : 1-25.

Taylor, G.I., 1919. Tidal friction in the Irish Sea. Philosophical Transactions of the Royal Society of London, A, 220 : 1-93.

Thompson, K.R., 1980. An analysis of British monthly mean sea level. Geophysical Journal of the Royal Astronomical Society, 63(1) : 57-73.

Thomson, R.E. and Chow, K.Y., 1980 . Butterworth and Lanczos-window cosine digital filters : with application to data processing on the Univac 1106 computer. Pacific Marine Science Report 80-9, 60 pp. Institute of Ocean Science, Canada. (Unpublished manuscript).

Williamson, D.I., 1956. The plankton in the Irish Sea, 1951 and 1952. Bulletins of Marine Ecology, 4(31) : 87-114.

Wilson, T.R.S., 1974. Caesium-137 as a water movement tracer in St. George's Channel. Nature, 248 : 125-127.

THE DYNAMICS OF THE LOOP CURRENT AND SHED EDDIES IN A NUMERICAL MODEL OF THE
GULF OF MEXICO

HARLEY E. HURLBURT and J. DANA THOMPSON
Environmental Simulation Branch (Code 322), Naval Ocean Research and Development
Activity, NSTL Station, MS 39529   USA

ABSTRACT

The dynamics of the circulation in the Gulf of Mexico have been investigated using simple, efficient numerical models capable of simulating consis-
tently observed dynamical features, including the Loop Current and the shedding
of large anticyclonic eddies from the Loop. Over 150 model experiments were
integrated to statistical equilibrium, typically 3-5 years.

One popular hypothesis holds that the Loop Current sheds anticyclonic eddies
in response to annual variations in the inflow through the Yucatan Straits.
However, a striking result from the models is their ability to simulate the
observed quasi-annual eddy shedding period with no time variations in the inflow.
The model-predicted eddy diameters, amplitudes, and westward propagation speeds
are also realistic. The dominant instability mechanism in the eddy shedding is
a horizontal shear instability of the first internal mode, a barotropic rather
than a baroclinic instability. Therefore, a reduced-gravity model with one
vertical mode is able to simulate the basic dynamics of the Loop Current-eddy
system. Rossby-wave theory and a conservation of absolute vorticity trajectory
analysis were used to explain the behavior of the Loop Current, including its
northward penetration into the Gulf, the latitude of westward bending, the
shedding period for the eddies, as well as their diameter, and their westward
propagation speed.

A regime diagram for the reduced-gravity model was constructed in terms of
the Reynolds number Re and the beta Rossby number $R_B = v_c/\beta L_p^2$, where v_c is the
velocity at the core of the current, L_p is half the port separation distance and
β is differential rotation. Eddy shedding can be prevented by reducing Re or
by increasing R_B.

Bottom relief acts to inhibit baroclinic instability, yielding solutions
more closely resembling those from the reduced-gravity model than the two-layer
flat-bottom model. Topography also influences the paths of the shed eddies and,
in the presence of sufficient deep water inflow through the Yucatan Straits,
prevents Loop Current penetration, westward bending, and eddy shedding. In
effect, the West Florida Shelf acts to reduce the port separation, increase
R_B, and shift the Loop Current into a stable regime.

The signatures of barotropic and baroclinic instabilities in the two-layer
Gulf of Mexico model were studied using upper and lower layer pressure fields
and eddy-mean energetics. Both instability processes tend to drive a deep flow
characterized by modon[1] generation and they exhibit similar vertical phase
relationships. However, in these experiments the westward propagation speeds
associated with baroclinic instability are typically two to three times faster.

---

[1] For convenience and in the spirit of Stern's (1975) application to observations
we have generalized the term "modon" to refer to any counter-rotating vortex pair
in the lower layer generated by a single vortex in the upper layer.

1. INTRODUCTION

Semi-enclosed seas are attractive domains for ocean modeling partly because
they allow the use of numerical grids that resolve strong meandering currents
and associated eddying phenomena also found in major ocean basins. The Gulf of
Mexico is particularly attractive because it contains a major current system
that sheds energetic anticyclonic eddies which are comparable in size to warm-
core Gulf Stream rings. This system is illustrated in Fig. 1 by the depth of
the $22^{0}C$ isotherm in the eastern Gulf of Mexico based on a hydrographic survey
by Liepper (1970). It shows the Loop Current entering from the south through
the Yucatan Straits and exiting to the east through the Florida Straits. The
mean transport through the straits is ~ 30 m^3/s (Nowlin, 1972). In Fig. 1 a
large anticyclonic eddy is about to break-off from the Loop Current, as
confirmed by subsequent observations (Elliott, 1979). The Loop Current penetrates into the Gulf and sheds these large anticyclonic eddies with a quasi-
annual period. The eddies have a typical radius of 180 km and translate into
the western Gulf at a mean speed of 2.4 cm/s   (Elliott, 1979).

In this paper we present some basic dynamical ideas and numerical results
concerning the behavior of the Loop Current-eddy system. The dynamical
topics include 1) the nature of the instability associated with the eddy
shedding, 2) the external and/or internal factors which determine the eddy
shedding period, 3) the trajectory dynamics of the Loop Current and how they
affect the penetration of the Loop into the Gulf, the eddy shedding, and the
diameter of the eddies, 4) the existence of different regimes for the Loop
Current, 5) two important roles of topography in the dynamics, and 6) the
distinctive signatures of barotropic and baroclinic instability in the flow
and in the energetics. Over 150 numerical experiments have been performed to
explore the model parameter space, but more importantly to aid in the formulation and testing of dynamical hypotheses. This paper is both a distillation
and an extension of Hurlburt and Thompson (1980), hereafter referred to as HT.
That paper discusses the only previous numerical model of the Gulf of Mexico
which was integrated to statistical equilibrium or which simulated the basic
repetitive features of the eddy shedding by the Loop Current.

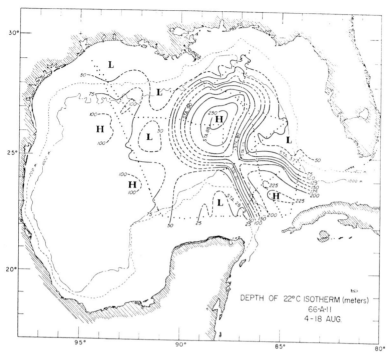

Fig. 1. Topography of the 22°C isothermal surface, 4-18 August 1966 (Alaminos cruise 66-A-11) from Leipper (1970). Subsequent data (Elliot, 1979) indicates that an anticyclonic eddy separated from the Loop Current within several months.

2. DESIGN OF THE NUMERICAL MODELS AND NUMERICAL EXPERIMENTS

The three numerical models of HT are used to elucidate the Loop Current-eddy shedding dynamics. These models were designed to be as simple as possible while retaining the ability to simulate the basic phenomena of interest. The three models are 1) reduced gravity, 2) barotropic, and 3) two-layer. The first two are mathematically identical except for parameter values, particularly the gravitational acceleration. The reduced gravity model is designed to represent the first internal mode and contains an upper active layer and a lower layer which is infinitely deep and at rest. In the reduced gravity and two-layer models the pycnocline is represented by an immiscible interface between two layers with a prescribed density contrast. In the reduced gravity model bottom topography and baroclinic instability are not permitted. Two active layers is the minimum to allow baroclinic instability and to allow coexistence of topography and the pycnocline. The barotropic and reduced gravity models demonstrate the behavior of the individual modes and provide insight into how they interact in the two-layer model. They also allow the investigation of some phenomena in the simplest context.

The models are primitive equation on a β-plane and retain a free surface. Using the hydrostatic and Boussinesq approximations and a right-handed Cartesian coordinate system, the vertically integrated model equations are

$$\frac{\partial \mathbb{W}_i}{\partial t} + (\nabla \cdot \mathbb{W}_i + \mathbb{W}_i \cdot \nabla) w_i + \hat{k} \times f \mathbb{W}_i = -h_i \nabla p_i$$

$$+ (\mathbb{t}_i - \mathbb{t}_{i+1})/\rho + A\nabla^2 \mathbb{W}_i \tag{1}$$

$$\frac{\partial h_i}{\partial t} + \nabla \cdot \mathbb{W}_i = 0 \tag{2}$$

where i = 1,2 for the two-layer model, i=1 for the barotropic and reduced gravity models and

$$\nabla = \frac{\partial}{\partial x} \hat{i} + \frac{\partial}{\partial y} \hat{j}$$

$$p_1 = g\eta_1$$

$$p_2 = p_1 - g'(h_1 - H_1)$$

$$\mathbb{W}_i = h_i w_i = h_i(u_i\hat{i} + v_i\hat{j})$$

$$g' = g(\rho_2 - \rho_1)/\rho$$

$$f = f_0 + \beta(y - y_0) \tag{3}$$

$$\mathbb{t}_i = \tau_i^x \hat{i} + \tau_i^y \hat{j}$$

See Appendix A for symbol definitions. In the reduced gravity model the lower layer momentum equation is $g\nabla\eta = g'\nabla h_1$.

Fig. 2 shows the model domain superimposed on a topographic map of the Gulf of Mexico. The 20^0 counter-clockwise rotation of the model domain is neglected. The numerical models were driven from rest by prescribed inflow through the Yucatan Straits (southern port) compensated by outflow through the Florida Straits (eastern port). Except at the ports the boundaries are rigid and in almost all cases the no-slip condition is used. $\mathbb{W}_i$ is prescribed at the southern (inflow) port. In most cases a parabolic inflow profile is used for $\mathbb{W}_i$. Due to the geostrophic tilt in the interface across the port, the velocity maximum is west of the center of the inflow port. At the eastern (outflow) port the normal flow is self-determined using the full x-momentum equation. At inflow points the boundary condition is $u_x = 0$. At outflow points the computational boundary condition is $u_{xx} = 0$. The latter results in upstream differencing for the $(Uu)_x$ term, which is lagged in time in this case. The normal pressure gradient is assumed uniform across the port and is determined by an integral constraint requiring the net outflow through the eastern port to compensate the inflow through the southern port. The tangential velocity component at the ports is usually set at zero 1/2 grid distance outside the physical domain. This weak overspecification eliminates the possibility of outflow at unrealistic angles. Outflow through a channel modeling the Florida Straits is a more realistic approach. This was done in a few cases, but with negligible effect. The semi-implicit numerical models of HT are used in this study. The implicit treatment of the external and internal gravity waves allows much longer time steps in the numerical integration than comparable explicit primitive equation models with a free surface. See HT for further discussion of the numerical models.

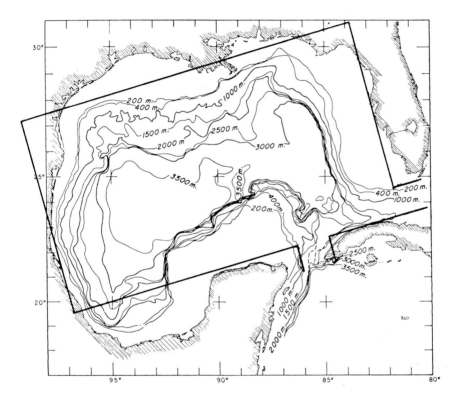

Fig. 2. Bathymetry of the Gulf of Mexico based on U. S. Coast and Geodetic Survey Chart 1007 and soundings on file at the Dept. of Oceanography, Texas A&M University. From Nowlin (1972). The rectangle shows the approximate domain of the numerical model. Inflow and outflow ports are also indicated.

Table 1 presents the parameters of the pivotal experiment for each numerical model. These parameters imply a maximum upper layer inflow velocity of 70-75 cm/s and an internal radius of deformation, $\lambda = (g'h_1)^{1/2}/f \approx 45$ km, about four times less than the observed radius of major eddies shed by the Loop Current. In the two-layer model the value of g' in the table is multiplied

by $(H_1+H_2)/H_2$ to yield the same internal values for the gravity wave speed as
in a reduced gravity model. The inflow transport is spun up with a time
constant of 30 days to minimize the excitation of high frequency waves. Poten-
tially important wind driving is neglected to allow focus on the Loop-driven
circulation.

TABLE 1

Model parameters for standard case

A	$10^7 cm^2 sec^{-1}$		β	$2\times10^{-13} cm^{-1} sec^{-1}$
f_0	$5 \times 10^{-5} sec^{-1}$		ρ	$1\ gm\ cm^{-3}$
g	$980\ cm\ sec^{-2}$		τ_i	0
g'	$3\ cm\ sec^{-2}$		Δx	20 km*
H_1	200 m		Δy	18.75 km*
H_2	2800 m		Δt	1.5 hr

Domain Size, x_L by y_L	1600 x 900 km
Southern Port Width, L_{pw}	160 km
Eastern Port Width, L_e	150 km
Center of southern port at x_p	1200 km
Center of eastern port at y_p	75 km
Upper Layer Inflow Transport**	$20 \times 10^6 m^3 sec^{-1}$ (20 Sv)
Lower Layer Inflow Transport	$10 \times 10^6 m^3 sec^{-1}$ (10 Sv)
Angle of inflow from x-axis, Θ_I	90^0
Inflow spin-up time constant	30 days

For the barotropic model the initial maximum depth is H=3000 m and the inflow
transport is 30 Sv.
* for a given variable
** also for the standard reduced gravity model

Horizontal friction provides the only dissipation in the models.
Because Laplacian friction is a crude parameterization, for convenience
$Ah_i\nabla^2 w_i$ was replaced by $A\nabla^2 w_i$ (with minimal effect). The standard eddy
viscosity (A) is greater than required for stable integration of the models.
HT showed this value yields a constant eddy-shedding period for the Loop
Current. Smaller values introduced some irregularity into the period without
substantially altering the long-term mean. Although lower eddy viscosities
are utilized in some experiments, most employ the larger value to reduce the
length of the integration required to obtain stable statistics, and to facilitate the analysis of the results. Fig. 3 shows the idealized Gulf of Mexico

topography used in some of the numerical experiments. Typically the models were integrated five years to statistical equilibrium.

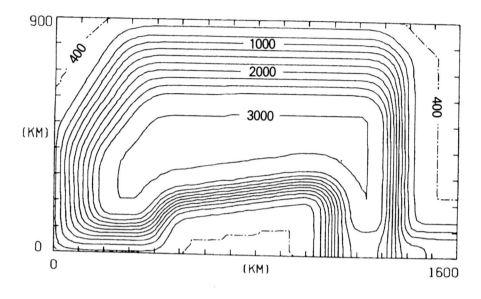

Fig. 3. Bathymetry of the idealized Gulf of Mexico model. The deepest water is at 3000 m and the shallowest topography is 400 m deep. The contour interval is 250 m. (From HT).

3. AN ATTEMPT TO SIMULATE THE EDDY SHEDDING BY THE LOOP CURRENT

Our first goal was to determine which, if any, of the models could demonstrate eddy shedding with a realistic eddy diameter, amplitude, shedding period, and propagation. Within the framework of the two-layer model, the first simulation was made as realistic as possible including the idealized topography shown in Fig. 3. A longstanding hypothesis (Cochrane, 1965) maintains that the Loop Current exhibits an annual eddy shedding cycle due to seasonal variations in the flow through the Yucatan Straits which affect the penetration distance of the Loop Current. When the Loop retreats, eddy shedding is presumed to occur. Despite this hypothesis, the model was first driven by a steady inflow to see if the Loop Current would shed eddies due to purely internal mechanisms. This might then establish a natural frequency for the eddy shedding.

The first experiment utilizes the parameters of Table 1 and the topography of Fig. 3 except that the upper layer inflow transport is 25 Sv, the lower layer 5 Sv. Fig. 4 illustrates an eddy shedding cycle from this experiment using a sequence of four synoptic maps of the pycnocline anomaly (PA). The PA is the

250

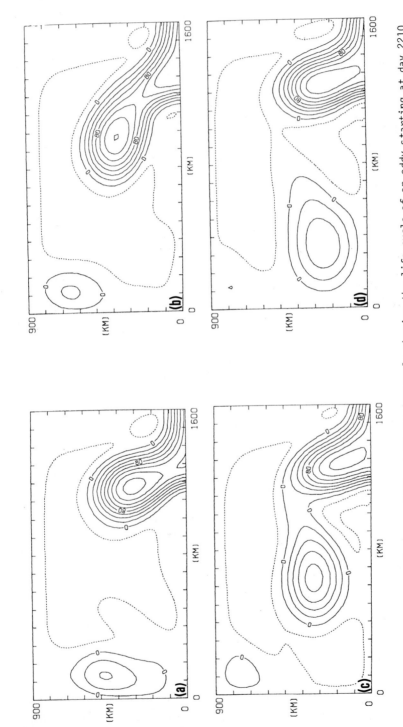

Fig. 4. Sequence of synoptic maps of PA at 70-day intervals showing the life cycle of an eddy starting at day 2210. The contour interval is 20 m. In all the figures dashed contours are negative. PA is positive downward. The case shown here uses the parameters of Table 1 and the topography of Fig. 3 except that the upper layer inflow transport is 25 Sv, the lower layer 5 Sv. (From HT).

deviation of the interface between the layers from its initial flat elevation and is positive downward (upper layer thickness greater than initial). Fig. 4a shows the Loop Current has penetrated into the Gulf and is beginning to form an anticyclonic eddy. In Fig. 4b the Loop Current has bent westward and an eddy is about to break off. Fig. 4c shows the Loop Current and an eddy just after an eddy-shedding event. In Fig. 4d the eddy has drifted westward while the Loop Current has penetrated further into the Gulf. Fig. 4a, b shows that when an eddy reaches the western boundary, it drifts northward with final decay in the northwest corner of the basin.

The cycle of Loop Current penetration into the Gulf, westward bending and eddy shedding is repeated with a period of about 290 days, close to the quasi-annual period observed. Contrary to the popular hypothesis, time variations of the inflow are not required for the model Loop Current to exhibit realistic quasi-annual eddy shedding, a striking result first noted by HT. The model also predicts a realistic eddy diameter, amplitude, and westward propagation speed. In subsequent experiments HT found that realistic time variations in the upper layer inflow can have a significant influence on the eddy shedding. However, the eddy shedding is dominated by the natural period, not the period of the forcing, a topic we shall not pursue here. In Section 7 we do examine an important effect of topography and lower layer inflow through the Yucatan Straits on the eddy shedding.

4. A SIMPLE TEST FOR THE INSTABILITY MECHANISM

The remaining sections are designed to provide some insight into the dynamics of the Loop Current-eddy system. We might be tempted to undertake a stability analysis to find instability mechanisms, unstable wavelengths, and growth rates, but we would anticipate that the configuration of the current would be troublesome. However, there are more fruitful approaches than this. Nevertheless, we will start with one simple test for the primary instability mechanism by using the reduced gravity model. If it produces results similar to the two-layer model, then we have eliminated baroclinic instability as an essential element of the dynamics, and the primary instability mechanism is a horizontal shear instability of the internal mode, a barotropic instability.

Fig. 5 compares (a) the experiment with topography discussed in Section 3, (b) a two-layer flat-bottom experiment using the standard parameters from Table 1, and (c) a reduced gravity experiment using appropriate parameters from Table 1. Shown is a latitude vs. time (y vs. t) plot of PA at a longitude 190 km west of the center of the southern port. In all three cases the PA shows a regular progression of discrete eddies with similar eddy diameter, amplitude, and shedding period. However, the experiment with topography (Fig. 5a) did not begin to shed eddies for almost three years, a point addressed in Section 7. With standard parameters the barotropic model evolved to a steady state without shedding eddies, a matter discussed in Section 6.

The results shown in Fig. 5 lead us to conclude that a horizontal shear instability of the internal mode is dominant. The two-layer model with Fig. 3 topography, the two-layer flat-bottom model, and the reduced gravity model do not agree in all the parameter space we explored (see Section 8), but they do agree for a regime in accord with observed features of the Loop Current-eddy system. Since the reduced gravity model is the simplest of the models to provide a realistic simulation, it is used in much of our analysis. The question of barotropic vs. baroclinic instability is addressed further in Section 8 using eddy-mean energetics and other signatures of the instability mechanisms.

5. CAV TRAJECTORIES AND ROSSBY WAVE THEORY ELUCIDATE THE LOOP CURRENT - EDDY SHEDDING DYNAMICS

Constant absolute vorticity (CAV) trajectories and Rossby wave theory are useful aids in understanding the dynamics of the Loop Current and the eddy shedding including the penetration of the Loop Current into the Gulf and the eddy diameter, shedding period, and westward propagation.

5.1 CAV trajectory analysis

CAV trajectories are based on conservation of potential vorticity on a β-plane and on steady, frictionless, geostrophically balanced flow. In the reduced gravity model this implies that contours of upper layer depth are streamlines, and thus absolute vorticity is also conserved. The CAV

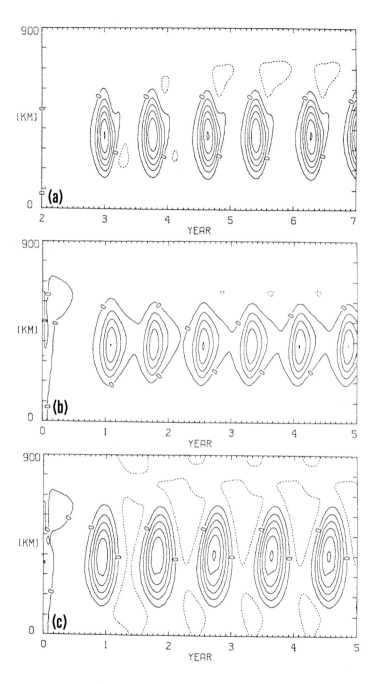

Fig. 5. Time variations of PA 190 km west of the center of the inflow port for three cases: (a) case shown in Fig. 4 which includes topography, (b) standard two-layer flat-bottom case using parameters from Table 1, and (c) standard reduced gravity case using appropriate parameters from Table 1. A regular progression of eddies through the north-south cross section is shown in each case. The contour interval is 30 m. (From HT).

trajectories are calculated from

$$\sin\Theta \frac{d\Theta}{dy} = -\frac{\beta}{v_c} y + \frac{v_{co}}{v_c r_o} \tag{4}$$

where Θ is the angle of the current with respect to the positive x-axis, v_c is the velocity at the core of the current, r_o is the radius of curvature, and the subscript, 0, indicates a value at the origin of the trajectory calculation (e.g., see HT; Reid, 1972; Haltiner and Martin, 1957).

Fig. 6 shows CAV trajectories superimposed on the model domain for $v_c = 75$ cm/s, $r_o = \infty$ and six different values of Θ_o. Since $r_o = \infty$, the origin is the first inflection point after inflow (see Fig. 4), and not the inflow port as implied by the figure. As Θ_o increases, the trajectory increasingly tends to loop back on itself. When $\Theta_o = 130^o$, the CAV trajectory intersects itself at the origin, a physically impossible situation for a steady flow. Thus, when Θ_o becomes large some physical instability of the Loop Current can be anticipated.

In Fig. 6 Θ_o is varied to simulate the formation of an eddy, but it really represents a sequence of steady state solutions to (4). Although the eddy-shedding Loop Current is not steady, its evolution is sufficiently slow to consider it in isostatic adjustment with respect to CAV trajectories. In the time a fluid particle in the Loop moves from the west side to the east side, the Loop bends westward only 5 to 10% of the Loop diameter.

5.2 Influence of Rossby waves

How does the model Loop Current bend westward when the angle of inflow through the Yucatan Straits is not varied? We can gain some insight into this by examining the continuity equation, (2). If the mass divergence is geostrophic, it will propagate westward as a nondispersive internal Rossby wave. (Note the converse is not true near the equator). For geostrophic divergence (2) becomes

$$\frac{\partial h_1}{\partial t} - \beta V_g/f = \frac{\partial h_1}{\partial t} - c_{ir} \frac{\partial h_1}{\partial x} = 0 \tag{5}$$

where V_g is the geostrophic meridional transport and

$$c_{ir} = \beta g' h_1/f^2 = \beta \lambda^2 \tag{6}$$

is the nondispersive internal Rossby wave speed.

The importance of nondispersive Rossby wave propagation can be anticipated from appropriate isolated vortex theory (McWilliams and Flierl, 1979), because 1) $r/\lambda \approx 4$ where r is the eddy radius and λ is the internal radius of deformation, and 2) the beta Rossby number, $R_B = v_c/(\beta r^2) \approx 1$ for the eddies. From the linear

255

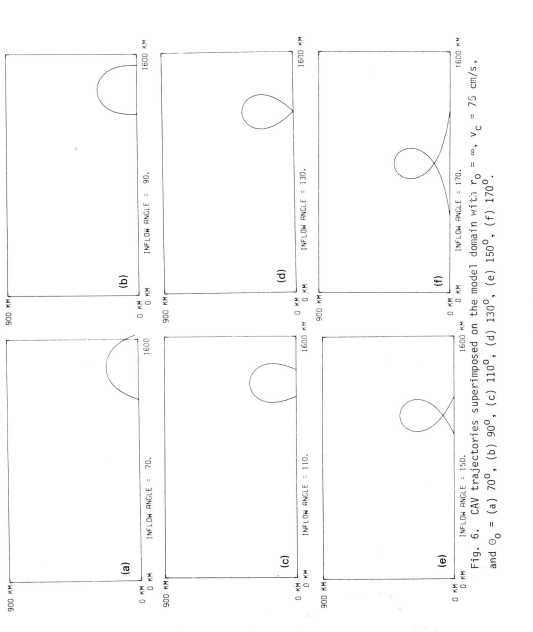

Fig. 6. CAV trajectories superimposed on the model domain with $r_0 = \infty$, $v_c = 75$ cm/s, and Θ_0 = (a) 70°, (b) 90°, (c) 110°, (d) 130°, (e) 150°, (f) 170°.

phase speed for Rossby waves

$$c_r = \beta/(k^2 + \ell^2 + \lambda^{-2}) \tag{7}$$

where k and ℓ are zonal and meridional wavenumbers, respectively, the dispersive and nondispersive contributions are equal for circular eddies when $r/\lambda = \pi/\sqrt{2} =$ 2.22. Hence, we also expect a significant but secondary contribution from dispersive Rossby wave propagation.

Fig. 7 compares the instantaneous mass divergence $(\nabla \cdot W_1)$ and the geostrophic mass divergence $(-c_{ir} \frac{\partial h_1}{\partial x})$ for the standard reduced gravity experiment at two different stages in the eddy shedding cycle. The usefulness of the instantaneous mass divergence fields must be questioned, since they are easily dominated by rapid oscillations and computational noise. The absence of these contaminations was verified by showing that the instantaneous mass divergence and the 20-day mean are virtually identical. From (2) the 20-day mean can be determined from the change in h_1 in 20 days.

Near the ports and near the western boundary the mass divergence is far from geostrophic. Note particularly in Fig. 7e the ageostrophic mass convergence in the southeastern part of the basin associated with the northward penetration of the Loop Current. Also note that mass convergence occurs at the center of the eddy during its formation (an anticyclonic inflow), while mass divergence occurs at the center (anticyclonic outflow) after the eddy separates from the Loop and slowly decays. However, in the westward bending Loop and in the recently shed eddy the total mass divergence and the geostrophic mass divergence are quite similar. This clearly demonstrates an important contribution of non-dispersive internal Rossby wave propagation to the westward bending of the Loop Current and the westward propagation of the eddies. Other contributions such as nonlinear and dispersive Rossby wave propagation are not accounted for here. Still, we have identified an important mechanism which acts to bend the Loop Current westward. Thus, it also produces a counterclockwise rotation of the current at the first inflection point after inflow (see Fig. 4). This in turn produces changes in the CAV trajectory (Fig. 6) which leads us to anticipate the formation and shedding of an eddy.

5.3 Two time scales associated with the eddy shedding

Note that westward bending of the current and the tendency for it to loop back on itself can be understood without invoking an instability mechanism. An instability mechanism appears essential only to explain the separation of the eddy from the Loop. Thus, two time scales are associated with the eddy shedding period: 1) the long time scale for the Loop Current to penetrate into the Gulf and bend westward into an unstable configuration, and 2) the much shorter time scale for the growth of the instability as the eddy separates from

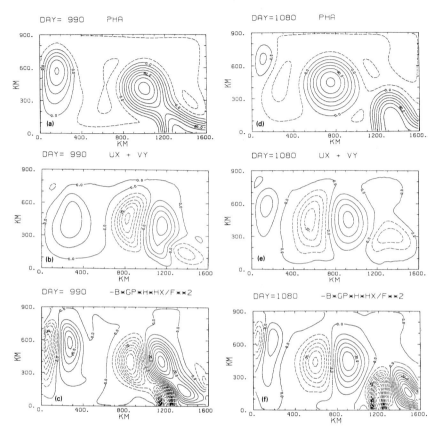

Fig. 7. Shows (a,d) the PA for the standard reduced gravity experiment, which uses the pertinent parameters from Table 1, and compares the associated (b,e) instantaneous mass divergence ($\nabla \cdot \mathbb{W}_1$) and (c,f) geostrophic mass divergence ($-c_{ir}\partial h/\partial x$). Two different stages of an eddy cycle are illustrated at days 990 (left) and 1080 (right). The contour intervals are 20 m for PA and 10^{-4} cm/s for mass divergence.

the Loop Current. This suggests a repeated spin-up of the Loop Current which eventually becomes unstable. Although it may, it is not clear that the Loop Current must satisfy any criterion for instability during much of the eddy cycle.

5.4 Hypothesis testing

The CAV trajectory analysis, Rossby wave theory, and the vorticity equation can be used to formulate a number of quantitative hypotheses concerning the northward penetration of the Loop Current into the Gulf, the latitude at which the westward bending occurs, and the eddy diameter, shedding period, and westward propagation. We will formulate the appropriate scales and then test them as hypotheses for the dynamics governing the Loop Current-eddy system predicted by the reduced gravity numerical model. The vorticity equation for the reduced gravity model is

$$\frac{\partial \zeta_1}{\partial t} + \mathbf{v}_1 \cdot \nabla \zeta_1 + (f+\zeta_1)\left(\frac{\partial u_1}{\partial x} + \frac{\partial v_1}{\partial y}\right) + \beta v_1 = A\nabla^2 \zeta_1 \tag{8}$$

where $\zeta = v_x - u_y$ is the relative vorticity.

5.5 Eddy diameter, Loop Current penetration, and latitude of westward bending.

The beta Rossby number, R_B, is the ratio of relative to planetary vorticity advection, and $R_B=1$ provides a minimum inertial length scale, $L_{\beta I}=(v_c/\beta)^{1/2}$, over which β is important. We hypothesize that this determines the latitude at which the Loop Current bends westward. The frictional length scale over which β is important, $L_{\beta F}=(A/\beta)^{1/3}$, is much smaller. $L_{\beta I}=191$ km and $L_{\beta F}=37$ km for our standard reduced gravity experiment. This implies that inertia will prevent Rossby wave action from bending the Loop Current westward at a higher latitude than friction.

We also find that $R_B=1$ and $r=(v_c/\beta)^{1/2}$ are appropriate values for the radius of the eddies formed by the Loop Current. However, without further analysis it is not clear why the eddies from the Loop Current select this scale. McWilliams and Flierl (1979) have studied persistent isolated eddies with $R_B \gg 1$ and note that typically $R_B > 1$ for Gulf Stream rings.

For insight into the scale selection by the Loop Current eddies, we turn to the CAV trajectory analysis and present a discussion similar to HT. Integration of (4) assuming v_c = constant along a streamline at the core of the current yields

$$\cos\theta = \cos\theta_0 + \frac{\beta}{2v_c} y^2 - y/r_0 \tag{9}$$

This neglects the point that $v_c \neq$ constant along a streamline, if there are variations in radius of curvature. The north-south diameter of an eddy between speed maxima can be estimated by setting $\Theta_0=\pi$ at the southernmost extent (the origin) and $\Theta=0$ at the northernmost extent. Then for $r_0=\infty$, (9) becomes

$$d = 2r = 2(v_c/\beta)^{1/2} \qquad (10)$$

where d is the desired diameter, a north-south "dimension" for "stationary planetary eddies" noted by Rossby (1940, p. 82). This implies that $R_B=v_c/(\beta r^2)=1$ for the Loop Current eddies.

The northernmost penetration of the core of the current, b, from the latitude of Θ_0 can be estimated from (9) by setting $\Theta=0$ at the northernmost extent. This yields

$$b = \left[\frac{r^2}{r_0} + \frac{r^4}{r_0^2} + 2r^2(1-\cos\Theta_0) \right]^{1/2} \qquad (11)$$

For $r_0=\infty$, (11) reduces to

$$b = d \sin\tfrac{1}{2}\Theta_0 \qquad (12)$$

Thus, with $r_0=\infty$ the maximum amplitude for a CAV trajectory occurs when Θ_0 This is what (10) really represents, since in this case the CAV trajectory loops back on itself northwest of the origin (see Fig. 6). For $\Theta_0=130^0$ the CAV trajectory loops back on itself at the origin in a figure 8 (Fig. 6d) and $\sin\tfrac{1}{2}\Theta_0 \approx .9$. We might anticipate that the horizontal shear instability would occur when the first inflection point of the current after inflow rotates counterclockwise to ~ 130^0. In the numerical solutions where the flow is not steady, potential vorticity is not perfectly conserved, and other conditions of the CAV analysis are not perfectly met, we find that eddy separation occurs when this angle is somewhat > 130^0 (see Fig. 4). In this case a CAV trajectory would loop back on itself northwest of the first inflection point after inflow. However, a col is configured such that eddy separation actually occurs southeast of this inflection point. From the standpoint of estimating the amplitude of the CAV trajectory (with $r_0=\infty$) and thus the eddy diameter, the value of Θ_0 when the eddy separates from the Loop Current is not critical, since $\sin\tfrac{1}{2}\Theta_0$ varies only 10% from $\Theta_0=130^0$ to $\Theta_0=\pi$.

5.6 Tests of some dynamical hypotheses

Tests of some hypotheses concerning the dynamical behavior of the Loop Current are summarized in Table 2. Immediately apparent is the pervasive role of differential rotation β. The results are based on 35 reduced gravity experiments (34 for $L_{\beta I}$ and L_{np}) from Table 2 of HT, the same ones they used in similar hypothesis testing.

TABLE 2

Tests of some dynamical hypotheses for the Loop Current–eddy system.

	% bias	correlation	Standard reduced gravity case numerical	theoretical
1. Eddy radius				
$r=(v_c/\beta)^{1/2}$	6	.87	186 km	191 km
2. Distance from the southern boundary to the latitude of westward bending by the Loop Current.				
$L_{\beta I} = (v_c/\beta)^{1/2} = r$	-7	.75	201 km	186 km
	-1	.77	201 km	191 km
3. Maximum northward penetration of the Loop Current.				
$L_{np} = L_{\beta I} + b = 3r$	-2	.99	574 km	560 km
	4	.89	574 km	573 km
4. Westward propagation speed of the eddies.				
$c_{ir} = \beta\lambda^2 = \beta g'h_1/f^2$	40	.99	3.21 cm/s	4.57 cm/s
$c = \beta/(k^2+\ell^2+\lambda^{-2})$	-2	.97	3.21 cm/s	3.49 cm/s
5. Eddy shedding period.				
$p_e = A_0 + A_1r(1+\cos\Theta_I)^{1/2}/c_e$	-	.95	327 days	359 days
	-	.96	327 days	338 days

The % bias and the linear correlation are statistics for the theoretical prediction vs. the values observed in the reduced gravity numerical model. They are based on 34 to 35 numerical experiments from Table 2 of HT, the same ones they used in their hypothesis testing for similar quantities. The % bias $\equiv$ $((m_o-m_p)/m_o)$ where m_o and m_p are the means of the observed and predicted values, respectively. The two rightmost columns present the results observed and predicted for the standard reduced gravity experiment which uses the pertinent parameters from Table 1. Results from two tests are presented for $L_{\beta I}$, L_{np} and p_e. On the upper line values of r and c_e observed in the numerical model were used in the predictor. On the lower line the theoretical values were used for r and c_e (i.e. c_r for c_e).

In estimating r, $L_{\beta I}$, and L_{np} the maximum speed at inflow was used for v_c. One-half the north-south diameter between speed maxima was used for the eddy radius from the reduced gravity numerical model. The distance from the southern boundary to the southern end of the eddy diameter was used for $L_{\beta I}$ and from the southern boundary to the northern end of the diameter for L_{np}. These were measured as the eddy center passed a longitude 110 km west of the western boundary of the inflow port. This was also close to the inflection point which exhibited a large angle at this time (see Figs. 4 & 7). Thus, the theoretical estimate of b was simplified by setting $\Theta_0=\pi$ and $r_0=\infty$. This yields b=2r.

The agreement between the theoretical estimates of r, $L_{\beta I}$, and L_p and the values calculated from the numerical model is remarkably good. In most cases the agreement for r was within 5%. However, at low Reynolds numbers and low latitudes, (10) overestimated the model value by > 10%. In the experiments with low Reynolds numbers downstream attenuation of the current appears to explain this. At low latitudes the assumption of isostatic adjustment with respect to CAV trajectories is not as good due to an increased westward propagation speed. Also r/λ is less, so the Loop and the eddies are more subject to dispersion. In estimating $L_{\beta I}$ and L_{np}, values of r from the numerical model were used for the upper line and theoretical values for the lower line.

In estimating λ, h_e from Table 2 of HT was used for h_1 and the value of f at the latitude of the eddy center was used. The correlation between c_{ir} and the westward propagation speed of shed eddies is extremely high, but the theoretical speed is 40% greater than observed in the reduced gravity numerical model. When the dispersive contribution is included, the mean Rossby wave speed and the mean observed westward propagation speed differ by < 2%. The value of $k^2+\ell^2$ was estimated by assuming circular eddies and using the theoretical values for r.

In Table 2 a regression equation is used to test the hypothesis that the eddy shedding period is a multiple of the time required for an eddy to move one eddy radius westward. The multiple depends on the angle of inflow for the current, Θ_I. The upper line presents the results when values measured from the numerical model are used for r and c_e (the westward propagation speed). On the lower line theoretical values (c_r and c_e and (10) for r) are used. The regression coefficients are $A_0=45.1$ days and $A_1=4.67$ for the upper line and $A_0=-.2$ days and $A_1=5.34$ for the lower line. The regression coefficient, $\frac{1}{2}A_1$, is a kind of inverse Strouhal number (nondimensional period) if we take the eddy diameter, d, as the appropriate diameter, and the westward propagation speed of the eddies (rather than the injection velocity) as the appropriate velocity. The Strouhal numbers ($S=2/A_1$) implied by the two regression results are .43 for the upper line and .37 for the lower line. If d was the half-wavelength for a continuous wavetrain, then the Strouhal number would be $S=.5$.

The eddy shedding period also exhibits a weak dependence on the eddy viscosity A, primarily because this affects the amount of entrainment or detrainment downstream. The result is an eddy-shedding period which increases with increasing Reynolds number, $Re=v_{ci}L/A$ where v_{ci} is the maximum velocity at inflow and L is half the inflow (southern) port width. At high Reynolds numbers, secondary circulations of the Loop-eddy system become significant and introduce some irregularity into the eddy shedding period.

6. REGIMES FOR THE LOOP CURRENT IN THE REDUCED GRAVITY MODEL

6.1 The eddy-shedding regime (E)

The preceding section examined some of the dynamics of the eddy shedding by the Loop Current and demonstrated the usefulness of CAV trajectory analysis and Rossby waves in explaining the behavior. It also demonstrated the important role of differential rotation (β) in most aspects of the eddy-shedding dynamics. We will call the eddy-shedding regime the E regime.

6.2 The steady westward spreading regime (W)

This section investigates the existence of other flow regimes in the neighboring parameter space. One such regime was found by reducing the Reynolds number, $R_e = v_c L/A$, where L is the half-width of the port. This acts both to damp physical instabilities in the current and to decrease potential vorticity conservation, thus reducing the tendency of the current to loop back on itself. The result is a steady solution with a westward bending Loop Current as shown in Fig. 8a. We will call this the W regime. Fig. 8a was obtained by increasing the eddy viscosity (A) from 10^7 to $3 \times 10^7 \, cm^2/s$ in the standard reduced gravity model. Steady linear viscous solutions (where $\beta v_1 = A \nabla^2 \zeta_1$) and weakly nonlinear solutions belong to the W regime. As mentioned in Section 5, the latitude of westward bending after inflow is determined by the larger of $L_{\beta I}$ and $L_{\beta F}$. As noted by HT, the mean of the standard reduced gravity experiment over an eddy cycle is very similar to Fig. 8a. This implies that in the mean the eddies drive a northward-flowing western boundary current.

Between the E and W regimes there is a transition regime (T) with eddies superimposed on a westward bending Loop Current. This is illustrated in Fig. 8b using the standard reduced gravity model except that $A = 2.5 \times 10^7 \, cm^2/s$. Experiments that exhibited both eddy shedding and an unbroken, westward bending zero contour (like Fig. 8b) were assigned to the T regime.

6.3 Steady source-sink regime (N)

A third major regime we call the N regime is found by increasing the beta Rossby number, $R_B = v_c/(\beta L_p^2)$, where L_p is half the distance separating the centers of the inflow and outflow ports. The N regime occurs when $R_B \gtrsim 2$. At sufficiently low Reynolds numbers the transition between the N and W regimes is determined by the beta Ekman number, $E_B = A/(\beta L_p^3)$, as discussed in the next subsection. In either case the N regime is characterized by a steady source-sink flow with no westward bending by the Loop Current. It is illustrated in Fig. 9 by two variations on the standard reduced gravity experiment. In Fig. 9a $\beta = 0$ and $R_B = \infty$. Note that $\beta > 0$ is essential for the westward bending of the Loop Current and the eddy shedding shown in Figs. 4 and 7. With Re sufficiently high, we would expect some instability to occur in the source-sink current, but not the quasi-annual eddy shedding exhibited by the Loop Current.

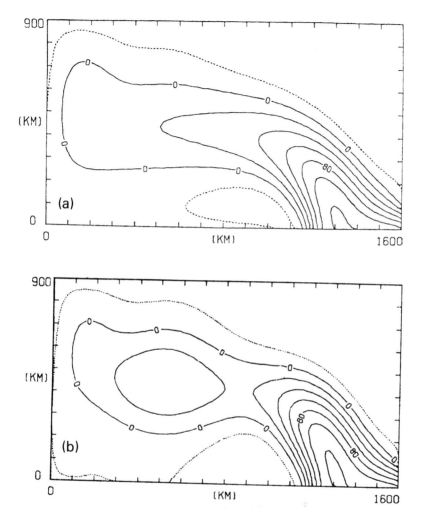

Fig. 8. Illustration of (a) steady regime W and (b) time-dependent regime T. The standard parameters for the reduced gravity model were used except that in (a) $A = 3 \times 10^7$ cm^2/sec and in (b) $A = 2.5 \times 10^7$ cm^2/s. The contour interval is 20 m. In regime W the Loop Current bends westward and is steady. In regime T eddy shedding is superimposed on a westward bending loop instead of being discrete as in Fig. 7a, d.

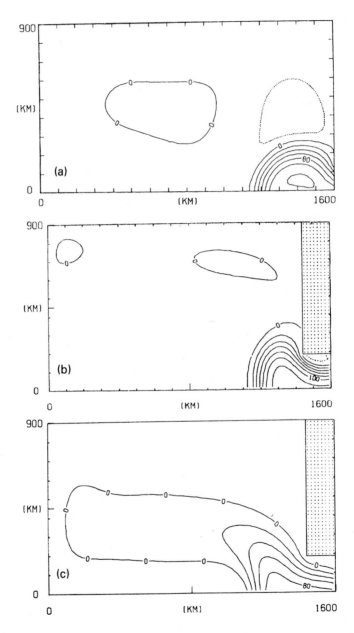

Fig. 9. Illustration of the steady regime N for the standard reduced gravity experiment except that β = 0 and (b) a section of land was added to approximate the west Florida shelf. Steady mixed regime M is shown in (c) with parameters chosen to approximate those of Mellor and Blumberg (1981), including Re = 10.8 and R_B = 1.19.

In a second experiment the port separation was reduced by inserting a land mass which approximates the location of the West Florida Shelf (Fig. 9b). In this case L_p was measured using a port centered 75 km south of the western boundary of the inserted land mass. From Section 5 $r=L_{\beta I}=(v_c/\beta)^{\frac{1}{2}}$, thus the beta Rossby number can also be expressed as $R_B=(r/L_p)^2$ or $R_B=(L_{\beta I}/L_p)^2$. Since the N regime occurs for $R_B \gtrsim 2$, this implies a critical port separation $2L_{pc} \simeq \sqrt{2}r = \sqrt{2}L_{\beta I}$. From the definition of R_B, both β and L_p play a similar role in determining the N regime. Otherwise, their roles are not similar. As long as R_B is small enough for eddy shedding to occur, the E regime is quite insensitive to L_p, but most aspects of the dynamics are very sensitive to β.

The N regime occurs when the Loop Current reaches a steady state before penetrating far enough into the Gulf to bend westward. From (12) and Fig. 6d a CAV trajectory with $r_0=\infty$ can penetrate into the Gulf with no westward bending a distance $b = \sqrt{2}r = \sqrt{2}L_{\beta I}$ (the same as the critical port separation). Using this as an estimate of the maximum possible Loop Current penetration in the N regime is consistent with our present numerical results (see HT for further discussion).

The transition between regimes N and E is quite abrupt and a transition regime has not been found in any of our numerical experiments. The transition between regimes N and W is broader. In this mixed regime (M) the westward spreading of the Loop Current is significantly less than it would be if the port separation were infinite. The numerical simulation of the Loop Current by Blumberg and Mellor (1981) belongs to this M regime. Fig. 9c shows a reduced gravity analog of that experiment using our estimates of appropriate parameters, including Re=10.8 and R_B=1.19 (See Appendix B for other parameters used). Considering our neglect of the 20° counterclockwise rotation of the basin, our pattern for the Loop Current is remarkably similar to that from the much more complicated and expensive model of Blumberg and Mellor (1981). Experiments were assigned to the M regime if the central contour on inflow exhibited any westward bending, but the amplitude of the Loop PA was < 30% of the maximum a distance $(v_{ci}/\beta)^{\frac{1}{2}}$ west of the center of the inflow, where v_{ci} is the maximum velocity at inflow.

6.4 Stability regime diagram

Three nondimensional parameters from the vorticity equation (Eq. (8)) play an important role in determining the stability regimes for the Loop Current in the reduced gravity and flat-bottom barotropic models. They are the Reynolds number (Re), the beta Rossby number (R_B), and the beta Ekman number (E_B). Only two of these are independent. Provided the same scales are used, $E_B=R_B/Re$. Fig. 10 shows the parameter space occupied by the various regimes on a stability diagram of Re vs. R_B. Eddy shedding occurs for $R_B \lesssim 2$ and Re$\gtrsim 25$ for the reduced

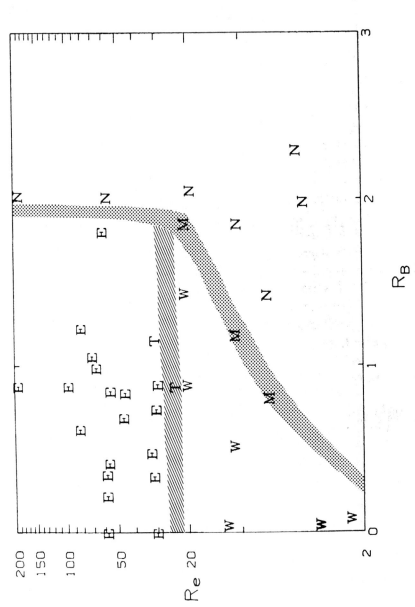

Fig. 10. Regime diagram for three stability regimes and transition regimes between them for a reduced gravity model of the Gulf of Mexico. The axes are the Reynolds number (Re) and the beta Rossby number (R_B). The regimes are (E) eddy shedding (Figs. 5c and 7a, d), (W) steady westward spreading (Fig. 8a), (N) steady source-sink (Fig. 9a, b), (T) transition between (Figs. 9a, b), (N) steady source-sink (Fig. 9a, b), (N) transition between steady regimes N and W (Fig. 9c). E and W with eddy shedding superimposed on a mean loop (Fig. 8b) and (M) transition between steady regimes N and W (Fig. 9c).

gravity model, Re$\geq$40 for the flat-bottom barotropic model (not shown). Apparently, the dispersive nature of Rossby waves in the barotropic model is a catalyst which leads to a higher critical Reynolds number (Re$_c$). The transfer of energy to the lower layer in the two-layer models seems to have a similar effect on Re$_c$.

At low Reynolds number the transition between regimes N and W depends upon $E_B=R_BL/(ReL_p)$. The correction factor L/L_p is required because we have not used L_p in our definition of Re. This transition is clearly defined on our stability diagram only if L/L_p is fixed. From Section 5.5 R_B and E_B can be expressed in terms of the latitude of westward bending by the Loop Current, i.e. $R_B=(L_{\beta I}/L_p)^2$ and $E_B=(L_{\beta F}/L_p)^3$. Whether R_B or E_B determines the transition to the N regime depends upon the relative importance of $L_{\beta F}$, the frictional length scale, and $L_{\beta I}$, the inertial length scale, in determining the latitude of westward bending by the Loop Current. From the regime diagram, the transition between these two criteria occurs when $2.5\ L_{\beta F}\simeq L_{\beta I}/\sqrt{2}$.

Other parameters not accounted for here such as inflow angle, basin geometry, and basin orientation may also have some influence on the regime selection. Additional influences in the two-active-layer model are discussed in the next two sections.

7. PREVENTION OF EDDY SHEDDING BY TOPOGRAPHY AND DEEP-WATER INFLOW THROUGH THE YUCATAN STRAITS

In this section the two-layer model is used to demonstrate a dramatic effect of topography on the eddy-shedding by the Loop Current when there is sufficient deep-water inflow through the Yucatan Straits. Fig. 11a shows the domain-averaged upper layer (upper curve) and lower layer kinetic energy vs. time for a two-layer experiment the same as shown in Fig. 4, except that during the first six years of model integration the lower layer inflow was zero. This includes the topography of Fig. 3. At the beginning of year 7 the lower layer inflow was increased to 10 Sv with a time constant of 30 days. While the lower layer inflow was zero, eddy shedding occurred in a manner similar to that shown in Fig. 4. The signature of the eddy shedding cycle is depicted in the upper layer energy curve of Fig. 11a. When the lower layer inflow was increased, the eddy shedding ceased and the solution evolved to a steady state as shown in Fig. 11a. This steady solution is shown in Fig. 11b, c in terms of the PA (Fig. 11b) and the lower layer pressure, p_2 (Fig. 11c). The PA depicts a source-sink flow like regime N, while the flow in the lower layer follows the f/h contours of the topography. HT uses a kinematic analysis to illuminate the dynamics of this phenomenon. From the continuity equation (2), the divergence term $h_1\nabla \cdot w_1$ is balanced by the advective term $w_1\cdot\nabla h_1$ in a steady state. Since the flow is nearly geostrophic, $w_1\cdot\nabla h_1 \simeq w_{1g}\cdot\nabla h_1 = w_{2g}\cdot\nabla h_1$, where w_{ig} is the geostrophic

268

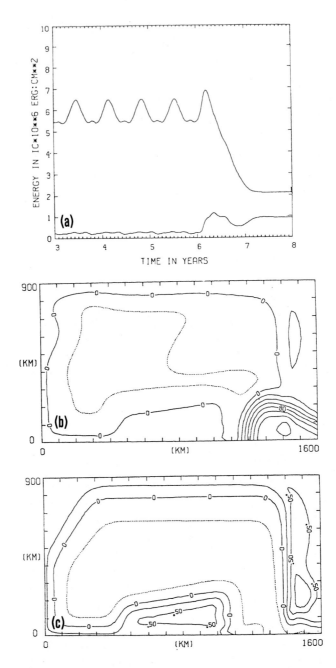

Fig. 11. Results for the bottom topography experiment shown in Fig. 4 except that T_1 = 25 Sv and T_2 = 0 until year 6 when T_2 increases to 10 Sv. (a) domain-averaged upper layer (top curve) and lower layer kinetic energy, (IC = 1.5). (b) Nearly steady PA at day 2880. The contour interval is 20 m. (c) Lower layer pressure normalized by density (p_2) at day 2880. The contour interval is .25 m^2/s^2

velocity component in layer i. The magnitude of $w_{2g} \cdot \nabla h_1$ is greatest when relatively strong lower layer currents flow at large angles to contours of h_1. Comparison of Fig. 11b and 11c shows that this occurs where the Loop Current intersects a current following the f/h contours of the West Florida Shelf. If the lower layer current is strong enough for the advection to balance the divergence in (2) associated with the approaching Loop, then the interface deepening and Loop Current penetration in this region are halted.

Thus, the West Florida Shelf along the eastern boundary of the domain (see Fig. 3) and lower layer flow act in conjunction to effectively reduce the port separation by locally limiting the northward penetration of the Loop Current. If this results in $R_B \gtrsim 2$, when we measure $2L_p$ as the distance between the center of the inflow port and the point where the upper and lower layer currents intersect, then the upper layer current exhibits the source-sink flow characteristic of the N regime described in Section 6. This is illustrated by comparing Fig. 11b with Fig. 9b, the reduced gravity experiment with a land mass in the location of the West Florida Shelf.

In the experiment shown in Fig. 11 the Loop Current had already penetrated far into the Gulf and shed eddies when the lower layer inflow was increased. When this increase occurred, a current following the f/h contours developed in the lower layer and the advection term ($w_1 \cdot \nabla h_1$) began to exceed the divergence term in the continuity equation where the Loop Current crossed the shelf slope, causing h_1 to decrease there. Thus, the Loop Current retreated southward until an equilibrium occurred near the southern end of the shelf.

In terms of vorticity dynamics, the northward penetration of the Loop Current is halted when the interaction between the topography of the West Florida Shelf and the pressure field results in a near balance between the pressure torques and the nonlinear terms in the mass transport vorticity equation. HT discuss and document this topic in more detail.

The results in this section suggest that certain time variations in the deep flow through the Yucatan Straits may have a greater effect on the Loop Current than fluctuations in the upper ocean current through the Strait. The effects of the latter are discussed by HT but not in this paper.

8. BAROTROPIC VS. BAROCLINIC INSTABILITY AND THE IMPORTANT ROLE OF TOPOGRAPHY

Section 6 examined stability regimes for the reduced gravity model. In Section 7 we studied a steady regime for the two-layer model which results from a particular combination of topography and deep flow following f/h contours. In this section we will investigate additional regimes of the two active layer model, confining ourselves to unsteady regimes with eddies. In particular we will search for cases of barotropic, baroclinic, and mixed instability.

The reduced gravity and barotropic models can exhibit barotropic, but not baroclinic instability. The reduced gravity model has demonstrated an eddy shedding regime with a horizontal shear instability of the first internal mode (a "barotropic" instability) which produces a remarkable simulation of observed features of the Loop Current - eddy shedding system. We know from Section 4 that in some cases the two active layer model exhibits similar results with similar parameters. In this section we will investigate the potential importance of baroclinic instability and the role of topography in determining its importance.

8.1 Eddy-mean energetics

We begin this investigation by surveying the eddy-mean energetics for the seven numerical experiments listed in Table 3. We then illustrate some characteristic features of the different regimes using synoptic maps of upper and lower layer pressure (p_1 and p_2) and curves of domain-averaged energy vs. time. Fig. 12 shows the eddy-mean energetics in terms of energy box diagrams. Fig. 12a labels the energy transfers. See Appendix A for symbol definitions and Appendix C for the energy transfer integrals. All of the model domain was used in calculating the energetics except the parts within 100 km of the eastern boundary and 37.5 km of the southern boundary. Thus, the eastern and southern boundaries of the energetics calculations are open. Kinetic energy and pressure work fluxes through these open boundaries are represented by arrows at the top (bottom) of the K_1 (K_2) boxes. In all cases most of the energy flows into $\overline{K}_1$. In some cases there is significant efflux from K_1', but always must less than the $\overline{K}_1 \to K_1'$ transfer. The arrows pointing outward from the sides represent dissipation of a particular type of energy due to Laplacian horizontal friction. Arrows between the boxes represent conversions of energy from one type to another as indicated by the direction of the arrow.

Fig. 12b shows the eddy-mean energetics for Experiment 1 on Table 3, a two-layer flat-bottom experiment using the standard parameters given in Table 1. The $\overline{K}_1 \to K_1'$ energy conversion is characteristic of a barotropic instability. The potential energy transfer is actually reversed with eddy potential energy (P') feeding the mean.

Angling the inflow 27^0 west of normal in the standard two-layer flat-bottom model (Experiment 2) produced a dramatic change in the eddy-mean energetics which

TABLE 3

Model experiments discussed in Section 8

Exp #	Differences from standard two-layer flat-bottom experiment in Table 1	Figures in HT from these experiments (HT Fig. #)
1	None	Figs. 5b, 11b, 14a
2	$\theta_I = 27^0$, $Sv_2 = 0$	Figs. 12, 13a, 14d
3	Reduced gravity, Yucatan and Florida Straits added to model domain	Figs. 20a, 21a, HT Table 2 case RG32
4	$A = 3 \times 10^6$ cm^2/s, $Sv_2 = 0$	Experiment in HT Figs. 10, 11a, 14c exhibits similar behavior
5	$A = 3 \times 10^5$ cm^2/s, $Sv_2 = 0$ Fig. 3 topography	
6	$Sv_1 = 25$, $Sv_2 = 0$	Figs. 24b, 25b
7	$Sv_1 = 25$, $Sv_2 = 0$, Fig. 3 topography	Figs. 24c, 25c

Sv_i is the inflow in layer i in 10^6 m^3/s or Sv.

is shown in Fig. 12c. (The lower layer inflow was also reduced to zero, but other experiments show this has a relatively minor role in altering the energetics in this case). Fig. 12c illustrates a classic signature of baroclinic instability in the eddy-mean energetics with $\bar{P} \rightarrow P'$ dominating the mean to eddy energy transfer and feeding the upper and lower layers almost equally. There is even a reverse cascade in the kinetic energy ($K_1' \rightarrow \bar{K}_1$) with eddies feeding the mean flow.

The eddy-mean energetics for the reduced gravity model (Experiment 3 and Fig. 12d) illustrates a pure barotropic instability, since this model excludes baroclinic instability. In this case the dominant mean to eddy energy transfer is $\bar{K} \rightarrow K'$. Even though this is a pure barotropic instability, there is a net transfer from $\bar{P} \rightarrow P'$. Thus, the existence of such a transfer does not necessarily imply any contribution from baroclinic instability.

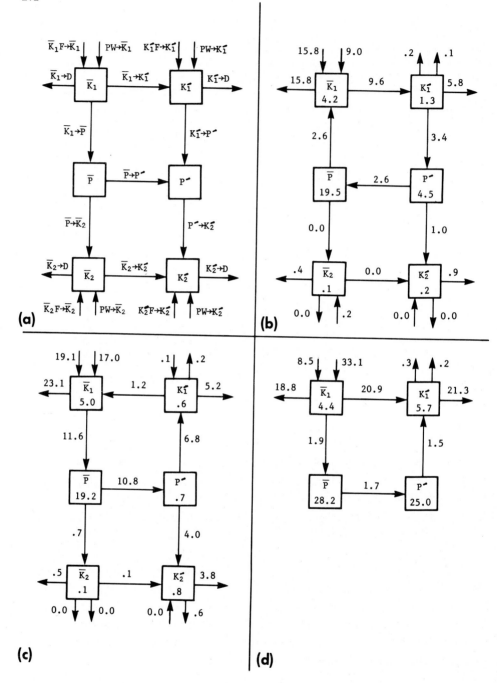

Fig. 12. Eddy-mean energetics for the experiments listed in Table 3: (a) labels for the energy pathways and energy reservoirs, (b) energetics for Experiment 1, standard flat-bottom case, (c) Experiment 2, flat bottom with non-normal inflow, (d) Experiment 3, reduced gravity, (e) Experiment 4, flat bottom with low

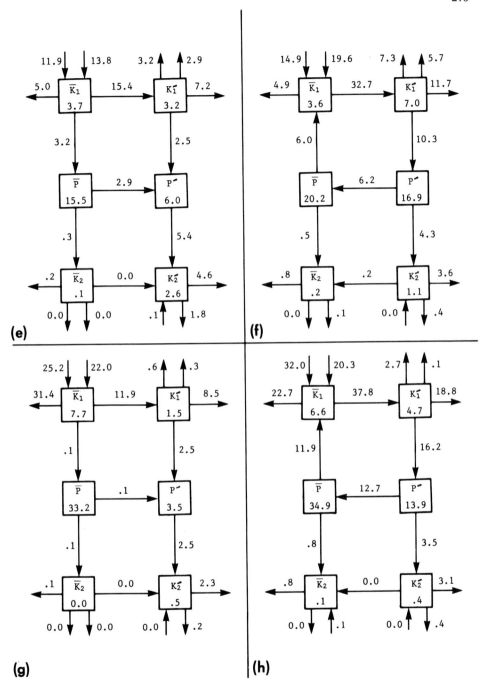

(e)

(f)

(g)

(h)

viscosity, (f) Experiment 5, same as the preceding but with topography, (g) Experiment 6, flat bottom, (h) Experiment 7, same as preceding but with topography. The energy reservoirs are in units of 10^{15} joules and the energy transfers are in units of 10^8 joules/s.

Fig. 12e is particularly interesting because it illustrates a mixed instability and because it demonstrates the value of separating the kinetic energy
into upper and lower layer components. These results were obtained primarily
by reducing the eddy viscosity in the two-layer flat-bottom model by a factor of
three (Experiment 4). If K_1 and K_2 were combined to produce a 4-box diagram,
the results would look much like those for the reduced gravity model and we
might conclude that this is a case of barotropic instability. In contrast, the
6-box diagram (Fig. 12e) illustrates a striking result. Although a barotropic
energy conversion $(\overline{K}_1 \rightarrow K_1')$ is dominant in the upper layer, the lower layer eddies
are fed almost equally by transfers from $\overline{P} \rightarrow P'$ and $K_1' \rightarrow P'$. In view of the reduced
gravity results, this is insufficient evidence for an important contribution from
baroclinic instability to the lower layer eddies. Additional evidence for this
will be provided shortly.

Figs. 12e and 12f compare the results for Experiments 4 and 5. The experiments are identical except that Experiment 4 (Fig. 12e) has a flat bottom and
Experiment 5 (Fig. 12f) includes the idealized Gulf of Mexico topography shown
in Fig. 3. The topography strongly suppresses any baroclinic instability. With
the topography added, the energy box diagram (Fig. 12f) indicates a strong baro-
topic instability $(\overline{K}_1 \rightarrow K_1')$ and a strong reverse potential energy flux $(P' \rightarrow \overline{P})$.

Figs. 12g and 12h again compare experiments with and without the topography
of Fig. 3 (Experiments 6 and 7). They differ from the preceding by a three-fold
increase in the eddy viscosity and a 25% increase in the upper layer inflow.
The experiment with the topography (Fig. 12h) exhibits essentially the same
energy pathways as the previous frame with the same topography (Fig. 12f). The
reverse potential energy transfer $(P' \rightarrow \overline{P})$ is even stronger. Almost 1/3 of the
eddy energy makes a complete circuit. Although this reverse transfer is clearly
augmented by the topography, it is not restricted to experiments with topography
(see Fig. 12b). Without the benefit of the energetics analysis, HT correctly
identified the baroclinically unstable case (Fig. 12c) and a mixed instability
case similar to Fig. 12e. However, they also conjectured that Experiment 6
(Fig. 12g) is a case of mixed instability. This is not corroborated by the
domain integrated eddy-mean energetics. Eddies in both layers are fed by energy

conversions appropriate for a barotropic instability, the lower layer fed indirectly via energy transfer from the upper layer. In this case, increasing the eddy viscosity has suppressed the contribution from baroclinic instability. Experiment 6 (Fig. 12g) differs from Experiment 1 (Fig. 12b) by having 25% greater inflow in the upper layer and none in the lower layer. The energy pathways in the two experiments are similar, but Fig. 12g shows more energy transfer to the lower layer and lacks the reverse ($P' \to \overline{P}$) transfer of the standard flat-bottom experiment (Fig. 12b).

The energy transfers in all these experiments are strongly inhomogeneous in space. Thus, as stressed by Harrison and Robinson (1978), energy transfers averaged over the model domain may not be characteristic of any important subregion.

8.2 Kinetic energy vs. time

In the following discussion, we will illustrate features of the flow which are characteristic of the three regimes identified in the eddy-mean energetics with barotropic, baroclinic, and mixed instabilities. We will utilize the four experiments which do this most simply and clearly, (a) Experiment 1 for barotropic instability with a flat bottom, (b) Experiment 7 for barotropic instability with topography, (c) Experiment 2 for baroclinic instability, and (d) Experiment 4 for mixed instability. Fig. 13 shows the curves of K_1 and K_2 vs. time for these four experiments.

Fig. 13a, b represents the barotropically unstable experiments and clearly shows a relatively long period for the eddy shedding cycle, 273 days for Experiment 1 (Fig. 13a) and 250 days for Experiment 7 (Fig. 13b). Fig. 13c shows a much faster 57 day oscillation for the baroclinically unstable experiment, Experiment 2. The corresponding reduced gravity experiment (not shown), in which baroclinic instability is not permitted, has a 284 day period. The period in Fig. 13c is very similar to that found by Holland and Lin (1975) for mid-latitude mesoscale eddies in a two-layer model with baroclinic instability. They also noted a similar maximum in K_1 near the onset of baroclinic instability which is followed by a rise in K_2. We have not found this type of signature in any of our barotropically unstable experiments. Fig. 13d shows K_1 and K_2 vs. time for Experiment 4, the experiment for which the eddy-mean energetics (Fig. 12e) suggest a mixed instability. Two periods which are not harmonically related are clearly indicated, a long period of 300 days, which is typical of barotropically unstable experiments, and a much shorter 56 day period similar to that for the baroclinically unstable experiment. Also notable are the dramatic spikes in K_2 lagging the maximum in K_1. This resembles the behavior of K_2 at the onset of baroclinic instability shown in Fig. 13c.

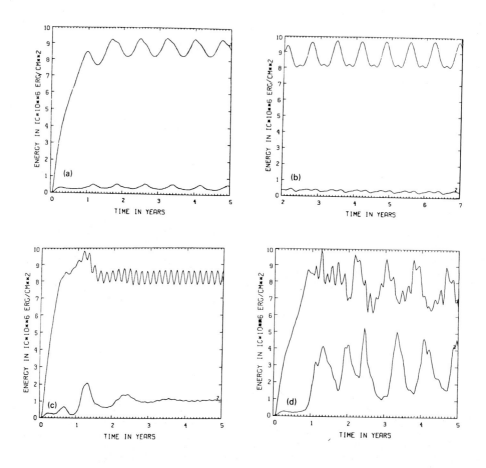

Fig. 13. Average kinetic energy over the rectangular domain (upper curve for upper layer) for (a) Experiment 1, the standard two-layer flat-bottom case, (b) Experiment 7, with the topography of Fig. 3, (c) Experiment 2, with non-normal inflow, and (d) Experiment 4, identical to Experiment 1 but with $A = 3 \times 10^6 \, cm^2/s$ and $Sv_2 = 0$. The value of IC is (a) .5, (b) 1.0, (c) .55, (d) .7.

8.3 Modon generation in the barotropically unstable experiments

We begin examining the characteristic features of the flow in different regimes by studying two experiments where the eddy-mean energetics indicate barotropic instability. One experiment has a flat bottom, and the other includes the idealized Gulf of Mexico topography shown in Fig. 3. The two experiments which illustrate the basic features of this flow in the simplest and clearest fashion are Experiment 1 with Fig. 12b energetics (the standard flat-bottom experiment) and Experiment 7 with topography and Fig. 12h energetics.

Fig. 14 shows synoptic views of p_1 and p_2 for Experiment 1. At day 1710, p_1 (Fig. 14a) shows the Loop Current penetrating into the basin and beginning to bend westward. An eddy shed earlier lies in the western Gulf. A characteristic feature of the barotropically unstable experiments is the generation of a modon in the lower layer as the Loop Current begins to form an eddy (Fig. 14b). The relationship between p_1 and p_2 can be seen clearly by superimposing the fields. The modon intensity tends to follow that of the generating eddy in the upper layer. The axis of the modon is oriented close to the direction of propagation by the upper layer vortex with the anticyclonic member leading and the cyclonic member trailing. The orientation of the modon generated here is quite different from that found by McWilliams and Flierl (1979) for isolated, nearly circular vortices, but the tendency of the eddy in the upper layer to propagate toward the member of the modon with like rotation is similar. However, in this case the westward propagation speed of the modon slightly exceeds that of the upper layer vortex. Thus the flow actually becomes more baroclinic and in Fig. 14a, b we see the anticyclonic eddy in the upper layer situated over the cyclonic member of the modon. This behavior is common but not universal in our numerical experiments. It is quite unlike the coupled behavior of the isolated baroclinic vortex and barotropic modon studied by McWilliams and Flierl (1979). In their results the modon member with rotation unlike the baroclinic vortex eventually broke away and the barotropic and baroclinic vortices tended to become superimposed and to approach a state of deep compensation (no signature of the vortex in the lower layer). When the upper layer vortex reaches the western boundary and propagates northward (Fig. 14c), it is again associated with a modon in the lower layer (Fig. 14d) and again the modon is oriented in the direction of propagation with the like (anticyclonic) member leading and the opposite member trailing.

Fig. 14b, d shows an additional interesting phenomenon which occurs in the lower layer. If the lower layer were integrated separately as a barotropic model, the solution would evolve to a steady, westward-bending Loop Current as in regime W. The solution would be similar to Fig. 8a but the loop would bend westward at a lower latitude because $(v_c/\beta)^{\frac{1}{2}}$ is much less (see Section 5.5). The lower layer inflow velocity at the core of the current is only 3.35 cm/sec.

278

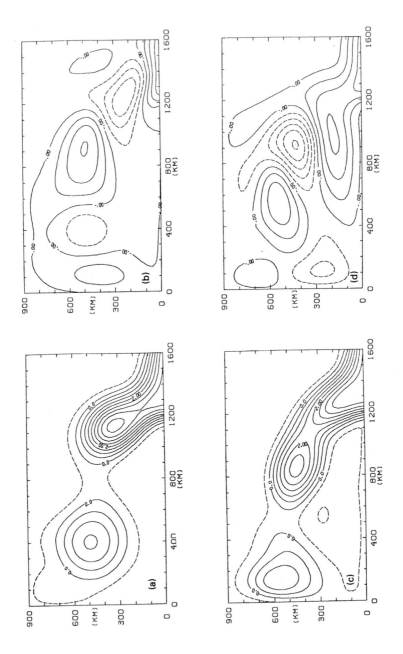

Fig. 14. (a) p_1 and (b) p_2 at day 1710 and (c) p_1 and (d) p_2 at day 1800 for Experiment 1. The contour interval is .5 m^2/s^2 for p_1 and .05 m^2/s^2 for p_2.

In this experiment with two active layers, the lower layer flow is quite different from the barotropic prediction. During the formation of the modon, the Loop Current in the lower layer exhibits a source-sink flow (Fig. 14b). The modon is the dominant flow and prevents the natural westward bending of the Loop. When the modon moves away (Fig. 14d), the lower layer Loop bends far to the west and sheds a weak eddy almost in phase with the upper layer (Fig. 14c). In the mean (Fig. 15) both the upper and lower layers exhibit a westward-bending loop like the W regime. As predicted by $(v_c/\beta)^{\frac{1}{2}}$ and the higher inflow velocity in the upper layer, the mean loop in the upper layer bends westward at a higher latitude. The lower layer also exhibits counter-rotating and zonally elongated mean gyres north of the loop. These are driven by downward flux of eddy energy from the upper layer and may also influence the latitude of the mean Loop Current in the lower layer.

Fig. 16 shows a synoptic view of p_1 and p_2 at day 1760 for a barotropically unstable experiment with Fig. 3 topography (Experiment 7 with Fig. 12h energetics). This experiment exhibits coupled upper layer vortex, lower layer modon behavior similar to the flat bottom experiment, except that the modon is mostly confined to the abyssal plain. Another difference is that the upper layer vortex remains between the modon pair. The modon is partially steered by the topography. Apparently, the back interaction from the modon to the upper layer is sufficient that the trajectory of the upper layer vortex is also modified by the topography. Fig. 17 compares upper layer eddy trajectories for Experiments 6 and 7, two experiments with no flow through the ports in the lower layer. The experiments are identical except that Experiment 6 has a flat bottom and Experiment 7 includes Fig. 3 topography. Because Experiment 7 includes no flow through the ports in the lower layer, there is no current following the f/h contours, unlike Fig. 11c. The addition of such a current had no major effect on the modon, provided the current was weak enough to permit the normal eddy shedding to occur.

Although eddy activity in the lower layer modified the propagation of the upper layer vortex, the propagation of both the upper layer vortex and the associated modon was dominated by internal Rossby wave propagation in both the reduced gravity and two active layer experiments which exhibited discrete eddy shedding and a horizontal shear (barotropic) instability of the internal mode. As we will see shortly, this is not the case in the experiment with a baroclinic instability.

280

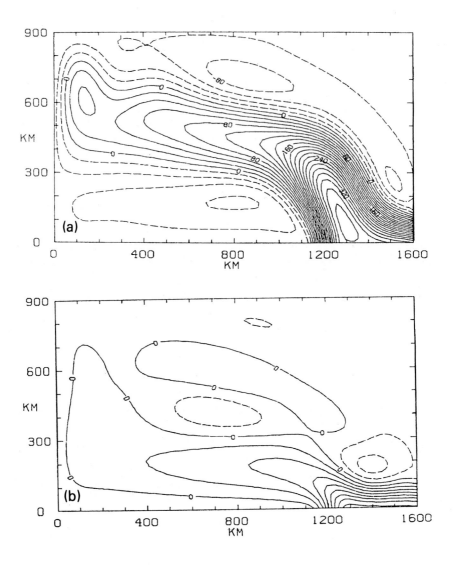

Fig. 15. Time mean of (a) p_1 and (b) p_2 for Experiment 1. The contour interval is .2 m^2/s^2 for p_1 and .02 m^2/s^2 for p_2.

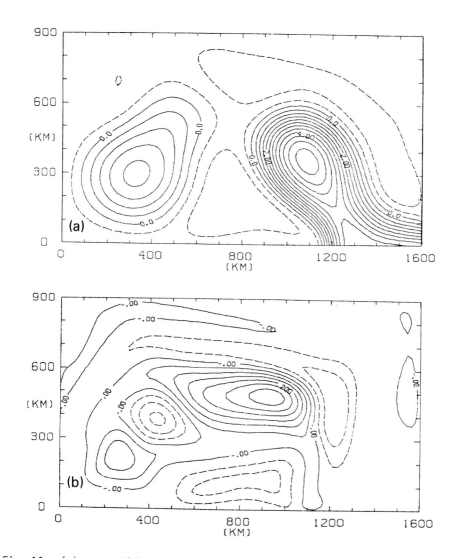

Fig. 16. (a) p_1 and (b) p_2 at day 1760 for Experiment 7. The contour interval is .5 m^2/s^2 for p_1 and .05 m^2/s^2 for p_2.

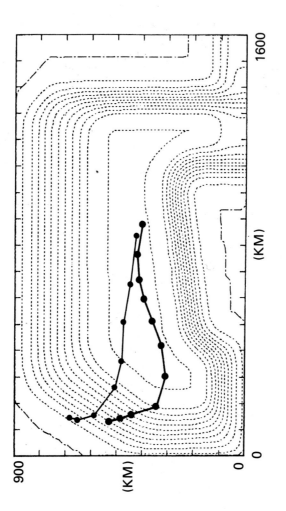

900

(KM)

0

0   (KM)   1600

Fig. 17. Shows the effect of bottom topography on eddy trajectories for identical experiments except that Experiment 6 (upper trajectory) had a flat bottom and Experiment 7 (lower trajectory) included the topography of Fig. 3 which is used as background in this figure. The trajectories are dotted at 30 day intervals.

8.4 Flow characteristics associated with baroclinic instability

Fig. 18 shows a synoptic view of p_1 and p_2 for Experiment 2 where the upper layer inflow is angled 27° west of normal and there is no flow through the ports in the lower layer. The eddy-mean energetics (Fig. 12c) indicate the occurrence of baroclinic instability. This experiment exhibits modon-like generation similar to that earlier associated with a barotropic instability. However, the eddies tend to be smaller and the greater population of eddies tends to mask the modon character of the eddy generation. The upper and lower layer eddies near the eastern part of the Loop bear a phase relationship which is similar to the barotropically unstable experiments. The modon axis is oriented close to the direction of propagation of the anticyclonic eddy in the upper layer, with the anticyclonic modon member leading and the cyclonic one trailing. One difference is that the modon axis is south of the upper layer vortex. Thus, the lower layer eddies tend to be strongest under the westward-flowing arm of the Loop Current as expected for a baroclinic instability (Gill, et al, 1974; Philander, 1976). Later, in the central basin the leading modon member shifts northward, away from the westward propagating vortex in the upper layer. The trailing vortex remains under the westward branch of the Loop. Thus the modon axis is no longer aligned with the direction of propagation. In general, the lower layer eddies tend to be elongated meridionally in the eastern part of the basin where they originate and zonally in the western part of the basin where they decay. In the western part of the basin the eddies also show some tendency toward barotropy. Except for the initial meridional elongation, these tendencies are consistent with results presented by Rhines (1977).

The most dramatic difference between the experiments with barotropic and baroclinic instability lies in the propagation speed of the eddies. In the barotropically unstable experiments with discrete eddies the internal Rossby wave speed associated with the upper layer vortex exerts primary control on the propagation in both layers. Even though the eddies in the baroclinically unstable case are smaller, they propagate westward at $\sim$ 10 cm/sec, typically 2 to 3 times faster than in the barotropically unstable experiments. Although it is difficult to estimate an appropriate shear velocity, the propagation speeds in our numerical model are quite consistent with those for baroclinic instability in a linearized two-layer model with a horizontally uniform basic flow (Pedlosky, 1979).

284

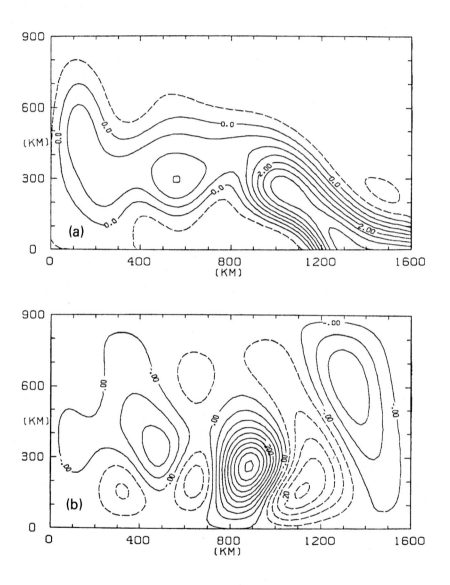

Fig. 18.   (a) p_1 and (b) p_2 at day 2450 for Experiment 2.   The contour interval is .5 m^2/s^2 for p_1 and .05 m^2/s^2 for p_2.

Gill, et al (1974) have suggested the upper to lower layer phase shift as a means of detecting baroclinic instability. In our results we find this is not very useful because the barotropic instability which occurs in the upper layer generates a modon in the lower layer with upper-lower layer phase relationships which are much like those of the baroclinic instability. In our results the westward propagation speed of the eddies is a much clearer distinguishing characteristic.

8.5 Flow characteristics of a mixed instability

Fig. 19 shows two synoptic views of p_1 and p_2 for Experiment 4 which has a flat bottom, no inflow in the lower layer, and one-third the eddy viscosity of the experiments discussed in Sections 8.3 and 8.4. The eddy-mean energetics (Fig. 12e) suggest that a mixed instability occurs in this experiment. Since there is no flow through the ports in the lower layer, all the energy in the lower layer is received from the upper layer. Apart from this the flows in the two layers are much more independent than those discussed in the two preceding subsections.

Eddies in the lower layer propagate westward at approximately the external Rossby wave speed ($\sim$ 10 cm/sec), and those with like rotation pass a given point with a periodicity of about 60 days. Unlike the experiments discussed in Sections 8.3 and 8.4 there is no clear phase relationship between the eddies in the lower layer and the eddy which forms on the Loop Current in the upper layer. This is true during most, but not all, of the eddy-shedding cycle of the Loop Current. In this experiment the eddy-shedding period is about 300 days and is depicted as a slow oscillation in K_1 (Fig. 13d). There is a back interaction from the lower layer eddies to the Loop Current in the upper layer which causes a strong undulation of the Loop with approximately a 60 day period. This is depicted in Fig. 13d as the high frequency oscillation in K_1. Except for this undulation, the Loop Current penetrates into the Gulf, bends westward and begins to form an eddy structure just as in the barotropically unstable experiments, but near the time an eddy would break off (Fig. 19a) in a barotropically unstable experiment, something quite different occurs. The Loop Current suddenly shoots far to the west at a speed appropriate for baroclinic instability and breaks into a series of smaller eddies. During this process lower layer eddies under the south side of the Loop strengthen dramatically and the upper and lower layer eddies develop distinct phase relationships. An anticyclonic eddy in the lower layer leads the westward advance on the Loop Current. At this stage phase relationships in the upper and lower layers are very similar to those for the baroclinically unstable case, and they exhibit the same differences from the barotropically unstable experiments. These phase relations disintegrate as soon as the rapid westward advance of the Loop Current is halted. Thus we have a

286

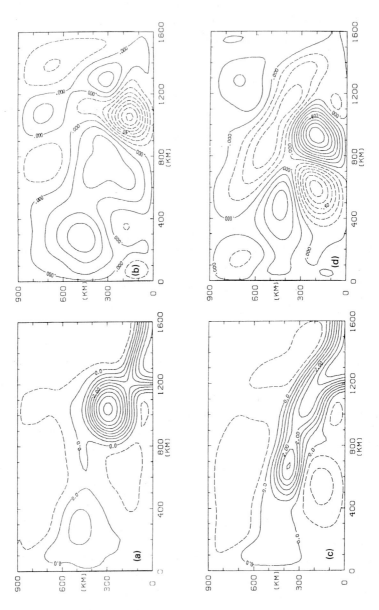

Fig. 19. (a) p_1 and (b) p_2 at day 1720 and (c) p_1 and (d) p_2 at day 1750 for Experiment 4. The contour interval is .5 m²/s² for p_1 and .1 m²/s² for p_2.

picture of episodic baroclinic instability associated with a small part of each 300 day eddy-shedding cycle of the Loop Current. This instability is strong enough to show up in the domain-averaged eddy-mean energetics (Fig. 12e) and to provide a sharp spike in the curve of K_2 vs. time (Fig. 13d). Day 1720 (Fig. 19b) is near the foot of the last spike and day 1760 (Fig. 19d) is near the top of it.

The much weaker coupling for the two layers than found in either the barotropically or baroclinically unstable experiments is explained in part by the peculiar episodic nature of the baroclinic instability in Experiment 4 and in part by the 3 times lower eddy viscosity. Because the eddies in the lower layer are governed by external Rossby wave propagation, they are dispersive in nature. With the lower eddy viscosity they are not dissipated as soon after generation and have greater opportunity to disperse and fill the basin. The importance of dispersion in spreading the eddy population in the lower layer has been noted by Rhines (1977) and in the study of isolated vortices by McWilliams and Flierl (1979).

A comparison of Fig. 16 (for the experiment with idealized Gulf of Mexico topography) and Fig. 19 (for the flat-bottom experiment with a mixed instability) indicates how the topography can suppress the episodes of baroclinic instability found in the latter case. When the topography of Fig. 3 is present, the eddies in the lower layer are mostly confined to the abyssal plain. Lower layer eddy generation over the strongly sloping topography is prevented because the eddy flow would have to cross the closely packed f/h contours at large angles, behavior not anticipated in geostrophically balanced flow which conserves potential vorticity. The strong eddies in Fig. 19d which form under the westward-flowing branch of the Loop Current lie over the region of the Campeche Bank and the slope of the bank. Thus, they are prevented from forming when the topography of Fig. 3 is included. We can now appreciate why the two-layer model with topography produces results more like the reduced gravity model than does the two-layer flat-bottom model. If the westward branch of the Loop Current were to flow over the abyssal plain, we might expect the model to exhibit episodes of baroclinic instability even when the topography is included.

9. SUMMARY AND CONCLUSIONS

In this paper we have demonstrated the ability of simple numerical models to perform remarkable simulations of the Loop Current - eddy system in the Gulf of Mexico. The models were designed for computational efficiency and simplicity, retaining only the essential physics and characteristics of the Gulf required to simulate the basic dynamical behavior of the system. The simplicity of the models facilitated the analysis of the system dynamics and the computational efficiency allowed us to perform over 150 multi-year integrations. The efficiency also allowed us to use horizontal resolution adequate to investigate interesting regions of the parameter space, regions where time dependent eddies dominated the circulation.

The numerous numerical experiments explored the model parameter space and aided in the formulation and testing of dynamical hypotheses. The most salient results from the model are summarized in the seven points which follow.

1) The simple models were able to simulate the anticyclonic eddy shedding by the Loop Current and to simulate eddies with realistic diameters, amplitudes, and westward propagation (Figs. 1,4). Most striking was the ability of the models to simulate the observed quasi-annual period of the eddy shedding with no time variations in the inflow through the Yucatan Straits (southern port). This is contrary to the popular hypothesis that the Loop Current sheds eddies in response to annual variations of the inflow.

2) The reduced gravity model proved to be the simplest model able to simulate the basic dynamics of the Loop Current and the eddy shedding (Fig. 5). This indicates that baroclinic instability is not an essential element of the dynamics. Instead a horizontal shear instability of the first internal mode (a barotropic instability) is the dominant instability mechanism.

3) We have demonstrated the usefulness of CAV trajectory analysis and internal Rossby waves in explaining the eddy-shedding behavior of the Loop Current, including the eddy diameter, the Loop Current penetration into the Gulf, the latitude of westward bending by the Loop Current, the westward speed of eddy propagation, and the eddy shedding period (see Table 2). The role of differential rotation (β) is pervasive. This theory also showed that it is not necessary to invoke an instability mechanism to explain the westward bending of the Loop Current, nor the tendency for it to loop back on itself. This suggests that an instability may be essential only to explain the final eddy separation from the Loop Current.

4) Two steady regimes were found in the parameter space neighboring the eddy shedding regime. The parameter space occupied by each regime was depicted on a regime diagram for the reduced gravity model (Fig. 10).

5) In the presence of sufficient deep water inflow through the Yucatan Straits the Florida Shelf topography may prevent Loop Current penetration, westward bending and eddy shedding by effectively reducing the port separation. This shifts the

Loop Current into one of the stable regimes (Section 7). Certain time variations in the deep flow through the Yucatan Straits may have a greater effect on the Loop Current than fluctuations in the upper layer flow through the strait.

6) Bottom topography plays another important role by inhibiting baroclinic instability. Thus the reduced gravity solutions were more like two-layer solutions with the idealized Gulf of Mexico topography (Fig. 3) than two-layer flat-bottom solutions. The topography also demonstrated some ability to steer eddies in the upper ocean through back interaction from eddies in the lower layer which were mostly confined to the abyssal plain.

7) Finally, we examined the characteristic signatures of barotropic and baroclinic instability in the pressure fields of both layers and in the eddy-mean energetics. In both cases there was a tendency for eddies in the upper layer to drive a modon in the lower layer. The upper and lower layer phase relations were surprisingly similar for both types of instability, but the westward propagation speeds associated with baroclinic instability were typically two to three times faster.

ACKNOWLEDGEMENTS

We extend our appreciation to Dr. L. B. Lin, who developed much of the analysis and display software, including the eddy-mean energetics. We thank Ruth Preller, John Harding, Monty Peffley, Marla Burson and Cynthia Seay for assisting us in various aspects of manuscript preparation. Dr. Daniel Moore of Imperial College, London provided the fast vectorized Helmholtz solvers for both rectangular and irregular domains. The CAV trajectory program was provided by Dr. Donna Blake. Some of the graphics software was supplied by the National Center for Atmospheric Research, which is sponsored by the National Science Foundation. Computations were performed on the two-pipeline Texas Instruments Advanced Scientific Computer at the Naval Research Laboratory in Washington, D.C. We thank Charlene Parker for typing the manuscript.

APPENDIX A

List of Symbols

A	horizontal eddy viscosity
c_{ir}	nondispersive internal Rossby wave speed
c_r	internal Rossby wave speed including dispersion
E_B	beta Ekman number, $A/(\beta L_p^3)$
f, f_0	Coriolis parameter; f_0 taken at southern boundary (y_0)
g	acceleration due to gravity
g'	reduced gravity, $g(\rho_2 - \rho_1)/\rho$
$H_1, H_2(x,y)$	initial thicknesses of the layers
h_1, h_2	instantaneous local thickness of the layers

K_i, $\overline{K}_i$, K_i'	kinetic energy $\frac{1}{2}(u^2 + v^2)$; of the mean flow; mean of the eddy flow, respectively, for layer i.
k, ℓ	zonal and meridional wave numbers, respectively
L	halfwidth of the southern port
$L_{\beta F}$	minimum frictional length scale over which β is important, $(A/\beta)^{1/3}$
$L_{\beta I}$	minimum inertial length scale over which β is important, $(v_c/\beta)^{\frac{1}{2}}$
L_{np}	maximum northward penetration of the Loop Current
L_p	half the port separation distance
P, $\overline{P}$, P'	potential energy $\frac{1}{2}\rho(gn_1^2 + g'n_2^2)$; of the mean flow; mean of the eddy flow, respectively.
p_1	upper layer density-normalized pressure, gn_1.
p_2	lower layer density-normalized pressure, $gn_1 - g'(h_1-H_1)$
Pe	eddy shedding period
R_B	beta Rossby number, $v_c/\beta L_p^2$
Re	Reynolds number, $v_c L/A$
r	eddy radius
t	time
Δt	time increment in the numerical integration
u_1, u_2	x-directed components of current velocity
v_{ci}	maximum inflow speed
v_c	speed at the core of the current
V_g	geostrophic meridional transport
W_1, W_2	$h_1 w_1$, $h_2 w_2$
x, y, z	tangent plane Cartesian coordinates: x positive eastward, y positive northward, z positive upward
x_L, y_L	east-west and north-south domain size
Δx, Δy	horizontal grid increments
β	differential rotation, df/dy
ζ	relative vorticity $v_x - u_y$
n_1	free surface anomaly; height of the free surface above its initial uniform elevation; $n_1 = h_1 + h_2 - H_1 - H_2$
n_2	$n_2 = H_1 + n_1 - h_1 = h_2 - H_2 = -PA$
Θ_I	angle of inflow with respect to the positive x-axis
λ	internal radius of deformation
ρ, ρ_1, ρ_2	densities of sea water
τ_i^x, τ_i^y	x and y directed tangential stresses at the top (i) and bottom (i + 1) of layer i

APPENDIX B

New Reduced Gravity Experiments for the Regime Diagram (Fig. 10)

Experiment	v_{ci}	L	A	L_p	β	Re	R_B	Regime
155	54.4	80	4.0	227.1	2.0	10.9	.527	W
157	54.1	80	4.0	150.9	2.0	10.8	1.19	M
158	73.4	80	2.0	203.5	2.0	29.4	.89	E
159	73.2	80	2.5	203.5	2.0	23.4	.88	T
160	40.3	80	7.3	203.5	.49	4.4	1.99	N
161	41.4	80	1.6	203.5	.537	20.7	1.86	M
162	41.2	80	1.6	203.5	.69	20.6	1.44	W
163	40.5	80	4.6	203.5	1.21	7.0	.81	M
164	40.8	80	4.6	203.5	.69	7.1	1.43	N

units: v_{ci} in cm/s; L, L_p in km; A in 10^7 cm^2/s; β in 10^{-13} cm^{-1}sec^{-1}

See Appendix A for symbol definitions. Note that L and L_p are the half-port width and half-port separation, respectively. The other parameters are the same as in Table 1 except that (1) in Experiments 155 and 157 a land mass was inserted in the location of the West Florida Shelf (See Fig. 9b, c) and the center of the eastern port was taken to be 75 km south of the western end of this land mass, (2) the southern port was centered at x_p = 1000 km in Experiment 155 and at x_p = 1160 km in Experiment 157, and (3) the inflow transport was 14 Sv in Experiments 155 and 157, and 10 Sv in Experiments 160-164.

APPENDIX C

Derivation of Eddy-mean Energetics for a Two-layer, Free-surface, Primitive-equation Model with Open Boundaries

Consider the momentum form of the primitive equations for a two-layer fluid with a free surface:

$$\frac{\partial w_i}{\partial t} + w_i \cdot \nabla w_i + \hat{k} \times f w_i = -\nabla p_i$$
$$+ (\tau_i - \tau_{i+1})/(\rho h_i) + A\nabla^2 w_i \tag{C1}$$

$$\frac{\partial \eta_1}{\partial t} + \nabla \cdot (h_1 w_1 + h_2 w_2) = 0 \tag{C2}$$

$$\frac{\partial \eta_2}{\partial t} + \nabla \cdot (h_2 w_2) = 0 \tag{C3}$$

where i=1,2 and η_1 and η_2 are the deviations of the free surface and the inter-face, respectively (see Appendix A). Also,

$$p_1 = g\eta_1 \qquad\qquad\qquad g' = g(\rho_2 - \rho_1)/\rho$$

$$p_2 = p_1 - g'(\eta_1 - \eta_2) \qquad\qquad \mathbb{T}_i = \tau_i^x \hat{i} + \tau_i^y \hat{j}$$

Note in (C1) that we have used the traditional form of Laplacian friction. Now define the kinetic and potential energies as

$$K_i = \tfrac{1}{2}\rho h_i (u_i^2 + v_i^2) \quad \text{where } i=1,2$$

$$P = \tfrac{1}{2}\rho (g\eta_1^2 + g'\eta_2^2). \tag{C4}$$

Multiplying (C1) by $\rho h_i w_i$ (i=1,2) and using (C2) and (C3) we obtain the kinetic energy equations:

$$\frac{\partial K_1}{\partial t} + \nabla \cdot (w_1 K_1) + \rho g \nabla \cdot (h_1 w_1 \eta_1)$$

$$= \rho g \eta_1 \nabla \cdot (h_1 w_1) + \rho A h_1 w_1 \nabla^2 w_1 \tag{C5}$$

and

$$\frac{\partial K_2}{\partial t} + \nabla \cdot (w_2 K_2) + \rho g \nabla \cdot (h_2 w_2 \eta_1)$$

$$+ \rho g' \nabla \cdot (h_2 w_2 \eta_2) = \rho g \eta_1 \nabla \cdot (h_2 w_2) \tag{C6}$$

$$+ \rho g' \eta_2 \nabla \cdot (h_2 w_2) + \rho A h_2 w_2 \nabla^2 w_2$$

Note that in deriving (C6) we have assumed $g'\nabla\eta_1 \ll g\nabla\eta_1$ and $\mathbb{T}_i=0$ for i=1,2,3. The potential energy equation is formed by multiplying (C2) by $\rho g\eta_1$ and (C3) by $\rho g'\eta_2$ and summing the results:

$$\frac{\partial P}{\partial t} + \rho g \eta_1 \nabla \cdot (h_1 w_1 + h_2 w_2) + \rho g' \eta_2 \nabla \cdot (h_2 w_2) = 0 \tag{C7}$$

Now define mean and perturbation quantities for u, v, h, and η such that

$$\overline{(\quad)} = \frac{1}{T}\int_{t_o}^{t_o + T} (\quad)dt$$

and

$$\overline{(\quad)}' = (\quad) - \overline{(\quad)},$$

where T is a suitable time interval. Also define the kinetic energy of the mean flow per unit area as

$$\overline{K}_i = \tfrac{1}{2}\rho h_i \,(\overline{u}_i^2 + \overline{v}_i^{\,2}), \quad i=1,2 \tag{C8}$$

and the mean kinetic energy of the eddy flow per unit area as

$$K_i' = \tfrac{1}{2}\rho h_i \overline{(u_i^2 + v_i^2)} - \overline{K}_i. \tag{C9}$$

Similarly, for the potential energy of the mean flow

$$\overline{P} = \tfrac{1}{2}\rho (g\overline{\eta}_1^2 + g'\overline{\eta}_2^{\,2}) \tag{C10}$$

and for the mean potential energy of the eddy flow

$$P' = \tfrac{1}{2}\rho (g\overline{\eta_1'^2} + g'\overline{\eta_2'^2}) \tag{C11}$$

The $\overline{K}_1$ equation is obtained by multiplying $(\overline{C1})$ with i=1 by $\rho \overline{h}_1 \overline{w}_1$:

$$\frac{\partial \overline{K}_1}{\partial t} = - \nabla \cdot (\overline{w}_1 \overline{K}_1) - \gamma_1 - \rho g \nabla \cdot (\overline{\eta}_1 \overline{h}_1 \overline{w}_1)$$
$$+ \rho g \overline{\eta}_1 \nabla \cdot (\overline{h}_1 \overline{w}_1) + \rho A \overline{h}_1 \overline{w}_1 \nabla^2 \overline{w}_1 \tag{C12}$$

where for layer i

$$\gamma_i = \tfrac{1}{2}\rho (\overline{u}_i^2 + \overline{v}_i^{\,2})\nabla \cdot (\overline{h_i' w_i'}) + \rho \overline{h}_i \overline{u}_i (\nabla \cdot (\overline{u_i' w_i'})$$
$$- \overline{u_i' \nabla \cdot w_i'}) + \rho \overline{h}_i \overline{v}_i (\nabla \cdot (\overline{v_i' w_i'}) - \overline{v_i' \nabla \cdot w_i'}).$$

The K_1' equation is $(\overline{C5}) - (C12)$ or

$$\frac{\partial K_1'}{\partial t} = - [\nabla \cdot \overline{w_1 K_1} - \nabla \cdot (\overline{w}_1 \overline{K}_1)] + \gamma_1$$
$$- \rho g \nabla \cdot (\overline{\eta_1 h_1 w_1} - \overline{\eta}_1 \overline{h}_1 \overline{w}_1) + \rho g [\overline{\eta_1 \nabla \cdot (h_1 w_1)} \tag{C13}$$
$$- \overline{\eta}_1 \nabla \cdot (\overline{h}_1 \overline{w}_1)] + \rho A [\overline{h_1 w_1 \nabla^2 w_1} - \overline{h}_1 \overline{w}_1 \nabla^2 \overline{w}_1]$$

Similarly, for $\bar{K}_2$ and K_2' we obtain

$$\frac{\partial \bar{K}_2}{\partial t} = - \nabla \cdot (\bar{w}_2 \bar{K}_2) - \gamma_2 - \rho g \nabla \cdot (\bar{\eta}_1 \bar{h}_2 \bar{w}_2)$$

$$+ \rho g \bar{\eta}_1 \nabla \cdot (\bar{h}_2 \bar{w}_2) - \rho g' \nabla \cdot (\bar{\eta}_2 \bar{h}_2 \bar{w}_2) \qquad (C14)$$

$$+ \rho g' \bar{\eta}_2 \nabla \cdot (\bar{h}_2 \bar{w}_2) + \rho A \bar{h}_2 \bar{w}_2 \nabla^2 \bar{w}_2$$

and

$$\frac{\partial K_2'}{\partial t} = - [\nabla \cdot (\overline{w_2 K_2}) - \nabla \cdot (\bar{w}_2 \bar{K}_2)] + \gamma_2$$

$$- \rho g [\nabla \cdot (\overline{\eta_1 h_2 w_2}) - \nabla \cdot (\bar{\eta}_1 \bar{h}_2 \bar{w}_2)]$$

$$+ \rho g [\overline{\eta_1 \nabla \cdot (h_2 w_2)} - \bar{\eta}_1 \nabla \cdot (\bar{h}_2 \bar{w}_2)]$$

$$- \rho g' [\nabla \cdot (\overline{\eta_2 h_2 w_2}) - \nabla \cdot (\bar{\eta}_2 \bar{h}_2 \bar{w}_2)] \qquad (C15)$$

$$+ \rho g' [\overline{\eta_2 \nabla \cdot (h_2 w_2)} - \bar{\eta}_2 \nabla \cdot (\bar{h}_2 \bar{w}_2)]$$

$$+ \rho A [\overline{h_2 w_2 \nabla^2 w_2} - \bar{h}_2 \bar{w}_2 \nabla^2 \bar{w}_2]$$

The $\bar{P}$ equation is obtained by multiplying $(\overline{C2})$ by $\rho g \bar{\eta}_1$ and $(\overline{C3})$ by $\rho g' \bar{\eta}_2$ and summing the results:

$$\frac{\partial \bar{P}}{\partial t} = - \rho g \bar{\eta}_1 \nabla \cdot (\bar{h}_1 \bar{w}_1 + \bar{h}_2 \bar{w}_2) - \rho g \bar{\eta}_1 \nabla \cdot (\overline{h_1' w_1'} + \overline{h_2' w_2'})$$

$$- \rho g' \bar{\eta}_2 \nabla \cdot (\bar{h}_2 \bar{w}_2) - \rho g' \bar{\eta}_2 \nabla \cdot (\overline{h_2' w_2'}) \qquad (C16)$$

By subtracting (C16) from $(\overline{C7})$, we obtain the P' equation:

$$\frac{\partial P'}{\partial t} = - \rho g [\overline{\eta_1 \nabla \cdot (h_1 w_1 + h_2 w_2)} - \bar{\eta}_1 \nabla \cdot (\bar{h}_1 \bar{w}_1 + \bar{h}_2 \bar{w}_2)]$$

$$+ \rho g \bar{\eta}_1 \nabla \cdot (\overline{h_1' w_1'} + \overline{h_2' w_2'})$$

$$- \rho g' [\overline{\eta_2 \nabla \cdot (h_2 w_2)} - \bar{\eta}_2 \nabla \cdot (\bar{h}_2 \bar{w}_2)] \qquad (C17)$$

$$+ \rho g' \bar{\eta}_2 \nabla \cdot (\overline{h_2' w_2'})$$

When the terms in the energy equations are calculated from a model solution in statistical equilibrium and a suitable time average is used, the tendency terms are negligible. Regional energy budgets can be obtained, if (C12) - (C17) are also integrated spatially. Integrated over a closed basin the divergence terms vanish, but in an open domain they must be retained. The energy balances are conveniently displayed using an energy box diagram such as Fig. 12a. Each term is represented by an arrow in or out of the box for the energy reservoir associated with that equation. When identical terms with opposite sign appear in two equations, they represent a conversion of energy from one type to another. The energy transfers shown in Fig. 12a were calculated from the spatially integrated terms in (C12) - (C17) as shown below.

$\overline{K}_1$ terms

$$\{\overline{K}_1 F \rightarrow \overline{K}_1\} \equiv -\iint \nabla \cdot (\overline{w}_1 \overline{K}_1) \, dx \, dy$$

$$\{\overline{K}_1 \rightarrow K_1'\} \equiv \iint \gamma_1 \, dx \, dy$$

$$\{PW \rightarrow \overline{K}_1\} \equiv -\rho g \iint \nabla \cdot (\overline{\eta}_1 \overline{h}_1 \, \overline{w}_1) \, dx \, dy \qquad (C18)$$

$$\{\overline{K}_1 \rightarrow \overline{P}\} \equiv -\rho g \iint \overline{\eta}_1 \nabla \cdot (\overline{h}_1 \, \overline{w}_1) \, dx \, dy$$

$$\{\overline{K}_1 \rightarrow D\} \equiv -\rho A \iint \overline{h}_1 \, \overline{w}_1 \nabla^2 \, \overline{w}_1 \, dx \, dy$$

K_1' terms

$$\{K_1' F \rightarrow K_1'\} \equiv -\iint \nabla \cdot (\overline{w_1 K_1} - \overline{w}_1 \overline{K}_1) \, dx \, dy$$

$$\{\overline{K}_1 \rightarrow K_1'\} \equiv \iint \gamma_1 \, dx \, dy$$

$$\{PW \rightarrow K_1'\} \equiv -\rho g \iint \nabla \cdot (\overline{\eta_1 h_1 w_1} - \overline{\eta}_1 \overline{h}_1 \, \overline{w}_1) \, dx \, dy \qquad (C19)$$

$$\{K_1' \rightarrow P'\} \equiv -\rho g \iint [\overline{\eta_1 \nabla \cdot (h_1 w_1)} - \overline{\eta}_1 \nabla \cdot (\overline{h}_1 \, \overline{w}_1)] \, dx \, dy$$

$$\{K_1' \rightarrow D\} \equiv -\rho A \iint [\overline{h_1 w_1 \nabla^2 w_1} - \overline{h}_1 \, \overline{w}_1 \, \nabla^2 \overline{w}_1] \, dx \, dy$$

$\overline{K}_2$ terms

$$\{\overline{K}_2 F \rightarrow \overline{K}_2\} \equiv - \iint \nabla \cdot (\overline{w}_2 \overline{K}_2)\, dx\, dy$$

$$\{\overline{K}_2 \rightarrow K_2'\} \equiv \iint \gamma_2\, dx\, dy$$

$$\{PW \rightarrow \overline{K}_2\} \equiv - \rho \iint \nabla \cdot [(g\overline{n}_1 + g'\overline{n}_2)\overline{h}_2\, \overline{w}_2]\, dx\, dy \qquad \text{(C20)}$$

$$\{\overline{K}_2 \rightarrow \overline{P}\} \equiv - \rho \iint (g\overline{n}_1 + g'\overline{n}_2)\nabla \cdot (\overline{h}_2\, \overline{w}_2)\, dx\, dy$$

$$\{\overline{K}_2 \rightarrow D\} \equiv - \rho A \iint \overline{h}_2\, \overline{w}_2 \nabla^2 \overline{w}_2\, dx\, dy$$

K_2' terms

$$\{K_2' F \rightarrow K_2'\} \equiv - \iint \nabla \cdot (\overline{w_2 K_2} - \overline{w}_2 \overline{K}_2)\, dx\, dy$$

$$\{\overline{K}_2 \rightarrow K_2'\} \equiv \iint \gamma_2\, dx\, dy \qquad \text{(C21)}$$

$$\{PW \rightarrow K_2'\} \equiv - \rho \iint \nabla \cdot [\overline{(gn_1 + g'n_2)h_2\, w_2} - (g\overline{n}_1 + g'\overline{n}_2)\overline{h}_2\, \overline{w}_2]\, dx\, dy$$

$$\{K_2' \rightarrow P'\} \equiv - \rho \iint [\overline{(gn_1 + g'n_2)\nabla \cdot (h_2\, w_2)} - (g\overline{n}_1 + g'\overline{n}_2)\nabla \cdot (\overline{h}_2\, \overline{w}_2)]\, dx\, dy$$

$$\{K_2' \rightarrow D\} \equiv - \rho A \iint [\overline{h_2\, w_2 \nabla^2 w_2} - \overline{h}_2\, \overline{w}_2 \nabla^2 \overline{w}_2]\, dx\, dy$$

$\overline{P}$ terms

$$\{\overline{K}_1 \rightarrow \overline{P}\} \equiv - \rho g \iint \overline{n}_1 \nabla \cdot (\overline{h}_1\, \overline{w}_1)\, dx\, dy$$

$$\{\overline{P} \rightarrow \overline{K}_2\} \equiv \rho \iint (g\overline{n}_1 + g'\overline{n}_2)\nabla \cdot (\overline{h}_2\, \overline{w}_2)\, dx\, dy \qquad \text{(C22)}$$

$$\{\overline{P} \rightarrow P'\} \equiv \rho \iint g\overline{n}_1 \nabla \cdot (\overline{h_1'\, w_1'} + \overline{h_2'\, w_2'}) + g'\overline{n}_2 \nabla \cdot (\overline{h_2'\, w_2'})]\, dx\, dy$$

P' terms

$$\{K_1' \rightarrow P'\} \equiv - \rho g \iint [\overline{n_1 \nabla \cdot (h_1\, w_1)} - \overline{n}_1 \nabla \cdot (\overline{h}_1\, \overline{w}_1)]\, dx\, dy$$

$$\text{(C23)}$$

$$\{P' \rightarrow K_2'\} \equiv \rho \iint [\overline{(gn_1 + g'n_2)\nabla \cdot (h_2\, w_2)} - (g\overline{n}_1 + g'\overline{n}_2)\nabla \cdot (\overline{h}_2\, \overline{w}_2)]\, dx\, dy$$

$$\{\overline{P} \rightarrow P'\} \equiv \rho \iint [g\overline{n}_1 \nabla \cdot (\overline{h_1'\, w_1'} + \overline{h_2'\, w_2'}) + g'\overline{n}_2 \nabla \cdot (\overline{h_2'\, w_2'})]\, dx\, dy$$

The bracket notation is dropped in Section 8. In our results $|\overline{K}_1 \to K_1'| \gg$ $|K_1'F \to K_1' + PW \to K_1'|$. Thus, any controversy over the formulation of these terms (Harrison and Robinson, 1978) should not cloud the interpretation of the basic results in Fig. 12. Also, the difference between the frictional formulation in the models and the energetics did not result in any serious imbalances in the energy equations.

REFERENCES

Blumberg, A. F. and G. L. Mellor, 1981: A numerical calculation of the circulation in the Gulf of Mexico. Dynalysis of Princeton Rept. No. 66. Prepared for Division of Solar Technology. U.S. Dept. of Energy., 159 pp.

Cochrane, J. D., 1965: The Yucatan Current and equatorial currents of the western Atlantic, Unpublished report, Dept. of Oceanography, Texas A&M University, Ref. (65-17T), 20-27.

Elliott, B. A., 1979: Anticyclonic rings and the energetics of the circulation of the Gulf of Mexico. Ph.D. thesis, Dept. of Oceanography, Texas A&M University, 188 pp.

Gill, A. E., J. S. A. Green, and A. J. Simmons, 1974: Energy partition in the large-scale ocean circulation and the production of mid-ocean eddies. Deep-Sea Research, 21, 499-528.

Haltiner, G. J., and F. L. Martin, 1957: Dynamical and Physical Meteorology, McGraw-Hill, 470 pp.

Harrison, D. E., and A. R. Robinson, 1978: Energy analysis of open regions of turbulent flows-mean eddy energetics of a numerical ocean circulation experiment. Dyn. Atmos. Oceans, 2, 185-211.

Holland, W. R., and L. B. Lin, 1975: On the generation of mesoscale eddies and their contribution to the oceanic general circulation. I. A preliminary numerical experiment. J. Phys. Oceanogr., 5, 642-657.

Hurlburt, H. E. and J. D. Thompson, 1980: A numerical study of Loop Current intrusions and eddy shedding. J. Phys. Oceanogr., 10, 1611-1651.

Leipper, D. F., 1970: A sequence of current patterns in the Gulf of Mexico. J. Geophys. Res., 75, 637-657.

McWilliams, J. C., and G. R. Flierl, 1979: On the evolution of isolated, nonlinear vortices. J. Phys. Oceanogr., 9, 1155-1182.

Nowlin, W. D., 1972: Winter circulation patterns and property distributions. Contributions on the Physical Oceanography of the Gulf of Mexico, Vol. II, L. R. A. Capurro and J. L. Reid, Eds., Gulf Publishing Co., 3-51.

Pedlosky, J., 1979: Geophysical Fluid Dynamics, Springer-Verlag. 624 pp.

Philander, S. G. H., 1976: Instabilities of zonal equatorial currents. J. Geophys. Res., 81, 3725-3735.

Reid, R. O., 1972: A simple dynamic model of the Loop Current. Contributions on the Physical Oceanography of the Gulf of Mexico, Vol. II, L. R. A. Capurro and J. L. Reid, Eds., Gulf Publishing Co., 157-159.

Rhines, P., 1977: The dynamics of unsteady currents. The Sea, Vol. 6, E. D. Goldberg, I. N. McCave, J. J. O'Brien and J. H. Steele, Eds., Wiley Interscience, 189-318.

Rossby, C. G., 1940: Planetary flow patterns in the atmosphere. Quart. J. Roy. Meteor. Soc., 66 (Suppl.), 68-87.

Stern, M. E., 1975: Minimal properties of planetary eddies. J. Mar. Res., 33, 1-13.

A NUMERICAL MODEL OF EDDY GENERATION IN THE SOUTHEASTERN CARIBBEAN SEA

G.W. HEBURN

Science Applications, Inc., 2999 Monterey-Salinas Highway, Monterey, CA, USA

T.H. KINDER and J.H. ALLENDER

Physical Oceanography Branch (Code 331), Naval Ocean Research and Development Activity, NSTL Station, MS 39529

H.E. HURLBURT

Environmental Simulation Branch (Code 322), Naval Ocean Research and Development Activity, NSTL Station, MS 39529

ABSTRACT

Previous oceanographic observations in the southeastern Caribbean suggested high levels of mesoscale variability. Because of the strong westward mean flow and because the Caribbean is a semi-enclosed sea, this variability must be formed locally. A joint observational and numerical modeling study of mesoscale variability in the southeastern Caribbean Sea was therefore initiated.

Satellite-tracked drifters have shown that the variability in the southeastern Caribbean is dominated by mesoscale (about 100 km diameter) eddies which originate close to the Lesser Antilles passages. The models of Hurlburt and Thompson (1980, J. Phys. Oceanogr. 10:1611-1651) were adapted to the southeastern Caribbean basin (720 km x 720 km model domain). The two-layer model, forced by inflow through the three southern passages and with the most realistic parameters, produced eddies similar to those observed. A one-mode reduced gravity model produced nearly identical results, demonstrating the negligible effect of bottom topography on eddy generation and that the eddies form by a horizontal shear instability. Comparisons between these model results and linear instability theory were in satisfactory agreement.

1. INTRODUCTION

Semi-enclosed seas such as the Caribbean (Fig. 1), exhibit hydrodynamical phenomena similar to oceans, but their partial isolation causes differences that are both interesting and useful. A natural laboratory for the study of fluid flow exists where strong flows enter seas through narrow passages. Inflow is restricted to a small part of the boundary where it is often concentrated into a narrow and well-defined jet. At the same time, the partial

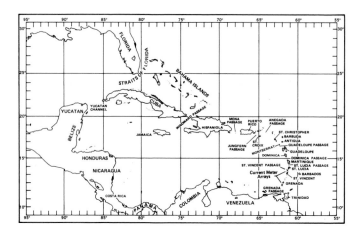

Figure 1. The Caribbean Sea. Much of the flow comprising the westward Caribbean Current originates in the narrow passages of the Lesser Antilles such as Grenada and St. Vincent.

enclosure of a sea prevents the entrance of large eddies from the adjacent ocean. Strong inflow through the narrow passages of the southern Lesser Antilles (Fig. 2) forms such a natural laboratory in the southeastern Caribbean Sea, where we have been using numerical modeling and field experiments to study the mesoscale (about 100 km) variability that is generated there.

Flow in the Caribbean has long interested oceanographers. Wust (1964) traced cores of hydrographic properties to define a westward flowing Caribbean current concentrated in the southern third of the sea and exiting at the Yucatan Strait. He used data that were widely separated spatially and temporally, but the gross pattern that he inferred has been confirmed by others. Gordon (1967) used historical hydrographic data from three different years and the dynamic method to construct 5 meridional sections of velocity. In the eastern Caribbean he showed westward speeds of 0.4 to 0.5 m/sec at the core of the Caribbean Current, but there was some eastward flow in all sections. Roemmich (1981) used inverse techniques on historical hydrographic data and obtained a strong Caribbean current. His analysis also suggested stronger spatial variability near inflow passages than farther downstream.

Recent applications of traditional methods have used more synoptic data. Febres-Ortega and Herrera (1976) used August 1972 hydrographic data to infer geostrophic flow in the southeastern Caribbean and adjacent Atlantic Ocean. They noted a meridional alternation of eastward and westward flow, superimposed on mean westward current, which they attributed to meanders or countercurrents.

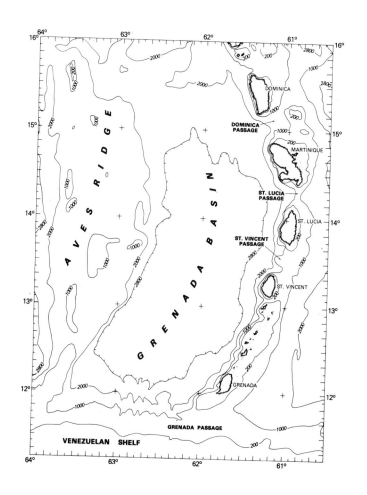

Figure 2. The Southeastern Caribbean Sea. The numerical model was designed to simulate the generation of mesoscale variability in this region. Depths are in meters.

They further conjectured that the complex flow patterns resulted from lee effects of the Lesser Antilles manifest as cyclonic and anticyclonic gyres. Morrison (1977) used meridional sections across the Caribbean to define two branches of the westward-flowing Caribbean Current and two eastward-flowing countercurrents which he believed lie to the north of each westward branch.

Other investigators concentrated directly on the variability. Wyrtki, Magaard and Hager (1976) used ship drift measurements from 1900-1972 to infer mean and eddy kinetic energy of surface flow. Their 1°x1° square averaged result for the North Atlantic showed large values (0.1 m^2/sec^2) in a local maximum of eddy kinetic energy in the southeastern Caribbean. Earlier Leming (1971) had used expendable bathythermographs to suggest that eddies form west of St. Vincent Passage. He suggested that anticyclonic eddies form north of the passage and cyclonic eddies to the south. Based on observations of two eddies he reported that the eddies were confined near the surface (75 and 300 m), that they were mesoscale (about 110 km diameter), and that they formed in about two weeks. More recently Molinari et al. (1981) have used satellite-tracked drifters to demonstrate that eddies are present over much of the Caribbean, including the southeast. We elaborate on their most pertinent data in a later section on observations.

We believe that these observations and analyses suggest that the south-eastern Caribbean is a region with abundant mesoscale flow variability. Inter-pretation of flow features variously described as countercurrents, gyres, eddies, and meanders probably refer to observations of various stages of the same process measured with different resolution. At least some of these features were defined sufficiently to show that they were too large (about 100 km) to have come through the passages (less than 40 km), but must have formed locally. Apparently many of them formed close to the passages. This suggests that the eddies are primarily a consequence of flow instabilities of the currents downstream from the Antilles passages. Because of the geography of the region and because of the strong mean westward flow, we have the advantage of studying the formation of the mesoscale variability without contamination from either the North Atlantic (narrow passages) or the western Caribbean (strong westward mean), and with the further advantage of knowing approximately where formation repeatedly occurs.

A combination of numerical modeling and field experiments has been used to address a number of descriptive and dynamical questions. For example, how well can a simple numerical model simulate mesoscale eddies observed in the eastern Caribbean in terms of generation locale, propagation, distribution, diameter, amplitude, period, vertical structure, and sense of rotation? Are the eddies an important component of the flow in the observations and in the models? What physical instability mechanisms are involved in the formation of the eddies? Are the model results consistent with linear instability theory? What is the influence of the flow through the Antilles passages and of dramatic topographic features, such as the Aves ridge (Fig. 2), on the eddy formation and propaga-tion? What is the importance of inflow angle and of time-varying inflow through the passages? What are typical life cycles of the eddies? To what extent do they behave like isolated eddies? Are they dispersive or nondispersive? How nonlinear is their propagation? What is the local importance of the persistent trade winds? Partial answers have been obtained for some questions, while some answers await work that is in progress. In this paper we concentrate on the success of the model in generating mesoscale eddies that resemble observations.

For the numerical modeling, we use the Hurlburt and Thompson (1980) Gulf of Mexico model adapted for use in the Caribbean. These adapted models are briefly described in section 2. In section 3, we present satellite-tracked drifter data which show the existence of mesoscale eddies within the eastern Caribbean. These observations are later compared with the numerical results. In sections 4 and 5 we examine the results of simulations with one and two active layers. We give particular attention to eddy generation in the upper ocean. The results from these two simulations are inter-compared and also compared to the drifter tracks. The physical characteristics of the eddies such as diameter, wavelength, and period are examined. We then compare these characteristics qualitatively with those predicted by linear stability theory for a horizontal shear flow. Molinari et al. (1981) suggest that topographic forcing is important for the generation of eddies in the eastern Caribbean Sea. We present horizontal shear instability of a zonal jet as an alternative hypothesis.

2. APPLICATION OF THE NUMERICAL MODEL

The numerical models used for this project are variants of the Hurlburt and Thompson (1980) Gulf of Mexico models. Hurlburt and Thompson showed that these models are useful tools in studying the dynamics of the Loop Current and eddy shedding in the Gulf. These models are efficient, and easily adaptable to other semi-enclosed sea such as the Alboran Sea (Preller and Hurlburt, 1982) and the Caribbean Sea.

The basic assumption for the use of a model with one or two active layers is that the dynamics of the flow can be represented by the barotropic and first baroclinic modes. The relatively strong stratification in the Caribbean Sea suggests that it is amenable to such idealizations. The models used here neglect thermodynamics and assume that layers with differing densities are immiscible. The hydrostatic, Boussinesq and β-plane approximations are used, but the primitive equations and a free surface are retained. Using a right-handed coordinate system the vertically integrated model equations are:

$$\frac{\partial \vec{V}_i}{\partial t} + (\nabla \cdot \vec{V}_i + \vec{V}_i \cdot \nabla) \vec{v}_i + \hat{k} \times f \vec{V}_i = -h_i \nabla P_i + \rho^{-1} (\vec{\tau}_i - \vec{\tau}_{i+1}) + A \nabla^2 \vec{V}_i, \quad (1)$$

$$\frac{\partial h_i}{\partial t} + \nabla \cdot \vec{V}_i = 0, \quad (2)$$

304

where i = 1,2 for the two-layer model, i = 1 for the barotropic and reduced
gravity models and

$$
\left.
\begin{aligned}
\nabla &= \frac{\partial}{\partial x}\hat{i} + \frac{\partial}{\partial y}\hat{j} \\
P_1 &= g\eta_1 \\
P_2 &= P_1 - g'h_1 \\
\vec{V}_i &= h_i\vec{v}_i = h_i(u_i\hat{i} + v_i\hat{j}) \\
g' &= g(\rho_2 - \rho_1)\rho^{-1} \\
f &= f_o + \beta(y - y_o) \\
\vec{\tau}_i &= \tau_i^x\hat{i} + \tau_i^y\hat{j}
\end{aligned}
\right\} .
\qquad (3)
$$

See Appendix A for symbol definitions.

The reduced gravity model is essentially a model of the first baroclinic
mode. It assumes an active upper layer, but a lower layer which is infinitely
deep and at rest. Thus, in the reduced gravity model the lower layer momentum
equation degenerates to $g\nabla\eta_1 = g'\nabla h_1$. For a more complete description of the
models and their numerical formulation, the reader is directed to the original
Hurlburt and Thompson (1980) paper.

2.1 _Model domain and boundary conditions_

The domain covered by the model extends from the Venezuelan shelf to Puerto
Rico (11.5 to 18°N) and from the Antillean Arc to the central Venezuelan Basin
(61.1 to 67.6°W) (see Fig. 1). The northern, southern, and eastern boundaries
of the model domain have natural analogues. Flow enters through the St. Lucia,
St. Vincent and Grenada passages. The western boundary through the central
Venezuelan Basin is completely open. Normal flow at this boundary is
self-determined with the integral constraint that the net mass transport out
from each layer match the total inflow through the Antilles passages. Any
phenomena originating at the western boundary are induced or reflected artificially by the open western boundary condition. Various formulations for this
boundary condition were tested and it was found that for our application the
use of a weak damping boundary layer was the most effective at reducing these
unwanted phenomena. The frictional boundary layer employs a linear drag law
proportional to velocity. The drag coefficient varies exponentially from zero
at 150 km from the western boundary to a maximum of 10^{-3} at the boundary.
Because the flow is artificially modified in the westernmost 150 km of the
basin, the solutions in this region are unrealistic and will not be included in
the discussions. The kinematic and no-slip boundary conditions are applied at
the rigid boundaries (heavy solid lines, Fig. 3).

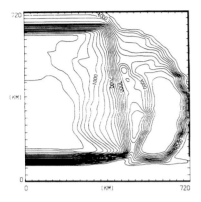

Figure 3. Caribbean Model Basin and Bottom Topography. Contour interval is
200 m. The values shown are heights above a reference level (the floor of the
Venezuelan Basin at 5000 m depth). The heavy lines denote solid boundaries
while the narrow lines denote open boundaries.

2.2 Inflow boundary conditions

The inflow through the eastern ports in the model is specified based on
observational data. The St. Lucia, St. Vincent and Grenada Passages provide at
least half the volume transport to the Caribbean Current and they are the most
important Caribbean passages for flow and water properties in the upper 1000 m
(Wust, 1964; Gordon, 1967; Stalcup and Metcalf, 1972; Mazeika, Burns and
Kinder, 1980a). Flow through these three southern passages profoundly affects
the flow to the west and these inflows are used to provide the forcing in the
model. Passages farther north (e.g. Dominica) and west (e.g. Mona) are
unlikely to influence the flow in the southeastern Caribbean and are not
included in the model.

The inflow boundary conditions are steady except for a spin-up with a time
constant of 30 days and are based on a review of existing measurements.
Experiments with fluctuating inflow will be reported in a later paper. Direct
current measurements have been made by moored current meters, by current meters
lowered from ships, and by free-fall (dropsonde) instruments over periods from
1 to 280 days (Stalcup, Metcalf and Zemanovic, 1971; Burns and Car, 1975;
Brooks, 1978; Mazeika, Burns and Kinder, 1980b). The model inflows were
designed to produce speeds and volume transports compatible with published
values. The mean outflow through the Yucatan Strait is well-established by the
work of Niiler and Richardson (1973) (assuming mean Yucatan Strait transport
and mean Florida Strait transport are equal) at 30×10^6 m^3/sec. It has
not been established, however, how the matching inflow is shared among the
various passages. We follow Mazeika, Burns and Kinder (1980a) who reviewed

the literature on transport estimates near the Lesser Antilles and suggested that the mean transport through the three southern passages is only 15 x 10^6 m^3/sec. This value is much lower than the Stalcup and Metcalf (1972) value of 26 x 10^6 m^3/sec based on lowered current meters, but it is close to their free-fall (dropsonde) measurements (about 15 x 10^6 m^3/sec). Roemmich (1981) estimated 22 x 10^6 m^3/sec for all passages east of 64°W. We also examined direct current measurements for speed and direction, since the kinetic energy and shear depend on velocity and not directly on transport. Table 1 shows the most representative speeds and directions synthesized from the various measurements.

TABLE 1.   INFLOW BOUNDARY CONDITIONS

Passage	Observations			Model		
	TRANSPORT ($10^6 m^3$/sec)	SPEED (m/sec)	DIRECTION (°T)	TRANSPORT ($10^6 m^3$/sec)	SPEED (m/sec)	DIRECTION (°T)
St. Lucia						
Upper layer	1.5	0.30	270	1.1	0.28	270
Lower layer	1.5	0.20	270	.9	0.10	270
St. Vincent						
Upper layer	3	0.60	310	3.6	0.50	310
Lower layer	3	0.15	310	2.0	0.15	310
Grenada						
Upper layer	3	0.50	270	3.1	0.27	270
Lower layer	3	0.20	270	1.8	0.20	270
Total	15	--	---	12.5	--	---

The inflow angle in the Grenada and St. Lucia passages was taken as due west (270°T), but current measurements in St. Vincent Passage indicated a flow north of west (a single exception is a current meter record taken within 30 m of the bottom). These not only included the moored current meters, lowered current meters, and dropsondes, but also drifter tracks just west of the passage (Figs. 4-6). We offer no explanation for this persistent northward flow component, but note that it may significantly influence the resulting flow downstream.

The actual model inflow conditions were selected by assuming that upper layer velocity was most critical, followed by total transport. The horizontal profile at the port was specified as uniform because actual profiles are not well-known (especially in St. Vincent Passage) and because the model has few grid points to define the profile in the ports. Work to examine the effect of the profile, which Nof (1978) argues is important, is planned. Because the model port geometry was selected independently to match the passage geometry, selecting the upper layer velocity and total transport thus specified velocity and transport in both layers for each port (directions were the same in both layers). The maximum model speeds are a little lower than the observations because the observations tended to be near the higher speed core of the inflow. Our transports are selected towards the lower estimates because this permits numerical stability at longer time steps and reduces the cost of the computations.

2.3 Bottom topography

Idealized bottom topography was used in the two-layer experiments. The bottom topography for the rectangular model domain described above was digitized at about a 10-20 km interval from Naval Oceanographic Office charts, interpolated to 7.5 km, and smoothed to eliminate two-grid-length variations. The resulting model topography is shown in Fig. 3. The algorithm used for the numerical solution does not allow islands, so the Antilles are represented as the minimum model depth (500 m). We justified the "sunken islands" a posteriori by noting that the total flow over these regions of minimum depth was a small fraction of the total flow in the model. We made no attempt to include realistic topography in the western third of the model domain. Depth contours there were purposely straightened to reduce the effects of the open boundary.

2.4 Model validation tests

Before the validity of the model results can be accepted, the sensitivity of the model to changes in the numerical design (e.g. sensitivity to changes in such non-physical parameters as the time step, grid spacing, east-west basin extent, spin-up time, open boundary condition specification, and eddy viscosity) must be tested. A series of experiments was conducted to determine the parameters for our standard cases and to determine the parameter range for which reasonable changes in the numerical design did not significantly alter the physical solutions. Table 2 lists the most significant model validation experiments and contains brief comments on the results.

The parameters for the pivitol experiment were selected following this series of experiments and are presented in Table 3. The values of g' and H_1 were chosen based on an envelope of density profiles derived from CTD data taken in the Grenada Basin (Teague, 1979).

Selection of the eddy viscosity required particular care. For our purpose, the eddy viscosity must be large enough to control the enstrophy cascade, but small enough so that the damping time scale for the primary eddies is much longer than the time for them to develop and propagate across the model domain.

TABLE 2. MODEL VALIDATION EXPERIMENTS

CASE	PARAMETER DIFFERENCES FROM TABLE 3	TO TEST EFFECT OF:	COMMENTS
1	(Standard Case)	Standard Case	Realistic eddies, no reflected (eastward propagating) waves. Minimal small scale variability. Generally acceptable results.
2	No FBL (Frictional Boundary Layer), $t_{spin-up}$=10 days, A=200	Changes in spin-up time	Solutions contaminated by reflected waves (unacceptable).
3	No FBL, A=200	Open boundary condition with different values of eddy viscosity	Generally good overall results with only slight indication of reflected waves. Solutions acceptable but not completely satisfactory.
4	No FBL	"	Same as Case #3.
5	No FBL, A=50	"	Increased reflected wave amplitude over Cases #3 & 4. Solution marginally acceptable.
6	No FBL, A=25	"	Significant reflected waves. Solution contaminated.
7	No FBL, A=200, $\frac{\partial v}{\partial x} = 0$ at western boundary	Change in specification of tangential velocity at open boundary	Significant reflected waves after 90-100 days. Solutions contaminated.
8	No FBL, A=200, XL=900 km	Increasing E-W extent	Results same as Case #3 in common basin area.
9	No FBL, A=200, XL=900 km $t_{spin-up}$=10 days	"	Results same as Case #2 in common basin area.
10	$t_{spin-up}$=10 days, A=200, B_L=90 km	Frictional boundary layer short spin-up	Significant reduction of reflected wave over Case #2. Results similar to Case #3.
11	A=25, B_L = km	FBL with various values of eddy viscosity and boundary layer (B_L) thickness	Low to moderate amplitude reflected waves present. Solutions contaminated.
12	A=25	FBL with various values of eddy viscosity	Significant reduction of reflected waves over Case #11. No apparent contamination due to eastward propagating waves. Results similar to Case #1 but with some indication of small scale variability.
13	A=50	FBL with various values of eddy viscosity	Same as Case #12 but with a reduction in small scale variability.
14	A=50, C_D=2.0 × 10^{-3}	Change in drag coefficient	No significant difference from Case #13.
15	XL=1500 km, A=50	Increasing E-W extent	Results same as Case #13 in common basin area outside of FBL.

CASE	PARAMETER DIFFERENCES FROM TABLE 3	TO TEST EFFECT OF:	COMMENTS
16	XL=900 km, A=50	"	Results same as Case #13 in common basin area outside of FBL.
17	XL=900 km	"	Results same as Case #1 in common basin area outside of FBL.
18	XL=1500 km	"	Results same as Case #1 in common basin area outside of FBL.
19	YL=360 km[1]	Reducing N-S extent. Compare with Case #20.	Generally results similar to Case #1, but with slightly smaller diameter eddies, slightly faster propagation speeds and only the northern anti-cyclonic and central cyclonic eddies present.
20	YL=360 km[1], $\Delta x = \Delta y = 3.75$ km, $\Delta t = 3/4$ hr	Reducing grid spacing and time step	Results same as Case #19

(1) Inflow through central port only. North/South extent of basin centered on central port.

TABLE 3. MODEL PARAMETERS FOR STANDARD CASE

A	$= 100 \text{ m}^2 \text{ sec}^{-1}$	β	$= 2.24 \times 10^{-1} \text{ m}^{-11} \text{sec}^{-1}$
f_o	$= 2.9 \times 10^{-5} \text{ sec}^{-1}$	ρ	$= 10^3 \text{ kg m}^{-3}$
g	$= 9.8 \text{ m sec}^{-2}$	$\vec{\tau}$	$= 0$
g'	$= 0.03 \text{ m sec}^{-2}$	Δx	$= 7.5 \text{ km }^{(1)}$
H_1	$= 250 \text{ m}$	Δy	$= 7.5 \text{ km }^{(1)}$
H_2	$= 4750 \text{ m}$	Δt	$= 1.5 \text{ hr}$
$t_{spin-up}$	$= 30 \text{ days}$	B_L	$= 150 \text{ km}$
$v_{outflow}$	$= 0 ^{(2)}$	C_D	$= 10^{-3}$
Domain Size, X_L by Y_L	$= 720 \times 720 \text{ km}$		

(1) For each dependent variable
(2) 1/2 grid point outside the outflow boundary

The value of the eddy viscosity was varied from A = 25 to 200 m^2/sec.
Although the model was stable at values as low as A = 25 m^2/sec, we found
that below A = 100 m^2/sec horizontal features smaller than the design
resolution of the grid (approximately 10 Δx) were present. Also, the tests
revealed that even with A = 200 m^2/sec the features with horizontal length
scale at or above the design resolution scale were not significantly different
from those with A = 100 m^2/sec. Therefore, A = 100 m^2/sec was chosen as
the standard value for the eddy viscosity.

The standard duration of a model experiment was one year. The model
required approximately four to five months to reach a quasi-steady state with
regular eddy shedding (see Fig. 10). A one year model integration allowed at
least six eddy shedding cycles after the model reached statistical equilibrium.
The reduced gravity standard case was run for an additional year to verify that
statistical equilibrium was achieved after six months.

3. OBSERVATIONS OF EDDIES BY DRIFTING BUOYS

Drifting surface buoys which follow shallow currents have been used in the
southeastern Caribbean. These surface buoys were located by satellite and
their tracks showed shallow current features with periods exceeding two days
and with sizes larger than about 20 km. Spatial scales and variability
patterns derived from drifter tracks were used to check model validity.
Drifters were deployed both by R. Molinari of the National Oceanic and
Atmospheric Administration (NOAA) and by us (NORDA) and the techniques used
were essentially identical. A small surface buoy was tracked by the Random
Access Measurement System of the NIMBUS-G satellite. Windowshade drogues
centered at either 30 m (NOAA) or 100 m (NORDA) depth ensured that the drifter
closely followed water motion. This system provided about two useful positions
daily with an accuracy of about 5 km, so that the daily speeds of the drifters
were accurate to about 0.05 m/sec. Editing removed the worst positions (based
on a criterion of excess speed, 2.5 m/sec for NOAA and 2.0 m/sec for NORDA).
The NOAA data were also smoothed. Molinari et al. (1981) report on their entire
data set, describe the technique more completely, and list several references
that discuss windage and other error sources.

A total of 15 drifters were released near the passages in 3 different
deployments during October 1975, January 1976, and November 1977. All but one
drifter continued transmission until leaving the area (arbitrarily defined as
passing westward of 64°W or northward of 16°N). Drifters remained within
the area for periods ranging from 3 to 76 days and moved with scalar speeds of
0.2 to 0.9 m/sec. Speeds were higher during the winter (January 1976)
deployment than during the two fall (October 1975 and November 1977)
deployments (a scalar mean of 0.6 m/sec versus 0.3 m/sec), but part of this

difference may have been caused by the different drogue depths. Eddies encountered by the drifters strongly affected drifter velocities, and an eddy was encountered during each deployment (Table 4).

TABLE 4. EDDIES OBSERVED BY DRIFTERS

Deployment	Number of Drifters in Eddy	Number of Loops Around Eddy	Sense of Rotation	Diameter (km) [2]	Drift (m/sec, ^{o}T) [3]	Swirl (m/sec) [4]
October 25-26 1975 NOAA 4 drifters (1) 30 m drogues	3	5.5	anticyclonic	60	0.1, 230	0.9
January 20-23 1976 NOAA 6 drifters 30 m drogues	1	1	cyclonic	90	0.2, 330	0.4
November 12-15 1977 NORDA 4 drifters 100 m drogues	1	2.5	anticyclonic	60	0.1, 290	0.2

(1) Buoy ID 343 failed after 4 days and is not included.

(2) Equivalent diameter defined as twice the square root of the product of the semi-major and semi-minor axes of the largest drifter loop. This is probably a minimum estimate because of drifter kinematics.

(3) Speed and direction of eddy movement.

(4) Scalar speed of drifter while entrained in eddy.

During the October 1975 deployment three drifters encountered an anticyclonic eddy about 200 km northwest of St. Vincent Passage (Fig. 4). Drifter 1417 (drifters are identified by their assigned satellite channel) completed only half a circumference, but 1421 circled the eddy once and 1450 made four complete loops and was still in the eddy when it passed 64°W. Because of its entrainment in the eddy, buoy 1450 had the longest residence time (42 days) but highest scalar speed (0.9 m/sec) of the deployment.

312

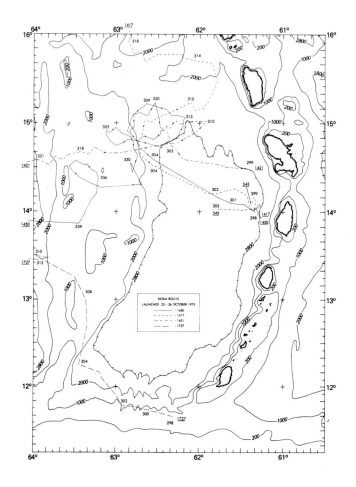

Figure 4. Buoy trajectories during NOAA October 1975 deployment. Note the
anticyclonic eddy near 15°N 62.5°W, especially the track of buoy 1450.
Underlined numbers are buoy identifications and the other numbers along the
tracks are Julian days.

Buoy 610, launched in January 1976, also detected an eddy with one cyclonic
loop south of the St. Vincent Passage inflow (Fig. 5). The buoy may have
remained in the eddy until it reached the 64°W meridian, but this is
uncertain. This buoy had the longest residence time (23 days) but, unlike buoy

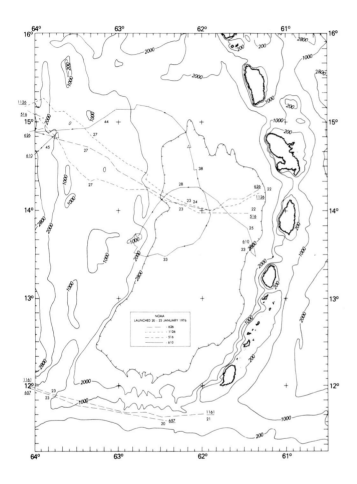

Figure 5. Buoy trajectories during NOAA January 1976 deployment. Note the cyclonic eddy near 14°N 62.5°W. Underlined numbers are buoy identifications and the other numbers along the tracks are Julian days.

1450 in October, this buoy also had the lowest scalar mean (0.4 m/sec) of the deployment. The relatively low scalar mean occurred in part because the other buoys were apparently located near the core of a westward current through one of the passages. Buoys 516, 626, and 1126 downstream of the St. Vincent and St. Lucia passages averaged nearly 0.5 m/sec. Buoys 657 and 1161 downstream of

314

the Grenada passage averaged almost 0.7 m/sec.

During the November 1977 deployment buoy 1600 completed two loops around an anticyclonic eddy southwest of St. Vincent Island (Fig. 6). Along with buoy 610 in January, this buoy had the longest residence time (76 days) and lowest scalar mean (0.17 m/sec) of the deployment.

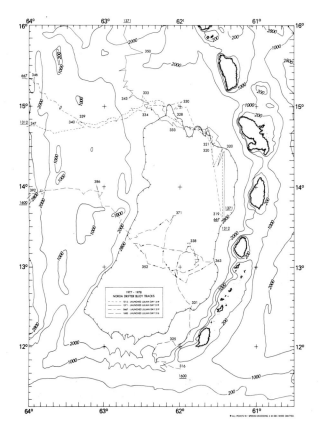

Figure 6. Buoy trajectories during NORDA November 1977 deployment. Note the anticyclonic eddy near 13°N 62°W. Underlined numbers are buoy identifications and the other numbers along the tracks are Julian days.

The two most energetic eddies, the anticyclonic eddy north of the St. Vincent Passage inflow (Fig. 4) and the cyclonic eddy south of the St. Vincent Passage inflow (Fig. 5) were consistent with Leming's (1971) hypothesis that anticyclonic (cyclonic) eddies form north (south) of the passage. The northern anticyclonic eddy appeared to be more energetic than the inflow through St. Lucia and St. Vincent Passages, while the southern cyclonic eddy seemed slightly less energetic. The anticyclonic eddy revealed in 1977 (Fig. 6) was not clearly associated with an inflow current, and all four 1977 drifters showed low speeds. Taken together, the drifter data suggest that mesoscale eddies are common in Grenada Basin (three of three drifter deployments detected an eddy), and that the presence of an eddy profoundly influences the shallow flow.

4. TWO-LAYER SIMULATION

4.1 Two-layer model results

We begin our discussion of the case studies by presenting the results of the most realistic model possible within the framework of the two-layer system. This is the two-layer model with the idealized bottom topography (Fig. 3) and the best estimates of the inflow through the eastern passages (Table 1). The parameters for this case are shown in Table 3. Following the analysis of these results we will examine the results of simpler models with one vertical mode and use them to elucidate the dynamics in the two-layer model. This first case will be referred to as the "Two-layer Standard Case", and it will be the experiment to which all others are compared. The inflow transport for this case is steady except for a spin-up with a 30-day time constant.

In Fig. 7, we present a sequence of synoptic views of the pycnocline height anomaly at 8-day intervals. The pycnocline height anomaly (PHA) is the deviation of the layer interface from its flat position at 250 m depth. The contour interval for the PHA is 5 m and positive contours represent downward deviations (increased thickness of the upper layer). This sequence depicts a typical eddy shedding cycle with the following salient features:

1) a meandering current emanating from the St. Vincent passage,

2) a meandering current emanating from the Grenada passage,

3) anticyclonic eddies forming in the northern Grenada Basin which propagate westward,

4) cyclonic eddies forming south of the St. Vincent inflow current which propagate west-southwestward,

5) anticyclonic eddies forming in the southeastern Grenada Basin which propagate west-northwestward and merge with the northern anticyclonic eddies, and

6) a suggestion of a boundary current along the eastern and northern boundaries.

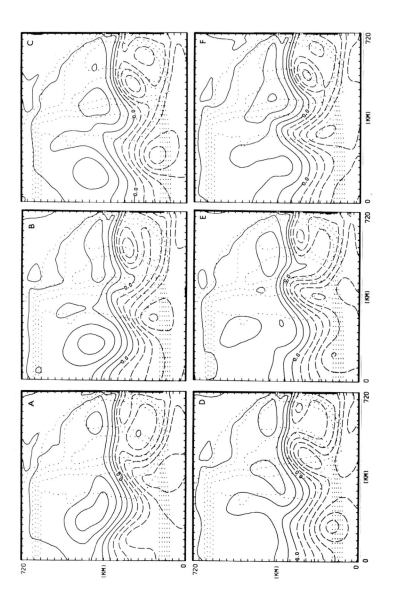

Figure 7. Pycnocline Height Anomaly (PHA) for the two-layer standard case. The contour interval is 5 m and the time interval between synoptic views is 8 days.

We also note that when the eddies first develop, their diameters are comparable to the radius of deformation, R_D, in the model. The internal Rossby radius, $R_D = (g'H)^{\frac{1}{2}}/f$, varies from about 97 km at the latitude of Grenada Passage to about 80 km at St. Vincent based on the parameters in Table 3.

The upper and lower layer pressure fields (not shown) demonstrate that the eddies observed in the synoptic views of PHA are present in the upper layer but are absent from the lower layer. Also the meandering westward currents (from St. Vincent and Grenada passages) are not visible in the lower layer but are confined to the upper layer. In the lower layer a mean boundary current flows along the slope near the eastern and northern boundaries (Fig. 8). There is also evidence of a cyclonic circulation in the lower layer of the Grenada Basin. A barotropic experiment developed a steady-state flow which was similar to the lower layer mean in the two-layer model. Roemmich (1981) inferred a similar deep cyclonic circulation for the Venezuelan Basin (west of the Aves Ridge) based on hydrographic data. The deep circulation appears to follow the f/h contours of the topography as expected from conservation of potential vorticity.

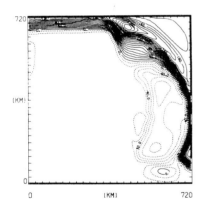

Figure 8. Lower Layer Mean Pressure anomaly (P_2) based on a six-month period (days 180 to 360). The contour interval is 0.025 N/m^2.

4.2 Comparison of model results to drifter observations

Examining Fig. 7 more closely we can relate the eddies observed in the model solutions to the eddies observed with the satellite tracked drifters. In Fig. 4

we see an anticyclonic eddy northwest of St. Vincent passage (in the
northwestern part of the Grenada Basin). Figure 7a, shows the development of
an anticyclonic eddy in the same area. Both the observed and the model eddies
drift westward.

The cyclonic eddy which forms just south of the current emanating from the
St. Vincent passage (Fig. 7a,b) and the cyclonic eddy detected by buoy 610 in
Fig. 5, also have similar positions and directions of propagation. The model
eddy has a diameter of approximately 75 to 100 km which is comparible to the
observed eddy (see Table 4). The anticyclonic eddy in the southeastern Grenada
Basin delineated by the drifting buoy 1600 (Fig. 6) also has a comparable
analogue in the numerical solution (Fig. 7c,d,f).

4.3 Instability mechanism

A preliminary analysis of the energetics for the upper and lower layer flow
fields revealed no evidence of baroclinic instability for the standard case
parameters. The dominant energy transfer was from kinetic energy of the mean
flow to eddy kinetic energy and occurred in the upper layer. This suggests
that the eddies result from a horizontal shear instability of the first
internal mode, a "barotropic" instability.

The upper and lower layer flows in this experiment are nearly decoupled.
This suggests that the simpler and less expensive models with a single vertical
mode should be useful to investigate the dynamics of the flow. In particular
we use the reduced gravity model to study the eddy shedding downstream of the
passages because the eddies are trapped near the surface and not substantially
influenced by the topography. The low cost of this model permits us to conduct
numerous numerical experiments with different model parameters and external
forcing.

5. REDUCED GRAVITY SIMULATIONS

5.1 Model results

The reduced gravity model is used to simulate the first baroclinic mode. It
contains an active upper layer and a lower layer which is infinitely deep and
quiescent.

In Fig. 9 we present synoptic views of the PHA for a typical eddy shedding
cycle from the reduced gravity standard case (based on appropriate parameters
from Table 3). Here the PHA can be used directly to infer the upper layer flow
field, since the lower layer is quiescent.

Comparing Fig. 9 to Fig. 7, we see the same upper layer features as
described for the two layer simulation. Although the match is not perfect, the
intensities, locations of eddy formation, directions of propagation, and eddy
shedding periods are similar, lending credence to the hypothesis that the

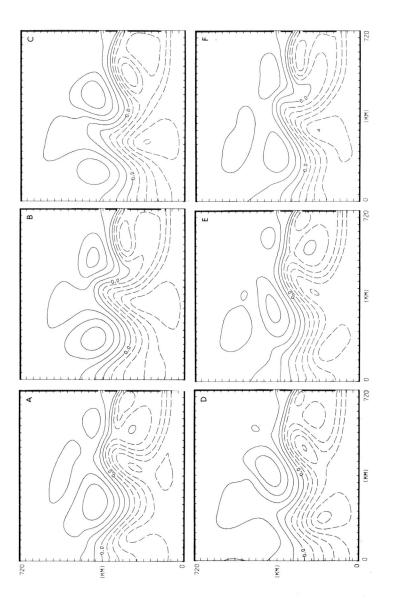

Figure 9. Pycnocline Height Anomaly (PHA) for the reduced gravity standard case. The contour interval is 5 m and the time interval between synoptic views is 8 days. This sequence shows a typical eddy shedding cycle starting at day 310.

reduced gravity model can be used to elucidate the dynamics of the dominant mesoscale phenomena.

Figure 9a clearly shows the three primary types of eddies (the northern and southern anticyclonic eddies and the cyclonic eddy forming south of the St. Vincent passage). Figure 9b shows that the two anticyclonic eddies have propagated westward and the southern eddy appears to be merging with the northern one. Also in this synoptic view a cyclonic eddy is about to separate from the eastern boundary. Figure 9c reveals that the cyclonic eddy has detached and is propagating west-southwestward at a speed of approximately 0.1 m/sec. Figures 9d and e show the development of the next set of anticyclonic eddies and the beginning of the next cyclonic eddy. Finally, in Fig. 9f, we see the next cyclonic eddy about to be shed.

Figure 10 shows north-south cross-sections of PHA vs. time at three different longitudes 40, 120, and 360 km west of the eastern boundary. Six months are required for the model to reach statistical equilibrium. The initial Rossby wave front can easily be tracked across the basin and it is apparent that well-defined westward currents exist only after the passage of this front. The meandering of these currents and the associated eddies are evident first in the western basin and later in the eastern basin. This indicates that the first perturbations on the stream grow more slowly as they propagate downstream than do those which follow them. This is evidence that meanders downstream increase the growth rate of new ones forming upstream, an important finite amplitude effect in these results. Figure 10a is a north-south cross-section 40 km west of the inflow boundary. Here we see nearly steady currents just downstream from the three active passages, although we see clear evidence of the formation of the cyclonic eddies south of the St. Vincent inflow. This figure also suggests the presence of a weak permanent anticyclonic circulation between the southern (Grenada) and central (St. Vincent) inflow ports.

Figure 10b is a section through the center of Grenada Basin (120 km west of the inflow boundary). It shows the presence of all three types of eddies and permits a good estimate of the eddy shedding period, which is approximately 35 days. We also note that the two northernmost currents, (i.e. the weak one emanating from St. Lucia passage and the strong one from St. Vincent passage) have merged into one current.

Finally in Fig. 10c, a section through the center of the model basin (360 km west of the inflow boundary), we see that the two anticyclonic eddies have merged and that the northern one has continued to intensify. The cyclonic eddy has propagated west-southwestward and has deflected the southernmost current northward (see Fig. 9). Furthermore, the southernmost current has merged with the central current.

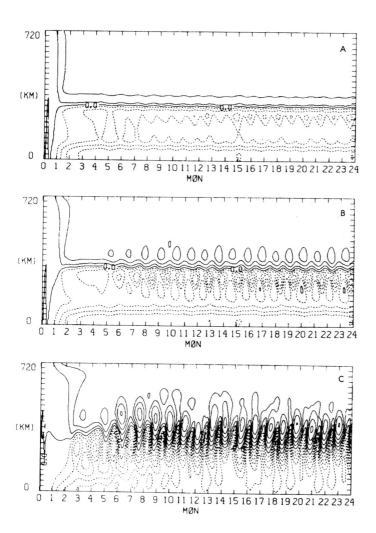

Figure 10. North-south cross-sections PHA vs. time for reduced gravity standard case: a) 40 km downstream of the inflow ports, b) through the center of the Grenada Basin (120 km downstream of the inflow boundary), and c) through the center of the model basin (360 km downstream of the inflow boundary). The contour interval is 5 m.

Wust (1964), Gordon (1967) and Roemmich (1981) inferred a westward flowing Caribbean current concentrated in the southern third of the basin. Figure 10 supports the idea of a single current but shows strong variability in the flow. A six-month mean of the upper layer flow (Fig. 11) shows a merger of the inflows in accord with the traditional image.

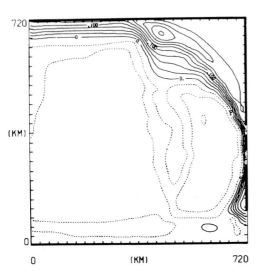

Figure 11. Upper Layer Mean Pressure Anomaly (P_1) based on a six-month period (days 180 to 360). The contour interval is 0.07 N/m^2 and the contour labels are scaled by 10^3.

5.2 Comparison to linear stability of a horizontal shear flow

It is clearly evident, from Figs. 9 and 10 that the eddies are growing spatially and temporally as they propagate downstream. These eddies apparently form as a result of horizontal shear instabilities, as indicated by the similarity of the solutions for the reduced gravity model and for the upper layer of the two-layer model, and by the type of mean to eddy energy transfer, i.e. kinetic energy of the mean flow to kinetic energy of the eddies.

Instabilities of currents in the ocean and atmosphere have been investigated for decades. We attempt to relate some of the results from these investigations, based on linear, normal-mode stability analysis, to the present model results. Early studies of instabilities in this context were done by Kuo (1949), Charney (1947) and Eady (1949). Numerous other studies have followed, and Killworth (1980) has published a more or less unified treatment of barotropic and baroclinic instability in unidirectional, geophysical flows. Most of these studies share a common foundation. The relevant equations are based on quasigeostrophic dynamics (e.g. Pedlosky, 1964). An unbounded flow is assumed along the axis of the mean current. The stability of the system to plane wave perturbations as a function of various nondimensional parameters is then determined. Unstable modes are those which grow exponentially in time all along the axis of the flow.

For the moment we adopt the viewpoint that the St. Vincent inflow is a westward jet in a rotating, stratified flow. From both the two-layer and reduced gravity model results it is clear that eddies amplify downstream by feeding on the mean flow, that is, we have spatially growing disturbances. Gaster (1962) has shown that the relationship between spatially growing and temporally growing disturbances in homogeneous shear flow is simple and involves only the group velocity provided the amplification rates of the disturbances are small. Thus, we proceed (without further justification) to look for similarities between our numerical results and published results from linear stability analyses for temporally growing waves.

For two layer flows, three non-dimensional parameters arise in these analyses: δ, the ratio of the upper to the lower layer depth: λ, the ratio of the length scale (L) of the horizontal shear to the internal radius of deformation, R_D; and the ratio of the planetary vorticity to the vorticity of the flow, $\beta* = \beta L^2/U_o$, where U_o is a characteristic speed. The ratio of the layer depths is small here ($\delta = 0.1$) as discussed above. Unfortunately, there is no unique choice for the characteristic scales. A particular choice for the horizontal length scale is L = 20 km, half the width of the model port that represents St. Vincent Passage. On the other hand the views of the PHA discussed above suggest that the scale of the horizontal shear is approximately 50 km. Similarly, the characteristic speed based on inflow in the upper layer is about $U_o = -0.5$ m/sec. However, this speed might be as low as -0.20 m/sec if we consider the speed at the core of the current around the model eddies. The β-effect appears to be quite small in any case because $-0.28 \le \beta* \le -0.02$, using the previous range of scales. The role of as a restoring force is well-known, though, and we cannot discount its effect on larger scales without further experiments.

The length scale (L) of the horizontal shear is small compared to the deformation radius ($0.2 \le R_D \le 0.6$) and according to Killworth (1980) each layer of the system may be unstable without the other in this situation. Charney (1963) has also noted this decoupling in equatorial systems where R_D is relatively large. If we regard the perturbed flow as O(1) in the upper layer, a much weaker flow of $O(\lambda^2)$ arises in the lower layer. Thus, we should expect primarily horizontal shear instabilities in our model ocean. The energetic features in the reduced gravity model results and the upper layer of the two-layer results are indeed similar as shown above. The linear theory seems to confirm the utility of the reduced gravity model in the present situation.

The wavelength and period of the fastest growing perturbations predicted by
linear theory are sensitive to the characteristic scales and to the profile of
the jet perpendicular to its axis. If on the one hand we choose the larger
speed and smaller length scales, then results from Fig. 1 of Killworth (1980),
suggest that the preferred wavelength and period (for a zonal jet with a
sech^2 profile in the north-south direction) are about 140 km and 7 days. If
on the other hand we choose the smaller speed and the larger length scale, then
results from Fig. 7 of Kuo (1973) suggest that the preferred wavelength and
period are about 310 km and 35 days, respectively. This latter wavelength and
period are in good agreement with the numerical model (e.g. see Figs. 9 and
10). In future work we plan to make further comparisons between the model
results and linear stability theory, when we vary the pertinent nondimensional
parameters.

6. SUMMARY

We have briefly presented the results of our standard case experiments using
the two-layer and reduced gravity models. These experiments used the most
realistic model configuration and parameters for the southeastern Caribbean Sea
based on our best estimates from the observational data.

In the upper layer of the two-layer model and in the reduced gravity model
eddies are generated which compare favorably to the NOAA and NORDA drifter
observations. The upper layer mean flow showed a westward flowing current in
the southern portion of the model basin which is consistent with the ideas
derived from historical hydrography (Wust, 1964; Gordon, 1967; Roemmich, 1981).
Febres-Ortega and Herrera (1976) and Morrison (1977) used meridional sections
to infer the westward-flowing Caribbean current and eastward-flowing counter
currents. By taking appropriate cross-sections through selected fields from
the numerical model, e.g. u(x,y,t), the same interpretation could be made, if
the total horizontal picture were not available. Furthermore, the apparent
correlation between meanders and loops in drifter tracks and the topography may
be fortuitous rather than causal, contrary to the hypothesis advanced by
Molinari et al. (1981). We have demonstrated that realistic eddies can be
generated in the reduced gravity model which does not have bottom topography.
The reduced gravity results suggest that horizontal shear instabilities are the
primary cause of eddy generation in the southeastern Caribbean Sea. The
primary energy transfer in both the reduced gravity and two-layer cases is
barotropic, i.e. kinetic energy of the mean flow to kinetic energy of the
eddies. This tranfer supports the horizontal shear instability hypothesis.
Further evidence for this hypothesis is that the wavelengths and periods
observed in the model are consistent with results from linear instability

theory for a reasonable choice of scaling parameters.

We have also shown in the two-layer case that the layers are nearly decoupled and that the primary effects of topography in the model are confined to the lower layer. As expected in a geostrophically balanced flow which conserves potential vorticity, the flow in the lower layer tends to follow the f/h contours of the topography. The result is a northward current along the topographic contours of the Antilles and a westward current following the topographic contours near the northern boundary. There is also a weak cyclonic gyre following the topographic contours of the Grenada Basin. Furthermore, if we had data on the deep flow along the Venezuelan Slope, we could specify a lower layer inflow near the southern end of the western boundary. Then we might also see a cyclonic circulation in the lower layer of the Venezuelan Basin similar to that found by Roemmich (1981).

We have presented tentative answers to some of the questions posed at the onset of this paper, but there is considerable work still to be done before definite answers are found. Work that is now in progress includes:

1) an investigation of time-dependent inflow (speed and direction),

2) a stability analysis of ideal zonal currents for various values of the Coriolis parameter (f) and differential rotation (β), and for actual zonal current profiles derived from model results,

3) further investigation of the effect of bottom topography,

4) an investigation of the effect of changing lower layer inflow,

5) an analysis of the eddy-mean energetics for key model experiments, and

6) an investigation of the effect of both steady and time dependent trade winds.

This present study is a first step in the use of numerical modeling in a joint modeling and observational program to examine the circulation in the eastern Caribbean Sea. We are optimistic that the results from the initial modeling effort can be used to formulate improved observational studies and that the data from observations can be used to refine the modeling effort.

ACKNOWLEDGEMENTS

We thank Robert Molinari, Irving Brooks and Carol Duckett for providing the NOAA drifter data. Albert Green and Donald Burns deployed the NORDA drifters and provided preliminary data processing. Joyce Ford prepared the final manuscript and typed many rough drafts. Janice Boyd contributed to the initial model setup. This is NORDA Contribution # JA 320:026:81.

APPENDIX A

List of Symbols for Model Equations

A	horizontal eddy viscosity
D	height of bottom topography above a reference level
f	Coriolis parameter
g	acceleration due to gravity
g'	reduced gravity, $g(\rho_2 - \rho_1)/\rho$
h_1, h_2	instantaneous local thickness of the layers
$H_1, H_2(x,y)$	initial thickness of the layers
t	time
u_1, u_2	x-directed components of current velocity
v_1, v_2	y-directed components of current velocity
$\vec{V}_1, \vec{V}_2$	$h_1 \vec{v}_1, h_2 \vec{v}_2$
x, y, z	tangent plane Cartesian coordinates: x positive eastward, y positive northward, z positive upward
β	differential rotation, df/dy
Δt	time increment in the numerical integration
$\Delta x, \Delta y$	horizontal grid increments
η_1	free surface anomaly; height of the free surface above its initial uniform elevation; $\eta_1 = h_1 + h_2 - H_1 - H_2$
η_2	$\eta_2 = H_1 + \eta_1 - h_1 = h_2 - H_2 = -PHA$
ρ, ρ_1, ρ_2	densities of sea water
τ_i^x, τ_i^y	x and y directed tangential stresses at the top (i) and bottom (i+1) of layer i

REFERENCES

Brooks, I.N., 1978. Transport and Velocity Measurements in St. Lucia Passage of the Lesser Antilles, EOS 59: 1102 (Abstract only).

Burns, D.A. and M. Car. 1975. Current Meter Data Report for the Eastern part of the Caribbean Sea, Naval Oceanographic Office TN 6110-6-75, 182pp.

Charney, J.G., 1947: The dynamics of long waves in a baroclinic westerly current, J. Meteorol.: 4, 135-163.

———, 1963: A note on large-scale motions in the tropics. J. Atmos. Sci., 20: 607-609.

Eady, E.T., 1949: Long waves and cyclone waves. Tellus, 1: 33-52.

Febres-Ortega, G. and L.E. Herrera 1976. Caribbean Sea circulation and water mass transports near the Lesser Antilles. Biol. Inst. Oceanogr. Univ. Oriente 15 (1): 83-96.

Gaster, M., 1962: A note on the relation between temporally increasing and spatially increasing disturbances in hydrodynamic stability. J. Fluid Mech., 14: 222-224.

Gordon, A.L. 1967. Circulation of the Caribbean Sea. J. Geophys. Res. 72 (24): 6207-6223.

Hurlburt, H.E. and J.D. Thompson, 1980: A Numerical Study of Loop Current Intrusions and Eddy Shedding. J. Phys. Oceanog., 10: 1611-1651.

Killworth, P.D., 1980: Barotropic and baroclinic instability in rotating stratified fluids. Dyn. Oce. and Atmos., 4: 143-184.

Kuo, H.L., 1949: Dynamic instability of two-dimensional non-divergent flow in a barotropic atmosphere. J. Meteorol., 6: 105-122.

Kuo, H.L., 1973: Dynamics of quasigeostrophic flows and instability theory. Adv. Appl. Mech., 13: 247-330.

Leming, T.D. 1971. Eddies west of the southern Lesser Antilles. In Symposium on Investigations and Resources of the Caribbean Sea and Adjacent Regions. UNESCO, Paris. 113-120.

Mazeika, P.A., D.A. Burns and T.H. Kinder, 1980a. Mesoscale circulation east of the southern Lesser Antilles. J. Geophys. Res. 85 (65): 2743-2758.

Mazeika, P.A., D.A. Burns, and T.H. Kinder, 1980b. Measured flow in St. Vincent and Grenada Passages in 1977. Naval Ocean Research and Development Activity Technical Note 62, 52 pp.

Molinari, R.L., M. Spillane, I. Brooks, D. Atwood and C. Duckett, 1981: Surface currents in the Caribbean Sea as deduced from Lagrangian observations. J. Geophys. Res. 86(C7):6537-6542.

Morrison, J.M., 1977: Water Mass Properties Used as Flow Indicators Within the Eastern Caribbean Sea During the Winter of 1972 and the Fall of 1973. Ph.D. Dissertation, Texas A&M University, College Station, TX, 75 pp.

Niiler, P.P. and W.S. Richardson, 1973. Seasonal variability of the Florida Current. J. Mar. Res. 31 (3): 144-167.

Nof, D., 1978: On geostrophic adjustment in sea straits and wide estuaries: theory and laboratory experiments. Part II - two layer system. J. Phys. Oceanogr. 8 (5): 861-872.

Pedlosky, J., 1964: The stability of currents in the atmosphere and the ocean. Part I. J. Atmos. Sci., 21, 201-219.

Preller, R. and H.E. Hurlburt, 1982: A reduced gravity model of the circulation in the Alboran Sea. In: J.C.J. Nihoul (Editor), Hydrodynamics of Semi-Enclosed Seas. Elsevier, Amsterdam, 75-89.

Roemmich, D., 1981: Circulation of the Caribbean Sea: a well-resolved inverse problem. J. Geophys. Res., in press.

Stalcup, M.C. and W.G. Metcalf, 1972: Current Measurements in the Passages of the Lesser Antilles. J. Geophys. Res. 77 (6): 1032-1049.

Stalcup, M.C., W.G. Metcalf, and M. Zemanovic, 1971: Current Measurements in the Lesser Antilles. Woods Hole Oceanographic Institute Technical Report 71-51, 14 pp. Figures, Tables. Unpublished manuscript.

Teague, W.J., 1979: CTD measurements in the eastern Caribbean Sea, August 1978. Naval Oceanographic Office Technical Note TN 3431-2-79, 24 pp.

Wust, G., 1964: Stratification and Circulation in the Antillean-Caribbean Basin. Columbia University Press, New York, 201 pp.

Wyrtki, K., L. Magaard and J. Hager, 1976: Eddy Energy in the Oceans. J. Geophys. Res. 81 (15): 2641-2646.

A MODEL FOR FRONTAL UPWELLING

C.L. TANG

BEDFORD INSTITUTE OF OCEANOGRAPHY, DARTMOUTH, NOVA SCOTIA, CANADA

ABSTRACT

To investigate the mechanism of frontal upwelling, a linear time-independant analytical model for the circulation below a frontal layer is developed. The role of the frontal layer in the model is to provide a drag at the lower boundary of the frontal layer to drive a motion below. The ambient fluid is viscous with constant vertical and horizontal eddy coefficients. An Ekman transport beneath the frontal layer is generated by the along-front movement of the frontal layer. This Ekman transport is in a direction away from the front and draws fluid in a vertical internal shear layer directly below the front upward, thus creating an upwelling. The thickness of the internal shear layer is $E^{\frac{1}{2}}L$, where E and L are the Ekman number and the horizonal scale of the frontal layer. Two outer Stewartson layers of thickness $E^{\frac{1}{4}}L$ feed the internal shear layer and also serve as return channels for the upwelled fluid. Outside the Stewartson layers, the motion is geostrophic. The vertical velocity is determined by the divergence of the interfacial and bottom Ekman transports and is independent of depth. Effects of stratification in the ambient fluid are discussed. Width of the upwelling layer is calculated and compared with observations in the Gulf of St. Lawrence frontal zone.

1. INTRODUCTION

A recent study of the temperature-salinity structure of the northwestern Gulf of St. Lawrence revealed the existence of a sharp salinity/density front near the entrance to the St. Lawrence Estuary, and strong evidence of upwelling along the front (Tang, 1980, hereafter referred to as T). This front is formed by the outflow of low salinity water from the estuary. The spatial structure and the cross-sectional view of the front is shown in Figs. 1 and 2. The low surface temperature and the hump in the isotherms just outside the frontal layer are signatures of upwelling of cold sub-surface water. The possibility of strong vertical mixing causing the low surface temperature can be ruled out by a close examination of the vertical profiles (not shown). In consistence with the T/S measurements, a filament of cold surface water along the front can often be seen in satellite imagery. Motivated by these observations, we construct this upwelling model to investigate

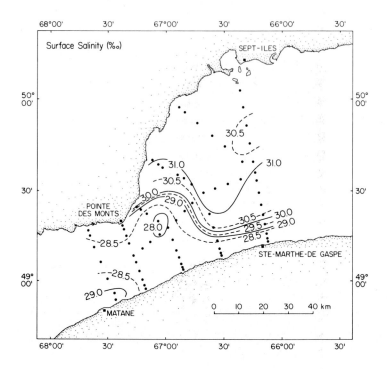

Fig. 1. Surface salinity in the northwestern Gulf of St. Lawrence.

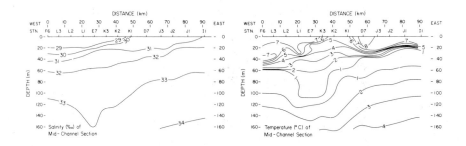

Fig. 2. Salinity and temperature sections (east-west) across the front.

the possibility that the along-front movement of a density front can drive a vertical circulation below and draw water to the surface.

The dynamics of oceanic fronts have been reviewed by Mooers (1978) and Joyce (1978). Mooers et al. (1976) analysed the dynamical structure of a frontal zone and emphasized the importance of comprehending the diffusive mechanism to the cross-front flow. Kao et al. (1978) solved a time dependent problem of frontal intrusion numerically. Their results show how a front is formed from a fresh water source, advances in position with time and finally a steady-state dominated by a strong along-front geostrophic flow is reached. In their model, the cross-front flow is controlled by specified upstream and downstream boundary conditions. A consequence of this is that the flow is forced to cross the interface to conserve mass. As we shall see, our model employs a different boundary condition resulting in a completely different flow pattern.

An important ingredient for the model is the concept of turbulent interfacial layer along the frontal interface. Csanady (1978) examined the experimental evidence of it and suggested (Horne et al., 1978) that such a frictional layer could provide a channel for the fluid beneath the frontal layer to move along the interface. From the point of view of modelling, the existence of an interfacial layer is a consequence of the assumption of small and constant eddy coefficient. Since such a turbulent interfacial layer has all the characteristics of a surface Ekman layer, we shall call it an interfacial Ekman layer.

Another element of the model is the internal shear layer. A front, due to the discontinuity of density at the surface, creates a sharp horizontal shear along a vertical line below the discontinuity (Csanady, 1971). Friction acts to weaken the shear. An internal shear layer is a vertical layer in which frictional effects are important. Killworth (1973) analyzed the layer structure around a current discontinuity caused by a sudden change in bottom slope and found that more than one internal shear layer were needed in order to satisfy all continuity requirements. The layer structure of the ambient fluid in this model is the same as that of Killworth. It should be emphasized that the layer structure is not an assumption. It is a consequence of parametrizing the horizontal turbulent mixing by a constant eddy coefficient, and its existence is independent of the method of solution. If no internal shear layer is found in nature, the conclusion we can draw is that our choice for the form of the horizontal turbulent mixing terms in the momentum equations is incorrect. The same argument holds for the interfacial Ekman layer.

With the concept of boundary layers discussed above, it was suggested in T that a mechanism similar to that for coastal upwelling could produce frontal upwelling. Coastal upwelling is caused by a wind-generated Ekman transport sucking a compensating flow from below through a coastal boundary layer. In the case of a density front, the interfacial Ekman flow on the lower side of the interface driven by the along-front vertical shear always moves in a direction away from the front. If there is no significant flow across the interface, the fluid that flows into the interfacial Ekman layer has to be drawn from the ambient fluid. It cannot be drawn from near the surface or directly from the interior since this would require a strong vertical shear near the surface or a high along-front pressure gradient, both of which do not exist in the absence of an external forcing. The flow transported out of the interfacial Ekman layer can be replenished by a vertical transport of subsurface fluid to the surface through an internal shear layer, and thus an upwelling is created.

In this paper, the cross-front circulation just described will be obtained from a model with the following basic assumptions:
a. time independent and two-dimensional motion,
b. slab-like structure for the frontal layer,
c. constant density, vertical and horizontal eddy coefficients for the lower layer,
d. linear dynamics for the lower layer,
e. a prescribed along-front velocity for the frontal layer,
f. no motion at infinity on both sides of the front in either layer,
g. no flow across the interface.
The governing equations we shall use are basically the same as those in Mooers (1978) and Kao et al. (1978). To solve the equations analytically, the standard boundary layer technique will be employed. The entire cross-section is divided into different regions (layers) according to the momentum balance in each region. The equations are solved in each region separately and then joined together by matching boundary conditions. In the following section, we define the mathematical problem and discuss the division of the regions. The solutions are obtained in the next three sections. From the solutions, several streamline patterns are calculated in section 6. A summary and discussion is given in the last section.

The density front in T will be used as an example to make order of magnitude estimates. The parameter values appropriate for this front are:

L = 30 km,   the cross-front length scale
U = 20 cm s^{-1},   the along-front velocity scale
H = 300 m,   the water depth

Before proceeding to the development of the model, we wish to emphasize that
(a) this model is not a frontogenisis model and we are not concerned with how the front is formed. The existence of the front is assumed and its along-front motion is given. We are here dealing with the small second order cross-front motion induced by the first order frontal movement.
(b) While the dynamics of the frontal layer itself are of great interest to oceanographers, our purpose here is to study the motion of the ambient fluid below the

frontal layer. Because of this, the frontal layer in this model is highly simplified and only serves as a moving boundary to drive the fluid below it. The
circulation within the frontal layer itself is not resolved.

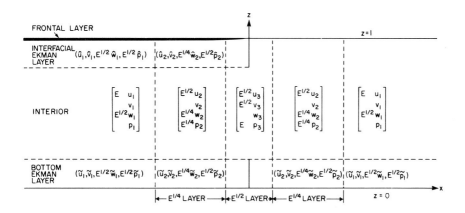

Fig. 3. Layer structure of the model and orders of velocity components and
pressure in each layer and region.

2. GOVERNING EQUATIONS AND STRUCTURE OF THE MODEL

We consider a frontal layer of negligible thickness embedded in a fluid of constant density in the f-plane moving in the negative y direction, where the coordinate system is x in the cross-front, y in the along-front and z in the upward
direction as shown in Fig. 3. The motion in the ambient fluid is governed by the
following set of equations:

$$- v = - \frac{\partial p}{\partial x} + \frac{1}{2} E_h \nabla^2 u + \frac{1}{2} E_v \frac{\partial^2 u}{\partial z^2} \tag{2.1a}$$

$$u = - \frac{\partial p}{\partial y} + \frac{1}{2} E_h \nabla^2 v + \frac{1}{2} E_v \frac{\partial^2 u}{\partial z^2} \tag{2.1b}$$

$$0 = - \frac{\partial p}{\partial z} + \frac{1}{2} \delta^2 E_h \nabla^2 w + \frac{1}{2} \delta^2 E_v \frac{\partial^2 w}{\partial z^2} \tag{2.1c}$$

$$\frac{\partial u}{\partial x} + \frac{\partial v}{\partial y} + \frac{\partial w}{\partial z} = 0 \tag{2.1d}$$

where $\nabla^2 = \frac{\partial^2}{\partial x^2} + \frac{\partial^2}{\partial y^2}$. The nonlinear terms in the momentum equations have been
neglected, and all the variables have been non-dimensionalized by the following

scalings

$$(x^*, y^*) = L\ (x,y)$$
$$z^* = Hz$$
$$(u^*, v^*) = U\ (u,v)$$
$$w^* = (HU/L)w$$
$$p^* = \rho ULfp$$

where the asterisks indicate dimensional variables. L is the horizontal length scale, H is the water depth, ρ is the density and f is the Coriolis parameter. Three dimensionless parameters appear in the equations. They are

$$E_v = 2A_v/(fH^2),\qquad \text{the vertical Ekman number}$$
$$E_h = 2A_h/(fL^2),\qquad \text{the horizontal Ekman number}$$
$$\delta = H/L,\qquad \text{the aspect ratio}$$

where A_v and A_h are the vertical and horizontal eddy coefficient respectively.

The first order solution of (2.1) without the friction terms is a geostrophic along-front flow with a discontinuity at x=0. Frictions act to eliminate the discontinuity. This is acheived by adding correction terms to the geostrophic solution in the internal shear layers around the discontinuity. A single shear layer cannot make all components of the velocity continuous. A Stewartson layer of thickness $E_h^{\frac{1}{4}}$ on each side of the discontinuity can smooth out the discontinuity in v (Veronis, 1970). Between the two Stewartson layers, there exist a thinner layer of thickness $E_h^{\frac{1}{2}}$ in which u can be made continuous. An even thinner layer of thickness δ serves to match w across x=0 (Pedlosky, 1968). Since the δ layer carries a transport smaller than the transport in other layers by a factor of $\delta/E_h^{\frac{1}{2}}$, we shall neglect this layer in the solution. The only consequence of this omission to the cross-front circulation is a discontinuity in the slope of the streamlines at x=0. Beneath the frontal layer and above the bottom, an interfacial Ekman layer and a bottom Ekman layer are developed, both of thickness $E_v^{\frac{1}{2}}$. They are required to satisfy the no-slip condition at the bottom and the interface.

To simplify the mathematics without at the time destroying the underlying physics, we assume $E_v = E_h \equiv E$. The condition $E \ll 1$ is required to allow us to use the boundary layer method to solve the equation. The layer structure and the order of magnitude of the correction terms in each layer are shown in Fig. 3. The total velocity and pressure in a given layer are the sum of the correction terms as given in the sections dealing with the individual regions.

We shall use the subscripts 0, 1, 2, 3 and 4 to denote the frontal layer, the $O(1)$ region, the $E^{\frac{1}{4}}$ layer and the $E^{\frac{1}{2}}$ layer respectively. The overhead symbols "^" and "~" refer to the interfacial and the bottom Ekman layers respectively. Variables without an overhead symbol denote the interior, which is defined to be the region between the two Ekman layers for $x < 0$, and the region above the bottom for $x > 0$.

3. THE O(1) REGION

This is the region outside the Stewartson layers. In the interior, the motion is geostrophic and independent of z. The equations of motion are

$$- v_1 + \frac{\partial p_1}{\partial x} = 0 \tag{3.1a}$$

$$u_1 = O(E) \tag{3.1b}$$

$$\frac{\partial p_1}{\partial z} = 0 \tag{3.1c}$$

$$\frac{\partial w_1}{\partial z} = 0 \tag{3.1d}$$

To order $E^{\frac{1}{2}}$, there is no horizontal flow. The vertical velocity is of order $E^{\frac{1}{2}}$ and is determined by the divergence in the two Ekman layers. The along-front velocity is of order 1 and is related to the pressure gradient. But because of the non-slip boundary condition, v_1 can be fixed by mass conservation alone.

The bottom boundary layer solutions with no-slip condition can be obtained by standard technique, and are given by

$$\tilde{u}_1 = -v_1 \exp\left(-E^{\frac{1}{2}}z\right) \sin\left(E^{\frac{1}{2}}z\right) \tag{3.2a}$$

$$\tilde{v}_1 = -v_1 \exp\left(-E^{\frac{1}{2}}z\right) \cos\left(E^{\frac{1}{2}}z\right) \tag{3.2b}$$

The cross-front mass transport is

$$\tilde{U}_1 = \int_0^\infty \tilde{u}_1 \, dz = -\frac{1}{2} E^{\frac{1}{2}} v_1 \tag{3.3}$$

The vertical velocity at z=0 is, by continuity,

$$\tilde{w}_1(x,0) = E^{-\frac{1}{2}}\frac{\partial \tilde{U}_1}{\partial x} = -\frac{1}{2}\frac{\partial v_1}{\partial x} \tag{3.4}$$

The condition of no normal velocity at the bottom determines the interior vertical velocity:

$$w_1(x,z) = w_1(x,0) = -\tilde{w}_1(x,0) = -\frac{1}{2}\frac{\partial v_1}{\partial x} \tag{3.5}$$

The solutions in the interfacial Ekman layer are similar to those in the bottom Ekman layer except that instead of the no slip condition the along-front velocity at the interface is equal to the frontal velocity, i.e.,

$$v_1(x,1) + \hat{v}_1(x,1) = v_0(x) \tag{3.6}$$

where v_0 is the velocity of the frontal layer. We then have a horizontal velocity of

$$\hat{u}_1 = -(v_0-v_1)\exp[E^{-\frac{1}{2}}(1-z)]\sin[E^{-\frac{1}{2}}(1-z)] \tag{3.7a}$$

$$\hat{v}_1 = (v_1-v_1)\exp[E^{-\frac{1}{2}}(1-z)]\cos[E^{-\frac{1}{2}}(1-z)] \tag{3.7b}$$

a cross-front mass transport of

$$\hat{U}_1 = \int_{-\infty}^{1}\hat{u}_1\ dz = \frac{1}{2}E^{\frac{1}{2}}(v_0-v_1) \tag{3.8}$$

and a vertical velocity of

$$\hat{w}_1(x,1) = -E^{-\frac{1}{2}}\frac{\partial\hat{U}_1}{\partial x} = -\frac{1}{2}\frac{\partial(v_0-v_1)}{\partial x} \tag{3.9}$$

The condition of zero normal velocity at z=1 gives

$$w_1(x,z) = w_1(x,1) = -\hat{w}_1(x,1) = -\frac{1}{2}\frac{\partial(v_0-v_1)}{\partial x} \tag{3.10}$$

For the along-front currents to satisfy both (3.10) and (3.5), v_0 and v_1 cannot be independently specified. They are related by

$$v_1 = \frac{1}{2}v_0 \tag{3.11}$$

We note that with (3.11) the mass transports in the two Ekman layers are equal in magnitude and opposite in sign, a necessary consequence of mass conservation.

In deriving (3.11), the boundary condition of no motion at $x = \pm\infty$ has been used. Since v_0 exists only in $x < 0$, we have

$$v_1 = w_1 = 0, \qquad \text{for } x > 0 \tag{3.10}$$

Eqs. (3.2), (3.5), (3.7) and (3.11) completely specify the motion in the $0(1)$ region. To summarize, the interior motion is geostrophic with no cross-front horizontal velocity. The along-front flow is driven by the frontal motion with a velocity equal to half of the frontal velocity. The shear across the interface and the along-front flow induce an interfacial and a bottom Ekman transport respectively. The excess mass resulting from the divergence of the interfacial Ekman transport moves straight downward and is received by the bottom Ekman layer.

4. THE $E^{\frac{1}{4}}$ LAYER

A function of this layer is to smooth v_1 across $x=0$. This requires the correction v to be of the same order of magnitude as v_1. Similar to the $0(1)$ region, the $E^{\frac{1}{4}}$ layer can be divided vertically into three regions.

4.1 The interior

The velocity components and pressure are decomposed as

$$u = E^{\frac{1}{4}} u_2 + \dots \tag{4.1a}$$

$$v = v_1 + v_2 + \dots \tag{4.1b}$$

$$w = E^{\frac{1}{2}} w_1 + E^{\frac{1}{4}} w_2 + \dots \tag{4.1c}$$

$$p = p_1 + E^{\frac{1}{4}} w_2 + \dots \tag{4.1d}$$

and obey (Veronis, 1970)

$$-\frac{\partial p_2}{\partial \xi} + v_2 = 0 \tag{4.2a}$$

$$-u_2 + \frac{1}{2} \frac{\partial^2 v_2}{\partial \xi^2} = 0 \tag{4.2b}$$

$$\frac{\partial p_2}{\partial z} = 0 \tag{4.2c}$$

$$\frac{\partial u_2}{\partial \xi} + \frac{\partial w_2}{\partial z} = 0 \tag{4.2d}$$

where $\xi = E^{-\frac{1}{4}} x$. From these equations, we immediately see that u_2, v_2 and p_2 are independent of z. u_2 and w_2 as functions of v_2 are given by

$$u_2 = \frac{1}{2} \frac{\partial^2 v_2}{\partial \xi^2} \tag{4.3a}$$

$$w_2(x<0,z) = \int_0^z \frac{\partial u_2}{\partial \xi} \, dz + w_2(\xi,0) = -\frac{1}{2} z \frac{\partial^3 v_2}{\partial \xi^3} + w_2(\xi,0) \tag{4.3b}$$

$$w_2(x>0,z) = \int_z^1 \frac{\partial u_2}{\partial \xi} \, dz = \frac{1}{2} (1-z) \frac{\partial^3 v_2}{\partial \xi^3} \tag{4.3c}$$

The interior velocity field can only be determined after the solutions in the Ekman layers are found.

4.2   The bottom Ekman layer

The dynamical variables can be expanded as

$$u = \tilde{u}_1 + E^{\frac{1}{2}} u_2 + \tilde{u}_2 + \dots \tag{4.4a}$$

$$v = v_1 + \tilde{v}_1 + v_2 + \tilde{v}_2 + \dots \tag{4.4b}$$

$$w = E^{\frac{1}{2}} w_1 + E^{\frac{1}{2}} \tilde{w}_1 + E^{\frac{1}{4}} w_2 + E^{\frac{1}{4}} \tilde{w}_2 + \dots \tag{4.4c}$$

$$p = p_1 + E^{\frac{1}{2}} \tilde{p}_1 + E^{\frac{1}{4}} p_2 + E^{\frac{1}{2}} \tilde{p}_2 + \dots \tag{4.4d}$$

The equations of motion in the stretched coordinate system $\xi = E^{-\frac{1}{4}}x$, $\zeta = E^{-\frac{1}{2}}z$ are

$$-\tilde{v}_2 + \frac{1}{2} \frac{\partial^2 \tilde{u}_2}{\partial \zeta^2} = 0 \tag{4.5a}$$

$$-\tilde{u}_2 + \frac{1}{2} \frac{\partial^2 \tilde{v}_2}{\partial \zeta^2} = 0 \tag{4.5b}$$

$$\frac{\partial \tilde{p}_2}{\partial \zeta} = 0 \qquad\qquad (4.5c)$$

$$\frac{\partial \tilde{u}_2}{\partial \xi} + \frac{\partial \tilde{v}_2}{\partial \zeta} = 0 \qquad\qquad (4.5d)$$

The solutions are

$$\tilde{u}_2 = \exp(-\zeta)\, [B(\xi)\, \sin\zeta - C(\xi)\, \cos\zeta] \qquad\qquad (4.6a)$$

$$\tilde{v}_2 = \exp(-\zeta)\, [B(\xi)\, \sin\zeta + C(\xi)\, \cos\zeta] \qquad\qquad (4.6b)$$

$$\tilde{w}_2 = - \int_{\infty}^{\zeta} \frac{\partial \tilde{u}_2}{\partial \xi}\, d\zeta \qquad\qquad (4.6c)$$

At $\zeta = 0$, the vertical velocity is given by

$$\tilde{w}_2\,(\xi,0) = \frac{1}{2} \frac{\partial}{\partial \xi}\,(B-C) \qquad\qquad (4.7)$$

The two unknowns B and C are to be determined from the boundary conditions at z=0, 1.

For $x < 0$, the no-slip condition at the bottom gives

$$C = 0 \qquad\qquad (4.8a)$$

$$v_2 + B = 0 \qquad\qquad (4.8b)$$

$$\tilde{w}_2(\xi,0) + \frac{1}{2} \frac{\partial}{\partial \xi}\,(B-C) = 0 \qquad\qquad (4.8c)$$

corresponding to the u,v and w components of the velocity. Eliminating B and C from (4.8), we obtain an equation for v_2:

$$\frac{\partial v_2}{\partial \xi} - 2\, w_2(\xi,0) = 0, \qquad \xi < 0 \qquad\qquad (4.9)$$

A similar equation linking v_2 and $w_2(\xi,0)$ will be derived when we consider the interfacial Ekman layer.

For $x > 0$, the counterpart of (4.9) does not have a term corresponding to the interior vertical velocity since there is no Ekman layer at $z=1$. Using the no-slip condition, (4.3d), (4.6) and (4.7), we obtain

$$\frac{\partial}{\partial \xi} \left(\frac{\partial^2}{\partial \xi^2} - 1\right) v_2 = 0, \qquad \xi > 0 \tag{4.10}$$

there are three general solutions for (4.10) but only one is bounded. The solution that vanishes as $\xi \to \infty$ is

$$v_2 = D \exp(-\xi), \qquad \xi > 0 \tag{4.11}$$

where D is a constant to be determined by matching v_2 at $\xi = 0$.

4.3   The interfacial Ekman layer

The variables in this layer obey a similar set of equation as the bottom boundary layer and the solutions have the same form as (4.6). Continuity of velocities at $z = 1$ leads to the equation

$$\frac{\partial}{\partial \xi} \left(\frac{\partial^2}{\partial \xi^2} - 1\right) v_2 - 2w_2(\xi,0) = 0, \qquad \xi < 0 \tag{4.12}$$

Eliminating $w_2(\xi,0) = 0$ from (4.12) and (4.9), we get

$$\frac{\partial}{\partial \xi} \left(\frac{\partial^2}{\partial \xi^2} - 2\right) v_2 = 0, \qquad \xi < 0 \tag{4.13}$$

The bounded solution of (4.13) is

$$v_2 = F \exp(2^{\frac{1}{2}} \xi), \qquad \xi < 0 \tag{4.14}$$

The two constants in the solutions for v_2, D and F, can be determined from the condition of continuity of the total along-front velocity, $v_1 + v_2$, and its first derivative, $\partial(v_1+v_2)/\partial \xi$, at $\xi = 0$. The results of the calculation are

$$v_2 = v_0/2 - K [v_0(0) + E^{\frac{1}{4}} v_0'] \exp(2^{\frac{1}{2}} \xi), \qquad x < 0 \tag{4.15a}$$

$$v_2 = K [2^{\frac{1}{2}} v_0(0) - E^{\frac{1}{4}} v_0'] \exp(-\xi), \qquad x > 0 \tag{4.15b}$$

where $K = 0.5/(1+2^{\frac{1}{2}})$ and v_0' is $\partial v_0/\partial x$ evaluated at $x = 0$.

Having obtained v_2, we can easily calculate u_2 and w_2 as well as the velocities in the boundary layer from (4.3) and (4.6). In particular, u_2 is given by (4.3a),

(4.10) and (4.13):

$$u_2 = \frac{1}{2} v_2, \qquad \xi > 0 \tag{4.16a}$$

$$u_2 = v_2, \qquad \xi < 0 \tag{4.16b}$$

u_2 is in general discontinuous at $\xi = 0$. This necessitates a thinner layer around $x = 0$ to smooth out the discontinuity as will be discussed in the following section.

The total cross-front mass transport in the interfacial and the bottom Ekman layer, $\hat{U}$ and $\tilde{U}$, are given by

$$\hat{U} = \tilde{U}_1 + \int_{-\infty}^{1} \hat{u}_2 \, dz = \frac{1}{2} E^{\frac{1}{2}}(v_1 - v_2), \qquad x < 0 \tag{4.17a}$$

$$\tilde{U} = \tilde{U}_1 + \int_{0}^{\infty} \tilde{u}_2 \, dz = -\frac{1}{2} E^{\frac{1}{2}}(v_1 + v_2) \tag{4.17b}$$

v_2 drives an interfacial and a bottom transports of equal magnitudes and directions.

To recap our findings in this section, to smooth the along-front geostrophic flow, a counter current in the $E^{\frac{1}{4}}$ layer on both sides of the discontinuity is developed, which in turn drives a bottom Ekman transport on both sides and an interfacial Ekman transport in $x < 0$. The two Ekman flows are connected through the interior of the $E^{\frac{1}{4}}$ layer giving rise to a cross-front circulation. However, the horizontal velocity so generated is discontinuous at $x=0$.

5.   THE $E^{\frac{1}{2}}$ LAYER

The horizontal velocity is made continuous in this layer. This requires the correction term for u be of order $E^{\frac{1}{2}}$. The vertical velocity is, by continuity, of order 1. Because of the large vertical velocity, we can identify this layer as the upwelling layer. The structure of the dynamical variables in the interior region on this layer can be represented by

$$u = E^{\frac{1}{2}} u_2 + E^{\frac{1}{2}} u_3 + \ldots$$

$$v = v_1 + v_2 + E^{\frac{1}{2}} v_3 + \ldots$$

$$w = E^{\frac{1}{2}} w_1 + E^{\frac{1}{4}} w_2 + w_3 + \ldots$$

$$p = p_1 + E^{\frac{1}{4}} p_2 + E p_3 + \dots.$$

The variables are governed by

$$- \frac{\partial p_3}{\partial \eta} + v_3 + \frac{\partial^2 u_3}{\partial \eta^2} = 0 \tag{5.1a}$$

$$- u_3 + \frac{\partial^2 v_3}{\partial \eta^2} = 0 \tag{5.1b}$$

$$\frac{\partial p_3}{\partial z} = 0 \tag{5.1c}$$

$$\frac{\partial u_3}{\partial \eta} + \frac{\partial w_3}{\partial z} = 0 \tag{5.1d}$$

where $\eta = E^{-\frac{1}{2}} x$.

A complete solution of (5.1) requires the specification of boundary conditions at $z = 0,1$, which can be found only if the solutions in the two $E^{\frac{1}{2}} \times E^{\frac{1}{2}}$ boxes are known. However, without knowing the detailed structure of the velocity field, it is still possible to calculate the transport in an out of the $E^{\frac{1}{2}}$ layer through the continuity relations. We thus shall not attempt to solve the difficult two-dimensional problem in the two corner boxes.

The volume of fluid that upwells to the frontal zone, W, is equal to that flowing out of the interfacial Ekman layer at x=0, and is given by, from (4.16b) and (4.17a),

$$W = -\hat{U}(0) = - \frac{1}{2} E^{\frac{1}{2}} [v_0(0) - v_1(0) - v_2(0)] \tag{5.2a}$$

$$= -K E^{\frac{1}{2}} (v_0 + E^{\frac{1}{4}} v_0')/2 \tag{5.2b}$$

(5.2a) states that the upward mass transport is proportional to the vertical shear at the front. For a front which has cross-front geostrophic balance, v_0 takes an exponential form and is negative (Csanady, 1971). We thus have a positive W indicating an upwelling. The upward mass transport and the width of the upwelling zone, $E^{\frac{1}{2}}$, increase with friction, while the vertical velocity remains of order 1.

The upwelling fluid is sucked into the interfacial Ekman layer and moves in the negative x direction. It leaves the interfacial Ekman layer by sinking to the interior of the $E^{\frac{1}{4}}$ layer and the O(1) region. A portion of it reaches the bottom Ekman layer, and then flows towards the $E^{\frac{1}{2}}$ layer. Along the way, it is forced upward by the divergence of the bottom Ekman transport. The fluid can also move directly from the interfacial Ekman layer to the $E^{\frac{1}{2}}$ layer through the interior of the $E^{\frac{1}{4}}$ layer. The volume of fluid that feeds the $E^{\frac{1}{2}}$ layer by way of the bottom Ekman layer, U_b, and through the interior, U_i, can be calculated from (4.17b) and (4.16b).

$$U_b = \tilde{U}(0) = -\frac{1}{2} E^{\frac{1}{2}} [v_1(0) + v_2(0)] \tag{5.3}$$

$$U_i = \int_0^1 u_2(0,z) \, dz = E^{\frac{1}{2}} v_2(0) \tag{5.4}$$

We note that the sum of U_b and U_i is equal to W, a consequence of mass conservation. v_2 is the correction term to the along-front geostrophic flow toeliminate the discontinuity at x=0. Its magnitude increases with the sharpness of the frontal velocity. v_2 drives a circulation cell counter the one driven by v_1 and partially cancels the flow in the lower part of the $E^{\frac{1}{4}}$ layer. Thus the larger v_2 is, the higher the circulation cell is situated. However, unless the total along-front velocity is zero, there is always fluid at the bottom that rises to the surface. In reality, we do not expect that a surface front in the open ocean can draw water from the deep bottom. The reason that the bottom water also participates in the circulation in our model is that we have assumed a homogeneous lower layer, hence no energy is required to lift the fluid from the bottom to the upper ocean. This situation can change in a model with stratification in the lower layer, in which conservation of energy would make the circulation confine to the upper part of the ocean.

The $E^{\frac{1}{2}}$ layer in this model is needed to eliminate the discontinuity created by the front at x=0. In the ocean if the length scale of the zone of high surface density gradient is greater than $E^{\frac{1}{2}}$, then an $E^{\frac{1}{2}}$ layer is not required. All the sunk fluid is returned to the surface through the $E^{\frac{1}{4}}$ layer.

6. NUMERICAL EXAMPLES

We define a stream function, Ψ, by

$$u = -\frac{\partial \Psi}{\partial z} \tag{6.1a}$$

$$w = \frac{\partial \Psi}{\partial x} \tag{6.1b}$$

$$\Psi = 0, \qquad x \to \pm\infty \tag{6.1c}$$

Outside the $E^{\frac{1}{2}}$ layer, the total velocity in any given region is the sum of all the interior and the boundary layer solutions. The stream function can be obtained by integration of the vertical velocity over x:

for x < 0

$$E^{-\frac{1}{2}} \Psi = \int_{-\infty}^{x} (w_1 + \hat{w}_1 + \tilde{w}_1) \, dx + \int_{-\infty}^{\xi} (w_2 + \hat{w}_2 + \tilde{w}_2) \, d\xi$$

$$= \frac{1}{2} (v_1 + v_2 - z \frac{\partial^2 v_2}{\partial \xi^2}) - \frac{1}{2} (v_1 + v_2) F(\zeta)$$

$$- \frac{1}{2} (v_0 - v_1 - v_2) F(\zeta') \qquad (6.2a)$$

and for x > 0

$$E^{-\frac{1}{2}} \Psi = \int_{x}^{\infty} (w_1 + \tilde{w}_1) \, dx + \int_{\xi}^{\infty} (w_2 + \tilde{w}_2) \, d\zeta$$

$$= \frac{1}{2} (1-z) \frac{\partial^2 v_2}{\partial \xi^2} - \frac{1}{2} v_2 F(\zeta) \qquad (6.2b)$$

where $\zeta = E^{\frac{1}{2}} z$, $\zeta' = E^{-\frac{1}{2}}(1-z)$ and $F(\zeta) = (\sin\zeta + \cos\zeta) \exp (-\zeta)$. $F(\zeta)$ and $F(\zeta')$ have non-zero values only in the bottom and interfacial Ekman layer respectively.

The structure of the cross-front circulation is now clearly exhibited in these simple expressions. the interior stream functions represented by the first terms of (6.2a) and (6.2b) have a linear z-dependence, implying a constant u. The second terms give the bottom Ekman transport which is proportional to the along-front interior velocity. The interfacial Ekman transport given by the third term of (6.2a) is determined by the shear between the frontal and the lower layers.

Fig. 4 shows the contours of $E^{-\frac{1}{2}}\Psi$ calculated from the following sets of parameters: (a) E = 0.01, v_0 = -exp(x) (b) E = 0.1, v_0 = -exp(x) and (c) E = 0.01, v_0 = -2exp(2x). The frontal velocity, v_0, and the interior along-front velocity, v = $v_1 + v_2$, are shown above and below the circulation diagrams respectively. Since the solution (6.2) is valid only in the $E^{\frac{1}{4}}$ layer and the O(1) region the streamlines within the $E^{\frac{1}{2}}$ layer are hand-interpolated.

From Fig. 4(a) to 4(c), we can see how the circulation patterns change with the frontal velocity and the friction. The interfacial and bottom Ekman layers in (a) and (c) can be identified by the crowed streamlines and have a thickness of $E^{\frac{1}{2}}$ =

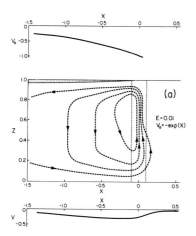

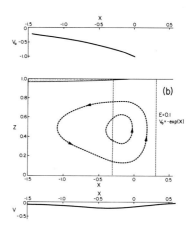

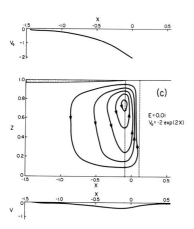

Fig. 4. Contours of $E^{-\frac{1}{2}} \psi$ calculated from the parameter sets: (a) $E = 0.01$, $V_o = -\exp(x)$ (b) $E = 0.1$, $V_o = -\exp(x)$ and (c) $E = 0.01$, $V_o = -2\exp(2x)$. V_o and the interior along-front velocity, V, are shown above and below the circulation diagrams respectively. Contour intervals are 50 for the dotted lines, and 100 for the solid lines.

0.1. In the O(1) region, there is no horizontal velocity and the vertical velocity is independent of z. The is most evident in (a). The consequences of a sharper frontal velocity can be seen by comparing (a) and (c). There is a relatively larger transport in the $E^{\frac{1}{4}}$ layer ($E^{\frac{1}{4}}$ = 0.32) and the circulation cell is closer to the surface in (c). The larger Ekman number in (b) gives rise to thickest boundary layers ($E^{\frac{1}{2}}$ = 0.32), which are not identifiable in the contour plot. The streamline pattern is almost symmetrical about z = 0.5. The along-front velocity in the lower layer, v, would be equal to $\frac{1}{2} v_0$ if there were no $E^{\frac{1}{4}}$ layer. The $E^{\frac{1}{4}}$ layer serves to smooth out the discontinuity at x = 0. It can be seen from the plots of v that the distance over which v changes from a (negative) maximum value to zero in x > 0 is greatest for (b). The absolute value of the maximum is controlled by the maximum of v_0 as can be seen by a comparison of (a) and (c).

As we noted in the introduction, a significant difference between this model and that of Kao et al. (1978) is that we impose the condition of no cross-front flow at x = ±∞, while in Kao et al., the cross-front flow originates from the frontal layer at x = -∞, which by continuity has to cross the frontal interface, and then moves on to x = ∞. This difference in the boundary condition results in quite dissimilar circulation patterns.

7. SUMMARY AND DISCUSSION

We have developed a model for the circulation below a frontal layer. Friction and the Coriolis force play a dominant role in the dynamics. In the absence of friction, the system is in geostrophic balance with a flow in the along-front direction with a discontinuity in the water column below the front. Frictional effects create several Ekman and internal shear layers. An interfacial Ekman layer beneath the frontal interface channels a transport of order $E^{\frac{1}{2}}$ in a direction away from the front. A compensating flow with a vertical velocity of order 1 upwells to the surface through a thin vertical internal shear layer of thickness $E^{\frac{1}{2}}$ around the discontinuity. The fluid in the $E^{\frac{1}{2}}$ layer is drawn from a thicker Stewartson layer of thickness $E^{\frac{1}{4}}$, which also serves as a return channel for the upwelled fluid.

A front maintains its sharpness by the movement of surface ambient water towards the front. Our results indicate that this surface convergence is achieved through upwelled water being sucked underneath the frontal layer by the Ekman transport. The distance over which the surface convergence occurs is $E^{\frac{1}{2}}$ from the front.

The effect of stratification in the ambient fluid to the circulated can be understood by drawing analogy from coastal upwelling problems (Barcilon and Pedlosky, 1967; Hsueh and Ou, 1975). We shall restrict our discussion to horizontal and vertical Ekmans of equal order of magnitude. Let us define a stratification parameter by S = $(N \delta/f)^2$, where N is the Brunt-Väsäila frequency. For a weak stratification, $\sigma S < E$, where σ is the Prandt number, the fluid in the lower layer behaves essentially as if it were homogeneous. For stratification in the range $E < \sigma S < E^{\frac{1}{2}}$, the development of an interfacial Ekman layer is not affected by the stratification. The internal shear layer around the discontinuity consists of an inner layer of thickness $(\sigma S)^{\frac{1}{2}}$ and two Stewartson layers on both sides of the inner layer. The $(\sigma S)^{\frac{1}{2}}$ layer assumes the role of the $E^{\frac{1}{2}}$ in the homogeneous fluid with a vertical transport of order $E^{\frac{1}{2}}$ and a vertical velocity of order $(E/\sigma S)^{\frac{1}{2}}$. In comparison with upwelling in a homogeneous lower layer, the vertical velocity is smaller, the width of the upwelling zone is greater and the vertical transport is the same. The Stewartson layers have the same function as in the homogeneous case. We thus see that the basic mechanism of upwelling is unchanged in a weakly stratified fluid. If σS is increased beyond $E^{\frac{1}{2}}$, no interfacial Ekman layer exists and the dynamics are governed mainly by dissipative processes.

We now use the observations in the Gulf of St. Lawrence frontal zone to obtain some order of magnitude estimates. From the CTD data, S is approximately 0.27 below the frontal layer. For the result of the homogeneous case to be applicable we need a vertical eddy coefficient $E > \sigma S$, which corresponds to an interfacial Ekman layer of a thickness of 150 m or greater (assuming $\sigma = 1$). This is apparently too large since the water depth is only 300 m. Consequently, we use the result for weak stratification, i.e., $E < \sigma S < E^{\frac{1}{2}}$. The corresponding range for E and the width of the upwelling zone, Δx, are given by

$$0.07 < E < 0.27 \tag{7.1}$$
$$\Delta x = (\sigma S)^{\frac{1}{2}} L = \sigma NH/f = 15 \text{ km} \tag{7.2}$$

Although the upwelling width is difficult to define and determine from the data, from the width of the zone of cold surface water in Fig. 2, the upwelling zone appears to be 10 to 20 km wide, which is consistent with the calculated width. The vertical velocity of the upwelling layer in the stratified case is of order $(E/\sigma S)^{\frac{1}{2}}$. Using (7.1), we obtain a vertical velocity of 0.1 to 0.2 cm s^{-1}. This represents a very strong vertical motion and should be able to detect with a vertical current meter.

An alternative interpretation of the results is to identify the $x > 0$ half of the $E^{\frac{1}{4}}$ layer as the upwelling layer. As we noted earlier, the $E^{\frac{1}{2}}$ layer is required if there is a discontinuity in the frontal velocity. In a frontal zone, there are high horizontal gradients of along-front velocity across the front, but the distance over which the rapid change in velocity occurs may not be smaller than $E^{\frac{1}{2}}$. Under such circumstances, there does not exist an $E^{\frac{1}{2}}$ layer. Sinking takes place in the $E^{\frac{1}{4}}$ layer and the $O(1)$ region below the frontal layer, and upwelling takes place on the other side of the $E^{\frac{1}{4}}$ layer. We thus have

348

$$\Delta x = E^{\frac{1}{4}} L = (A_h/f)^{\frac{1}{4}} L^{\frac{1}{2}}$$

Using 15 km for Δx, we get $A_h = 5 \times 10^7$ cm^2 s^{-1}. This value is large for a shallow sea under normal conditions. But in a frontal zone, vigorous mixing caused by small-scale processes such as double diffusion and interleaving can drastically increase the value of A_h. The vertical velocity in the $E^{\frac{1}{4}}$ layer depends on the value of E. Assuming an interfacial Ekman layer of 15 m thick, we have $E = 2.5 \times 10^{-3}$. This gives a vertical velocity of the order $E^{\frac{1}{4}} \delta U = 0.04$ cm s^{-1}, which is one order of magnitude smaller than our previous estimate and appears to be a more reasonable number.

ACKNOWLEDGEMENTS

The author wishes to thank Dr. C.N.K. Mooers for reading the manuscript and for offering useful comments.

REFERENCES

Barcilon, V. and Pedlosky, J., 1967. A unified linear theory of homogeneous and stratified rotating fluid. Journal of Fluid Mechanics, 29: 609-621.
Csanady, G.T., 1971. On the equilibrium shape of the thermocline in a shore zone. Journal of Physical Oceanography, 1: 263-270.
Csanady, G.T., 1978. Turbulent interface layer. Journal of Geophysical Research, 83: 2329-2342.
Horne, E.P.W., Bowman, M.J. and Okubo, A., 1978. Cross-front mixing and cabbeling. In: M.J. Bowman and W.E. Esaias (Editors), Oceanic fronts in coastal processes. Spring-Verlag, Berlin Heidelberg New York, pp. 105-113.
Hsueh, Y. and Ou, H., 1975. On the possibilities of coastal, mid-shelf and shelf break upwelling. Journal of Physical Oceanography, 5: 670-682.
Joyce, T.M., 1978. Dynamics of oceanic fronts. American Geophysical Union Transaction, 5: 490-491
Kao, T.W., Pao, H. and Park, C., 1978. Surface intrusions, fronts and internal waves : a numerical study. Journal of Geophysical Research, 83: 4641-4650.
Killworth, P.D., 1973. A two-dimensional model for the formation of Antartic bottom water. Deep-Sea Research, 20: 941-971.
Mooers, C.N.K., 1978. Frontal dynamics and frontal genesis. In: M.J. Bowman and W.E. Esaias (editors), Oceanic fronts in coastal processes Spring-Verlag, Berlin Heidelberg New York, pp. 16-22.
Mooers, C.N.K., Collins, C.A. and Smith, R.L., 1976. The dynamic structure of the frontal zone in the coastal upwelling region off Oregon. Journal of Physical Oceanography, 6: 3-21.
Pedlosky, J., 1968. An overlooked aspect of wind-driven oceanic circulation. Journal of Fluid Mechanics, 32: 809-821.
Tang, C.L., 1980. Mixing and circulation in the northwestern Gulf of St. Lawrence: a study of a buoyancy driven current system. Journal of Geophysical Research, 95: 2787-2796.
Veronis, G., 1970. The analogy between rotating and stratified fluid. Annual Review of Fluid Mechanics, 2: 37-66.

NUMERICAL TIDAL SIMULATIONS WITHIN THE HAURAKI GULF, NEW ZEALAND

MALCOLM J. BOWMAN
Marine Sciences Research Center, State University of New York,
Stony Brook, New York, 11794, U.S.A.

STEPHEN M. CHISWELL
Physics Department, University of Auckland,
Auckland, New Zealand.*

ABSTRACT

The application of a nonlinear numerical tidal model to the Hauraki Gulf, a semi-enclosed shelf sea on the east coast of the North Island, is described. It has provided a preliminary assessment of tidal elevations and currents, overtides, tidal residual currents, vorticity, energy dissipation rates and the stratification index.

The M_2 tide closely approximates a standing wave. As the resonant tidal period along the longitudinal axis of the Gulf is ~5.2 hours, significant nonlinear M_2:M_4 resonant interaction is expected. The model suggests an influence of tidal scouring and mixing on sediment deposition and the intensity of summer water column stratification.

INTRODUCTION AND SIGNIFICANCE OF REGION

The Hauraki Gulf is a semi-enclosed shallow sea of area ~5,000 km^2 bounded by the eastern shore of the New Zealand mainland north of Auckland City, the western side of the Coromandel Peninsula and Great Barrier Island (Figs. 1 and 2). It is a continuation of a downfaulted rift valley which apparently extends from the Firth of Thames to the Colville Channel at the northern tip of the Coromandel Peninsula. Tamaki Strait and the Waitemata Harbour (tr. "sparkling waters") are drowned river valleys cut in marine sediments of Miocene Age (15-25 x 10^6 years ago). The region has a history of active seismic activity. Auckland City is built around 50 extinct volcanoes. The most recent, the island of Rangitoto (tr. "blood red sky") lies at the entrance to Waitemata Harbour and was active some 750 years ago during the early Maori occupation of New Zealand (c. 1100 AD -).

* Present affiliation: Marine Sciences Research Center.

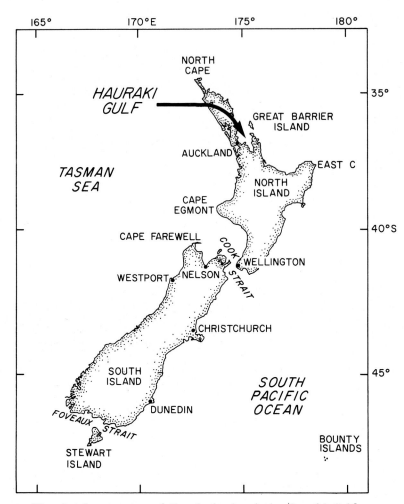

Fig. 1. Locator map of New Zealand and the Hauraki Gulf.

Of the total area, about 5% are shallow tidal harbours, 40% shoal waters less than 20 m in depth, 30% waters of depth 20 to 40 m, and 25% waters deeper than 40 m (Paul, 1968). The major source of fresh water discharge into the Gulf is near Thames from the Waihou River (Fig. 2) which drains a large portion of the fertile Hauraki Plains to the south. The Gulf is exposed to the South Pacific Ocean only along its northern approaches which suggests the origins of its Maori name "hau" meaning wind and "raki" meaning north.

The subtropical East Auckland Current flows southwards down the North Island east coast, is deflected and swept southeastwards by the shelving bottom across the entrance to the Gulf (Brodie, 1960). Currents reach 1.5 m s^{-1} at times near Great Barrier Island (Admiralty Hydrographic Department, 1958). Winds are most frequent from the westerly or southwesterly quarter,

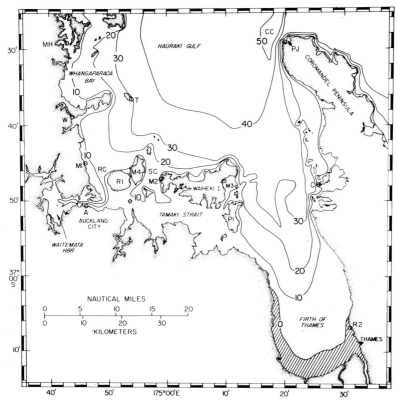

Fig. 2. Depth contours in metres, tide gauge locations
(open circles) and geographical locations.

A	Auckland	PI	Ponui Island
C	Coromandel Harbour	PJ	Port Jackson
CC	Cape Colville	R1	Rangitoto Island
MH	Mahurangi Harbour	R2	Rocky Point
M1	Murrays Bay	RC	Rangitoto Channel
M2	Matiatia Bay	SC	Sergeant Channel
M3	Man O'War Bay	T	Tiri Tiri Matangi Is
M4	Motutapu Island	W	Weiti River

with most gale force winds coming from the northeast.

The semi-diurnal tide over the New Zealand continental shelf forms a resonant trapped wave which rotates counterclockwise with a 12.42 hour period (Bye and Heath, 1975). The New Zealand land mass is thus centred on a degenerate antiamphidrome (Heath, 1977). The tidal wave sweeps up the coast of the North Island, into the Hauraki Gulf and progresses northward to North Cape.

Many inlets and embayments are located along the western and southern shoreline, with the Waitemata Harbour serving as New Zealand's major seaport and the focal point of Auckland City (pop. ~8 x 10^5). Facilities of the Royal New Zealand Navy are located here, and the harbour is also an important commercial fishing centre. Numerous islands within the Gulf near the Harbour entrance together with easily navigable waterways provide good shelter and berthage for large ships. From time to time, the possibility of constructing a sea level canal across the Auckland Isthmus (minimum width ~2 km) to link the Pacific Ocean and Tasman Sea has been proposed. The Hauraki Gulf is also a region of great natural beauty and a major recreational area for boating, fishing and swimming.

As a contribution to the oceanography of the Gulf, and to provide input to wise decision making for municipal, commercial and recreational development around its perimeter, tidal simulations were performed with a nonlinear numerical model which has already been successfully applied to a number of other areas (e.g., Bowman et al, 1980). This model is able to accurately predict tidal elevations and currents; the nonlinear terms in the model lead to the generation of residual (mean) tidal flows and higher order harmonic tides. Energy dissipation rates and the influence of tidal mixing on summer water column stratification can also be estimated from the model results.

THE MODEL

The model is a vertically integrated, two dimensional, nonlinear, finite difference model based on the algorithms of Leendertse (1967). A grid dimension of 0.926 km (0.5 nautical mile) was chosen to give adequate spatial resolution. The model contained 3742 active cells. Water depths were digitized from Royal New Zealand Navy Navigation Charts Nos. NZ532 and NZ533.

The model ran without instability with a time step of 124.2 seconds (2 lunar minutes). In the absence of open sea tide gauge data, the amplitudes and phases along the northern model boundary were derived from linear interpolations of the M_2 semidiurnal tidal predictions available from nearby coastal tidal stations (R. Gillbanks, RNZN Hydrographic Office; pers comm).

The model calculated tidal elevation and velocity components in each interior cell for every time step. It was calibrated by running to a steady state (transient decay time ~6 tidal periods) and adjusting bottom friction for an optimal fit between published and model predictions. The M_2 and other tidal harmonics (M_4, M_6, etc) generated by nonlinear effects were evaluated with Fourier analyses of the tides and currents for each cell.

The locations of tidal stations in the Gulf are shown in Fig. 2; of these only Auckland maintains a permanent station. The remainder represent locations where a temporary tide gauge has at some time been installed. These periods have been of varying duration and hence predictions are of varying and

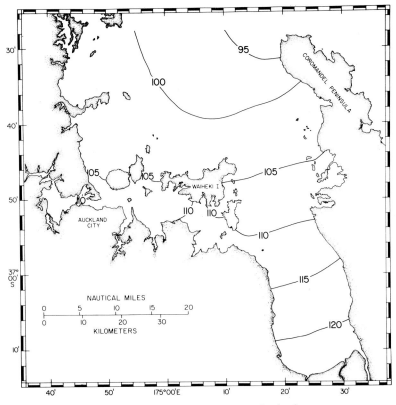

Fig. 3. Amplitude of M_2 tide (cm).

sometimes uncertain accuracy.

TIDAL AMPLITUDES AND PHASES

The tide derived from the model within the Gulf closely approximates a standing wave where the amplitude increases towards the head (i.e., Firth of Thames), rising from a minimum of 95 cm at Port Jackson to over 120 cm near the city of Thames (Fig. 3). Cotidal lines (Fig. 4) show that high tides are almost synchronous (to within a few minutes) over the entire region with the southern Firth lagging by ~3° due to frictional retardation of the tidal wave.

Table I lists model versus tidal station M_2 predictions for amplitude and phase relative to Auckland. Values with question marks indicate tide gauge data of dubious accuracy, designated as such by large discrepancies from the model and by departures from regional trends along the coastline. Stations located on the open coast usually show much better agreement with model results than those located near river mouths or harbours (e.g., Mahurangi Harbour). By using all data from Table I (excluding boundary stations) the

354

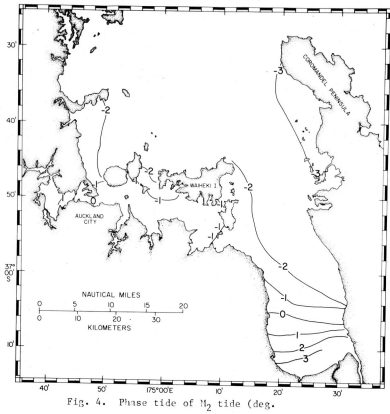

Fig. 4. Phase tide of M_2 tide (deg.
w.r.t. high tide at Auckland).

root mean square (rms) errors in amplitude and phase are ±4.5 cm (9 stations)
and ±8.6° (9 stations). If questionable values are deleted, the rms error in
amplitude is ±2.9 cm (7 stations) and phase ±6.8° (7 stations). It may be
possible to reduce these errors by further adjustment of bottom friction, but
a careful assessment of tidal station data quality is needed before attempting
any finer tuning of the model.

The tidal wave along the axis of the eastern Gulf and Firth (345°T)
closely resembles a co-oscillating tide. Ignoring rotational and frictional
effects, predicted elevations and currents are (Neumann and Pierson, 1966):

$$\eta(x) = \eta(L) \frac{\cos kx}{\cos kL} \cos \omega t$$

$$U(x) = \eta(L) (g/h)^{\frac{1}{2}} \frac{\sin kx}{\cos kL} \sin \omega t$$

where wavenumber $k = \omega(gh)^{-\frac{1}{2}}$, the origin is taken at the south end of the
Firth and the positive x direction is 345°T.

Using Hauraki Gulf values of $L = 8 \times 10^4$ m, h = 30 m, $\eta(L)$ = .95 m (see

TABLE I

Comparisons of model a_m, and tidal station a_{ts}, amplitude and phase of M_2 tide.

Location	Symbol	a_m	a_{ts}	$a_m - a_{ts}$	g_m	$*g_{ts}$	$g_m - g_{ts}$
		cm	cm	cm	deg	deg	deg
Mahurangi Hbr	H	103	†	†	-3	7	-10
Tiri Tiri Matangi Is.	T	103	103	0	-3	6	-9
Weiti River	W	103	95?	8?	-2	2	-4
Murrays Bay	M1	103	105	-2	-2	-14?	12?
Mataita Bay	M2	106	108	-2	-2	-5	3
Man O'War Bay	M3	106	114?	-8?	-2	-6	4
Rocky Point	R	120	120	0	0	-14?	14?
Coromandel Hbr	C	106	101	5	0	-6	6
Port Jackson	PJ	92	91.5	-0.5	-3	-11	8
Auckland		111	116	-5	0	0	set

* with respect to Auckland
† not available

TABLE II

Comparisons of model and published current strengths and directions.

Location	speed (cm s^{-1})			direction (^{O}T)		
	Model	Chart	Ratio	Model	Chart	Δ
A	0.23	0.103?	2.23?	103	095	8
B	0.23	0.51	0.45	100	0?	100?
C	0.15	0.51	0.29	057	020	37
D	0.05?	0.41	0.122?	150	145	5
E	0.34	0.77	0.44	014	020	-6
F	0.16	0.51	0.31	082	015?	67?
G	0.23	0.15?	1.53?	004	335	29
H	0.14	0.23	0.61	030	023	7
I	0.10	-	-	043	065	-22
J	0.25	0.31	0.81	347	000	-13
K	0.37	0.51	0.73	020	020	0
L	0.26	0.36	0.72	351	350	1
M	0.20	-	-	015	020	-5
N	0.09	-	-	006	335	31
O	0.26	0.51	0.51	320	320	0
P	0.28	0.51	0.55	351	335	16
Q	0.31	0.64	0.48	343	326	17
R	0.27	0.77	0.35	346	335	11
S	0.16	1.03?	0.155?	315	330	-15

Figs. 2 and 3), we find

$$\eta(0) = 120 \text{ cm}$$

and

$$U(L) = 42 \text{ cm s}^{-1}$$

These compare favourably with the model predictions (Figs. 3 and 9).

TIDAL CURRENTS

Four vector plots of hourly tidal currents are presented. These have been selected to cover ebb tidal streams at 0, 1, 3, and 5 solar hours after high tide at Auckland. Flood tidal patterns are essentially the reverse of ebb. To accomodate a wide dynamic range in currents, tidal stream vectors were scaled nonlinearly by preserving their directions but plotting amplitudes proportional to the square root of the current. The true current strengths are easily obtained by using the nonlinear scale on each chart.

0 hours (Fig. 5) Slack water occurs over the southern half of the Gulf. A southward current flows down the northwestern margin of the Gulf through Whangaparaoa Bay and sweeps across the open reaches and northward around Coromandel Peninsula as a narrow jet over the relatively deep Cape Colville Channel.

+1 hour (Fig. 6) Ebb currents flow towards the open sea over the entire region except in the northwestern approach where currents flow southeastward. Strong flows are found in the Rangitoto Channel as Waitemata Harbour discharges, between Mototapu and Waiheke Islands (Sergeant Channel), and east of Waiheke Island. This is a consequence of the water in Tamaki Strait ebbing, diverging and flowing around Waiheke Island.

+3 hours (Fig. 7) Flows intensify as ebb currents peak over the Gulf. A strong convergence forms north of Waiheke Island as the flows meet from around its western and eastern extremities.

+5 hours (Fig. 8) Most of the Gulf continues to ebb, except near Cape Colville where flood tide commences. Elsewhere most currents are directed to the northerly quarter.

Maximum tidal streams are contoured in Fig. 9. Highest values are located in the constricted Rangitoto and Sergeant Channels (~50 and 65 cm s^{-1}, respectively) and in the Colville Channel (~60 cm s^{-1}). Elsewhere in the Gulf currents are typically ~20 cm s^{-1}.

Tidal current ellipticities and major axis orientations are plotted in Fig. 10. Again the currents were scaled with a square root law. In the relatively open seas of the northern approaches currents are rotary in the expected anticlockwise sense for the southern hemisphere. In coastal areas and in most of the southern Gulf tidal streams are essentially rectilinear, except near islands and headlands where inertial effects in regions of sharp curvature cause flow separation and hence generate rotation as the ebb and flood currents follow slightly different paths.

Table II presents comparisions of model predictions with historical tidal current measurements (RNZN Navigation Charts Nos. NZ532 and NZ533). The locations of these measurements are plotted in Fig. 10.

Although no details on experimental procedure or analysis methods were available at the time of writing, we have assumed that published values represent surface spring tidal streams. An appropriate ratio of spring/neap currents for the Gulf is 1.35 (Bye and Heath, 1975). We reduced surface currents U_s to depth-mean currents U from the empirical power law

$$U(z) = U_s (z/h)^\alpha$$

The shape of the velocity distribution in tidal regions can be quite variable with reported values of the exponent α lying between 1/5 and 1/11 (Van Veen, 1936). For a typical value of α = 1/7 (Dronkers, 1964) we found

$$U_{M_2} \sim 0.75\, U_s \text{ springs}$$

This compares with a value of 0.52 ± 0.17 obtained from Table II.

The question marks in column 2 represent current speed data that appear of dubious quality or are influenced by river runoff (viz., station S, Fig. 10). For example, proximate stations A and B would be expected to possess similar tidal streams, as might stations G and E.

Differences between predicted and observed current directions are also presented in Table II. Excluding question marked values, the mean error is 6.0° ±16.5°, which is in good agreement given the approximations inherent in the model and the difficulties of making accurate current measurements in shallow water. The two major discrepancies in direction are from stations B and F. These are both located in regions of low ellipticity and difficulties in establishing the direction of the semi major axes from limited duration data would be expected.

A map of M_2 tidal vorticity is presented in Fig. 11. These contours conform to expected patterns where highest values are associated with regions of flow intensification and curvature around the various islands and peninsulas. Vorticity values $\sim 3 \times 10^{-4}$ s^{-1} and 1×10^{-4} s^{-1} roughly correspond to those inter island channels where tidal currents peak near 40 and 20 cm s^{-1} respectively (Fig. 9). It is not yet known whether vorticity generated in these regions has any influence on offshore tidal sand bank formation. Pingree (1978) and Pingree and Maddock (1979) have conducted interesting numerical experiments near some headlands on the south coast of Dorset and Devon, England, which suggest asymmetric formation of submarine

358

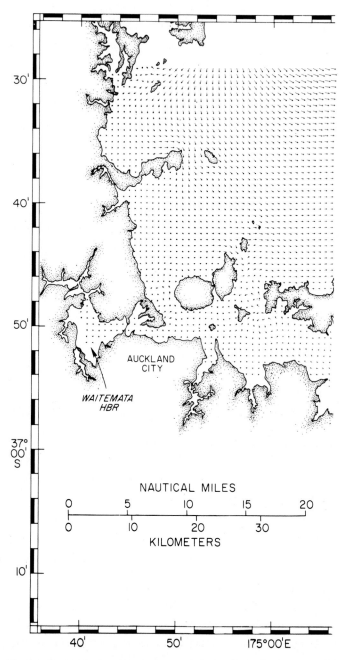

Fig. 5. Tidal currents at time of high tide at Auckland.

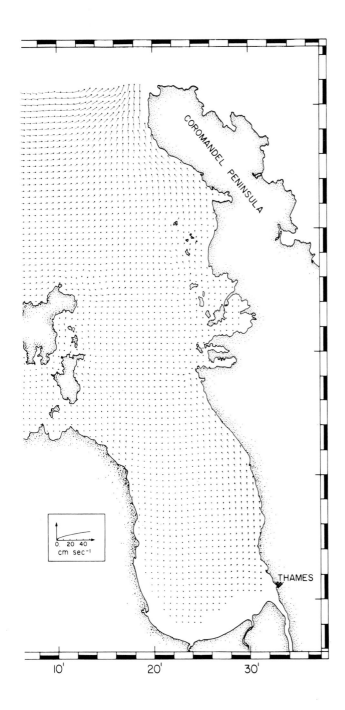

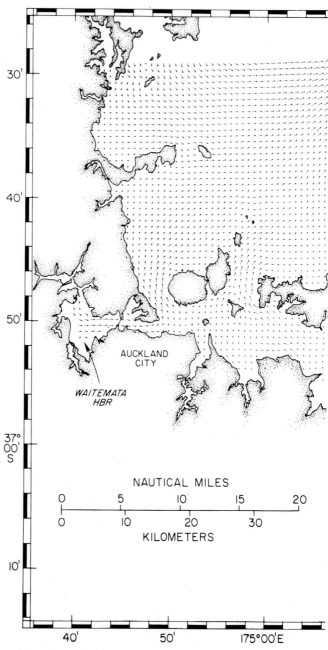

Fig. 6.   Tidal currents 1 hour after high tide at
          Auckland.

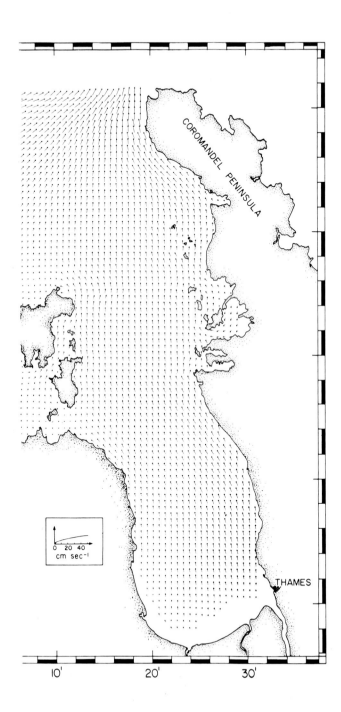

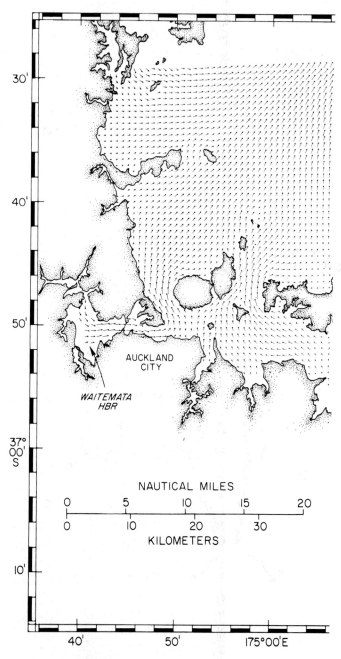

Fig. 7. Tidal currents 3 hours after high tide at Auckland.

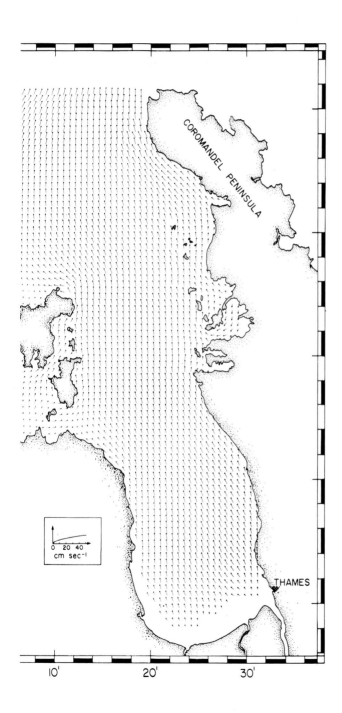

364

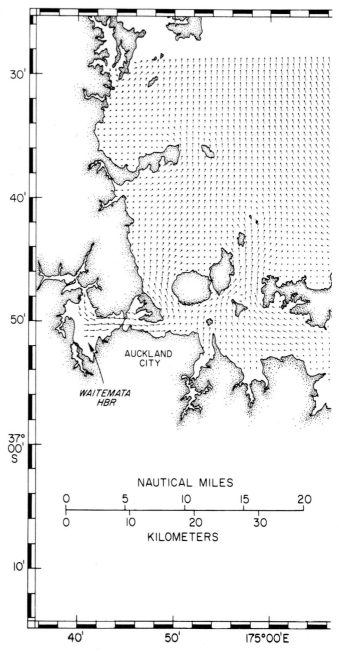

Fig. 8. Tidal currents 5 hours after high tide at
Auckland.

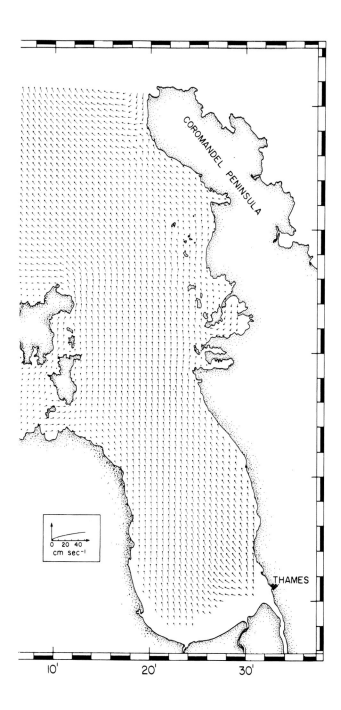

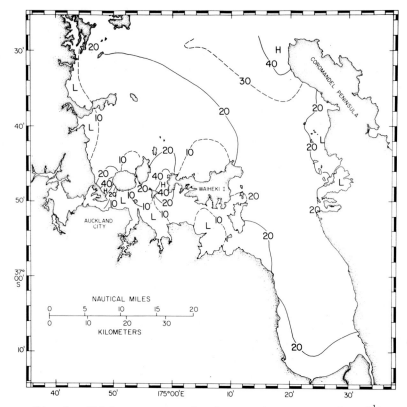

Fig. 9. Tidal current speeds along semi-major axes (cm s^{-1}).

banks near these promontories under the influence of planetary and relative vorticity. Currents around the islands of the Gulf are of the order of one third of those in the English Channel and thus bottom stresses are about one tenth.

TIDAL RESIDUAL CURRENTS

Nonlinear terms in the model equations of motion and continuity generate residual flows (Eulerian tidal streams averaged over a tidal cycle) even when the northern boundary is driven purely at the M_2 frequency.

Eddies in the residual flow are generated by the transfer of vorticity from the tidal to the mean flow as a consequence of the field acceleration terms in the equation of motion. These effects are often associated with strong oscillatory flows around promontories (Pingree and Maddock, 1977; Maddock and Pingree, 1978; Tee, 1976, 1977).

The proper procedure for computing tidal residuals is a matter of some controversy. Nihoul (1975) and Nihoul and Runfola (1981) claim that the residual tidal signal to numerical noise ratio is of the order one in many regions i.e., the computational error is comparable to the residual current itself. Nihoul claims that it is necessary to first time average the equations of motion, and apply these with known boundary values of mean sea level or currents. On the other hand, Pingree and Griffiths (1980), for example, have produced with a very large finite difference model some apparently realistic plots of wind driven residual currents over the northwestern European shelf by computing Eulerian averages of the tidal plus wind driven solutions. Another problem which affects either method of computation relates to the correct specification of the boundary conditions. Small changes in amplitude and phase along the boundary can cause significant changes in residual current patterns in the model interior.

As an initial approach to the study of mean circulations we have calculated the Eulerian tidal residual current from the tidal solutions,

$$\overline{\underset{\sim}{U}} = \frac{1}{T} \int_{o}^{T} \underset{\sim}{U} \, dt,$$

where T is the tidal period and $\underset{\sim}{U}$ the instantaneous vertically averaged velocity vector. One measure of success in separating the signal from the noise is the apparent spatial coherency of the residuals, although subtle problems can appear. For example, grid scale eddies generated by abrupt depth changes and corner effects must be considered suspicious. We have concentrated attention on mesoscale features of the residual flow and vorticity around the islands and headlands where similar effects have been documented in other shallow seas.

Fig. 12 is a plot of residual circulation computed in the absence of wind stress. Several features emerge:

i) A broad westward drift occurs over the northern Gulf which passes both sides of Tiri Tiri Matangi Island and sweeps into Whangaparaoa Bay.

ii) A number of counter rotating eddies form around the major island groups. These are particularly well developed off the northeastern corner of Waiheke Island, where a strong offshore (eastward) net flow results. Another pair of eddies is located north and south of western Waiheke Island resulting in a northward flow northeast off the island and a southward flow towards the northern coast. These eddying motions also become apparent in the residual vorticity map (Fig. 13). Alternating regions of positive and negative vorticity are located either side of the various headlands and islands of the Gulf. The relative vorticity of the strongest eddy is ~-0.4f and is located off the northeastern corner of Waiheke Island which lies in the path of the discharge from both the Tamaki Strait and the Firth of Thames.

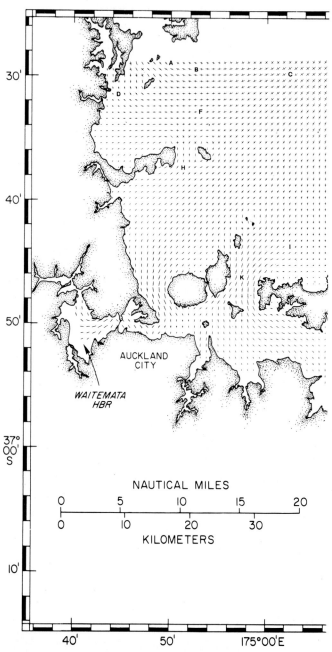

Fig. 10. Tidal current speeds and ellipticities. Letters A through S represent locations where current data are available.

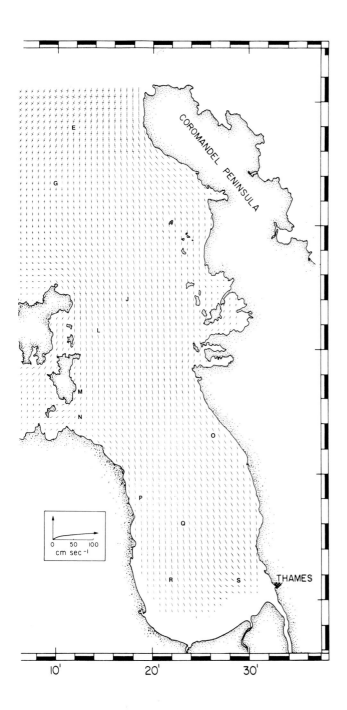

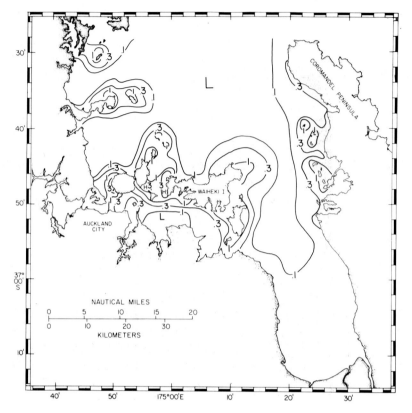

Fig. 11. Amplitudes of M_2 tidal vorticity (10^{-4} s^{-1}).

HIGHER TIDAL HARMONICS

While the M_2 tidal solution depends only weakly on the nonlinear terms in the governing equations, these terms still generate tidal harmonics in the model interior. The M_4 harmonic with period 6.21 hours is generated by those terms which contain products of variables oscillating at the M_2 frequency (*viz.*, the advective terms $\frac{U \partial U}{\partial x}$ etc., and the continuity terms $\frac{\partial}{\partial x}(HU)$ etc.).

The frictional term $U|U|$ can be approximated for a co-oscillating tide with zero residual current as

$$U|U| \approx \frac{16 U_o^2}{15 \pi} [U/U_o + 2(U/U_o)^3]$$

$$= U_o^2 [8/3\pi.\cos \omega t + 8/15\pi.\cos 3\omega t]$$

Hence, quadratic friction generates only odd harmonics (M_6, M_{10}, etc.). However, when divided by the time varying depth

$$H(x,y,t) = h(x,y) + \eta(x,y,t),$$

friction generates a small contribution to the M_4 acceleration. For rectilinear flow in a standing wave pattern, it can be shown that the respective contributions to the M_4 accelerations are (Pingree and Maddock, 1978)

$$\left|\frac{\partial U_{M_4}}{\partial t}\right| \sim 4gU_o^2\eta_o/3\pi C^2h^2 + kU_o^2/2 + k^2g\eta_o U_o/\omega$$

$$\qquad\qquad\qquad\text{friction}\qquad\quad\text{advection}\qquad\text{continuity}$$

With $U_o \sim .2$ m s^{-1}, $\eta_o = 1.0$ m, h = 30 m and k = 8.2 x 10^{-6} m^{-1} the relative magnitudes in generating M_4 oscillations are ~1:3:20. Clearly the nonlinearities in the continuity equation dominate, with the frictional term being the smallest. Locally, where considerable curvature exists in the neighbourhood of promontories and islands, the advective terms may dominate. In such areas, the inshore lowering of sea level by centrifugal effects during both ebb and flood streaming generates oscillations at twice the tidal frequency as well as a lowering of mean sea surface topography.

To correctly simulate M_4 tides and currents in the model interior it is necessary to accurately specify M_4 tidal oscillations generated externally and propagated through the northern boundary. Unfortunately no published data were available and so this contribution could not be evaluated. We thus investigated only the presence of higher harmonics within the model interior (Figs. 14 and 15).

The resonant length L for the second harmonic (M_4) tide is (Kreiss, 1957)

$$L = (gh/8)^{\frac{1}{2}} T[(1 + \beta^2/4)^{\frac{1}{2}} - 1]^{\frac{1}{2}}/\beta \sim 96 \text{ km}$$

where $\beta = gU_o T/2\pi hC^2 \sim .12$ for h = 30 m and $U_o = 0.2$ m s^{-1}

This is close to the length of Hauraki Gulf along its north-south axis and hence we might expect significant nonlinear resonant interaction. In such cases an estimate of M_4 to M_2 currents ratio is

$$U_4/U_2 \sim (\eta_o/2h\beta) (4 + \beta^2)^{\frac{1}{2}} (\frac{1 + \beta^2}{1 + \beta^2/4})^{\frac{1}{4}}$$

$$\sim .45 \text{ for } \eta_o = 1.2 \text{ m, h = 2 m, } \beta \sim 4.34$$

This compares well with a modelled value of $U_4/U_2 = .60$ at locations S (Fig. 10) in the shallows near the city of Thames. However, the modelled value of $U_4/U_2 = .054$ in the deeper central Firth water (location J; h = 31 m) is considerably less than Kreiss' prediction of 0.35.

The M_4 tide generated by the divergence term $\nabla\eta\underset{\sim}{U}$ in the continuity equation produces an assymetry in the tidal wave near the head of embayments such that the stronger flood tide is of shorter duration than the longer but weaker ebb tide (Fig. 16). At location S, for example, currents flood for 5

372

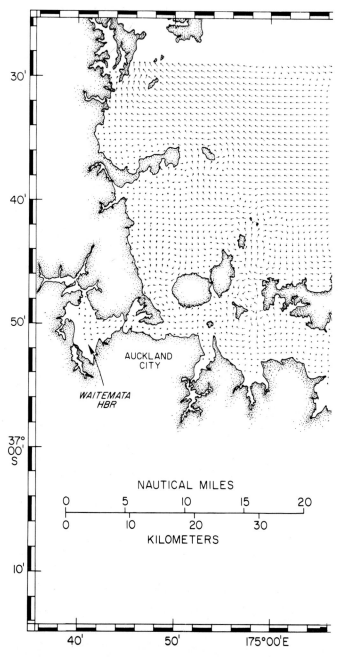

Fig. 12.   Tidal residual currents.

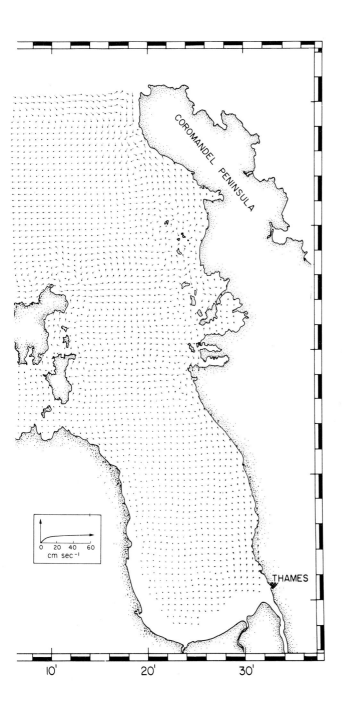

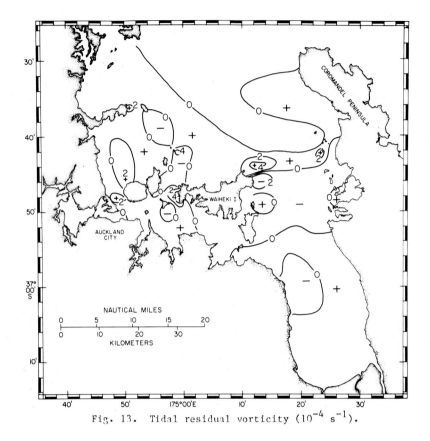

Fig. 13. Tidal residual vorticity (10^{-4} s^{-1}).

hours 10 minutes, peaking at 21 cm s^{-1}, while ebb currents flow for 7 hours 15 minutes, and peak at 17 cm s^{-1}. Since shear stresses near the sea bed follow a square law, this can produce sediment transport towards the head of the bay, although it is doubtful if $M_2 - M_4$ interactions have much effect over most of the Firth.

The M_6 and higher harmonics were of very small amplitude (<2 cm) over the Gulf, as were deviations in mean sea surface topography (around Waiheke Island mean sea topography dropped ~1 cm).

BOTTOM STRESS AND ENERGY DISSIPATION RATES

The mean bottom frictional stress during a tidal cycle $\rho g/C^2 \cdot |U|^2$ is of interest in sediment resuspension and deposition. High stress regions should correspond with gravel or boulder bottom and low stress regions with mud or clay.

When plotted on logarithmic scales contours of the energy dissipation rate $\rho g/C^2 \cdot |U|^3$ are similar to those of bottom stress. Accordingly only the latter are plotted (Fig. 17). Highest dissipation rates occur in the

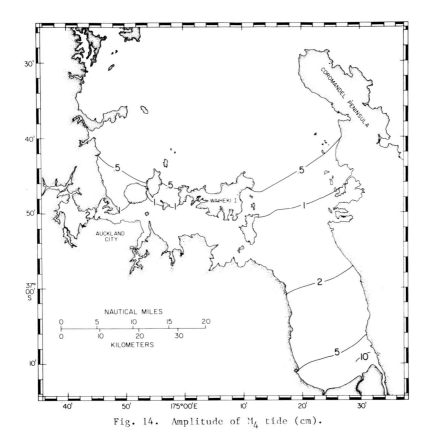

Fig. 14. Amplitude of M_4 tide (cm).

Rangitoto and Sergeant Channels and around the northern tip of the Coromandel Peninsula (>100 erg cm^{-2} s^{-1}). Lowest values are found north of Whangaparaoa Peninsula (<0.1 erg cm^{-2} s^{-1}), and in sheltered embayments around the perimeter of the Gulf. A broad band of intermediate dissipation (10 - 100 erg cm^{-2} s^{-1}) lies along the eastern Gulf extending south into the Firth of Thames.

A simplified interpretation of bottom sediments (dominant components) is given in Fig. 18 (after Carter and Eade, 1980). Regions of calcareous gravel (>50% calcium carbonate in gravel fraction) are located in the southern Firth, around Cape Colville and south of Tiri Tiri Matangi Island and in Sergeant Channel. Some of these materials are probably associated with shellfishing beds, but Cape Colville and Sergeant Channel are regions of elevated dissipation. A broad band of sandy sediment lies across the northern Gulf and this appears to lie between the 1 and 2 contours. Muddy sediments are generally found in regions with dissipation less than 1 (10 erg cm^{-2} s^{-1}), although the southern Firth with its clay bank does not conform to this interpretaton. It is possible that an upstream (i.e., southerly) estuarine

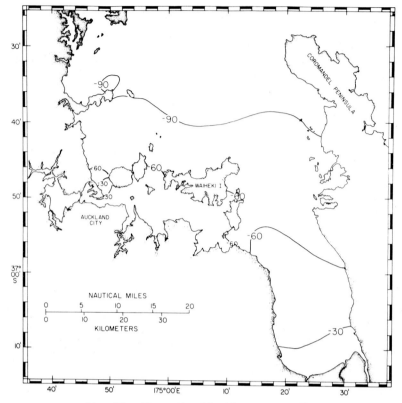

Fig. 15. Phase M_4 tide (deg. w.r.t. M_2
high tide at Auckland).

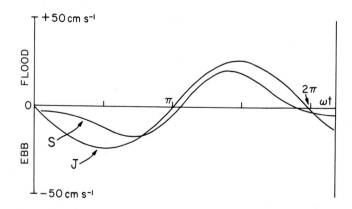

Fig. 16. Tidal current curves for locations J and S (see Fig. 10).

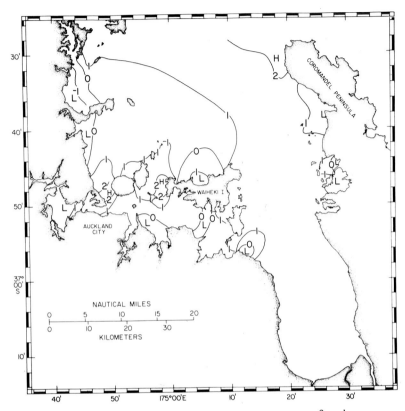

Fig. 17. Energy dissipation rates (erg cm^{-2} s^{-1}).

flow at depth recirculates and traps fine sediments originating from the Waihou River within the southern Firth.

A strong correlation between sediment grade and bottom stress would be expected only if an initial mix of sedimentary types were uniformly spread over the entire region and subsequentially reworked by bottom currents. Fines would be deposited in low stress regions and coarser sands in higher stress regions. Boulder sized gravel would then exist in the higher stress regions as tidal scouring removed all smaller particles. The real situation is much more complex. Fine sediments are brought down by rivers and streams emptying into the basin, calcareous sediments accumulate in shellfishing beds, lahars (volcanic mud flows) and debris from Rangitoto and other Auckland Isthmus volcanoes have undoubtedly affected the Gulf. Changing sea levels since the last glaciation ($\sim 10^4$ years ago) and sediment accumulation in local depressions each have an influence on the present day sediment structure. Nevertheless, the model demonstrates an influence of tidal streaming on reworking and distributing sediments.

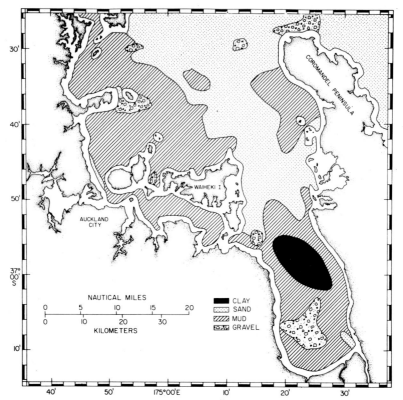

Fig. 18.   Dominant sediment types according to Carter and Eade (1980).

SUMMER STRATIFICATION

Simpson and Hunter (1974) derived a "stratification index" h/U^3 (where h is water depth and U is the surface current amplitude for spring tides) as a measure of the intensity of summer water column stratification.   High values of h/U^3 often correlate with regions of strong stratification, whereas low values correspond to regions which remain well mixed.   Intermediate values ($\sim$30 - 100 m^{-2} s^{-3} depending partly on latitude) have been associated with frontal structures produced by tidal stirring variations in the shelf seas of Great Britain (e.g., Simpson, 1976; Simpson et al, 1977, 1978; Pingree and Griffiths 1978), Bay of Fundy (Garrett et al, 1978), Long Island Sound, New York (Bowman and Esaias, 1981) and Cook Strait, New Zealand (Bowman et al, 1980).   The almost fixed positions of these fronts, as detected by satellite, hydrographic or biological measurements (e.g., phytoplankton concentrations) are often well predicted by the contours of h/U^3.

Fig. 19 is a plot of the inverse of energy dissipation rate per unit mass ($viz.$, $C^2 h/(g|\underset{\sim}{U}|^3) = s$ [T^3 L^{-2}]), which is proportional to h/U^3 (apart from small variations in C which in turn is weakly dependent on depth).

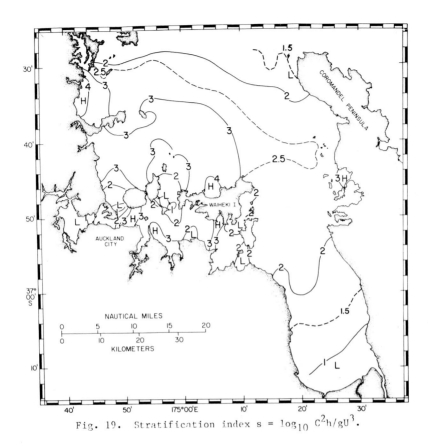

Fig. 19. Stratification index $s = \log_{10} C^2 h/g U^3$.

According to these predictions most of the Gulf is expected to stratify in summer with localized mixed regions located in Rangitoto and Sergeant Channels, and the southern reaches of the Firth. A marginally stratified frontal zone, $s \sim 1.5$ concentrations is also predicted near the northern tip of Coromandel Peninsula where strong tidal rips are present (e.g., Fig. 5). Results from hydrographic surveys generally confirm these predictions. The central Gulf sustains a modest seasonal thermocline (Fig. 20) with maximum temperature contrasts of about 4° occurring in the spring. The surface mixed layer deepens in summer until it intersects the bottom at 40 m at this particular location. A weak temperature inversion occurs in winter, density compensated by a corresponding increase of salinity from about 34% at the surface to 35.6% at depth (Cassie, 1960).

The spatial distribution of water column stratification is well illustrated with an example from late spring (Fig. 21). Bottom temperatures were fairly uniform near 14.5° - 15.0° so surface contours were a good indicator of stratification. (Top and bottom salinity contrasts typically are ~ 0.1 - ~ 0.4% in January; Cassie, 1960). Surface temperatures over much of the

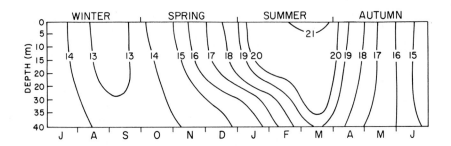

Fig. 20. Seasonal temperature contours for a mid Gulf
profile (after Paul, 1968).

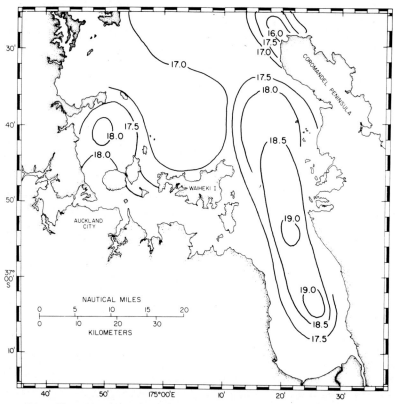

Fig. 21. Distribution of surface temperature (November 22 –
December 10, 1965; after Paul, 1968).

Gulf lay in the range $17^O - 18^OC$, with strongest stratificatiion ($\Delta T \sim 4^OC$), occurring as a shallow thermocline within an elliptical patch in the offshore waters of the Firth. A region of cold, mixed water ($\Delta T \sim 1^OC$), corresponding to the 1.5 contour, was located off Cape Colville, which may be a consequence of tidal mixing and/or centrifugal upwelling effects (Garrett and Loucks, 1976). This is also an area of increased turbidity (Paul, 1968) some of which may be related to phytoplankton blooms. Marginal stratification, coupled with a favourable light regime often foster enhanced primary production in such areas. The major discrepancy to be explained between predictions and observations lies in the southern Firth. It may be that salinity stratification created by Waihou River discharge adds sufficient buoyancy flux to prevent stratification breakdown by tidal stirring.

CONCLUSIONS

The application of a nonlinear tidal model to the Hauraki Gulf has provided a preliminary assessment of tidal elevations, tidal and residual currents, vorticity, overtide generation, bottom stress, energy dissipation rates and the stratification index. The agreement with available experimental data is encouraging. Hopefully this modelling effort will stimulate further field efforts to investigate tidal and current characteristics. Measurements of elevation and currents along the northern open boundary would be especially useful in evaluating possible errors associated with our assumptions of linear phase and amplitude gradients. These data would also be helpful in accurately modelling the propagation of higher tidal harmonics from the exterior region into the model. Bottom sediment samples taken in areas of high residual vorticity might determine if preferential offshore sand bank formation occurs. A good place to start looking would be in the region of negative residual vorticity off the northeastern coast of Waiheke Island for there both relative and planetary vorticity have the same sign and hence stronger bottom convergences and sediment accumulation may result.

ACKNOWLEDGEMENTS

This project was conceived and initiated when the authors were with the Physics Department, University of Auckland. We thank Professor A.C. Kibblewhite for his help and encouragement. Mr. George Carroll is also thanked for his computing assistance. Support was provided by the State University of New York and the University of Auckland, facilitated by the Memorandum of Understanding in marine science between the two institutions.

Contribution 297 of the Marine Sciences Research Center.

APPENDIX

The differential equations of motion and continuity are

x momentum

$$\frac{\partial U}{\partial t} + U\frac{\partial U}{\partial x} + V\frac{\partial U}{\partial y} = -g\frac{\partial \eta}{\partial x} + fV - \frac{gU(U^2 + V^2)^{\frac{1}{2}}}{C^2 H}$$

y momentum

$$\frac{\partial V}{\partial t} + U\frac{\partial V}{\partial x} + V\frac{\partial V}{\partial y} = -g\frac{\partial \eta}{\partial y} - fU - \frac{gV(U^2 + V^2)^{\frac{1}{2}}}{C^2 H}$$

continuity

$$\frac{\partial \eta}{\partial t} + \frac{\partial}{\partial x}(HU) + \frac{\partial}{\partial y}(HV) = 0$$

NOTATION

C   Chezy friction coefficient: the Chezy coefficient is related to the Manning coefficient N by (in MKS units)

$$C = (h + \eta)^{1/6} / N(m^{\frac{1}{2}} s^{-1})$$

         A constant value of $N = 0.028$ was used as a model

f   Coriolis parameter $\sim -8.75 \times 10^{-5}$ s^{-1} at $37°S$

g   acceleration of gravity = 981 cm s^{-2}

H   total water depth = $h + \eta$

h   depth of water at mean sea level

k   horizontal wavenumber $k = \omega(gh)^{-\frac{1}{2}}$

L   length scale of Gulf

s   stratification index

T M_2 tidal period = 12.42 hr

t   time

U,V   depth-averaged velocity components in direction x,y

U_o amplitude of tidal current in direction x

U(z)   x component of velocity at depth z (z measured vertically upwards from sea floor)

ω angular frequency of M_2 tide = $2\pi/T$

β ratio of tidal period to frictional time scale

η sea surface elevation with respect to mean sea level

M_2,M_4 semidiurnal, quarter diurnal tides

REFERENCES

Admiralty Hydrographic Department. 1958. New Zealand Pilot, 12th ed. London. 500 pp.

Bowman, M.J., A.C. Kibblewhite, and D.E. Ash. 1980. M_2 tidal effects in greater Cook Strait, New Zealand. J. Geophys. Res. 85:2728-2742.

Bowman, M.J. and W.E. Esaias. 1981. Fronts, stratification and mixing in Long Island and Block Island Sounds. J. Geophys. Res. 86:4260-4264.

Brodie, J.W. 1960. Coastal surface currents around New Zealand. N.Z. J. Geol. & Geophys. 3:235-252.

Bye, J.A.T. and R.A. Heath. 1975. The New Zealand semi-diurnal tide. J. Mar. Res. 33:423-442.

Carter, L. and J.V. Eade. 1980. Hauraki Sediments, N.Z. Oceanogr. Inst. Chart, Coastal Series 1:200 000.

Cassie, R.M. 1960. Hydrology of Hauraki Gulf. N.Z. Ecol. Soc. 1:40-43.

Dronkers, J.J. 1964. Tidal computations in rivers and coastal waters. North Holland Publishing Co. Amsterdam. 518pp.

Garrett, C.J.R., J.R. Keeley and D.A. Greenberg. 1978. Tidal mixing versus thermal stratification in the Bay of Fundy and Gulf of Maine. Atmosphere-Ocean. 16:403-423.

Garrett, C.J.R. and R.H. Loucks. 1976. Upwelling along the Yarmouth shore of Nova Scotia. J. Fish. Res. Board Can. 33:116-117.

Heath, R.A. 1977. Phase distribution of tidal constituents around New Zealand. N.Z. J. Mar. Freshw. Res. 11:383-392.

Kreiss, H. 1957. Some remarks about nonlinear oscillations in tidal channels. Tellus. 9:53-68.

Leendertse, J.J. 1967. Aspects of a computational model for long period water wave propagation. Mem. RM 5294-PR, Rand Corporation, Santa Monica, Calif.

Maddock, L. and R.D. Pingree. 1978. Numerical simulation of the Portland tidal eddies. Estuarine Coast. Mar. Sci. 6:353-363. Prentice - Hall Inc., New Jersey. 545pp.

Nihoul, J.C.J. 1975. Effect of the tidal stress on residual circulation and mud deposition in the Southern Bight of the North Sea. Pageoph. 113:577-581.

Nihoul, J.C.J. and Runfola, Y. 1981. The residual circulation in the North Sea. In: J.C.J. Nihoul (Editor), Ecohydrodynamics. Elsevier, Amsterdam, 219-271.

Paul, L.J. 1968. Some seasonal water temperature patterns in the Hauraki Gulf, New Zealand. N.Z. J. Mar. Freshw. Res. 2:535-558.

Pingree, R.D. 1978. The formation of the shambles and other banks by tidal stirring of the seas. J. Mar. Biol. Ass. U.K. 58:211-226.

Pingree, R.D. and D.K. Griffiths. 1978. Tidal fronts on the shelf seas around the British Isles. J. Geophys. Res. 83:4615-4622.

384

Pingree, R.D. and D. K. Griffiths. 1980. Currents driven by a steady uniform wind stress on the shelf seas around the British Isles. Oceanol. Acta. 3:227-236.

Pingree, R.D. and L. Maddock. 1977. Tidal residuals in the English Channel. J. Mar. Biol. Ass. U.K. 57:339-354.

Pingree, R.D. and L. Maddock. 1979. The tidal physics of headland flows and offshore tidal bank formation. Mar. Geol. 32:269-289. Estuarine Coast Mar. Sci. 4:71-81.

Simpson, J.H. and J.R. Hunter. 1974. Fronts in the Irish Sea. Nature. 250:404-406.

Simpson, J.H., D.G. Hughes and N.C.G. Morris. 1977. The relation of seasonal stratification to tidal mixing on the Continental Shelf. Deep Sea. Res. 24:327-340.

Simpson, J.H., C.M. Allen and N.C.G. Morris. 1978 Fronts on the Continental Shelf. J. Geophys. Res. 83:4607-4614.

Tee, K.T. 1976. Tide-induced residual current, a 2-D nonlinear numerical tidal model. J. Mar. Res. 34:603-628.

Tee, K.T. 1977. Tide-induced residual current - Verification of a numerical model. J. Phys. Oceanogr. 7:396-402.

Veen, J. Van. 1936. Onderzoekingen in de Hoofden (Measurements in the Straits of Dover, and their relation to the Netherlands coasts; English and French summary) (Landsdrukkerij, The Hague). 152pp.

THE SENSITIVITY OF THE BALTIC SEA TO NATURAL AND MAN-MADE IMPACT

FL. BO PEDERSEN

ABSTRACT

Hydrographic observations in the Baltic Sea during nearly a century have shown the picture of a highly non-steady system. The two major sources for these variations are the barometric pressure (the wind) and the river runoff. As the wind speed is only known by visual judgement, and, into the bargain, by a large number of observers, no reliable secular variation of the wind is known. This has been overcome by correlating the monthly mean wind speed squared to the monthly peak to peak value of the barometric pressure at Copenhagen, the last one being known with high accuracy since 1873.

As the natural variations show a high correlation between the wind and the runoff, it is hard to separate the effect on for instance the salinity from the variation in the wind and in the runoff, respectively, unless one makes use of a mathematical model, which is based on knowledge of the hydrodynamics of the system. A first step (steady-state) model has been outlined and used to investigate the effect on the Baltic Sea from a diversion of part of the river Neva. The calculations show that if a 25% river diversion had been executed in the beginning of this century, a 30 to 40% higher salinity-variation would have been encountered in the Baltic Sea - compared to the actual variations during this century.

INTRODUCTION

The growing concern for our aquatic environment and the expansion of our agricultural and industrial activities quite often result in a political conflict. When we are dealing with a semi-enclosed sea, such as the Baltic Sea, this conflict may even attain international dimensions, due to the large number of countries bordering the Sea. This was the case in 1978 in connection with the Danish project of building a bridge across the Great Belt (Bo Pedersen, 1978), and it will be the case, if the Russian plans for river diversions will involve the river Neva. Before this sort of major interference with nature is decided upon, a qualified estimate of the long-term environmental consequences ought to be evaluated and commented/agreed upon by all the concerned countries. The *first condition* for such a procedure is an extension of the international laws/conventions. The *second condition* is the development of a predictive mathematical model, i.e. a model reasonably representative for the dynamics of the sea. The *third condition*

386

is a knowledge of the natural variations in the external forces of major importance for the system (such as runoff, wind, tide, etc.) to be used as input to calibrate the mathematical model, and furthermore as input and reference data in the
simulation run of the man-made interference. The *fourth condition* is the ability
to estimate the environmental impact, when the hydrodynamic changes are known.

The fulfilment of condition no.1 - the international laws - is not necessary
for making an effort in regard to the other tasks - on the contrary, a mathematical
model will create a growing understanding of the sensitivity to a local interference of the whole system, and, hence, may act as a catalyzer for further development of the highly needed international conventions. In the following, we shall
first give a brief description of the Baltic Sea estuary system with focus on the
dynamics and the time scales in relation to the establishment of a long-term predictive mathematical model. Next, we shall comment on the fundamental difference
in the response of the Baltic Sea to a natural and to a man-made variation of the
external forces, exemplified by a diversion of 25% of the discharge of the river
Neva. Finally, we shall discuss the problem of establishing a reliable secular
time series of the wind force, which is one of the most important external forces
in the Baltic Sea, and which has hitherto been unknown.

A STEADY-STATE MODEL OF THE BALTIC SEA

In Figure 1 is shown a schematic longitudinal cross-section of the Baltic Sea
estuary system, which comprises eight sub-areas, chosen in such a way that a reasonably simple dynamic description can be given for each region (Bo Pedersen &
Møller, 1981). This model was developed for the consequence analysis of the possible diversion of part of the river Neva. At that time no reliable time series
of the wind power was available, and hence it was only possible to consider an
artificial, two-layer steady-state situation.

For each sub-area steady-state continuity equations for mass and volume were
established. The mixing across the interface constitutes the dynamic contribution to these equations. This mixing is due to the generation of turbulence by
the external forces, which primarily originate from the wind, as will be explained
in the following. The wind is a highly non-steady force, and hence a proper dynamic transformation from the non-steady to the steady system has to be performed.
According to the author's (1980) comprehensive analysis of the mixing processes
for a large class of two-layer stratified flows, a universal relationship exists
between the energy available for the turbulence production and the energy gained
(potential as well as turbulent kinetic energy) owing to the entrained mass.
Hence the proper transformation from the non-steady to the steady system is obtained by applying a *dynamic mean velocity V*, reflecting the energy production,
namely

$$\tilde{V} = (\frac{1}{T} \int_0^T |v|^3 \, dt)^{\frac{1}{3}}$$

(1)

where T is the averaging time scale and v is the mean velocity.

The *kinematic mean velocity* in the continuity equations is the simple mean velocity and not the velocity defined by Eq. 1. The problem of obtaining consistency in the dynamic balance as well as in the mass-balance was solved by introducing a circulation-velocity with no net transport inside some of the sub-areas.

Before the results of the analysis are commented upon, it is convenient to summarize our knowledge of the system.

THE SHORT-TERM DYNAMICS OF THE BALTIC SEA

A brief supplement to the description of the normal, overall dynamics of the Baltic Sea, given by G.Kullenberg (page 399), can most conveniently start from Fig. 2, which shows a typical time series of the measured discharge through the Great Belt. The figure illustrates the highly non-steady in-and outflow of huge amounts of stratified brackish water. The flow is caused by a water-level difference between Kattegat and the Arkona Basin, mainly due to the wind setup/setdown. The varying wind field is created by the nearly cyclic passage over the area by high/low air pressure. In the Kattegat region, this nearly cyclic movement is reflected in a similar pendling forward/backward movement of the Kattegat/Skagerak front in the upper layer. The overall mixing in the two shallow sub-areas is governed by the energy input - i.e. in accordance with the above-mentioned, primarily the wind - and the stability - i.e. the fresh water content. This fresh water content is in turn determined by the net sea-ward transport of the river runoff, which amounts to, say, only 10% of the typical amplitude in the nearly cyclic varying discharge.

The Great Belt and the Sound are separated from the Arkona Basin by two shallow sill regions. The high mixing rate in the shallow transition area, combined with a net outward directed flow in the upper layer, creates a high longitudinal salinity (and hence density) gradient, which means that part of the inward flowing water is trapped by the sills as it, due to the density excess, plunges down and descends as a dense, entraining bottom current into the lower layer of the Bornholm Basin. The residence time here (volume/discharge) is about 4 months, which means that the main part of the intermittently inflowing dense water continues as a delayed, nearly steady dense bottom current through the Stolpe Channel into the lower layer of the Central Baltic, while a minor part is entrained in the upper layer due to wind-induced mixing. The balance between the lower layer discharge input and the rate of upwards directed entrainment in the Central Baltic govern the position of the interface there. Again, the fresh water input (primarily the river runoff), the dense water input into the lower layer (primarily caused by the wind) and the energy input (again the wind) are the most important external forces of the Baltic Proper. The time scale for the Central Baltic (volume/discharge) is of the order of magnitude of decades.

No rules without exceptions. Under very severe wind conditions the inwards directed flow may persist for so long a time that huge amounts of highly saline water pass the sills. These water masses may then renew the deepest parts of the succeeding basins, creating a nearly stagnant bottom layer. The long-term effect of the major inflows is the formation of stagnant ocean deserts, suffering from oxygen deficience.

In summary: the most important factors governing the hydrography of the Baltic Sea estuary system are the river runoff, the wind, and the geometry of, especially, the shallow transition region, including the sills. The order of magnitude of the discharges, the salinities, and the depths is indicated on the table in Figure 1.

THE LONG-TERM DYNAMICS OF THE BALTIC SEA

The overall decrease in oxygen content in the deep waters, the overall increase in salinity and temperature, and the rise of the halocline are some of the general trends encountered in the Baltic Sea during this century, the causes of which have not found their final solution. In Figures 3 and 4 are shown some long-term time series representative of this evolution. The correlations between all the parameters are evident, although the runoff has been subject to man's interference (agriculture, industry, water power development). As a long-term non-steady mathematical model for the Baltic Sea has not yet been developed, a detailed analysis of the time series cannot be given. One general trend concerning the forcing functions is obvious, namely a decrease in the river runoff as well as in the wind, probably because both are correlated to the barometric pressure. The runoff/barometric pressure correlation is unknown. The wind/barometric pressure correlation is elaborated upon below.

THE INFLUENCE OF NATURAL AND MAN-MADE IMPACT ON THE BALTIC SEA

As demonstrated on Figure 4, a natural change in the runoff has always been associated with a change in the wind force also. Hence the effect of a man-made change of, for instance the runoff, can *not* be extracted from the observed natural changes; it has to be evaluated by use of a mathematical model. In 1978 the author developed such a type of consequence analysis model for estimating the influence on the Baltic Sea from the building of a bridge with large embankments across the Great Belt. The crucial role of the mixing in the shallow transition (the Great Belt) was demonstrated above, and the consequence analysis clearly showed that a measurable change of the hydrography of the Baltic Sea would have been the result, if the bridge had been built in accordance with the proposed design.

The two other important factors for the hydrography of the Baltic Sea estuary system are the runoff and the wind. It is therefore natural to investigate the effect of a man-made change of the runoff - especially because the USSR's Council of Ministers in their 5-year plan 1976- 80 has initiated the preliminary planning for diverging up to 2000 m^3/s from the river Ob (which drains to the Arctic Sea) to the river Volga in order to meet the increasing water demand for irrigational purposes in the dry regions north of the Caspian Sea and Lake Aral. From an engineering point of view the river Neva is also attractive as a source for this irrigation project. As the river Neva contributes about 20% of the runoff to the Baltic Sea, any decrease in its discharge would have a great bearing on the hydrography of the Baltic Sea and on the Danish inland waters.

Hence a steady-state model was developed which gave an overall quantitative description of the Baltic estuary system as it behaves under the present average meteorologic and hydrographic conditions. If it is assumed that the man-made changes have a minor effect on the meteorological conditions, then the governing equations shall be satisfied by the conditions after - as well as before - the man-made changes. Hence, by introducing the new parameters (discharges, depths, and salinities) equal to the previously used ones with an added minor correction, the 22 highly non-linear equations in the Neva analysis could be transformed to a set of 22 linear equations in the correction terms, which could then be solved directly.

In order to quantify the consequences a hypothetical runoff reduction of 25 % of the river Neva discharge was investigated. This corresponds to an only 5 % reduction of the total average runoff to the Baltic. Nevertheless, the influences will be significant. A detailed discussion of all the calculated hydrographic effects can be found in the papers referred to. The most striking difference between the response to a natural and to a man-made impact is most clearly illustrated in the runoff and in the Baltic upper layer salinity time series, Fig. 3.

The man-made reduction in the total runoff amounts to only 15 % of the natural runoff variations encountered in this century. Nevertheless, the associated salinity change in the upper layer of the Baltic Proper (S_{F75}) was calculated to be nearly 50 % of the natural salinity variation in the same period. This large difference in response may have two explanations. The yearly runoff to the Baltic Sea amounts to only 2 % of the total volume, which means that any response to non-steady external forces as the runoff or the wind will be highly damped and delayed due to the large response time of the system (the so-called reservoir effect). A permanent change in the runoff will on the contrary after about half a century yield a permanent, undamped change in the response. Another factor -

not taken into account in the calculation performed - is the possible damping/
amplifying effect of a variable wind. It is most probable that the effect will
be even more pronounced than the calculated effect, because the reduced stability
of the estuary system will make the system more sensitive to the inevitable changes
in the wind forces, which were held constant in the calculations.

A LONG-TERM WIND DATA SERIES

The general applicability of the outlined mathematical model is restricted,
mainly due to lack of knowledge of the time series for the important wind force.
Without this time series a lot of questions concerning the Baltic Sea remains
unanswered, such as: What has caused the general trend in the hydrography of the
Baltic Sea as demonstrated in Figure 3? How long time will elapse from the stop-
ping of a certain pollution source till the effect can be recognized in the various
parts of the estuary system?

The long-term variations of most oceanographic parameters in the Baltic Sea are
relatively well-known, but not the very important wind data. In Denmark, for
instance, the wind force and the wind direction have systematically been observed
at several locations since the foundation of the Danish Meteorological Institute
in 1872. Nevertheless, these observations are not reliable in long-term time
series, partly because they have been obtained by visual judgement (not by an
anemometer), and partly because a time series covering a century must comprise
the observations of a large number of individual observers. Hence, the importance
of the wind data series makes it necessary to seek for new, untraditional data
treatment. The following approach is a first approximation to obtain a secular
time series for the wind.

CHOICE OF TIME STEP

The time step chosen in a mathematical model has a great bearing on the formulation of the equations and of course on the computer cost. Figure 2 illustrated
that significant changes may take place within days. Figures 5 and 6 illustrate
accordingly that the seasonal variations of the wind power and the temperature
are significant, although the response of the water is damped due to the reservoir
effect (damping and delaying a step input). Finally Figure 4 shows that even the
secular variations are pronounced, and, moreover, that they themselves show
trends which mean that they are only part of an even longer varying time series.

The existence of systematic meteorological and hydrographical observations
since the last half of the 19th century makes it obvious to deal with a time
horizon of a century. The choice of a reasonable time step is, according to the
above-mentioned, not as obvious. The summer-thermocline formation in the Baltic
acts as a lid over the halocline and thus prevents the wind from eroding the

halocline during the period May - October (see Figure 6). Hence, a model representative for the dynamics of the sea cannot operate with time steps larger than
half a year. A shorter time step, on the other hand, increases the complexity
of the model significantly, because if the time step becomes less than the typical
time-scale of a sub-area, then the non-steady terms have to be retained for that
area.

In the present approach the summer and the winter period, i.e. half a year
has been chosen as the time step in the time series for the wind. As the response
time for the Central Baltic is of the order of decades, this implies that this
region has to be treated as non-steady. For all the other sub-areas the response
time is less than half a year, and hence they will attain a steady-state condition
before the lapse of each time step. As will be demonstrated below, a time step
of a month could have been used, but then the Bornholm Basin and probably the
Kattegat region would be non-steady. Especially a non-steady Kattegat/Skagerak
front would be extremely difficult to handle in a mathematical model. Finally,
a time step of less than a month is not possible with the present approach.

WIND VELOCITY OR SPEED

The superior role of the Danish Straits in governing the hydrography of the
Baltic Sea is demonstrated above. The characteristic flow pattern here is either
an inwards or an outwards directed flow, which makes it reasonable to operate with
only two types of wind, one creating inflow, the other creating outflow. As the
Baltic Sea is a semi-enclosed basin, the net long-term outflow must be equal to
the net fresh water input. Hence, if the strength of the wind contribution to
the in- and outflow, respectively, are taken equal (in the simple, long-term
model), a non-accumulation condition is ensured. This is a parallel to a semi-
enclosed sea connected to an ocean with tide of varying strength. If the averaging
time (the model time step) is well above the time scale of the phenomena, only
one parameter is needed to characterize the force, namely the average wind speed
or - in the other example - the tidal amplitude.

WIND-AIR PRESSURE CORRELATION

By physical reasoning the average wind must depend on the air-pressure gradient.
This may either be evaluated in a Lagrangian frame, for instance from two separate
observation stations, or in an Eulerian frame, from a single observation station,
located at a point where the lows and the highs pass by. The latter is chosen
here, with the station at the Danish Meteorologic Institute in Copenhagen as
reference. This does not mean that the conditions at this particular station is
representative of the wind force for the whole Baltic Sea system; the station is
merely chosen for convenience's sake, in order to demonstrate the basic approach.

By dimensional reasoning the wind speed must be proportional to the square root
of the representative barometric pressure, which is taken as the monthly peak-to-
peak value. In order to test the value of this simple hypothesis, the monthly
wind speed observed at Christiansø Light Tower (the Bornholm Basin) has in Figure
7 been plotted against the square root of the peak-to-peak value of the air pressure in Copenhagen. The wind speed is converted from the Beaufort scale (B) to
a metric value (V [m/s])by use of the old (before 1931) conversion formula:

$$V = (0.5 + 2 B_C) \pm 0.5 [m/s]$$

The weak elliptic distribution of the month-to-month values are probably caused
by the seasonal variations in the wind pattern. If we take the summer (May to
October) and the winter (November to April) average values respectively, this
minor effect disappears. From Figure 7 we conclude that the variation in the
monthly peak-to-peak values of the barometric pressure is representative for the
variations in the monthly mean wind. As the barometric pressure at Copenhagen
has been measured without interruption since 1873, we are able to outline the
crucial secular time series for the wind. Figure 8 shows a ten-year gliding mean
of the wind squared, calculated by use of the air pressure. In the same figure
is shown the time series of the three-year gliding mean of the wind speed to the
third power from Gedser Reef observations, referred to by Kullenberg (1977). The
three separate observation series resemble the calculated secular time series,
while the general trend of the wind is totally different, due to the above-mentioned problem of having individual observers.

A preliminary sensitivity test by the author, in which the wind force and the
runoff have been assumed correlated (see Figure 4), gives further support to the
validity of the calculated wind force time series.

SUMMARY AND CONCLUSIONS

Semi-enclosed seas - such as the Baltic - are bordered by a large number of
countries. This calls for an active international environmental policy based on
a detailed knowledge of how the meteorology, the oceanography, the biology, the
industry, the agriculture etc. are influencing one another.

For the Baltic Sea two examples of these types of consequence analysis have
been mentioned, namely in connection with the Danish project of building a bridge
with embankments across the Great Belt, and the (possible?) Russian project of
diverting part of the river Neva. Both examples illustrate that "minor" man-made
changes have "major" environmental consequences.

In an attempt to develop a mathematical consequence model for the Baltic Sea, which takes into account the non-steadiness of the external forces (temperature, wind, runoff), a secular time series for the major external force (the wind) has been established. This has been demonstrated by correlating the wind speed to the monthly peak-to-peak barometric pressures at Copenhagen.

When this time series is known, a lot of hitherto unanswered questions concerning the natural long-term variability of the hydrography of the Baltic Sea can be answered. To this end the set of governing equations has to be supplemented with the non-steady terms, and the flow in the system has to be expressed as functions of the wind field. Furthermore, this non-steady mathematical model can be used to predict the response of the Baltic Sea to a major man-made interference, and hence acts as a necessary tool in an active environmental policy for the Baltic Sea.

REFERENCES

Bo Pedersen, Fl., 1978. On the influence of a bridge across the Great Belt on the hydrography of the Baltic Sea. 11th Conference of the Baltic Oceanographers-Rostock, DDR.
Bo Pedersen, Fl., 1980. A monograph on turbulent entrainment and friction in two-layer stratified flow. Series Paper, No. 25, Institute of Hydrodynamics and Hydraulic Engineering, Technical University of Denmark.
Bo Pedersen, Fl. and Møller, J.S., 1981. Diversion of the river Neva - how will it influence the Baltic Sea, the Belts and the Cattegat. Nordic Hydrology, 12:1-20
Danmarks Klima. Belyst ved tabeller og kort. [The climate of Denmark]. Publ.by the Danish Meteorologic Institute. Copenhagen 1933. (In Danish)
Fonselius,S.H., 1969. Hydrography of the Baltic deep basins III. Fishery board of Sweden, Series hydrography, Report no. 23.
Hela,I., 1966. Secular changes in the salinity of the upper waters of the northern Baltic Sea. Commentationes Physico-Mathematicae, Vol.31, no.14. Helsingfors.
Kullenberg, G.E.B., 1977. Observations of the mixing in the Baltic thermo- and halocline layers. Tellus, 29:572-587
National Agency of Environmental Protection, Denmark, 1976. The Belt project. Interim report on the Danish Belt project. Miljøstyrelsen, Kampmannsgade 1, DK-1604 Copenhagen. (In Danish)
Nilsson,H. and Svansson,A., 1974. Long term variations of oceanographic parameters in the Baltic and adjacent waters. Meddelande från Havsfiskelaboratoriet, Lysekil, no.174 .

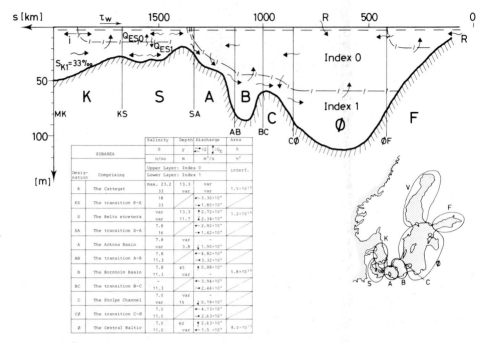

Fig. 1. The Baltic estuary system divided into eight subareas. The specific characteristics of the six outermost subareas are summarized in the table. From Bo Pedersen and Møller, 1981.

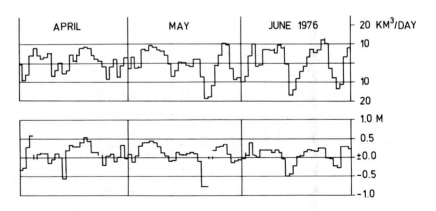

Fig. 2. Typical time series of the measured outward (positive) and inward discharge through the Great Belt. From Bo Pedersen, 1978.

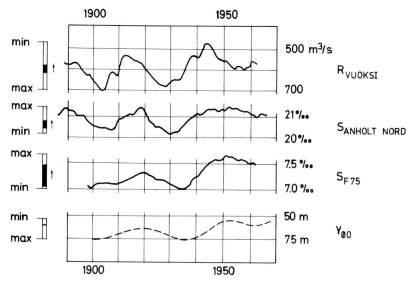

Fig. 3. The secular changes in the Baltic Sea estuary illustrated by the ten-year gliding mean of the runoff from the river Vuoksi (Nilsson and Svansson, 1974), the surface salinity at Anholt Nord (Nilsson and Svansson, 1974), the upper layer salinity at Station F75 (the Central Baltic, Hela 1966), the upper layer depth in the Central Baltic (Fonselius, 1969).

In the column diagram to the left is shown the min/max values observed and the changes calculated for a 25% reduction of the river Neva's runoff. From Bo Pedersen and Møller, 1981.

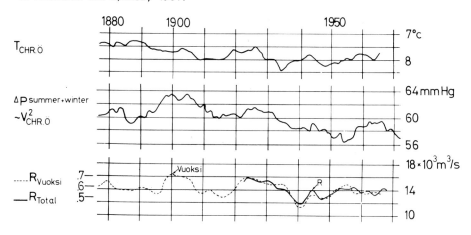

Fig. 4. The secular variations of the ten-year gliding mean values of $T_{CHRØ}$ = the air temperature at Christiansø (the Bornholm Basin), $\Delta p_{summer + winter}$ = the sum of the summer and winter average of monthly peak-to-peak barometric pressure, proportional to the wind speed squared at Christiansø, R_{Vuoksi} = the discharge of the Vuoksi river, R_{Total} = the total fresh water runoff to the Baltic, $T_{CHRØ}$, $\Delta p_{summer + winter}$ based on data published by the Danish Meteorologic Institute. R_{Vuoksi}, from Nilsson and Svansson, 1974. R_{Total}, from the Belt Project.

396

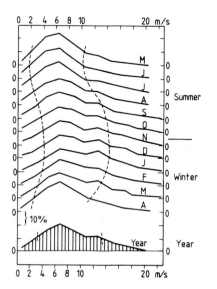

Fig. 5. The monthly and annual wind speed probability curves at Anholt lighttow (the Kattegat region). The half-peak probabilities are indicated to illustrate the seasonal variation. From Danmarks Klima, 1933.

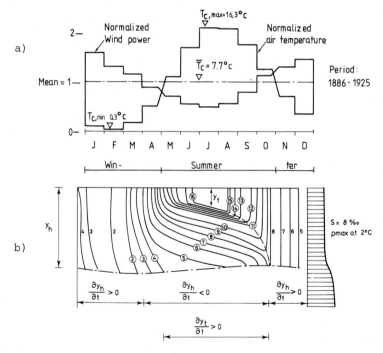

Fig. 6. a) The seasonal variation of the air temperature (T_c), the wind power ($\Delta p^{3/2} \sim$ (wind speed)^3) and b) the water temperature in the Bornholm Basin for a nearly continuous supply of dense water to the deep water. y_H = halocline depth, y_t = thermocline depth; water temperature in ^{0}C. Figure a) 1886-1925; b) 1949-1961.

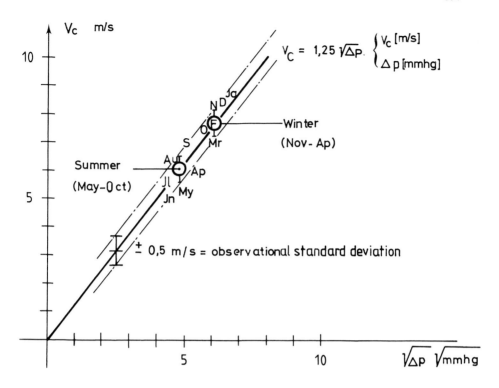

Fig. 7. The monthly 50 years average wind speed V_c[m/s] at Christiansø lighttower (the Bornholm Basin) versus the square root of the monthly peak-to-peak air pressure at Copenhagen [mm Hg] averaged over the same 50 years period, namely 1876-1925. Original data taken from "Danmarks Klima", 1933.

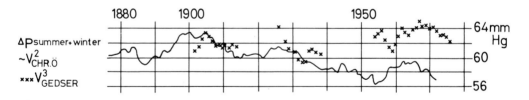

Fig. 8. Secular time series of the calculated ten-year gliding mean of the wind speed squared compared with the three-year gliding mean of third power of the observed wind speed from Gedser Rev lightvessel. The opposite trend in the individually observed time series is obvious.

V^2CHRØ - present calculations

V^3Gedser - from Kullenberg, 1977.

MIXING IN THE BALTIC SEA AND IMPLICATIONS FOR THE ENVIRONMENTAL CONDITIONS

GUNNAR KULLENBERG

Institute of Physical Oceanography
University of Copenhagen
Haraldsgade 6, 2200 Copenhagen N, Denmark

ABSTRACT

The Baltic Sea is a semi-enclosed sea with narrow and shallow connections to the open ocean and an annual river runoff amounting to about 2% of its volume. In some respects the Baltic Sea can be regarded as a series of estuaries. The mean cyclonic circulation is very weak and the wind-generated motion is dominating. There is a marked permanent stratification (halocline) at 50 - 70 m depth, and a summer thermocline around 20 m. The mean residence time is about 30 years.

The Baltic Sea is subject to considerable human influence, for instance as recipient of waste, and both the living and non-living resources, including recreational uses, are of great importance to the countries around the Baltic.

Experimental results have been obtained on mixing rates by means of natural and artificial tracers in the open sea, and in the coastal zone current meter records combined with repeated sections have been used to determine various exchange rates. The wind, heat input and stratification have a decisive influence on the vertical mixing. It is shown that both the vertical exchange in the open sea and the coastal zone are important for the fluxes.

The mixing in the deep and bottom waters is investigated using short and long term observations, and some consideration is given to long term fluctuations. Implications of the results for the environmental conditions in the Baltic are presented.

INTRODUCTION

The Baltic Sea is the largest brackish water body in the world. A population of about 19 million people in seven states around it contributes a considerable amount of waste input, including natural organic material, metals, organochlorines and petroleum hydrocarbons. In addition, the atmospheric input of anthropogenic substances is considerable. Harmful effects on the Baltic mammals and sea birds have been demonstrated. An increase in the primary production has been indicated along with local changes of dominating primary producers, and decreasing production at depths below about 70 m, as well as a change in the structure of the benthic and the pelagic ecosystem.

The concentration levels of pollutants in Baltic biota are, however, generally not elevated compared to the levels found in North Sea coastal areas.

The rivers entering the Baltic have a profound influence on the system. They have been subject to regulations in relation to hydro-electric power constructions, but no flow has as yet been reversed.

The living resources of the Baltic are important, the yield during the last decade being approximately constant around 800.000 tonnes per year, with no decreasing trends. The Baltic Sea is a very important transportation medium for the states around it, and the recreational importance is also great.

The overall problem is to what extent the natural Baltic ecosystem can adjust to the human use of the area without being completely destroyed. This clearly depends on a combination of many factors, involving physics, chemistry, biology. Here in particular the mixing conditions and their implications will be considered. It seems clear that the vertical transfer, and its space and time variation, is a very important factor for the environmental conditions. A thorough assessment of the state of the Baltic marine environment based on recent data has been carried out during the last 2-3 years under the auspices of the Helsinki Convention (Melvasalo et al. 1981), and a treatment of Baltic Sea oceanography is given by Voipio (Ed. 1981).

AREA DEFINITION AND TOPOGRAPHY

The Baltic Sea, an intra-continental mediterranean sea with an area of about 370.000 km^2 and volume of about 21.000 km^3, consists of the Gulf of Bothnia, including the Åland Sea, the Gulf of Finland, and the Baltic proper with the Central, Bornholm and Arkona basins. The Central basin includes the Eastern and Western Gotland basins and the Northern Central basins (Fig. 1). The Danish Sounds and the Kattegat, constituting the Transition Area, are sometimes included in the Baltic Sea although it is a different oceanographic regime. The sill depth in the Sound between Sweden and Denmark (the Øresund) is 7-8 m and in the Belt Sea the sill depth is 17-18 m at Darsser. One of the outstanding features of the Baltic topography is the division into a series of basins separated from each other by shallow areas and sills (Table 1). The mean depth is 56 m but roughly 17% of the area is shallower than 10 m.

The northern boundary of the Transition Area is defined by the line Skaw - Marstrand, and the oceanographic boundaries between the Baltic proper and the Transition Area are the lines Gedser Rev - Darsser Ort and Dragør - Limhamn (Wattenberg 1949). The area is generally shallow, the mean depth of the Kattegat being 23 m, with the largest depths in the Øresund about 50 m, SE of the island Ven, and in the Great Belt up to 80 m in narrow trenches. A very important characteristic is that the connections between the Baltic Sea and the open ocean are both shallow and narrow. The section area over the sill in the Øresund is 0.1 km^2 and in the Belt Sea 0.16 km^2.

TABLE 1

Major Baltic divisions with maximum depths, sill depths at outer boundary, volumes and mean depths.

Name	Max depth m	Sill depth m	Volume km^3	Mean depth m
Baltic Sea (total)	459	17	20900	56
Arkona Sea	55	17	430	23
Bornholm Sea	106	45	1780	46
Eastern Gotland Sea	–	–	–	–
Gdansk/or Danzig Bay	116	88	1460	57
Gotland Deep	249	60	3570	81
Fårö Deep	205	140	1270	–
Northern Central Sea	459	115	2090	72
Landsort Deep	459	138	780	–
Western Gotland Sea	205	100	1640	61
Gulf of Riga		–	410	23
Gulf of Finland		–	1100	37
Åland Sea	300	70	410	75
Archipelago Sea	40	40	170	19
Bothnian Sea	293	90	4300	67
Bothnian Bay	126	25	1490	41

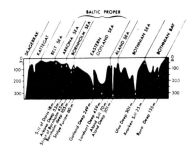

Fig. 1. Baltic Sea subdivisions with section showing depth of various basins (from Janson 1978). Dotted line in left hand figure shows position of topographic section shown on right hand side.

THE WATER BALANCE

The dominating factor is the river inflow which according to investigations covering slightly different periods falls in the range 473-440 km^3 per year, or about 2% of the total volume of the Baltic Sea (Witting 1918, Brogmus 1952, Soskin 1963, Mikulski 1970). Long-term records of the river inflow show a variability of about 20% between maximum and minimum.

Remaining significant terms in the fresh water budget are the precipitation and evaporation which on a yearly basis for the whole area very closely balance. However, they both show marked regional and seasonal variations.

Considerable amounts of various substances are brought to the Baltic Sea through the river runoff, including humic substances, particulate matter, nutrients and metals.

The water exchange between the Baltic Sea and the open ocean is driven both by the river runoff and by the meteorological conditions over the North Sea - Baltic Sea area.

The average circulation in the Transition Area is a two-layered flow. However, due to the influence of meteorological conditions, the flow is often a one-layer flow with the whole water column moving either from or towards the Baltic. For south-westerly to north-westerly winds above about 10 m s^{-1} and with a minimum duration of several days over the North Sea - Skagerrak area, the current in the Transition Area is towards the Baltic in the whole water column. For other wind directions with wind forces of 10 m s^{-1} or more over the Baltic - North Sea area the current is out of the Baltic (Dietrich 1951).

The most favorable conditions for inflows of saline water into the Baltic occur with a high pressure over Jutland and a low pressure over Sweden, whereas outflow situations occur with high pressure over Scandinavia. Particularly strong inflows can occur when an outflow situation is followed by a series of intense west wind situations. This was the case in November-December 1951 when about 200 km^3 of highly saline water of about 22 $^o/oo$ penetrated into the Baltic over a three week period (Wyrtki 1954).

Using the classical Knudsen hydrographical theorem to calculate the long-term average water exchange, it is found that the inflows of fresh water and salt water are almost equal, or about 470 km^3 per year, and the outflow about twice as large. An important characteristic of the water transport is its large variability. Recent studies using long-term current measurements in several sections in the Belt Sea show that the total transport is in the range 3-4000 km^3 per year (Jacobsen 1980)

For the conditions in the Baltic bottom waters the major inflows of saline water are particularly important. They occur aperiodically at intervals of 2-5 years. There has been a tendency for the frequency of these inflows to increase during the last decades. Dickson (1971, 1973) found a rather good correlation between positive salinity anomalies in the European shelf seas and the occurrence of major inflows into the Baltic. It should be noted that on an average there is a continuous inflow of deep water into the Baltic. This water does not penetrate down to the bottom in tha Baltic basins except during major inflows.

The residence time for the water in the Baltic is about 35 years, calculated using the yearly average water exchange and taking into account that about 1/3 of the water in the outflow from the Baltic is mixed down into the return flow.

SALINITY AND TEMPERATURE DISTRIBUTIONS

The fresh-water surplus, constituting a positive water balance, the narrow and shallow connections with the ocean, and the topographic division into several basins have a major influence on the oceanographic conditions of the Baltic Sea.

An important characteristic of the Baltic is the marked permanent salinity stratification (Fig. 2). The fresh-water supply is mixed downwards by a combination of wind-generated mixing and thermohaline convection during fall and early winter. This process generates an almost homohaline layer separated from the deep and bottom waters by a permanent halocline layer of about 20 m thickness. The thickness of the surface layer varies from about 40 m in the south-west basins to about 60 m in the Central basin (Fonselius 1969). According to Matthäus (1979) the mean depth of the halocline layer has not varied more than 10% during this century, and the mean depth of the top of the halocline layer has decreased by about 6 m.

The water exchange between the Central basin and the Gulf of Bothnia goes essentially through the Åland Sea. The incoming water originates from the top 70 m layer of the Central basin, which has small salinity and density variations. The mixing during the inflow further reduces the density variations, implying that the stratification in the Gulf of Bothnia is considerably weaker than in the Baltic proper. The stratification is stable throughout the year but the depth of the weakly developed halocline varies strongly and the halocline can be absent during part of the year.

The deep water salinities in the Gulf of Bothnia are 3-7 $^{o}/oo$, in the Gulf of Finland 5-9 $^{o}/oo$ and in the Baltic proper 10-13 $^{o}/oo$. In connection with particularly strong inflows from the Kattegat the bottom water salinity in the Bornholm basin can reach 23 $^{o}/oo$ and in the eastern and western Gotland basins 14 $^{o}/oo$ and 11 $^{o}/oo$, respectively. In connection with such inflows a secondary halocline layer develops at a depth of 110-130 m (Voipio and Mälkki 1972).

The residence time of the bottom waters depends primarily on the density difference to the overlying waters, which is essentially determined by the salinity. After strong inflows of highly saline waters, replacing the old bottom waters, the density of the new bottom water normally must decrease significantly by vertical mixing before a new inflow can replace it. During these periods, which can

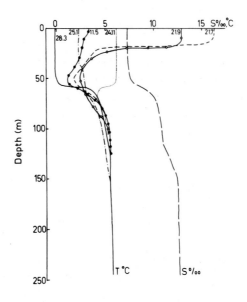

Fig. 2. Profiles of salinity and temperature from the Gotland basin showing
halocline and development of seasonal thermocline.

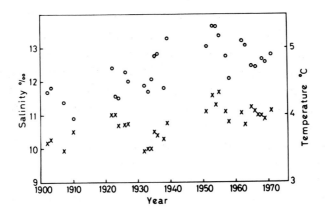

Fig. 3. Long-term variations of salinity (x) and temperature (o) at 300 m depth
in the Landsort Deep.

last up to about 5 years, the motion in the bottom water is very weak and they
are therefore often called periods of stagnation. In the Arkona basin and normally
in the Gulf of Bothnia the bottom water is renewed every year due to a combination
of water exchange and thermohaline convection.

The vertical temperature distribution shows marked seasonal variations (Fig. 2).
During fall and early winter the convection reaches the top of the primary halocline, where it is stopped by the strong stratification. During the spring a
strong thermocline is developed over the whole Baltic Sea at depths between 15
and 20 m. The temperature maximum occurs in August with up to $18^{\circ}C$ at 20 m.
During fall the temperature decreases, and the depth of the thermocline may then
increase to 50 à 60 m.

On top of the halocline the so-called winter water remains which was formed
during the preceding fall-winter period. The summer thermocline effectively
suppresses vertical mixing and nutrient transfer from deeper layers to the euphotic
zone, which is about 20 m deep.

The deep water temperature in the Bornholm basin varies between about 2 and
$14^{\circ}C$ whereas in the Central basin the deep water temperature normally lies between
3 and $6^{\circ}C$.

LONG-TERM VARIATIONS AND THEIR CAUSES AND EFFECTS

Both temperature and salinity show important long-term fluctuations (Soskin
1963, Hela 1966a, Fonselius 1969, Matthäus 1979), with a clear trend towards an
increase (Fig. 3). The salinity in the deep and bottom waters has increased by
0.8 - 1.7 $^{\circ}\!/oo$ and the temperature by 0.6 - $2.7^{\circ}C$ during the present century. The
salinity increase in the surface layer is slightly less, by about 0.2 - 0.5 $^{\circ}\!/oo$,
than in the deep water. These variations can be caused both by the variations
of the river runoff and of the water exchange with the Kattegat-North Sea. There
seems to be a coupling between periods of low salinity and periods of high runoff
and vice versa (e.g. Fonselius 1969, Kaleis 1976). The changes of the river runoff are in turn probably related to changes in the atmospheric circulation (e.g.
Soskin 1963) although there has not been found any clear correlation between certain types of climatic fluctuations (Hela 1966a) and the river runoff fluctuations.
There does not seem to be any significant long-term decreasing trend in the river
runoff during the last 100 years, although there are shorter periods with marked
trends, (Launiainen and Koljonen, 1981). The salinity increase may be related
·to variations in the river runoff as well as to changes in the frequency of major
inflows of high salinity water from the Kattegat, especially when these are coupled
to a positive salinity anomaly over the European shelf seas as shown by Dickson
(1972).

The temperature and salinity fluctuations have important implications for the
conditions in the Baltic Sea. The density stratification across the halocline

layer and in the deeper waters is mainly determined by the salinity. The fluctuations generate varying degrees of stratification in the deep and bottom water implying different conditions of vertical mixing. Studies of the long-term variations of the salinity gradient across the halocline in the Gotland basin do not show any significant trend of change during the century (Matthäus 1979), which would suggest that the stability has not changed significantly. This is important in relation to vertical mixing since the stability has a major influence on the mixing (e.g. Kullenberg 1974). The temperature increase in the deep waters may be due to a shift of inflows towards the warmer season. It implies an increased rate of oxygen consumption and also that less oxygen enters with the inflowing water. This may well have influenced the development of the oxygen conditions (e.g. Kullenberg 1970).

Features of the circulation

There is a weak cyclonal mean circulation in the Baltic Proper and the Gulfs of Finland and Bothnia, with velocities of the order of centimeters per second. This circulation is essentially thermohaline, the mean winds over the Baltic being very weak.

The fluctuating part of the motion, which can reach velocities of 50 cm s^{-1}, is generated by the meteorological conditions, wind and pressure gradients. Strong storms often occur over the Baltic Sea. In the top layer the fluctuating motion is directly proportional to the wind stress, and in the deeper layers the motion is related to the divergence and curl of the wind stress. Important features of the motion are the inertial oscillations and various types of seiches generated by fluctuating winds and air pressure. The tidal motion is weak, of the order of centimeters per second.

MIXING IN THE BALTIC

General

The mixing in the Baltic Sea is weaker than in the open ocean and than in areas of strong tidal currents like the North Sea. The mixing can be generated by processes at the boundaries, by breaking of internal waves which have been generated in the interior or have radiated into the interior from the boundaries, by inertial motion, by fall and winter time convection in the surface layer down to the primary halocline.

The main energy source for the mixing is the wind, and during fall and early winter the loss of heat through cooling. The layer down to the primary halocline will always become thoroughly mixed during some periods in fall and winter. The primary interest in relation to mixing is the exchange across the halocline layer and the mixing in the deep and bottom waters. The latter mixing has a great influence on the exchange rate of the bottom waters, and is thus of great significance in relation to the oxygen conditions in these waters.

The deep water inflow from the Danish Straits, across the Bornholm sill and the Stolpe Channel into the Baltic Proper is also a main source of energy for the interior mixing. Entrainment of water into the inflowing water from below and to some extent from above will generate considerable vertical mixing. This is an important process since it occurs more or less continuously.

Several investigations have shown that internal small scale motion occur in the Baltic deep waters (e.g. Hollan 1969, Krauss et al 1973). The dominating type of fluctuating motion is the inertial motion, which is found in the whole water column in connection with suitable wind events and which generates shears with associated mixing.

Above the halocline

The efficiency of wind-generated mixing in eroding and deepening the seasonal thermocline has been demonstrated (e.g. Krauss 1978, Kullenberg 1978) on the basis of observations in relation to the passing of a sequence of storms over the southern Baltic Proper (Fig. 4). Considering that the frequency of storms over the Baltic is large, this constitutes a very important energy source for the mixing, in the interior as well as in the coastal zone. Results on the vertical mixing rates in the top layer obtained by means of different methods are also presented in Table 2. It should be noted that during calm or weak wind conditions of some length the mixing in the top layer can be very weak, especially during the warm season. These periods of very low mixing can extend for many days, and quite clearly they have biological significance in relation to the productivity. An example of dye profiles obtained during such a period in the central Baltic is shown in Fig. 5. It is noted that layers can be formed also during weak stratification.

Vertical mixing below the halocline

Mixing rates for the deep and bottom waters may be estimated from observed decreases of the salinity of the deep and bottom water following a bottom water renewal (Fig. 6), and assuming that the decrease of salinity is due to a vertical flux of salt. The time-interval between renewals can be rather well determined together with the salinity decrease. The total salt flux has been calculated using hydrographic data from a few stations in the Baltic Proper representing different parts of the area. The volumes were obtained from Ehlin et al (1974). The vertical mixing coefficient, K_z, was calculated using the expression

$$K_z = Q_s/A \cdot t \cdot \frac{dS}{dz}$$

where A is the area at the level in question (obtained from Ehlin et al 1974) and t is the time-interval. The salinity gradient, dS/dz, was determined for the appropriate level from the hydrographic data. Results are given in Table 2. The

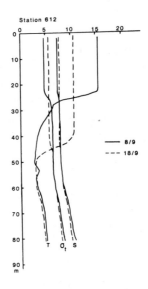

Fig. 4. Thermocline erosion during September storm in the southern central
Baltic.

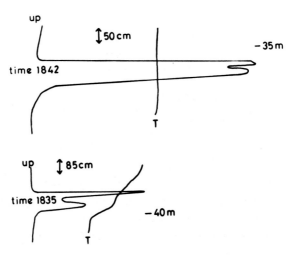

Fig. 5. Rhodamine dye layers after 20 hours of in situ tracing during a period
of several days of calm in the Eastern Gotland basin.

TABLE 2

Vertical mixing coefficients, K_z, for various layers in the Baltic.

Method and remarks	Depth range m	Range of $K_z \cdot 10^6$ $m^2 s^{-1}$	Reference
Dye diffusion, calm weather	45- 55 22- 35	0.8-3.9 5 - 15	Kullenberg (1974b, 1977)
Seasonal heat penetration	50- 70	10 - 100	Matthäus (1977)
Seasonal heat penetration "	0- 20 20- 30 40- 50	$10^2 - 10^4$ $30 - 3 \cdot 10^3$ $10 - 3 \cdot 10^3$	Matthäus (1977) Matthäus (1977) Matthäus (1977)
Seasonal heat penetration	20- 30 50- 60	$60 - 200$ $5 \cdot 10^2 - 5 \cdot 10^3$	Hela (1966b)
Conservation calculations of salt flux	60- 70	Open Baltic 10 coastal zone 80	Shaffer (1979a)
Thermocline deepening during storm	30- 40	700	Jensen and Kullenberg (1981)
Dye diffusion, calm weather	30- 40	15 - 60	Jensen and Kullenberg (1981)
Salinity decrease after inflow	200-240 ≥ 100 ≥ 150	10 - 35 4 - 5 5 - 10	present " "

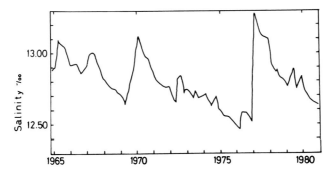

Fig. 6. Variations of salinity at 240 m depth in the Gotland Deep following inflows (data from S. Fonselius, pers.com.).

values appear reasonable, and are comparable to results from the halocline layer. The energy supply for the mixing is derived from the deep water inflow through the Danish Straits and from the wind. The latter transfers a substantial amount of energy to the top layer (Kullenberg 1977) and part of this energy will penetrate to the deep and bottom waters, inertial oscillations being one transfer mechanism.

The results summarized in Table 2 quite clearly show that the vertical mixing is very variable, with area, depth and depending upon the conditions. This is quite what should be expected, and the results are consistent with each other although very different methods have been used. The values for the deep and bottom waters obtained by means of observations from different times during this century do not suggest any significant change in the mixing rates during the present century.

Vertical fluxes

It is important to determine the rate of exchange between the various layers in the Baltic as well as to clarify the distribution in space of the transfer. In the coastal zone very efficient vertical transfer across the halocline layer may be generated by suitable winds giving rise to a divergence at the coast, with associated compensating flow and upwelling or downwelling in the coastal zone (e.g. Walin 1972a, Shaffer 1975, 1979a, b). The width, L_c, of the coastal dynamics zone may be estimated by the expression

$$L_c \simeq H_o \, N/f$$

where H_o is the depth of the halocline at the boundary between the coastal zone and the open sea. Using typical values from the Baltic one finds a width L_c in the range 5-10 km (e.g. Walin 1972b). This is in reasonable agreement with observations although typical coastal zone dynamics also have been observed over greater widths (Shaffer 1975). The vertical flux associated with wind events of this kind has been computed by Shaffer (1975, 1979b) on the basis of observations, over a period of some months in the fall, in repeated sections of salinity and temperature, nutrients and currents. He found an average vertical diffusive flux of $12 \cdot 10^{-6}$ kg salt m^{-2} s^{-1}, with an advective flux during the same period about an order of magnitude larger. In a later study in the same area Shaffer (1979a) calculated the fluxes across the 8.5 ‰ isohaline using observations from a six weeks period in the spring time. He found values for the diffusive and advective fluxes of $5 \cdot 10^{-6}$ kg salt m^{-2} s^{-1} and $70 \cdot 10^{-6}$ kg salt m^{-2} s^{-1}, respectively. For comparison, Shaffer calculated the flux across the 8.5 ‰ isohaline for the entire Baltic, finding the fluxes to be $1.1 \cdot 10^{-6}$ and $3.4 \cdot 10^{-6}$ kg salt m^{-2} s^{-1}, respectively. For these calculations he used inflow observations through the Bornholm Strait and the Stolpe Furrow presented by Rydberg (1978).

Shaffer's results demonstrate that large fluxes can occur in the coastal zone. However, how often and over how large a part of the total coast line of the Baltic Sea? These questions have not yet been answered. Here the results of Shaffer will be used to estimate the possible vertical flux in the coastal zone for the whole Baltic.

With a length of the coastline at the 60 m level of about 1200 km, and a width of the zone of coastal dynamics on an average of 10 km, we find an integrated diffusive flux of salt across the halocline layer in the coastal zone of up to 144 ton salt s^{-1}, and about an order of magnitude more as advective flux.

The diffusive flux may be compared with the corresponding flux in the open Baltic, calculated by means of observed vertical mixing coefficients, K_z, and salinity gradients across the halocline layer. These are on an average in the range 1-3 $^o\!/oo$ per 10 m. Values of K_z determined by various techniques for the halocline layer are presented in Table 2. The range is fairly large so maximum and minimum estimates of the integrated salt flux can only be given, assuming that the values are representative for the whole area. The values of K_z determined by Kullenberg (1971, 1977) from dye experiments of one or two days' duration during calm conditions are probably minimum values. The area of the Baltic Proper is $10^5 km^2$ at 60 m depth (Ehlin et al 1974), assuming this to be an average depth of the halocline layer. The minimum diffusive salt flux is 60 ton s^{-1}, using the maximum value of the salinity gradient. Taking the maximum average value of K_z for the whole open Baltic at the halocline to be $100 \cdot 10^{-6} m^2 \ s^{-1}$ we find tha diffusive salt flux to be 10^3 ton s^{-1}, using the minimum value of the gradient. These values are certainly comparable with the diffusive flux for the coastal zone. The maximum value is comparable with the advective flux in the coastal zone. It appears that the vertical exchange in the Baltic occurs at comparable magnitudes over the whole sea area.

It is of interest to compare the yearly inflow of salt to the Baltic with the vertical salt flux. Considering an annual inflow of 500 km^3 through the Danish Straits with a salinity of 17 $^o\!/oo$ we find an inflow of 270 ton salt s^{-1}. This number compares well with the total diffusive flux across the halocline layer. An advective flux of about 10^3 ton s^{-1} in the coastal zone as an annual average appears, however, to be quite unrealistic. It can be concluded that the estimates for the interior vertical mixing are realistic, and that the values may be used to discuss implications for the Baltic ecosystem.

Horizontal mixing

Only a limited number of direct experimental studies of horizontal mixing exist. For the southern Baltic, Kullenberg (1977) found horizontal diffusion velocities in the range 3.5 m h^{-1} to 7.2 m h^{-1} in the thermo- and halocline layers. In the surface layer Schott et al (1978) found values in the range 9.7 m h^{-1} to 21 m h^{-1}.

These results are based on dye mixing observations, carried out during weak winds. In the Landsort area Kullenberg (1964) found values in the range 4-18 m h^{-1} for the surface layer to 25 m, based on the observation of dispersion of internal layers of suspended matter resulting from a sewage sludge dumping experiment. The horizontal mixing in the Baltic is weaker than it is for instance in the North Sea, by about a factor of 5 on similar scales. This is of some interest in relation to the transfer of material from the coastal zone outwards, in particular along the isopycnals in thermo- and halocline layers. Considerable periods of time, of the order of several months, will be required for material to become transferred across the coastal zone into the interior. The most efficient transfer will occur during strong wind conditions in the fall and late winter to early spring.

FACTORS INFLUENCING THE MIXING

The conditions in the Baltic have displayed a considerable variability during the present century. In particular the oxygen conditions in the deep and bottom waters have deteriorated. This can conceivably be related to several factors and processes, one being that the rate of vertical mixing has changed.

The rate of vertical exchange is essentially depending upon the density stratification (static stability) and the energy available for turbulent mixing against the buoyancy forces. The stability across the halocline layer has shown fluctuations but there has been no long-term increase (Kullenberg 1977, 1981; Matthäus 1980). It appears that no long-term decreasing trend of vertical exchange rate can be expected on the basis of stability changes. Considerable short-term fluctuations over several years of the vertical exchange rates can, however, be expected on the basis of stability fluctuations related to inflows. It should also be noted that there is no single relationship between stability and vertical mixing.

The stability is determined by the salinity difference across the halocline layer (Fig. 7) (Kullenberg 1981/82) and is therefore also related to fluctuations in the river runoff. This could be important for short-term variations but could not have generated a long-term significant change in the mixing rates, since the long-term runoff changes are very small.

The salinity difference across the halocline layers in the Bornholm, Gotland and Landsort Deeps are shown in Fig. 8. There are no marked overall trends. Ten years moving averages of the stability across the halocline layer calculated from light vessel observations in the Kattegat area are shown in Fig. 9, together with the series from the Bornholm Basin. A decrease of stability is shown for the latter area since about 1920, with a corresponding increase in the Kattegat area.

A rise of the halocline layer could imply an increased exchange between the surface and the deep water since the surface area of the layer would be larger,

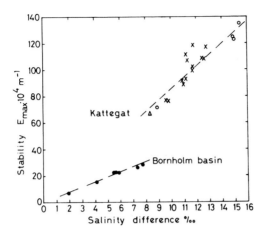

Fig. 7. Stability, given by $E_{max} = \Delta\rho/\rho\Delta z \ m^{-1}$, across halocline layer versus salinity differences in the Kattegat and the Bornholm basins.

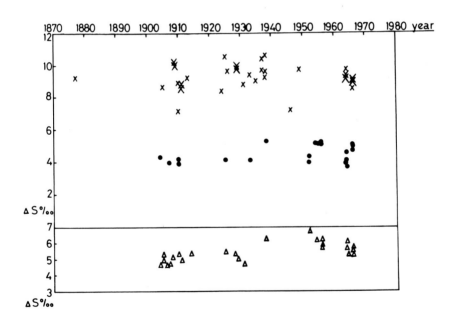

Fig. 8. Variations of salinity differences across the halocline layer in the Bornholm (x), Landsort (o), and Gotland (Δ) Deeps during the present century.

and the wind energy driving the mixing would penetrate to the halocline in a
shorter time. However, the halocline has only become about 5 m shallower during
the century (Matthäus 1980) which can hardly give rise to a large transfer change.

The major driving force for the fluctuating circulation and mixing in the Baltic, the wind, has shown considerable fluctuations (Kullenberg 1977). These are
related to the climatic variability with alternating predominance of cyclonic and
anticyclonic atmospheric circulation over the north-eastern European continent
(e.g. Hela 1966a). It is difficult to ascertain any long-term trend in the wind
strength, mainly because of different observation techniques. The record used
by Kullenberg (1977) from Gedser Rev light vessel over the period 1900 to 1960
did not display any marked trend. However, a longer record appears to show a
long-term trend (see Pedersen, this volume).

On the basis of the present calculations of vertical exchange rates in the
deep waters of the Baltic Proper, there does not appear to be any significant
trend of changing mixing rates. It is concluded that long-term changes in the
vertical exchange rates cannot be the main cause for long-term deteriorating
oxygen conditions in the deep and bottom waters of the Baltic Sea.

IMPORTANCE OF THE MIXING FOR THE CONDITIONS IN THE BALTIC

It is of interest to consider briefly the importance of the vertical exchange
rates for the exosystem of a semi-enclosed sea like the Baltic. The nutrient
content and its variability in the surface layer is of central importance. Limiting nutrients for different parts of the Baltic during different seasons are phosphate and nitrate. The importance of the nitrogen as a possibly dominating limiting factor has, however, been emphasized in recent years.

It is pertinent to separate between the conditions in the Baltic Proper and
the Gulf of Bothnia. In the latter area the vertical stability is comparatively
weak, the oxygen conditions have not deteriorated as in the Baltic Proper, and
the nutrients have not increased as much in the surface layer. This shows the
importance of the vertical exchange for the oxygen conditions. It also suggests
that the nutrient increase in the Baltic Proper cannot alone be due to an increased
input from land through rivers and waste water input.

In the Baltic Proper the phosphate concentrations have increased since about
the mid-1950's (Fonselius 1969), both in the deep and surface waters. Around
1969 the rate of increase of phosphate concentrations in the mixed surface layer
winter water showed a marked increase (Nehring 1979), and since that year an
increase of the nitrate concentrations in the same water has also been established
(Nehring 1979). Nehring's data show that maxima and minima of both nitrate and
phosphate concentrations are alternately occurring during coinciding periods.
The periods of concentration maxima seem to coincide with the periods of good
oxygen conditions in the bottom water (Table 3) and the minima with the periods

TABLE 3

Correlation between nutrient extreemes in the winter surface water and oxygen extreemes in the bottom water in the Gotland basin (data from Fonselius 1978 and Nehring 1979).

Year	PO_4-P	NO_3-N	O_2	H_2S
	In winter surface layer		at 240 m	
	μg at ℓ^{-1}	μg at ℓ^{-1}	ml ℓ^{-1}	ml ℓ^{-1}
1954/55	0.3 - 0.4	–	1 - 2	0
1961/62	0.1	–	0	1
1962/63	0.7 - 0.9	–	2	0
1963/64	~ 0.1	–	0	0.8
1964/65	0.2 - 0.4	–	1 - 2	0
1966/67	0.1 - 0.2	–	0	1
1967/68	0.3 - 0.5	–	1 - 2	0
1968/69	≤ 0.1	–	0	2 - 2.5
1970/71	1.3 - 0.4	2.5 - 3	0.5 - 1.5	0
1972/73	0.2	1.0	0	1.5
1973/74	0.5	3 - 4	1 - 2	0

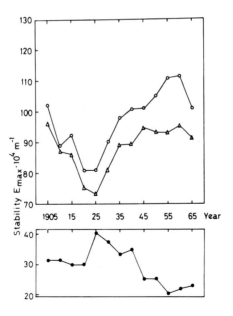

Fig. 9. Stability, given by $E_{max} = \Delta\rho/\rho\Delta z$ m^{-1}, across the halocline layer in the Bornholm basin (●) and in the Kattegat at the Anholt N(Δ) and the Kattegat SW (o) light vessel during the present century.

of hydrogen sulphide there (Table 3). The peaks occur with only a slight time delay after bottom water renewals. This suggests that the deep and bottom waters are significant sources of nutrients. The storage there is gradually transferred towards the surface layer in connection with bottom water renewal and deep water inflow. Nehring (1979) demonstrated a correlation between the salinity increase and the nutrient increase, and concluded that probably an increasing amount of Kattegat water intruded into the Baltic, leading to an increasing upward transfer of nutrients and salt to the surface layer. An increase of the inflow cannot be substantiated at present, but the results show that nutrients are supplied from the deep and bottom waters through vertical transfer to the surface layer. The vertical transfer occurs over the whole Baltic Proper.

It should be noted that the increase in the rate of increase of nutrient concentrations around 1969 coincided with a temporary breaking of the trend of an increasing volume of hydrogen sulphide containing deep and bottom waters, as given by Jansson (1978). This supports the conclusion above.

The phosphate and nitrate concentrations in the Gotland basin surface layer winter water have increased by factors of 3 and 2.5, respectively (Nehring 1979), from about 0.2 μg at ℓ^{-1} and 1.5 μg at ℓ^{-1}, respectively, in 1968. The phosphate concentration in the deep and bottom waters is a factor of 3 to 10 larger than in the surface winter water (Fonselius 1969). The total volume beneath the 100 m level of the Baltic Proper is about 1700 km^3 (Ehlin et al 1974), mostly found in the Gotland basin, whereas the 0-50 m volume in the Gotland basin is about 3000 km^3 A couple of inflows of about 200 km^3 water from the Kattegat, leading to inflows of about 400 km^3 into the Gotland basin, would be able to generate the transfer of the required amount of nutrients to the surface winter water. Since 1968 at least three inflows of that category have occurred (Fonselius 1978).

Biologically the changes have implied an increase in nutrients and a slight decrease in the ratio N:P in the water. It remains to be seen whether this trend of changing N:P ratio continues, and if it can imply that nitrogen becomes increasingly important as a most limiting factor for the primary production. The supply of nutrients may also have become more pulsating, occurring over different periods of the year. This may imply that an unbalance between the primary and secondary productions is established, so that the zooplankton grazing cannot cope with pulses of phytoplankton production which occur outside the 'normal' production cycles, provided no other factor such as light limits the primary production. The result will then be an increased transfer of organic matter to the halocline layer and the deep water through dead phytoplankton. This, in turn, leads to an increasing oxygen consumption rate in these waters. Shaffer (1979b) calculated that the rate of oxygen consumption had increased since the 1930's in theintermediate waters.

Most of the implications above point at the great importance of vertical mixing for the conditions in a semi-enclosed sea like the Baltic. A close cooperation between hydrodynamicists and scientists from other marine sciences is clearly required to solve ecosystem problems of such regions and make forecasts of the development which can be reliably used for environmental management.

REFERENCES

Brogmus, W., 1952. Eine Revision des Wasserhaushaltes der Ostsee. Kiel. Meeres-forsch., 9: 15-42.

Dickson, R. R., 1971. A current and persistent pressure-anomaly pattern as the principal cause of inter-mediate hydrographic variation in the European shelf sea. Dtsch. Hydrogr. Z., 24: 97-119.

Dickson, R. R., 1973. The prediction of major Baltic inflows. Dtsch. Hydrogr. Z., 26: 97-105.

Dietrich, G., 1951. Oberflächenströmmungen im Kattegatt, im Sund und in der Beltsee. Dtsch. Hydrogr. Z., 4: 129-140.

Ehlin, U., Mattisson, I. and Zachrisson, G., 1974. Computer based calculations of volumes of the Baltic area. Proc. 9th Conf. Baltic Oceanogr. Kiel, 17-20 April 1974, pp. 115-128

Fonselius, S., 1969. Hydrography of the Baltic Deep basins III. Fish. Board Swed., Ser. Hydrogr., 23: 97 pp.

Fonselius, S. H., 1978. On nutrients and their role as production limiting factors in the Baltic. Acta Hydrochim. Hydrobiol., 6: 329-339.

Hela, I., 1966a. Secular changes in the salinity of the upper waters of the northern Baltic Sea. Comm. Phys.-Math. Soc. Sci. Fenn., 31, 14: 21 pp.

Hela, I., 1966b. Vertical eddy diffusivity in the Baltic Sea. Geophysica 9: 219-234.

Hollan, E., 1969. Die Veränderlichkeit der Strömmungsverteilung im Gotlandbecken am Beispiel von Strömmungsmessungen im Gotland Tief. Kieler Meeresforsch., 25: 19-70.

Jacobsen, T., 1980. Sea water exchange of the Baltic: Measurements and methods. The Belt Project. The National Agency of Environmental Protection, Copenhagen.

Jansson, B.-O., 1978. The Baltic - A systems analysis of a semi-enclosed sea. In: H. Charnock and G. Deacon (Editors), Advances in Oceanography. Plenum Press, Oxford, pp. 131-184.

Jensen, T. G. and Kullenberg, G., 1981. On the efficiency of the wind to generate vertical mixing. Geophysica 17: 47-61.

Kaleis, M. V., 1976. Present hydrographic conditions in the Baltic. Ambio, Spec. Rep., 4: 37-44.

Krauss, W., 1978. Inertial waves and mixing in the thermocline (BOSEX-results). Proc. XI Conf. Baltic Oceanogr. paper 56: 709-728, Rostock, DDR, 1979.

Krauss, W., Koske, P. and Kielmann, J., 1973. Observations on scattering layers and thermoclines in the Baltic Sea. Kieler Meeresforsch., 29: 85-89.

Kullenberg, B., 1964. Försökstippning av rötslam i Östersjön 8-12 juli 1963. Report to Stockholm municipality, in Swedish, 75 pp.

Kullenberg, G., 1970. On the oxygen deficit in the Baltic deep water. Tellus, 22: 357.

Kullenberg, G., 1971. Vertical diffusion in shallow waters. Tellus, 23: 129-135.

Kullenberg, G., 1974a. An Experimental and Theoretical Investigation of the Turbulent Diffusion in the Upper Layer of the Sea. Rep. No. 25, Inst. Phys. Oceanogr., University of Copenhagen, 272 pp.

Kullenberg, G., 1974b. Some observations of the vertical mixing in the Baltic. Proc. 9th Conf. Baltic Oceanogr, Kiel, 17-20 April 1974, pp. 129-137 (mimeogr.).

Kullenberg, G., 1977. Observations of the mixing in the Baltic thermo- and halocline layers. Tellus, 29: 572-587.

Kullenberg, G., 1981. Physical Oceanography. In: A. Voipio (Editor), The Baltic Sea, Ch. 3. Elsevier Oceanography Series 30, Elsevier, Amsterdam, pp. 135-181.

Kullenberg, G., 1982. The Baltic Sea. In: B. H. Ketchum (Editor), Ecosystems of the World, vol. Estuaries and Enclosed Seas, Ch. 13, Elsevier, Amsterdam, in press.

418

Launiainen, J. and Koljonen, J., 1981. Seasonal and long-period variation of temperature at Finnish fixed observation stations. In Proceedings of 3rd Seminar on the Gulf of Bothnia, SNV, in press.

Matthäus, W., 1977. Mittlere vertikale Wärmeaustauschkoeffizienten in der Ostsee. Acta Hydrophys. Berlin, 22, 2: 73-92.

Matthäus, W., 1979. Long-term variations in the primary halocline in the Gotland Basin. ICES, C.M. 1979/C:22, mimeo.

Matthäus, W., 1980. Zur Variabilität der primären halinen Sprungschicht in der Gotlandsee. Beiträge zur Meereskunde, 44/45, pp. 27-42.

Melvasalo, T., Pawlak, J., Grasshoff, K., Thorell, L. and Tsiban, A. (Editors), 1981. Assessment of the effects of pollution on the natural resources of the Baltic Sea. Baltic Sea Environment Proceedings No. 5A and 5B, Helsinki Commission 1981.

Mikulski, Z., 1970. Inflow of river water to the Baltic Sea in the period 1951-1960. Nord. Hydrol., 4: 216-227.

Nehring, D., 1979. Relationships between salinity and increasing nutrient concentrations in the mixed winter surface layer of the Baltic from 1969 to 1978. ICES C.M. 1979/C:24, and Ann. Biol., ICES 1980.

Rydberg, L., 1978. Deep water flow and oxygen consumption within the Baltic. Rep. No. 27, Oceanographic Institute, University of Gothenburg, 12 pp.

Shaffer, G., 1975. Baltic coastal dynamics project - the fall downwelling regime off Askö. Contrib. Askö Lab. No. 7, University of Stockholm, 69 pp.

Shaffer, G., 1979a. Conservation calculations in natural coordinates (with an example from the Baltic). Journal Physical Oceanography 9, 4: 847-855.

Shaffer, G., 1979b. On the phosphorous and oxygen dynamics of the Baltic Sea. Contrib. Askö Lab. No. 26, University of Stockholm, 90 pp.

Soskin, I. M., 1963. Long-term Changes in the Hydrological Characteristics of the Baltic. Hydromet. Press, Leningrad, in Russian, 159 pp.

Voipio, A., and Mälkki, P., 1972. Variations of the vertical stability in the northern Baltic. Havsforskningsinst. Skr. 23: 3-12.

Voipio, A. (Editor), 1981. The Baltic Sea. Elsevier Oceanogr. Ser. 30, Amsterdam 1981, 418 pp.

Walin, G., 1972a. On the hydrographic response to transient meteorological disturbances. Tellus, 24: 169-186.

Walin, G., 1972b. Some observations of temperature fluctuations in the coastal region of the Baltic. Tellus, 24: 187-198.

Wattenberg, H., 1949. Entwurf einer naturlishen Einteiling der Ostsee. Kieler Meeresforsch., 6: pp 10.

Witting, R., 1918. Hafsytan, Geoidytan och Landhöjningen utmed Baltiska Hafvet och vid Nordsjön. Fennia, 39, 5: 1-346.

Wyrtki, K., 1954. Der grosse Salzeinbruch in der Ostsee in November und Dezember 1951. Kieler Meeresforsch., 10, 1: pp. 19.

FINESTRUCTURE OF THE OPEN PART OF
THE BALTIC SEA

A. Aitsam, J. Laanemets, M-J. Lilover
Institute of Thermophysics and Electrophysics
Academy of Sciences of the Estonian S.S.R.

INTRODUCTION

Data from profiling instruments are widely used to study the processes responsible for the vertical structure of oceanic variables. One of the goals of the fine- and microstructure studies is the parametrization of unresolved processes in circulation models. The model of Osborn and Cox (Osborn and Cox, 1973) may serve as an example. According to this model, the mean coefficients of vertical mixing in a given layer can be obtained from the balance between the turbulent production and the dissipation of temperature inhomogeneities. However, this model works only under certain conditions. At the present time, there is no general theory about the generation of finestructure in the oceans and seas. Relying on the available data, the following processes have been proposed: 1) random deformation of the density field by internal waves; 2) intrusions caused by fronts; 3) processes of double diffusion (Woods, 1980). The study of finestructure in a synoptic eddy is of interest because, as suggested by Woods (1980), the energy of eddies may be transferred to small-scale processes through internal waves and frontal processes.

In this paper, we analyze the finestructure of the deep waters of the open part of the Baltic Sea under calm weather conditions on the one hand and within a synoptic eddy on the other hand.

MEASUREMENTS AND METHODS OF ANALYSIS

In order to study the formation of the vertical structure in the deep layer of the Baltic Sea, several series of vertical profiles were obtained with a Neil Brown Mark III probe at the central station of the BOSEX area in 1979. All these profiles were measured in calm weather from a drifting vessel at depths ranging from 65 m to 95 m. The time interval between profiles was 3 minutes. The probe was lowered at a rate of 30 cm/s, and the recording frequency was 31 times per second for each parameter. The resulting vertical resolution is about 1 cm.

In 1979 and 1980, series of surveys with the Neil Brown Mark III probe were performed in the BOSEX area in an attempt to detect eddies of synoptic scale (Aitsam and Elken, 1980). The dimensions of the survey area were 20 x

25 miles and the grid spacing was 5 miles. The duration of each survey was one day. All these profiles were analyzed with the aim of detecting the influence of the synoptic scale phenomena on the vertical finestructure of the deep layer of the Baltic Sea.

The preliminary processing of the CTD data is described in detail by Laanemets and Lilover (1981). Let us simply mention that the rolling of the vessel and the time lag of the temperature sensor are taken into account to reduce the errors in the salinity and density calculations. The temperature and salinity data are interpolated at constant depth intervals of $\Delta z = 2$ cm. For this study, we use only data collected during the lowering of the probe.

As the fluctuations at finestructure scales of the temperature, salinity, and density fields are essentially random, statistical methods are widely used in their study. In this paper, the variances and spectra of the fluctuations are calculated. The measured series are divided into mean and fluctuating components using a 5 m cosine filter. Spectra are calculated by the FFT method after preliminary smoothing with a 4-sample Kaiser-Bessel filter (Harris, 1978). The wavenumber bandwidth of the calculated spectra is $0.2 \leq k \leq 24 \text{ m}^{-1}$.

RESULTS AND DISCUSSION

In the BOSEX area the effect of the coasts and of the Danish Sounds can be considered unimportant. The vertical profiles of temperature, salinity and density vary monotonously with depth in the deep layer (60 to 95 m.). We analyzed the data with the presumption that three processes can be responsible for the formation of vertical structure within the scales of finestructure and microstructure: i) small-scale turbulence; ii) double-diffusive convection (both temperature and salinity increase with depth in the deep layer of the Baltic Sea); iii) kinematic effects of internal waves.

To determine the importance of double-diffusive convection, we calculated the function

$$R\rho(i\Delta z) = -\beta(i\Delta z) \, \Delta Si/\alpha(i\Delta z)\Delta Ti$$

with $\Delta z = 10$ cm, and using a density formula appropriate for the Baltic Sea (Millerò and Kremling, 1976) in the calculation of $\alpha = -(\partial\rho/\partial T)_{p,S=const}$ and $\beta = (\partial\rho/\partial S)_{p,T=const}$. The analysis of the function $R\rho(i\Delta z)$ shows that its numerical value is smaller than 15 only at a few separate points of the vertical profiles; in general $R\rho(i\Delta z) > 15$, which indicates that only molecular diffusion is taking place. Certainly, the final assessment of the importance of double-diffusion convection in the generation of the vertical structure and mixing in the deep layer of the open part of the Baltic requires a more detailed analysis.

The spectral analysis of the vertical profiles observed in the deep layer of the BOSEX area shows that the averaged spectra of temperature $S_T(k)$, salinity $S_S(k)$ and relative density $S_{\sigma_t}(k)$ can generally be well approximated by the power law

$$S_T(k) \sim S_S(k) \sim S_{\sigma_t}(k) \sim k^{-3}$$

for wavenumbers in the range $0.7 < k < 25 \text{ m}^1$ (Fig. 1).

In individual spectral curves, a local maximum can be noticed in the interval $3 < k < 6 \text{ m}^{-1}$. No subinterval of small-scale turbulence was observed on any single spectrum. Figure 2 shows a section of isotherms, isohalines and isopycnals based on one series of profiles. The absence of mixed layers and the smallness of the amplitudes of the internal waves can be noticed in Figure 2. The mean amplitude of the vertical displacements in this layer, as determined from the various spectra, is about 0.2 m.

The agreement between the mean amplitudes determined from the temperature, salinity and density spectra indicates that all isolines are similarly deformed. This supports the assumption that the observed fluctuations of the physical variables at finestructure scales are the result of the influence of internal waves.

We now turn our attention to the study of finestructure and mixing in synoptic eddies. In earlier papers on this topic, Dykman et al. (1980) and Fjodorov et al. (1981) have analyzed the results of vertical profiles obtained during the POLYMODE program. The results of the spectral analysis (Dykman et al., 1980) showed that the normalized variance of the displacements of internal waves is smaller in the eddy center that at the periphery. It has also been shown that the rate of energy dissipation, ε, increases in the eddy center. On the basis of their analysis of the θ, S characteristics, and of anomalies in the distribution of hydrogen and pH, Fjodorov et al. (1981) have suggested a hypothesis about water transformation in eddies as a result of mixing, which in turn is connected to vertical motions in the eddy center.

We now discuss the results of three of our own surveys in the Baltic Sea: the 6th and the 7th surveys of the R/V "Ayu-Dag" cruise No. XIV in 1979, and the second survey of cruise No. XVIII in 1980. On the basis of maps of the relative dynamic topography (RDT), eddylike perturbations of synoptic scale were detected for surveys No. 7 and 2 (Aitsam and Elken,

422

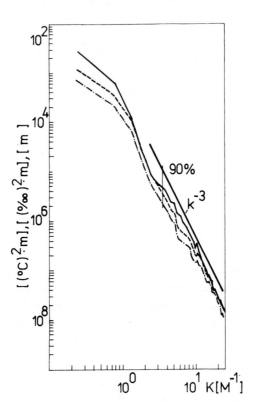

Fig. 1. Ensemble averaged spectra of temperature (-), salinity (- - -) and relative density (-·-) for the first series of measurements. The spectral curves are well approximated by the "k^{-3}" power law.

1980). On the RDT maps of the 6th survey there were no similar perturbations.

We chose to use the variances of the temperature, salinity, and relative density fluctuations, denoted by σ_T^2, σ_S^2, and $\sigma_{\alpha_t}^2$, respectively, as measures of the horizontal variability of the vertical finestructure in the synoptic scale eddy. From the results discussed earlier, it is obvious that the main mechanism of the finestructure generation is the random deformation of the density field by internal waves. By normalizing the variances with

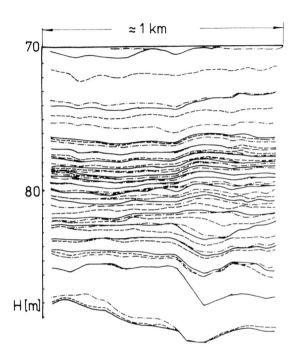

Fig. 2. Isotherms (--), isohalines (-) and isopycnals (-·-) of the first series of measurements in the depth interval 70 to 90 m. The horizontal length scale is about 1 km and the interval between profiles is about 40 m.

the squares of the gradients of the corresponding physical parameters, we obtain estimates of the mean square displacements of the internal waves. Therefore, variations of the normalized variances in the synoptic scale eddy can be interpreted as variations in the energy flow from the eddy to the internal wave field. The variances and spectra of the temperature, salinity and relative density fluctuations were calculated for the profiles of the 6th and 7th surveys. Only data from depths between 65 and 90 m were inclu-ded in the calculations. For the 7th survey, the variances are one or two order of magnitude larger at the periphery of the eddy than in the center. The distributions of the variances calculated from the profiles of the 6th survey (in the same depth range) show no regular pattern.

The same conclusion can be drawn from a comparison of the spectra: the spectral levels of the 7th survey are higher on the edges of the eddy than in the center, and those of the 6th survey are irregular. In general, the shapes of the spectra are well approximated by power laws, a fact which indicates the dominating effect of the internal wave field.

A different method was used to analyze the data of the second survey of the R/V "Ayu-Dag" 18th cruise. The variances and spectra of the physical parameters (T, S, σ_t) were also calculated over a 25 m depth interval, but the depth of the isopycnal surface $\sigma_t = 6.75$ (the beginning of the halocine) was chosen as the reference level of the interval.

Such a choice of reference level eliminates the distorting effect of the synoptic scale variability for the following reason. The Baltic, in its open part, may be divided into four layers: the upper mixed layer, the thermocline, the intermediate layer of winter convection and the halocline (Fig. 3). The amplitude of the isopycnal displacement in the halocline can be about 20 m on the periphery of a synoptic eddy. Hence, when statistics are calculated over a fixed depth interval, the contribution of layers having different characteristics may vary within a synoptic eddy. This may be the reason for the high variability in the variances calculated from the 7th survey. The 2nd survey of the 18th cruise took place at the end of May. At that time, the seasonal thermocline was missing, and an eddylike perturbation was present in the halocline (Fig. 4). Figure 5 shows the distribution of the natural logarithm of the temperature fluctuations variance (ln σ_T^2) in the lower layer (extending 25 m below the reference level).

It can be seen that the temperature variance (for vertical scales smaller than 5 m) is minimum in the center of the eddy and increases towards the periphery. The distribution of the normalized temperature variance is shown in Figure 6. The pattern of the normalized variance is similar to that of the variance. The normalized variances at the periphery are twice as large as the center values. The variability factor of the normalized variance over the whole experiment area is 8.

In summary, the data of the seventh and second surveys exhibit a certain regularity in the distribution of variance in synoptic scale eddies, although the variability is smaller than that reported by Dykman et al. (1980). In the upper layer (extending 25 m above the reference level), the variability of the normalized variance is larger than 10 and no regularity is observed. In this layer the mean gradient of temperature also varies by more than one order.

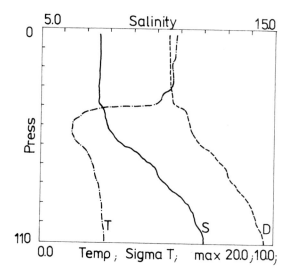

Fig. 3. Characteristic vertical profiles of temperature (T), salinity (S) and relative density (D) in the BOSEX area.

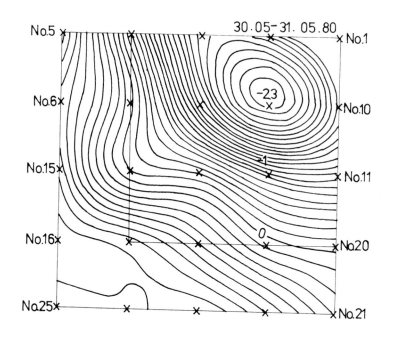

Fig. 4. Map of the relative dynamic topography (RDT) for survey No. 2. Crosses indicate the position of the stations. The smaller frame delimits the area of the finestructure study.

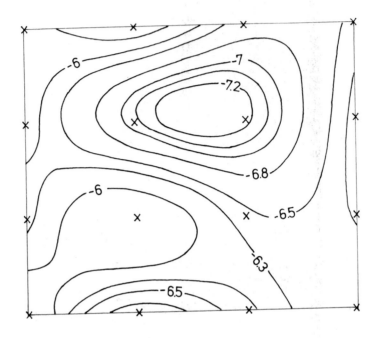

Fig. 5. Distribution of the natural logarithm of the temperature variance ($\ln \sigma_T^2$) in the lower layer. Survey No. 2.

The spectra of temperature, salinity and relative density were calculated for all profiles in both the upper and lower layer. The spectral slopes vary over a wide range (from -2.8 to -3.6) in the lower layer (Fig. 7). However, most spectra have a slope close to -3, so that one can interpret the fluctuations as the result of the interval wave influence. Neither the spectra (Fig. 7b) nor the vertical profiles of the temperature, salinity and relative density gradients (Fig. 8) show any evidence of small-scale turbulence in the center of the eddy in the lower layer.

Some upper layer spectra at stations located above the eddy (the method used to detect an eddy does not reveal anything in this layer, due to weak stratification) have slopes close to -3 up to wavenumbers of about 25 m^{-1} (Fig. 9a). In some spectra there is a break in slope at wavenumber k_x in

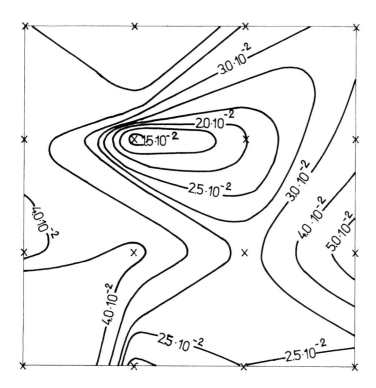

Fig. 6. Distribution of the normalized temperature variance $[\sigma_T^2/(d\bar{T}/dz)^2]$ in the lower layer. Survey No. 2.

the range $1 < k_* < 2m^{-1}$, and for $k > k_*$ the spectra have slopes typical of small-scale turbulence (Fig. 9b,c). When this is the case, the vertical profile of the relative density gradient above the center of the eddy exhibits patches of small-scale inversions accompanied by turbulence (Fig. 10). The vertical scale of these layers is about 0.5 to 1.0 m. Existing data do not permit to relate these turbulent events to the eddy.

It should be emphasized that the lack of evidence in our data of small-scale turbulence in the center of an eddy in the halocline (where the manifestations of the synoptic eddy are strongest) could be fortuitous. Because of the strong stratification in the halocline of the Baltic Sea, the small-scale turbulence is characterized by great intermittency in space and occurs as a rare event in time. Therefore, we believe that single profiles may not be representative, and that long series of profilings at a fixed location are needed.

In conclusion, we may say that the internal waves are the main factor affecting the vertical finestructure in the halocline. The processes of

428

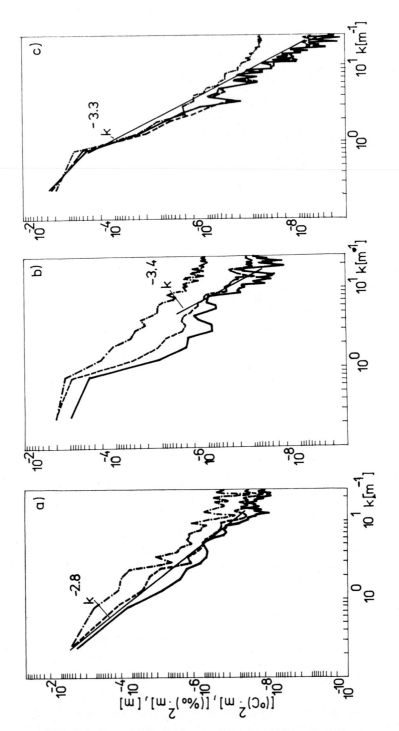

Fig. 7. Spectra of temperature (—), salinity (- - -) and relative density (-·-·-) in the lower layer, calculated from the profiles at station No. 1 (a), No. 9 (b) and No. 14 (c).

429

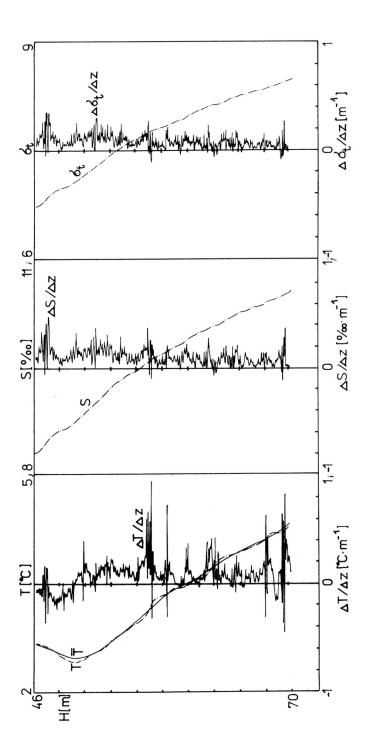

Fig. 8. Vertical profiles of temperature, salinity and relative density gradients in the lower layer at station No. 9. No active regions are apparent on the profiles.

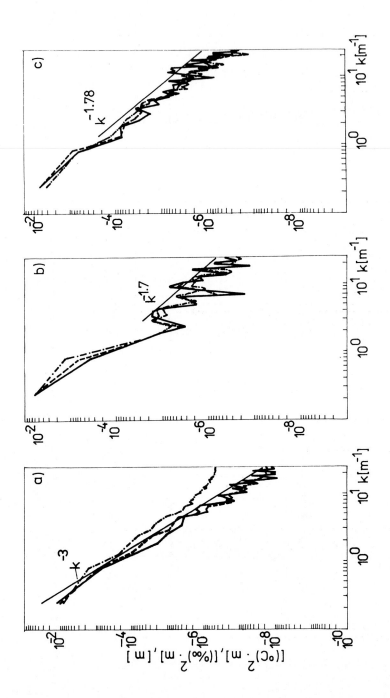

Fig. 9. Spectra of temperature (-), salinity (- - -) and relative density (-·-) in the upper layer, calculated from the profiles at station No. 1(a), No. 9(b) and No. 11(c).

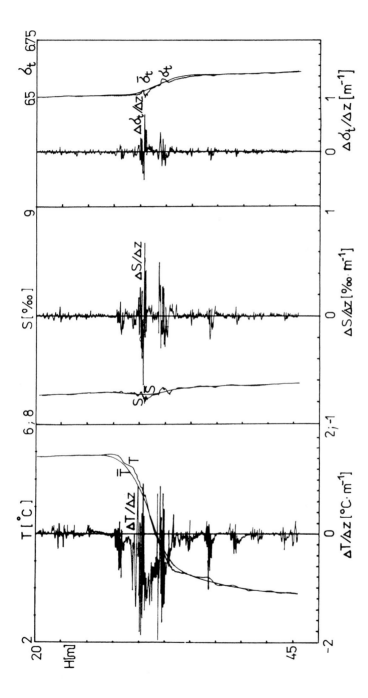

Fig. 10. Vertical profiles of temperature, salinity and relative density gradients in the upper layer at station No. 9. Patches of small-scale density inversions can be noticed.

432

double diffusion and small-scale turbulence are of minor importance, although they certainly require further study. Finally, the distribution of
the variances of temperature, salinity and relative density exhibits a certain regularity in synoptic eddies.

REFERENCES

Aitsam, A. and Elken J., 1980. Results of CTD surveys in the BOSEX area of
    the Baltic Sea (in Russian). In: Tonkaya struktura i sinopticheskaja
    izmenchivost morei, Tallinn, pp. 19-23.
Dykman, V.Z., Efremov, O.I., Kiseleva, O.A. and Panteleev, N.A., 1980.
    Internal waves and turbulence in the synoptic scale (in Russian). In:
    Tonkaya struktura i sinoticheskaja izmenchivost morei, Tallinn, pp.
    64-68.
Fedorov, K.N., Ginzburg, A.I. and Zatsepin, A.G., 1981. Thermohaline
    structure and traces of mixing in synoptic eddies and Gulf stream rings
    (in Russian). Okeanologiya, $\underline{21}$: 25-29.
Harris, Fr.J., 1978. On the use of windows for harmonic analysis with the
    discrete Fourier transform. Proc. of the IEEE, $\underline{66}$: 51-83.
Laanemets, J. and Lilover, M.-J., 1981. The data processing scheme of
    measurements with the Neil Brown Mark III CTD. In: The Investigation
    and Modelling of Processes of the Baltic Sea. Tallinn, pp. 10-19.
Millero, Fr. J. and Kremling, K., 1976. The densities of Baltic Sea waters,
    Deep-Sea Res., $\underline{23}$: 1129-1138.
Osborn, T. and Cox, C., 1972. Oceanic fine-structure. Geophysical Fluid
    Dynamics $\underline{3}$: 321-345.
Woods, J.D., 1980. Do waves limit turbulent diffusion in the ocean? Nature
    $\underline{288}$: 219-224.

SYNOPTIC SCALE VARIABILITY OF HYDROPHYSICAL FIELDS IN THE BALTIC PROPER ON THE BASIS OF CTD MEASUREMENTS

A. Aitsam, J. Elken
Institute of Thermophysics and Electrophysics
Academy of Sciences of the Estonian S.S.R.

ABSTRACT

The results of CTD surveys in the Baltic Proper on rectangular grids with spacing of 5 nautical miles are analyzed. Eddylike perturbations of the relative dynamic topography (RDT), with diameters equal to 2 to 5 times the internal Rossby radius of deformation R_d ($\cong$ 10 km), are described. The typical migration speed of these perturbations is a few cm/sec and it is directed along the averaged isobaths with shallower water on the right. It is shown that the speed and direction of migration of the eddies can be explained in terms of topographic waves. The hypothesis that some of the observed eddies might be generated by baroclinic instability of sheared mean flows is discussed on the basis of a simple model. An attempt is made to estimate absolute velocities using a generalization of the beta-spiral method. Synoptic scale processes in the Baltic are compared to their oceanic counterparts.

INTRODUCTION

Synoptic eddies (Koshlyakov and Monin, 1978; Woods and Minnett, 1979) or "mesoscale" eddies (the latter term is widely used by the MODE Group, 1978) are a common phenomenon in the open ocean as well as near frontal currents. The Baltic Sea is one of the most thoroughly investigated semi-enclosed seas (Jansson, 1978); yet, synoptic scale variability has not been studied here as much as in the ocean. Previous observations worth mentioning include the section of thermocline anomaly observed by Keunecke and Magaard (1974) using a towed thermistor string; interesting data from the sixties in the Arcona Basin (Kielmann et al., 1973) and in the Gotland Basin (Sustavov et al., 1978); and results of the Baltic-75 experiment in the Bornholm Basin (Kielmann et al., 1976). As for numerical model studies, eddylike motions can be simulated if the resolution of the model is sufficient (Simons, 1978; Kielmann, 1978).

The aim of our studies is to broaden our knowledge of the three-dimensional structure of synoptic scale perturbations and of their evolution. The field experiments described in the next section took place mainly in the BOSEX area.

In this paper, we consider the results of vertical CTD casts obtained during several surveys. At the present time, this is the only possible way to achieve sufficient spatial coverage and resolution to document low frequency motions from the surface down to the bottom layers. The complete list of measurements also includes direct current measurements at various mooring stations, and CTD profiles obtained with an undulating underwater unit towed in the upper layer. Unfortunately, the most intensive density anomalies were not covered by direct current measurements. Some of the earlier results of this complex project are described in another paper (Aitsam et al., 1981).

METHODS

A large number of hydrographic measurements has been made in the ocean as well as in the Baltic Sea during the last century. However, historical data are too sparse in space and time to resolve the synoptic scale motions. A qualitatively new approach was implemented in the course of specially designed projects, such as POLYGON-67 (Koshlyakov et al., 1970), POLYGON-70 (Koshlyakov and Grachev, 1973), MODE (McWilliams, 1976) and POLYMODE; in these experiments, hydrographic casts were obtained at stations covering a regular grid with proper grid spacing. We have no information about similar measurements in the Baltic Sea and our task was to apply "oceanic" methods and historical experiences to the Baltic. However, the Baltic Sea is not simply a reduced model of the ocean, so that the application of oceanic results to the Baltic case requires caution.

For the design of an oceanographic experiment, the optimal sampling rate and the optimal configuration and spacing of stations can be found if the correlation and spectral characteristics are known (Bretherton et al., 1976). The spatial correlation functions were not known at the start of our investigations, so we elected to make measurements on a rectangular grid with a spacing of 5 nautical miles between grid points. The latter choice was based on the hypothesis that the scales of the eddies and of the internal Rossby radius of deformation, R_d, are similar in the ocean and in the Baltic. In the Baltic, R_d is about 10 km. We selected experimental areas with relatively smooth bottom slopes, and with depths greater than 80 m in order to include the halocline. The orientation of the grid was chosen according to the pecularities of the bottom topography. The number of stations was limited to ensure that surveys could be completed in two days or less.

The various surveys were performed during cruises of the R/V "Ayu-Dag". Most surveys were conducted in the BOSEX area (Aitsam and Elken, 1980), and some took place in the Bornholm Basin and in the Gotland Basin to the north of the BOSEX are (Fig. 1). The surveys are listed in Table 1. In this table, the first item of the survey number denotes the cruise number of the R/V "Ayu-Dag". The lengths (in nautical miles) of the sides of the grids in the x- and y-directions are tabulated under the heading "Survey area". The x- and y-axes are directed eastward and northward, respectively, for the 1981 surveys; the axes are rotated 30° clockwise for the surveys of 1979 and 1980. The lower left and upper right coordinates define the geographical coordinates of the working area; they correspond to the corners of the "boxes" shown in Figure 1.

In the BOSEX area the bottom topography is sloping mainly in the x-direction (see the maps in Aitsam et al., 1981, and in Aitsam and Talpsepp, 1980). On the left side of the area the slope exceeds $5 \cdot 10^{-3}$, in the central part the slope is more moderate, ranging from $5 \cdot 10^{-4}$ to 10^{-3}, and on the right side the depth decreases. A typical depth is 100 m.

The instrument used is the Neil Brown Mark III CTD-profiler, whose characteristics are described elsewhere (Laanemets and Lilover, 1981). The data were collected on a REVOX audio tape recorder, and subsequently transferred to a HP-9825A microcomputer for preliminary data processing and storage on HP-9885 flexible disks.

In the preliminary data processing phase, temperature and conductivity data are interpolated at pressure intervals of 0.1 dbar; salinity and density values are then calculated as described in Laanemets and Lilover (1981). To facilitate further analyses, temperature, salinity and density values at selected pressure levels as well as temperature, salinity and pressure values at selected density levels are compiled in easily retrievable format. Also some integrated properties, such as the relative dynamic topography (i.e. the difference of dynamic heights), henceforth denoted RTD, are calculated between selected pressure levels. The RDT is calculated according to the formula:

$$D\,(p_2,\ p_1) = \frac{1}{g} \int_{p_1}^{p_2} \frac{dp}{\rho} \tag{1}$$

where p_1 and p_2 denote pressure values (in dbars in the argument of RDT, with $p_1 < p_2$); g, the acceleration due to gravity; ρ, the density of the water; and $D(p_2, p_1)$, the RDT in cm, or with the accuracy of 10^{-3} g in dynamic cm.

The data in pressure coordinates and the RDT have minor instrumental errors for synoptic scale studies, except for the salinity in the thermocline layer where negative spikes can occur. When density is used as the vertical coordinate, special care must be taken. For long-term processes

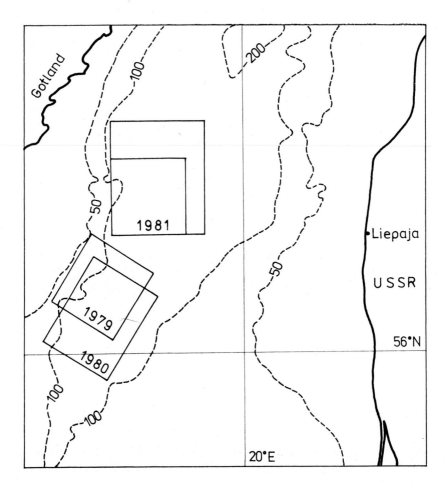

Figure 1. Basic areas for CTD surveys in 1979, 1980 and 1981 (boxes), with depth contours (dashed lines) labeled in meters.

the water is assumed to be stably stratified. However, density inversions are present in some of the observed profiles. These inversions are removed to guarantee one-to-one correspondence of pressure and density. The esti-

TABLE 1. List of the CTD surveys

Survey Number	Time day	Time month	year	Duration (hrs)	Survey area	Number of casts	Lower left Latitude	Lower left Longitude	Upper right Latitude	Upper right Longitude
13/1	27	05	79	18	20X20	21	50°14.5'N	18°21.3'E	56°21.1'N	19°11.1'E
13/2	28	05	79	21	20X20	21	50°14.5'N	18°21.3'E	56°21.1'N	19°11.1'E
13/3	29-30	05	79	34	30X20	38	50°14.5'N	18°21.3'E	56°15.7'N	19°25.0'E
13/4	2-3	06	79	20	20X20	21	50°14.5'N	18°21.3'E	56°21.1'N	19°11.1'E
13/5	10-11	06	79	20	20X20	21	50°14.5'N	18°21.3'E	56°21.1'N	19°11.1'E
15/1	5-6	08	79	24	20X20	21	50°14.5'N	18°21.3'E	56°21.1'N	19°11.1'E
15/2	15-16	08	79	20	20X20	21	50°14.5'N	18°21.3'E	56°21.1'N	19°11.1'E
16/1	25-26	09	79	23	20X20	21	50°14.5'N	18°21.3'E	56°21.1'N	19°11.1'E
17/1	8-9	05	80	24	20X25	30	56°03.4'N	18°18.8'E	56°14.8'N	19°12.4'E
18/1	30-31	05	80	32	20X25	30	56°03.4'N	18°18.8'E	56°14.8'N	19°12.4'E
18/2	8-9	06	80	33	20X25	30	56°03.4'N	18°18.8'E	56°14.8'N	19°12.4'E
18/3	10-11	06	80	27	25X20	27	56°05.4'N	18°31.1'E	56°09.3'N	19°27.8'E
19/1	1-3	07	80	39	20X25	30	56°03.4'N	18°18.8'E	56°14.8'N	19°12.4'E
20/1	10-11	08	80	37	25X25	36	56°03.4'N	18°18.8'E	56°12.1'N	19°20.1'E
20/2	2-3	09	80	30	20X25	30	56°03.4'N	18°18.8'E	56°14.8'N	19°12.4'E
22/1	25-26	04	81	34	25X25	36	55°00.0'N	15°30.0'E	55°25.0'N	16°13.4'E
22/2	29-30	04	81	32	25X25	36	55°00.0'N	15°30.0'E	55°25.0'N	16°13.4'E
23/1	3-5	06	81	44	25X30	42	56°31.0'N	18°55.4'E	57°01.0'N	19°40.7'E
23/2	15-16	06	81	26	20X20	25	56°31.0'N	18°55.4'E	56°51.0'N	19°32.1'E
23/3	21-22	06	81	26	20X20	25	56°31.0'N	18°55.4'E	56°51.0'N	19°32.1'E
23/4	26-27	06	81	25	20X20	25	56°31.0'N	18°55.4'E	56°51.0'N	19°32.1'E
23/5	4-5	07	81	25	20X20	25	56°31.0'N	18°55.4'E	56°51.0'N	19°32.1'E

mates of the measurement error based on "total difference" type expressions are not good because the profiles can be too jagged within the density error intervals. The error on the quantity ϕ (temperature, salinity or pressure) at the density value $\bar{\sigma}_t$ is determined as follows. Let $\Delta\phi$ and $\Delta\sigma_t$ be the instrumental errors on ϕ and σ_t, and let $\phi(\sigma_t)$ be the relation obtained from the measured profiles of $\phi(p)$ and $\sigma_t(p)$. Consider all the values of ϕ within the density interval $(\bar{\sigma}_t - \Delta\sigma_t, \bar{\sigma}_t + \Delta\sigma_t)$, and find ϕ_{min} and ϕ_{max}. Then the true value of ϕ at $\bar{\sigma}_t$ is between the limits $(\phi_{min} - \Delta\phi, \phi_{max} + \Delta\phi)$, and it should be determined individually every time.

The typical vertical stratification of the Baltic waters is well known. The upper boundary of the halocline is located between 60 and 80 m, and it separates the upper cold/fresh waters from the lower warm/salty waters. During summer, a very steep thermocline at a depth of 15 to 30 m separates the warm upper "quasi-homogeneous" layer and the cold intermediate layer.

When interpolating nonsimultaneous and nonaveraged measurements on a horizontal grid, it is not easy to extract the synoptic scale component of the variability. Among the several possible interpolation and filtration techniques, the optimal interpolation (Gandin, 1965) has the favor of most "mesoscale" oceanographers (McWilliams, 1976). For special purposes, if statistics are not well known, the least squares polynomial fitting (Nikitin and Vinogradova, 1980) could be useful.

Whatever the technique, the signal to noise ratio is a very important parameter which indicates how justified the interpolation procedure can be. In the algorithm of optimal interpolation, the error norm (ratio of the dispersions of noise and signal) is explicitly calculated, and if the value of this norm is close to one, the maps constructed by the interpolation method are only slightly influenced by the measurements.

In order to estimate the error norms, we collected series of profiles at given stations in different seasons. The duration of each series to measure the error dispersions was one day, and the time interval between casts one hour. During horizontal surveys, the duration and the time interval were about the same, but the measurements were made at different stations. The error dispersion, ε^2, includes the random measurement errors and the high frequency noise (internal waves), which can be assumed statistically stationary, homogeneous and uncorrelated in space; it also includes contamination of "instantaneous" patterns due to diurnal variations and trends in the synoptic scale perturbations. The latter factor imposes certain limitations on the survey duration and on the number of stations. Our experience indicates that maps obtained from surveys taking more than two days cannot be considered instantaneous, and some dynamical and/or statistical time corrections are required. The signal dispersion, σ^2, is determined from the deviations from the mean of the data obtained in the horizontal surveys; σ^2 includes both the dispersion of the "cooled" synoptic scale perturbations, and its time contamination and high frequency noise.

Some typical distributions of the error norms, $\eta = \varepsilon^2/\sigma^2$, for the summer stratification in the BOSEX area are presented in Figure 2, with either pressure or density as the "vertical" coordinate. Note that η can be larger than one due to statistical uncertainties and because the implicit hypothesis of statistical homogeneity and stationarity is not always valid.

Figure 2 shows that, when the pressure is used as the vertical coordinate, the density, temperature and salinity profiles above the 70 dbar level (i.e. above the halocline) are disturbed by "errors"; hence it is not possible to try to "separate" or identify "cooled" patterns in such data. This conclusion does not apply to the salinity in the layer above the thermocline, which is not disturbed by vertical displacements of internal waves and diurnal heat exchange variations. Typical values of η below the 70 dbar level are 0.1 to 0.2, indicating that horizontal low frequency inhomogeneities dominate over short-term temporal variations in the halocline.

The error norms for the profiles of pressure, temperature and salinity as functions of density are smaller than those calculated in p-coordinate. For the pressure, typical values of η are 0.3-0.5 in the thermocline (σ_t = 5.5-6.5), and 0.1-0.2 in the halocline (σ_t = 7.5-8.5). In the intermediate layer, the higher value of η can be explained by measurement errors: the vertical density gradient is small in that layer. As to the temperature and salinity profiles in σ_t-coordinate, they should theoretically be free of the kinematic effect of internal waves. The relatively higher values of η above the σ_t = 7.5 level can be explained by measurement errors rather than by physical processes. In these layers the temperature and salinity variations (due to the finestructure) within each density error interval can be comparable to the thermoclinicity effects described by Woods (1979). In the halocline (below σ_t = 7.5), thermoclinicity clearly dominates and η is very small.

The values of η for the relative dynamic topography (RDT) are not presented in the figure. If the thermocline and/or the halocline lie between the limits of integration, the RDT anomalies are caused mainly by the total vertical displacement of these transition layers, and the manifestations of fine-scale/short-term phenomena are eliminated via the vertical integration procedure. Typical values of η are 0.2-0.5 for the thermocline, and less than 0.1 for the halocline. Note that for the MODE region the error norms are within the range of 0.1-0.3 (McWilliams, 1976).

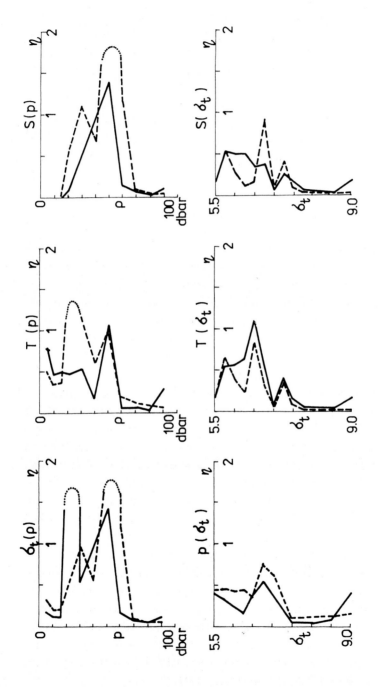

Figure 2. Vertical distribution of the error norms, $\eta = \varepsilon^2/\sigma^2$, of density (σ_t), temperature (T) and salinity (S) as function of pressure (above); error norms of pressure (p), temperature and salinity as function of density (below). The solid lines represent data from survey 20/1, the dashed lines data from survey 20/2.

From this study of the error norms, we conclude that, in the halocline, the amplitude of the "cooled" patterns of synoptic scale perturbations is larger than that of the short-term variations (with periods inferior to one day); it is therefore meaningful to map the observed fields. At the same time we doubt that it would be justified to plot horizontal maps (or sections) of the temperature, salinity or density fields at any given depth (pressure) level above 70 m (dbar) when more than a few hours elapse between neighbor stations.

The knowledge of the spatial correlation functions is required to draw maps using the optimal interpolation techniques (Gandin, 1965). Unfortunately, no data other than those collected during the various surveys are available for determining these correlation functions. When only a few data points from one survey are used, the statistical uncertainties are large, but variations from survey to survey are greater than the estimated confidence interval.

Figure 3 shows an example of the correlation function of D (70,30),the RDT between 30 and 70 db (i.e. the halocline anomalies), for the data of a single survey (lower panel) and the average correlations over 6 surveys (upper panel). The correlations were calculated in four directions with 45° increment. In the analytical fitting the anisotropy was taken into account by the correlation ellipses. The correlation radii are more than 10 miles in this example, so the grid spacing chosen for the measurements (5 miles) is almost optimal in terms of interpolation errors: the latter do not exceed 20%. However, some of the other RDT data gave too short correlation lengths in comparison with the grid spacing. As a rule, the parameters which have large error norms are uncorrelated at the distance of the grid spacing.

Various experiments show that the interpolated maps are visually not very sensitive to the variations of the correlation functions. However, this conclusion does not apply to the study of the spatial derivatives and the dynamical equations. Generally, for repeated surveys (close in time to each other) the averaged correlation functions were used. For some cases the correlation lengths were increased to obtain more effective points for the interpolation.

SYNOPTIC SCALE DISTRUBANCES

The relative dynamic topography (RDT), calculated by formula (1), is the main object of our interest for two reasons. First, the RDT has fairly small error norms and sufficiently large correlation lengths to ensure correct interpolation. Second, and more importantly, the RDT is a dynamical property: it is the geostrophic stream function of relative currents.

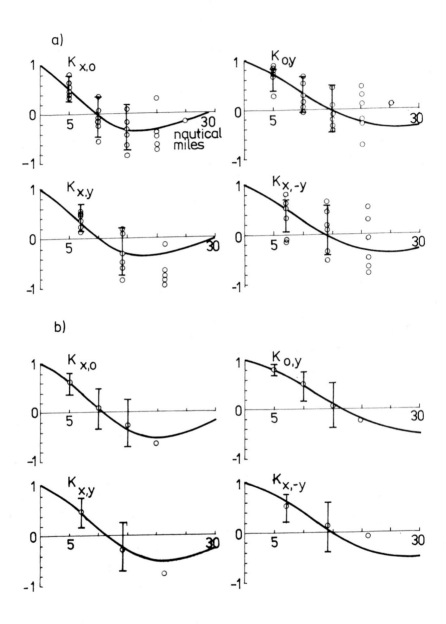

Figure 3. Spatial correlation functions of the relative dynamic topography (RDT) between 30 and 70 db, D (70,30), in four directions (indicated by subscripts). Circles represent data points, vertical bars indicate the 90% confidence limits, and solid lines are the results of two-dimensional analytical fits. Upper panel shows the average correlation functions over six 1980 surveys; lower panel shows results of the single survey 18/2.

Indeed, for the nondimensional parameter values characteristic of the Baltic Proper, the conditions for the quasi-geostrophic approximation to be valid are satisfied in the low frequency range. However, it should be emphasized that the reference level for geostrophic calculations of the absolute velocity by the dynamical method is not well known. Several methods have been proposed (Fomin, 1964), but in this section we shall only discuss relative currents. If the RDT is calculated by (1), it represents the velocity of the upper layer relative to that of the lower layer in the traditional sense of a stream function. An RDT change of 1 dyn.cm over 5 miles corresponds to a relative current speed of 8.65 cm/sec. If the isopycnals are displaced upward, the RDT anomaly is negative, and vice versa.

Three examples of the evolution of eddylike phenomena can be described on the basis of rapidly succeeding surveys in the BOSEX area.

The data of August 1979 show an eddylike perturbation of the RDT with a diameter of 20 km ($\cong 2R_d$). The left-hand side of Figure 4 shows three RDT integrals between different levels for survey 15/1; the right-hand side shows the same integrals for survey 15/2 ten days later. The deformations of the thermocline [D(30,10)] and of the halocline [D(90,30)] have the same sign, and both reflect an upward displacement from the mean position in the center of the perturbation. The difference in geostrophic currents above and below the halocline is 5 to 7 cm/sec. The comparison of the two series of maps shows that the eddy migrates 10 miles along the average isobaths in 10 days (migration speed $\cong 2$ cm/sec), with the shallower water remaining on the right. It can also be seen that the axis of the eddy is not vertical (the centers do not coincide in the halocline and thermocline maps) and it appears that the thermocline perturbation migrates faster than that of the halocline. The intensification of the halocline perturbation is also evident: the relative rotational speed doubles in 10 days.

The maps of surveys 13/1 to 13/4 (Figure 5) show a positive eddylike RDT perturbation of weak intensity in the upper central part of the area. The perturbation appears in the halocline only, because no thermocline has developed yet. On the basis of a single survey, it could be hypothesized that the perturbation is caused by internal waves. However, the presence of the perturbation on three successive daily maps (13/1-3) is convincing evidence that the perturbation (lowering of isopycnals, with axes $R_x \cong 15$ km, $R_y \cong 20$ km) is a synoptic feature. The speed of the perturbation drift is of the order of 1.5 cm/sec with the shallower water on the right. Although the current speeds are too weak for a correct comparison, the relative currents at the central station, determined on the basis of mooring station data and averaged over 5 days, correspond satisfactorily to the geostrophic

444

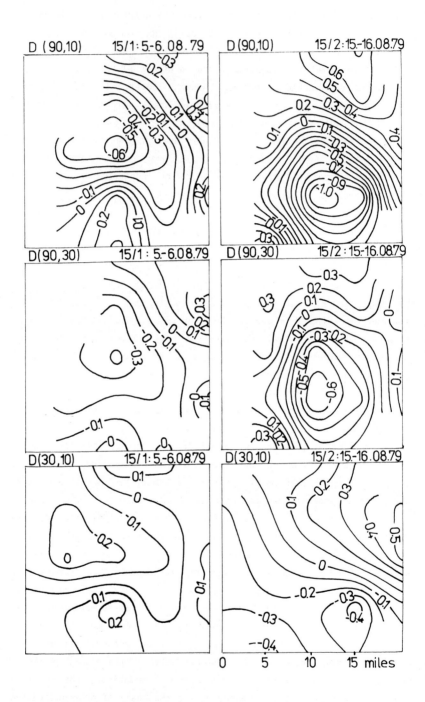

Figure 4. Maps of RDT anomalies (in dynamic cm) for surveys 15/1 (on the left) and 15/2 (on the right). The contour interval is 0.1 dyn.cm.

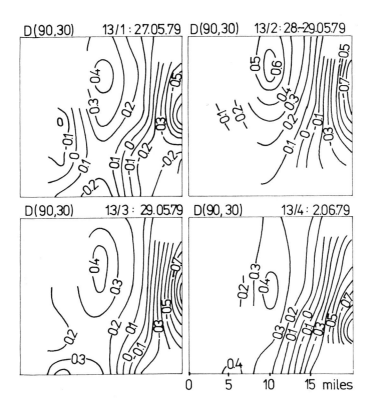

Figure 5. Maps of RDT anomalies (in dynamic cm) for surveys 13/1-4. The contour interval is 0.1 dyn.cm.

velocity determined from RDT. On the right side of the area, the edge of a large negative RDT anomaly can be observed. An extension of survey 13/3 allows us to document the scales and shape of this perturbation. The halocline intersects the bottom slope at the right edge of the survey extension (decreasing depth). The anomaly is tonguelike in shape, and it extends 40 km in the y-direction. The streamlines of D(90,30) remain unclosed along the line where the halocline disappears because of decreasing depths.

The data of surveys 18/1 to 18/3 (early summer 1980) show an intensive and large eddylike perturbation. The isopycnals are displaced upward by more than 20 m in the center of the eddy. The total depth is about 100 m. The diameter of this eddy is more than twice as large as that of the eddies previously observed; it exceeds 40 km. The difference in geostrophic current between the 60 m and 90 m layers is about 20 cm/sec. The contour maps of D(70,30) for three different surveys (Fig. 6) show the evolution of the perturbation. In 9 days (i.e. between survey 18/1 and 18/2), the center of the perturbation moves 5 to 10 miles eastward across the isobaths, and it "escapes" the survey area. At the periphery of the eddy, the lines of constant RDT become more distorted than in previous surveys; the contour lines on the left-hand side of the area tend to become parallel to the isobaths, with shallower water on the right. Survey 18/3 (which covers a different area selected on the basis of the observed migration of the eddy center, and which was completed immediately after survey 18/2) reveals a "splitting" of the large eddy into two smaller ones with diameters of about 20 km. At the time of the last survey, the splitting is not fully completed and the perturbations have a common area. It must also be pointed out that the time evolution of such an intensive perturbation is uneven. Between surveys 18/1 and 18/2, the time evolution was moderately slow, but survey 18/3 shows a "collapse-like behavior", i.e changes in the isopycnal depths occur much faster than during previous days. This rapid splitting of the perturbation leads to a rearrangement of the vertical structure of the density anomalies. The isopycnals observed during surveys 18/1 and 18/2 are displaced "together" for $7.5 \leq \sigma_t \leq 8.5$, and the cross-correlation between pressure at $\sigma_t = 7.0$ and RDT D(70,30) is larger than 0.95. For the data of survey 18/3, the latter correlation is reduced to 0.8 and less.

We find it also interesting to analyze the temperature field on given isopycnal surfaces. Figure 7 shows temperature maps on the surface $\sigma_t = 6.5$ (above te halocline) for surveys 18/1 and 18/2. Because the correlation radii are fairly small, these maps were not constructed by optimal interpolation, but by spline interpolation. The temperature is maximum at the center of the eddy; the local minimum, located at a distance of about 10

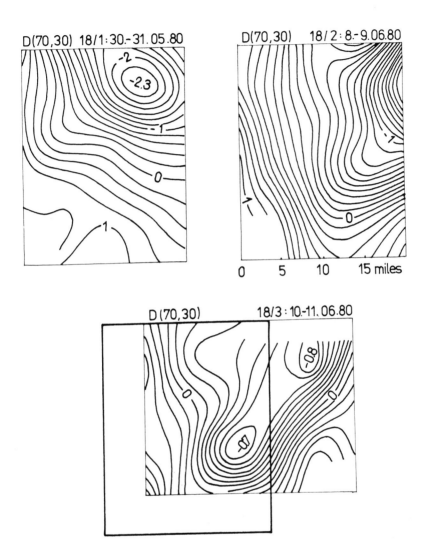

Fig. 6. Maps of RDT anomalies (in dynamic cm) for surveys 18/1 to 18/3. The contour interval is 0.2 dyn.cm for survey 18/2, and 0.1 dyn.cm for surveys 18/2 and 18/3.

448

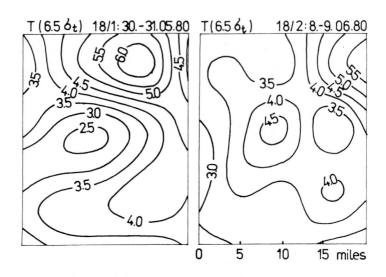

Fig. 7. Maps of temperature on the isopycnal surface σ_t = 6.5 for surveys 18/1 and 18/2. The contour interval is 0.5°C.

miles, is not reflected in the density field. This local minimum seems to have a stable orientation with respect to the center of the eddy. The variations in temperature are large ($\cong$ 4°C with error $\cong$ 1°C) compared to oceanic data (see Woods and Minnett, 1979, who report variations of about 0.1°C.) The temperature distribution on σ_t-surfaces can be considered a tracer under the assumption that the process responsible for the formation of the anomalies is slow. In such a case, the water in the center of the eddy should migrate with the eddy, and the eddylike perturbation could not be of wavelike origin since mass is actually transported in the direction which would be that of the phase speed. The other possibility is that the eddy permanently generates that kind of anomalies. Another feature of survey 18/1 is that the salinity above the halocline is markedly higher at the center of the eddy than elsewhere (in pressure coordinate); this provides evidence that pumping or mixing processes upwell salty halocline waters.

Figure 8 shows maps of RDT D(70,30) and temperature at σ_t = 6.5 for one of the single surveys, number 19/1. A negative RDT perturbation is located in the upper right corner of the area, but the contour lines are not closed.

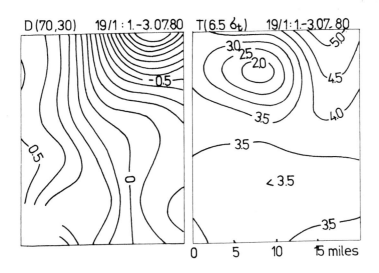

Fig. 8. Maps of RDT (left panel) and temperature on the isopycnal surface σ_t = 6.5 (right panel) for survey 19/1. The contour intervals are 0.1 dyn.cm for RDT and 0.5°C for temperature.

Assuming that the perturbation is eddylike, the diameter appears to be roughly equal to 30 to 40 km. The displacements of the thermocline and halocline appear to have the same sign. The pattern of the temperature field (right panel) is similar to that of surveys 18/1 and 18/2: the temperature is maximum at the center of the perturbation and a local minimum is observed nearby.

Some other perturbations have been observed during some of the single surveys conducted in the BOSEX area. The RDT D(70,30) of survey 17/1 indicates a jetlike anomaly (contour lines almost parallel to the isobaths) in the western part of the area. As observed in the surveys of spring and early summer of 1980, the isopycnals are deeper at the western edge of the area where the water is shallower. The data of survey 20/1 show two eddy-like perturbations with diameters of about 20 km ($2R_d$). The thermocline is depressed at the center of both perturbations, but the halocline is depressed in one case and uplifted in the other.

The processing of the 1981 data is not completed yet. Hence, we shall describe some of the perturbations without figures.

Two surveys - 22/1 and 22/2 - were carried out in the Bornholm Basin at the end of April 1981. The halocline in the Bornholm Basin is sharper than in the Baltic Proper. The Bornholm Basin and the Stolpe Furrow (in the eastern part of that basin) are the regions through which the salty North Sea waters enter the Baltic Proper in the bottom layers. Several density and RDT anomalies were observed in the Bornholm Basin, but their structure is more complicated than in the BOSEX area. A characteristic feature is the raising of the isopycnals in the shallower parts of the working area; the converse was observed in the BOSEX area. In the central part of the working area, the cross-correlations between the displacements of different isopycnals are poor: some displacements even change sign over small (5-10 m) vertical intervals within a given perturbation. Hence, it is hard to believe that the observed perturbations are synoptic scale eddies. Unfortunately, no error norm estimates are available.

In June of 1981, five surveys were performed in the Gotland area (north of the BOSEX area) during the joint Soviet-German Physical/Chemical Experiment. Two distinct perturbations and their evolution can be followed on the maps of surveys 23/3 to 23/5. In survey 23/3 a positive, tonguelike perturbation in RDT D(80,50) appears in the upper left part of the area; the perturbation extends 20 km in the x-direction. Over the next 5 days (survey 23/4), the perturbation seems to expand along the isobaths: the tip of the tongue migrates 20 km in the y-direction and the tongue widens to 30 km in the x-direction. In the upper part of the perturbation, a slight eddylike center begins to take shape. On the map of survey 23/5 (8 days later), the width of the perturbation has decreased to 20 km in the x-direction, and the eddylike center is stretched out in the y-direction. The other disturbance is a negative eddylike perturbation, 15 to 20 km in diameter, located in the right-central part of the map of survey 23/3. Between surveys 23/3 and 23/4, we collected data along a section of the eddy with a profiling interval of 1 mile. The results show that the RDT varies smoothly between the grid stations of the survey and that interpolation gives nearly the same picture as do measurements on a fine horizontal scale. On the map of survey 23/4, the eddy is at the same place, but in the upper left part of the eddy the streamlines of the relative velocity have become denser because the positive RDT perturbation described above is impinging on the negative eddylike perturbation. After 8 days (survey 23/5), the eddy has migrated about 11-14 km along the isobaths towards the northeastern corner of the area, i.e. with shallow water on the right. Migration along the isobaths is characteristic of both perturbations in spite of the fact that the average bottom slopes have completely different orientations below the different perturbations.

THEORETICAL INTERPRETATION

Generally speaking, the theory of synoptic scale motions is complicated and needs further study. The first eddies observed in the ocean were interpreted as the superposition of linear barotropic and baroclinic Rossby waves (Koshlyakov and Grachev, 1973; McWilliams and Flierl, 1976). In this section, we do not try to develop general theories, but we look for the simplest possible quasi-geostrophic motions consistent with parameter values characteristic of the Baltic Sea, and we point out some differences between the linear regimes of the oceans and of deep seas. In particular, some pecularities of topographic waves and baroclinic instability of sheared mean currents are discussed in connection with observational results.

Let x,y,z be Cartesian coordinates with x and y directed to the east and north, and z pointing down with z = 0 at the undisturbed surface. A sketch of the model is presented in Figure 9. Consider a basin with bottom sloping in the x-direction, i.e. with depth $H = H_0 + \alpha x$, and assume that $\alpha \ll 1$, so that as a first approximation the difference between H and H_0 can be neglected for moderate horizontal scales except in terms involving the depth gradients. Let us assume that the water column consists of two layers of thicknesses h_1 and h_2 respectively, and constant (but different) Väisälä frequencies N_1 and N_2. At the same time the density is assumed continuous at the interface. Consider also a mean flow $\bar{V}(z)$ in the y-direction, which is constant in the upper layer (V_s) and has a constant vertical gradient, $(V_s - V_b)/h_2$, in the lower layer. The Earth's rotation is taken into account by the usual β-plane approximation, $f = f_0 + \beta y$, where the difference between the Coriolis parameter f and the constant f_0 can be neglected except in the y-derivative of f. The linearized quasi-geostrophic equation expressing the conservation of potential vorticity can be written as follows

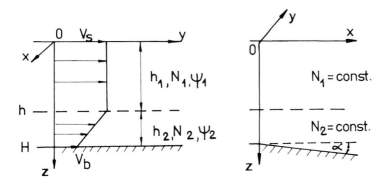

Fig. 9. Sketch of the two-layer model.

$$(\frac{\partial}{\partial t} + \bar{V}_k \frac{\partial}{\partial y})(\Delta\psi_k + \frac{\partial}{\partial z} \frac{f^2}{N_k^2} \frac{\partial\psi_k}{\partial z}) + \beta \frac{\partial\psi_k}{\partial x} = 0, \tag{2}$$

where ψ is the stream function, t denotes the time variable and Δ Laplace's operator. The subscript k = 1,2 identifies the upper and lower layer respectively. The vertical boundary conditions will be given later. Their form depends on the solution one is looking for, and their physical meaning is the requirement of zero normal velocity at the surface and at the bottom and of continuity at the interface.

A   Topographic Waves

Let us first consider the case of topographic waves (Rhines, 1970) without mean flow ($\bar{V} = 0$), and, for simplicity, let us analyze a one-layer model ($h_1 = 0$). The subscripts can then be omitted for these topographic waves. We look for wave solutions of the form

$$\psi = \phi(z) \exp [i(kx + ly - \omega t)] \tag{3}$$

where $\phi(z)$ is the vertical structure function, k and l are the wavenumbers and ω is the frequency. The substitution of (3) into equation (2) gives the following equation for $\phi(z)$:

$$\frac{d}{dz}(\frac{f^2}{N^2} \frac{d\phi}{dz}) - (\eta^2 + \frac{\beta k}{\omega}) \phi = 0, \tag{4}$$

where $\eta^2 = k^2 + l^2$. The boundary conditions are

$$\frac{d\phi}{dz} = 0 \quad \text{at } z = 0, \tag{5}$$

$$\frac{d\phi}{dz} = - \frac{\alpha l N^2}{f\omega} \phi \quad \text{at } z = H. \tag{6}$$

The 'system (4), (5), (6) has two classes of solutions depending on whether $\eta^2 + \beta k/\omega$ is positive or negative.

If $\eta^2 + \beta k/\omega > 0$, the solution is

$$\phi(z) = \phi_o \cosh[\frac{N\eta z}{f} (1 + (\beta k)/(\omega\eta^2))] \tag{7}$$

and the transcendental equation defining ω is

$$\omega = -\frac{N\alpha l}{\eta} \frac{\coth[\frac{N\eta H}{f} \ (1 + (\beta k/\omega\eta^2)]}{(1 + (\beta k/\omega\eta^2)}. \tag{8}$$

Parameter values characteristic of the BOSEX area are: $f = 1.25 \cdot 10^{-4}$ $\sec^{-1}$, $N = 10^{-2}$ $\sec^{-1}$, $H = 100$ m, $\alpha = 5 \cdot 10^{-4}$, $\beta = 1.3 \cdot 10^{-13}$ cm^{-1} $\sec^{-1}$, and wavelengths $|\lambda_x| = |\lambda_y| = 40$ km, where $\lambda_x = 2\pi/k$, and $\lambda_y = 2\pi/l$. For these values, the second term under the radical is of order 10^{-2}. As long as the parameters vary within reasonable limits, the role of β does not increase considerably. Therefore, in the Baltic Sea, the β-effect can be neglected for the "fast baroclinic" waves (Rhines, 1977), and equation (8) takes the form of the well-known dispersion relation for topographic waves

$$\omega = -\frac{N\alpha l}{\eta} \coth \frac{N\eta H}{f}. \tag{9}$$

In the limit $N\eta H/f \gg 1$, (9) reduces to the dispersion equation for bottom-trapped topographic waves, $\omega = -N \alpha \sin\theta$, where θ is the angle between the wave vector and the bottom slope. For $N\eta H/f \ll 1$, equation (9) becomes $\omega = -\alpha l f/\eta^2 H$, appropriate for barotropic waves. Since β has no effect on the solution, the orientation of the bottom slope and of the coordinate axes can be arbitrary.

If $\eta^2 + \beta k/\omega < 0$, the solution describes slow baroclinic waves. The β-effect dominates that of the bottom slope; the presence of a slope is important, but the variation of its magnitude has only minor influence. For the parameter values corresponding to the Baltic Sea, the periods of these waves are longer than years. Therefore, such waves are not relevant to the study of synoptic variability.

Consequently, in the absence of a mean shear flow and with a linearly sloping bottom, only bottom-intensified or nearly barotropic (for large wavelengths) topographic waves can exist. These waves have no modal structure and a single frequency ω corresponds to each pair of wavenumbers k and l. As long as $d\phi(z)/dz$ does not change its (positive) sign in the vertical direction, the displacements of the free surface and of the isopycnal surfaces have the same sign. This is the reason why no attempt was made to distinguish cyclones and anticyclones in the description of the experimental data. If the eddies are formed by a superposition of topographic waves, then, unlike the oceanic case, an anticyclone has a cold center in the thermocline and a salty center in the halocline; a cyclone has warm and

454

fresh centers respectively in the thermo- and halocline.

Since N ≠ constant for the observed stratification, the problem consisting of equations (4), (5), (6) was also solved numerically using a finite difference method. The system of linear equations for discrete $\phi(z)$ values is homogeneous, so that, in order to obtain nontrivial solutions, the frequency ω has to be such that the determinant of the system is equal to zero.

Figure 10 shows various profiles of $\phi(z)$ calculated for a typical summer stratification. The various profiles correspond to different values of λ_y (we assume $k = 0$), and they are normalized by the condition

$$\frac{1}{H} \int_0^H \phi^2 \, dz = 1 \quad .$$

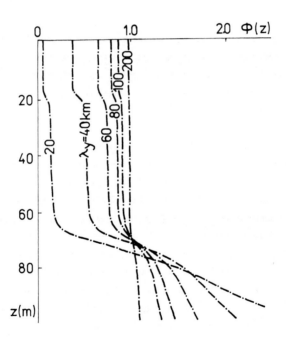

Fig. 10. Vertical structure function of topographic waves, $\phi(z)$, for the August stratification. The various curves correspond to different values of λ_y. The wavenumber in the x-direction, k, is set equal to zero in all cases.

Since $\phi(z)$ represents the amplitude of the stream function, it is proportional to the horizontal velocity. For $\lambda_y = 10$ km, we find that the motion is concentrated in the bottom layers. There are no vertical shear in the horizontal velocity and no displacements of the isopycnals in the thermocline. For $\lambda_y = 200$ km, the function $\phi(z)$ corresponds to the barotropic regime, and the whole water column moves with the same velocity. For intermediate wavelengths, there are vertical shears of velocity in both the thermocline and the halocline. The isopycnal displacements in the thermocline are largest for 20 km $\leq \lambda_y \leq 80$ km.

The observations presented in Figure 4 can be modeled by the superposition of two plane waves, $(k, 1)$ and $(-k, 1)$, with $\lambda_x = 40$ km, and $\lambda_y = -40$ km. For such a model, the numerically determined phase speed and period are: $\vec{c} = (0; 3)$ cm/sec; $T = 15.6$ days. The estimated migration speed of the RDT perturbation between surveys 15/1 and 15/2 is 2 cm/sec. Taking into account the uncertainties affecting the parameter values, the difference between the model and the observation is not significant. The direction and the speed of migration of the RDT perturbation, as well as the presence of geostrophic velocity shears in the thermocline and in the halocline, correspond satisfactorily to the topographic wave model.

The observations shown in Figure 5 can be interpreted in a similar way. Using estimated wavelengths $\lambda_x = 25$ km and $\lambda_y = -40$ km, the theory yields $\vec{c} = (0; 1.9)$ cm/sec and $T = 23.8$ days. On the basis of the experimental data, the migration speed of the RDT perturbation is 1.5 cm/sec. Hence, we believe that the conclusion of the previous paragraph is also valid in this case.

B. **Baroclinic instability**

Let us now consider equation (2) with $\beta = 0$, applied to a two-layer fluid without density jump, in the presence of a sheared mean flow, $\bar{V}(z)$, as described at the beginning of this section. We assume the solution to be of the form

$$\psi_k = \text{Re } \{\phi_k(z) \exp[il(y - ct)]\} \sin kx , \tag{10}$$

where both $\phi_k(z)$ and the phase speed, c, are complex. The function ϕ_k satisfies the equation

$$\frac{d^2\phi_k}{dz^2} - (N \eta/f)^2 \phi_k = 0 \tag{11}$$

subject to the following boundary conditions:

$$\text{at } z = 0, \qquad \frac{d\phi_1}{dz} = 0; \tag{12}$$

$$\text{at } z = h_1, \qquad \phi_1 = \phi_2, \text{ and} \tag{13}$$

$$\frac{(V_s - c)\dfrac{d\phi_1}{dz}}{N_1^2} = \frac{(V_s - c)\dfrac{d\phi_2}{dz} + [V_s - V_b)/h_2]\,\phi_2}{N_2^2} \; ; \tag{14}$$

$$\text{at } z = H, \qquad (V_b - c)\frac{d\phi_2}{dz} = \left(\frac{V_s - V_b}{h_2} - \frac{\alpha N_2^2}{f}\right)\phi_2 . \tag{15}$$

The general solution of equation (11) is a sum of hyperbolic sine and cosine, where the coefficients must be determined so as to satisfy the boundary conditions (12)-(15). The system of linear equations for the determination of the coefficients in the general solution is homogenous; in order to obtain a nontrivial solution, the phase speed c must be such that the determinant is equal to zero. Therefore, c must satisfy a quadratic equation. In some parameter range, the phase speed has a nonzero imaginary part; the corresponding solutions describe unstable waves. The calculations reported here were made by M. Pajuste.

In this paper, we present only the results for the one-layer case ($h_1 = 0$). (The solutions for the two-layer case are similar, but more complicated.) The phase speed is given by

$$c = \frac{V_s + V_b + c_o}{2} \pm \left\{\left(\frac{V_s - V_b + c_o}{2}\right)^2\right.$$

$$\left. - \frac{V_s - V_b}{\gamma}\left[(V_s - V_b)(\coth \gamma - \frac{1}{\gamma}) - c_o (\tanh \gamma - \gamma)\right]\right\}^{\frac{1}{2}} , \tag{16}$$

where c_o is the phase speed of topographic waves without mean flow ($c_o < 0$ if $\alpha > 0$) and $\gamma = N\eta H/f$.

In general, the phase speed is complex, $c = c_r + ic_i$. The solution for the stream function, ψ, is

$$\psi = \text{Re}\{(\phi_r + i\phi_i)\,\exp[il(y - c_r t)]\}\,\sin kx\,\exp(1\,c_i t)$$
$$= |\phi|\cos\{1[y - c_r t + \theta(z)]\}\,\sin kx\,\exp(1\,c_i t), \tag{17}$$

where ϕ_r and ϕ_i are the real and imaginary parts of the vertical structure function $\phi(z)$, $|\phi| = (\phi_r^2 + \phi_i^2)^{\frac{1}{2}}$, and the z-dependent phase, $\theta(z)$, is given by

$$\theta(z) = \text{arc tan } (\frac{\phi_i}{\phi_r}).$$

If the phase speed has a nonzero imaginary part, $c_i \neq 0$, we also have $\phi_i \neq 0$; the waves are then unstable, and their amplitude increases with time as $\exp(1\ c_i t)$. The phase is not constant vertically, and the axes of eddy-like perturbations are inclined with respect to the vertical.

The two-layer model with $\beta = 0$ contains, as particular cases, the model of Tang (1975) (corresponding to $\alpha = 0$, $V_b = 0$), and the baroclinic insta-bility model of Eady (1949) ($\alpha = 0$, $V_b = 0$, $h_1 = 0$).

For the calculations described hereafter, we used the following para-meter values: $H = 100$ m, $h_1 = 60$ m, $h_2 = 40$ m, $N_1 = 10^{-2}$ sec^{-1}, $N_2 = 2.5\cdot10^{-2}$ sec^{-1}; for the one-layer case, we chose $N = 1.25\cdot10^2$ sec^{-1}. Since the observed RDT anomalies were almost circular, only waves for which $\lambda_x = \lambda_y$ (or $k = 1$) were studied.

The instability region for $\alpha = 0$, $h_1 = 0$ is independent of the mean flow, and for $\gamma < 2.399$ ($\lambda_y > 2.6 \sqrt{2} R_d$) all the waves are unstable, as derived by Eady (1949). The same result holds for $\alpha = 0$, $h_1 \neq 0$, but the critical wavelength is equal to 44.5 km for the above-given parameter values. If $\alpha > 0$, the instability region depends on both the wavelength and the mean flow, but waves are more unstable if $V_s - V_b > 0$. In other words, the stability domain is smaller when the direction of the upper layer mean flow relative to the bottom current is opposed to that of the phase speed of the topographic waves.

Two-folding times for the amplitudes of the unstable waves are pre-sented in Figure 11 as function of the wavelength λ_y, for different shears of the mean current $V_s - V_b$. For $\alpha = 0$, the results obtained from the one- and two-layer models are close, but for $\alpha = 5.10^{-4}$ the one-layer model requires much greater values of $V_s - V_b$ for instability than the two-layer model. According to the two-layer model, for a mean current difference of 2.5 cm/sec between the surface and bottom layers, the amplitude of the most unstable waves doubles in 10 days. Both values are quite realistic for the Baltic Sea. These most unstable waves correspond to $\lambda_y \cong 50$ to 60 km ($\cong 4$ to 5 R_d). The dominating wavelength of the RDT perturbation observed during surveys 18/1 and 18/2, estimated by the correlation function, is 80 to 90 km; this is somewhat larger than the scale of the most unstable waves calcu-lated from the baroclinic instability theory. This difference, however, is

458

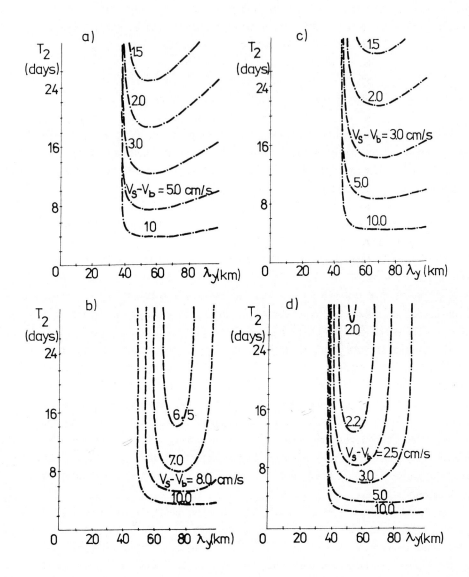

Fig. 11. Two-folding times (T_2) for the amplitudes of the unstable waves as functions of the wavelength λ_y. The various curves correspond to different values of the mean velocity shear $V_s - V_b$. Panels a and b show the results of the one-layer model, panels c and d those of the two-layer model. The bottom slope $\alpha = 0$ for panels a and c, and $\alpha = 5.10^4$ for b and d.

reasonably small, and we suggest that this RDT perturbation was generated by baroclinic instability. When the amplitude of the wave reaches some critical value, the linearized theory presented above ceases to be valid to describe the further development of the waves: the infinite amplitude growth predicted by (17) is limited by nonlinear processes. The data of survey 18/3 show the splitting of a large and intensive eddy into two smaller ones, and that is one plausible mechanism which would limit the amplitude growth.

It must be pointed out that such quasi-geostrophic waves in the presence of shear mean flow are very sensitive to parameter variations. Some inclination of the vertical axis of the eddy is characteristic of both oceanic (Koshlyakov and Grachev, 1973) and Baltic field observations, but the theoretical phase distribution $\theta(z)$ of the unstable waves can have vertical gradients of both signs. In the one-layer model, the amplitude $|\phi|$ of the unstable waves above a sloping bottom has maxima at the surface and at the bottom. In the two-layer model, $|\phi|$ is maximum at the interface (upper boundary of the halocline), and the amplitude decreases more rapidly towards the bottom than towards the surface. For stable waves there are two solutions for the above-mentioned models. In the one-layer model, one vertical structure function $\phi(z)$ decreases monotonously with depth, whereas the other increases. For the two-layer model, both $\phi(z)$ are very similar; they are maximum at the interface and decrease faster towards the bottom than towards the surface (as for the unstable waves of this model).

The linear quasi-geostrophic regime of the Baltic Sea is somewhat different from that of the ocean. In the Baltic, the effect of the bottom slope overwhelms the planetary β-effect in the constant slope model, but the role of the Rossby deformation radius as determinator of typical horizontal scales is common to both the Baltic and the oceanic cases. The mean current shear introduces new types of waves, but they are still influenced by the sloping bottom. It should be emphasized that the assumption of a constant bottom slope is a simplification, and that the real bottom topography is very irregular: this is in contrast to the regular variation of the Coriolis parameter, which dominates ocean dynamics. The perturbations of the bottom topography and of the atmospheric forcing, which can be important contributors to the dynamics of synoptic scale motions, are not considered here.

ON THE ESTIMATION OF ABSOLUTE VELOCITIES

The classical dynamic method (Fomin, 1964) allows the calculation of relative geostrophic currents from density data. For the determination of absolute velocities, it is necessary to know the current at some reference level either from direct measurements (McWilliams, 1976) or as a result of speculation. The old idea that deep water velocities are small does not fit in today's conceptions. Schott and Stommel (1978) proposed the beta-spiral method to overcome the problem of the reference level velocity for large-scale currents. This method uses the geostrophic relations together with the linear equation of vorticity conservation on a β-plane and it assumes the immiscibility of the density stratification.

The synoptic eddies cannot be treated by the β-spiral method, but the generalization proposed by Korotayev and Shapiro (1978) allows the calculation of the absolute velocity of nonstationary quasi-geostrophic currents and eddies. In this section, we use the method of Korotayev and Shapiro with a slightly different formulation. We choose to use density as the vertical coordinate, with the hope that these "Lagrangian" coordinates might lead to better vertical resolution than "Eulerian" pressure coordinates for the case of the very sharp density layering observed in the Baltic.

For the vertical discretization, consider a multi-layered water column consisting of N layers of constant densities. The potential vorticity conservation equation, which holds for each layer, has the form

$$(\frac{\partial}{\partial t} + u_k \frac{\partial}{\partial x} + v_k \frac{\partial}{\partial y}) (\frac{\xi_k + f}{h_k}) = 0, \tag{18}$$

where u_k and v_k are the velocities, ξ_k the vorticity, and h_k the thickness of the k-th layer. By definition,

$$\xi_k = \frac{\partial v_k}{\partial x} - \frac{\partial u_k}{\partial y}.$$

Decompose the velocities and the vorticity into a reference level value, denoted by an overbar, plus a value relative to that reference level, denoted by a prime, as follows:

$$\begin{aligned} u_k &= \bar{u} + u'_k , \\ v_k &= \bar{v} + v'_k , \\ \xi_k &= \bar{\xi} + \xi'_k . \end{aligned} \tag{19}$$

Note that the reference level values are independent of depth (or layer). If the data of two rapidly succeeding surveys are available, u'_k, v'_k, ξ'_k and h_k as well as their time and space derivatives can be calculated using the geostrophic relations for the velocities and the definition of relative vorticity.

Substituting (19) into (18), the following system of linear equations can be obtained

$$\sum_{i=1}^{5} A_{ki} X_i + F_k = 0, \quad k = 1,N \tag{20}$$

where the X_i's are functions of the unknown reference level values

$$X_1 = \frac{\partial \bar{\xi}}{\partial t} + \bar{u} \frac{\partial \bar{\xi}}{\partial x} + \bar{v} \frac{\partial \bar{\xi}}{\partial y},$$

$$X_2 = \bar{u}, \quad X_3 = \bar{v}, \tag{21}$$

$$X_4 = \frac{\partial \bar{\xi}}{\partial x}, \quad X_5 = \frac{\partial \bar{\xi}}{\partial y},$$

and where the A_{ki}'s and F_k's depend only on the relative values of the variables (which are known from the observations):

$$A_{k1} = 1,$$

$$A_{k2} = \frac{\partial \xi_k'}{\partial x} - \frac{f}{h_k} \frac{\partial h_k}{\partial x},$$

$$A_{k3} = \frac{\partial \xi_k'}{\partial y} - \frac{f}{h_k} \frac{\partial h_k}{\partial y},$$

$$A_{k4} = u_k', \qquad A_{k5} = v_k', \tag{22}$$

$$F_k = \frac{\partial \xi_k'}{\partial t} + u_k' \frac{\partial \xi_k'}{\partial x} + v_k' \frac{\partial \xi_k'}{\partial y} - \frac{f}{h_k} (\frac{\partial h_k}{\partial t} + u' \frac{\partial h_k}{\partial x} + v' \frac{\partial h_k}{\partial y}).$$

In order to solve (20), one must take $N \geq 5$. There is no need to include the surface and/or bottom layers among the layers selected for the solution of the system.

If the observational data are without errors and (18) holds exactly, and if $N > 5$, only 5 equations are linearly independent and the remaining $(N - 5)$ equations are linear combinations of the former. In practice, because of errors and small-scale noise, (20) is overdetermined for $N > 5$, and the solution can be found by a least squares method, i.e. by minimizing the sum

$$R = \sum_{k=1}^{N} (\sum_{i=1}^{5} A_{ki} X_i + F_k)^2. \tag{23}$$

This procedure is followed at every point x, y of the data grid. The values of $\bar{u}$, $\bar{v}$ and $\partial \bar{\xi}/\partial x$, $\partial \bar{\xi}/\partial y$ are calculated separately despite the fact

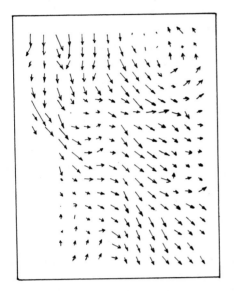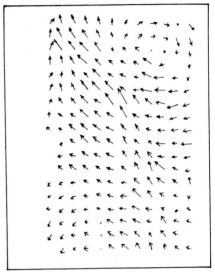

Fig. 12. Estimated absolute velocities for the near-surface layer (left) and on the σ_t = 8.5 surface (right) for survey 18/1. An arrow whose length equals the interpolation step corresponds to a velocity of 10 cm/sec.

that they are related through spatial derivatives. But the problem becomes enormously complicated if the horizontal fields are given as numerical tables and the equations solved for all points simultaneously.

For a test of the method, we chose the data of surveys 18/1 and 18/2 for which the time interval is 9 days. The pressure values as functions of density were interpolated by optimal interpolation to a denser grid (spacing of 0.25 σ_t units) and the values of A_{ki} and F_k were calculated. The time derivatives were calculated by one-sided differences and the space derivatives by central differences, the latter from the data of survey 18/1. The reference level was chosen at the surface, but the minimization of (23) involved only intermediate layers with N = 8 to 11.

The estimated absolute velocities are presented in Figure 12 for the surface layer and on the σ_t = 8.5 surface, which is in the middle of the halocline. The directions of the velocity vectors replicate the pattern of the RDT perturbation shown in Figure 6, and the velocity field is sufficiently smooth. However, we think that the magnitudes of the reference level (surface) currents are underestimated, and that the bottom currents should be weaker or even reverse.

In minimizing (23), the dominant terms of the system (20) were $A_{k4}X_4$ and $A_{k5}X_5$, which represent the advection of reference level vorticity by the relative velocity. The other terms of (20), after least squares fitting, are one order of magnitude smaller. The same qualitative results were obtained by Korotayev and Shapiro (1978), but they estimated the absolute velocity at one location only. Our larger horizontal data set allows us to compare "independently" estimated values of

$$\frac{\partial}{\partial x} \left(\frac{\partial \bar{v}}{\partial x} - \frac{\partial \bar{u}}{\partial y} \right) \quad \text{and} \quad \frac{\partial \bar{\xi}}{\partial x} \; .$$

The correlation between these values is bad, vorticity gradients being systematically higher. Hence, we are unable to estimate the balance of terms in the vorticity conservation equation and to determine which terms are the most important contributors to the dynamics of synoptic scale processes.

Nevertheless, we think that our attempt to estimate absolute velocities for synoptic scale processes was partially successful and that the shortcomings are due to the quality of the data rather than to the method. The data were not collected with the direct purpose of estimating the absolute velocity, and the temporal and spatial resolutions were probably not optimal for the calculation of the high-order derivatives which are necessary for the method.

DISCUSSION AND CONCLUSIONS

First, let us summarize the purely experimental results obtained from the CTD surveys:

1) It is evident that the stratification of the Baltic Proper is disturbed by low-frequency motions. Such motions can be distinctly separated from short-term variations (with periods shorter than one day), especially in the halocline.

2) The most common spatial structure of the synoptic scale perturbations consists of "mountains" and "valleys" of isopycnal surfaces. For many perturbations the geostrophic streamlines of relative velocity are closed, being nearly circular. For that reason we can consider them to be eddies. In the most distinctive eddies, the isopycnals rise in the center of the perturbation.

3)   The typical horizontal dimensions of the eddies are of the order of 2 to 6 R_d ($R_d \cong 10$ km). The eddy axis can be inclined with respect to the vertical.

4)   The usual direction of migration of the eddies is along the averaged isobaths with shallower water on the right. The typical migration speed is a few cm/sec.

5)   The vertical synoptic scale displacements of the isopycnals can be more than 20 m. The relative currents in the eddies can exceed 10 to 15 cm/sec.

6)   The typical life time of the eddies is more than 10 days. The intensification of an eddy was documented, as was the splitting of a large and intensive eddy into two smaller ones.

7)   The large and intensive eddies reveal significant thermoclinicity. In the intermediate layer between the thermocline and the halocline, the temperature distribution on a fixed density surface can have variations of up to 4°C.

8)   The eddies and other synoptic scale perturbations tend to have larger dimensions along the averaged isobaths than along the bottom slope. The streamlines of relative currents can intersect the bottom contours where the depth decreases.

From the section entitled "theoretical interpretation", the following points can be made:

1)   The speed and the direction of migration of the eddies can be explained in terms of topographic waves. Also, the vertical shears of the horizontal currents in the thermocline and in the halocline may correspond to those of topographic waves. The magnitude of the current shear is greater in the halocline than in the thermocline, for topographic waves, and the shear has the same sign in both layers.

2)   In the simple model of baroclinic instability, the wavelengths of the most unstable waves agree well with the dimensions of the larger eddies. A vertical shear of the mean flow of the order of a few cm/sec can produce reasonable growth rates for unstable waves. This leads us to the hypothesis that the observed eddies can be generated by baroclinic instability of sheared mean flows.

Comparing our results to those obtain for the ocean, we note that the nondimensional diameters of the eddies (with R_d as the scale unit) are the same in the Baltic and in the ocean. The Baltic Sea, however, is not simply a reduced model of the ocean. The migration and the evolution of the eddies are controlled by the bottom topography rather than by the planetary β-effect. From a theoretical point of view, it is only for the barotropic case that the β-effect (in the ocean) can be simply replaced by the influence of the bottom slope (in the Baltic). In the stratified water of the Baltic, the effect of bottom topography completely dominates that of beta, and many of the oceanic theoretical results cannot be directly applied to the Baltic case. The other complication is that, in contrast to the regular variation of the Coriolis parameter, the bottom topography is very irregular, and the assumption of a constant slope is only valid in a few cases. Disturbances of the bottom topography on a scale comparable to that of the eddies can also be important.

The limitations of the experiments did not allow to answer the "oceanic" question of whether the eddies are "closed-packed" (Koshlyakov and Monin, 1978) or singular (Nelepo and Korotayev, 1979). In the latter paper, the authors assert that eddies are singular nonlinear phenomena, between which exists a background of Rossby waves. They show theoretically that the nonlinear eddies migrate westwards like Rossby waves.

Woods (1980) distinguishes between wavelike motions that radiate energy and momentum, and advective-like motions (eddies and fronts) that transport momentum and energy by advection of water particles. At the present time, we are not able to classify the observed eddies (defined otherwise like Woods) in those terms.

The currents in the Baltic Sea are considered to be mostly wind-induced (Jansson, 1978). With the help of a linear numerical model, Kielmann (1978) shows that fluctuating winds can generate topographic eddies. The computations of Simons (1978), based on a nonlinear model, indicate that the eddies are not related in a straightforward manner to the wind forcing. Our observations indicate that the storm which occurred between surveys 18/1 and 18/2 had no obvious influence on the RDT patterns.

Numerous interesting phenomena were observed, the nature of which is not entirely clear. From our point of view, cooperative experiments such as BOSEX in 1977 should be useful to complement the knowledge of the dynamics of the Baltic Sea.

REFERENCES

Aitsam, A. and Elken, J., 1980. Results of CTD surveys in the BOSEX area of the Baltic Sea (in Russian). In: Tonkaya struktura i sinopticheskaya izmenchivost morei, Tallinn, pp. 19-23.

Aitsam, A., Elken, J., Pavelson, J. and Talpsepp, L., 1981. Preliminary results of the investigation of spatial-temporal characteristics of the Baltic Sea synoptic variability. In: The Investigation and Modelling of Processes in the Baltic Sea, Part I, pp. 70-98.

Aitsam, A., and Talpsepp, L., 1980. Investigation of the variability of synoptic scale currents in the Central Baltic in 1977-1980 (in Russian). In: Tonkaya struktura i sinopticheskaya izmenchivost morei, Tallinn, pp. 14-18.

Bretherton, F.P., Davis, R.E. and Fandry, C.B., 1976. A technique for objective analysis and design of oceanographic experiments applied to MODE-73. Deep-Sea Research, 23: 559-582.

Eady, E.T., 1949. Long waves and cyclone waves. Tellus, 3: 33-52.

Fomin, L.M., 1964. The dynamic method in oceanography. Elsevier Scientific Publishing Company, 212 pp.

Gandin, L.S., 1965. Objective analysis of meteorological fields. Israel Program for Scientific Translations, Jerusalem.

Jansson, B.-O., 1978. The Baltic - a system analysis of a semi-enclosed sea. In: Advances in Oceanography, Plenum Publishing Corporation, pp. 131-183.

Keunecke, K.-H., and Magaard, L., 1974. Measurements by means of towed thermistor cables and problems of their interpretation with respect to mesoscale processes. Mémoires de la Société Royale des Sciences de Liège, 6: 147-160.

Kielmann, J., 1978. Mesoscale eddies in the Baltic. In: Proc. of the XI Conference of Baltic Oceanographers, Rostock, pp. 729-755.

Kielmann, J., Holtroff, J. and Reimer, U., 1976. Data report Baltic '75. Ber. Inst. Meeresk. Kiel, 26: 23.

Kielmann, J., Krauss, W. and Keunecke, K.-H., 1973. Currents and stratification in the Belt Sea and Arcona Basin during 1962-1968. Kieler Meeresforschungen, 2: 90-111.

Korotayev, G.K. and Shapiro, N.B., 1978. On the calculation of absolute velocity of geostrophic currents from the data of synoptic surveys (in Russian). In: Eksperimentalnye issledovaniya po mezhdunarodnoi programme "POLYMODE", Sevastopol, pp. 83-95.

Koshlayakov, M.N., Galerkin, L.I. and Truong Din Hien, 1970. On the mesostructure of the open ocean geostrophic currents. Okeanologiya, 10: 805-814.

Koshlayakov, M.N. and Grachev, Y.M., 1973. Mesoscale currents at a hydrophysical polygon in the Tropical Atlantic. Deep-Sea Research, 20: 507-526.

Koshlayakov, M.N. and Monin, A.S., 1978. Synoptic eddies in the ocean. Ann. Rev. Earth Planet. Sci., 6: 495-523.

Laanemets, J. and Lilover, M.-J., 1981. The data processing scheme of measurements with the Neil Brown Mark III CTD. In: The Investigation and Modelling of Processes in the Baltic Sea, Part I, Tallinn, pp. 10-19.

McWilliams, J.C., 1976. Maps from the Mid-Ocean Dynamics Experiment: Part I, Geostrophic Streamfunction. J. Phys. Oceanogr. 6(6): 810-827.

McWilliams, J.C. and Flierl, G.R., 1976. Optimal, quasi-geostrophic waves analyses of MODE array data. Deep-Sea Research, 23: 285-300.

The MODE Group, 1978. The Mid-Ocean Dynamics Experiment. Deep Sea Research, 25: 859-910.

Nelepo, B.A. and Korotayev, G.K., 1979. The structure of synoptical variability from the data on hydrological surveys in the POLYMODE observational area (in Russian). Morskie gidrofizicheskie issledovanya, 3: 3-20.

Nikitin, O.P. and Vinogradova, K.G., 1980. Separation of the synoptic component of temperature field from XBT-survey data and some applications. Ocean Modelling (unpublished manuscript).

Rhines, P., 1970. Edge-, bottom-, and Rossby waves in a rotating, stratified fluid. Geophysical Fluid Dynamics, 1: 273-302.

Rhines, P., 1977. The dynamics of unsteady currents. In: The Sea, Wiley-Interscience, 6: 189-318.

Schott, F. and Stommel, H., 1978. Beta spirals and absolute velocities in different oceans. Deep-Sea Research, 25: 961-1010.

Simons, T.J., 1978. Wind-driven circulations in the southwest Baltic. Tellus, 3: 272-283.

Sustavov, J.V., Chernyshova, E.S. and Michaylov, A.E., 1978. On the synoptic eddy genesis in the Baltic Sea. In: Proc. of the XI Conference of Baltic Oceanographers, Rostock, pp. 795-805.

Tang, C.M., 1975. Baroclinic instability of stratified shear flows in the ocean and atmosphere. J. Geophys. Res., 80: 1168-1175.

Woods, J.D., 1979. Modelling oceanic transport in studies of climate response to pollution. In: Man's Impact on Climate, Elsevier Scientific Publishing Company, pp. 99-107.

Woods, J.D., 1980. Do waves limit turbulent diffusion in the ocean? Nature, 288: 219-224.

Woods, J.D. and Minnett, P.J., 1979. Analysis of mesoscale thermoclinicity with an example from the tropical thermocline during GATE. Deep-Sea Research, 26A: 85-96.

SYNOPTIC VARIABILITY OF CURRENTS IN THE
BALTIC PROPER

A. Aitsam, L. Talpsepp
Institute of Thermophysics and Electrophysics
Academy of Sciences of the Estonian S.S.R.

INTRODUCTION

The discovery of synoptic scale variability is one of the results of several experiments conducted in different parts of the World Ocean during the last two decades. Phenomena of synoptic scale include open sea eddies, Rossby waves, topographic waves and topographic Rossby waves, baroclinic instabilities of large scale motion of the ocean, etc. Theoretical investigations show that the latitude, the atmospheric conditions, the bottom topography, the stratification of the water, and the character of large scale motion are of crucial importance in determining the forms and scales of synoptic variability, and must be involved in theoretical models.

In view of the importance of synoptic variability in the energetics of the ocean, several expeditions for the study of the variablity at the corresponding scale were carried out in the Baltic Sea. Given the characteristic scale, the study of the Baltic is relatively less expansive than that of the ocean. As far as the Baltic Sea can be regarded as a model of the ocean, it is reasonable to study the aforementioned processes in that model. However, the identification of different phenomena is not simple because the bottom topography, the basin geometry, and the stratification of the Baltic Sea are complicated. At the Institute of Thermophysics and Electrophysics, Academy of Sciences of the Estonian S.S.R., experimental studies of synoptic variability have been made since 1977, and experiments using autonomous mooring stations with recording current meters were carried out in 1977, 1979 and 1980. In this paper, we describe the results of these experiments. During the same experiments, some temperature and salinity mappings were also made in certain regions of the Baltic Sea: the results of these density mappings are discussed in a previous paper (Aitsam et al., 1980). We also note that the results of the experiments with recording current meters were different in different years and in the following these results will have different interpretations.

MEASUREMENTS

The direct measurement of currents using autonomous mooring stations is one of the most reliable methods for studying synoptic scale processes.

Measurements of current velocities and temperature using autonomous mooring stations with recording current meters were carried out in the open part of the Baltic Sea in 1977, 1979 and 1980. The most important characteristics of the experiments are given in Table 1.

TABLE 1

The open sea experiments with autonomous mooring
stations (AMS) in 1977-1980

	1977	1979	1980
Number of AMS	2	5(4)	6(5)
Number of levels in AMS	4	2-6	2-3
duration (days)	20	35	102
time of year	September	May-June	May-August
separation distance	20 miles	10 miles	10 km

In 1977 two mooring stations located 20 miles apart were installed as part of the international BOSEX experiment. At both stations measurements were made at four depths during 20 days. Aanderaa instruments were used. In 1979, 5 autonomous mooring stations with one measuring instrument in the surface layer and one in the bottom layer were installed. Six current meters were installed at the central station of the area in order to study the vertical distribution of kinetic energy. Both VACM and Aanderaa instruments were used. The experiment took place in May-June and lasted for 36 days. In 1980, six mooring stations with instruments at depths of 45 and 80 meters were installed for 102 days. One station with two measuring instruments was lost and one current meter did not work.

Figure 1 shows the bottom topography of the site of the 1980 experiment. The mooring stations are deployed in a crosslike pattern. The location of the mooring stations of the 1979 experiment is slightly northward of this site. The station N of 1977 is located at the same slope. Three characteristic sections of the bottom topography are presented in Figure 2; the distance between these sections is 10 km.

RESULTS OF THE 1977 EXPERIMENT

In this section, we present and discuss the results of the current measurements made in 1977. The kinetic energies measured at station N and E are presented in Table 2. The mean velocities over the measuring period, denoted $\bar{u}$ and $\bar{v}$, and the total kinetic energy of the fluctuations, K, are

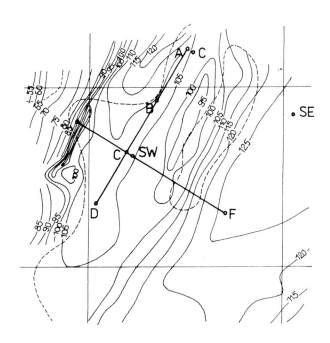

Figure 1. Bottom topography at the site of the 1980 experiment.

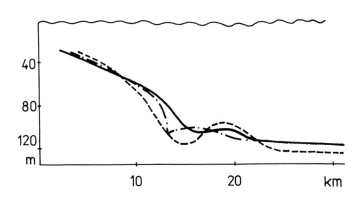

Figure 2. Characteristic sections of the bottom topography.

TABLE 2

The vertical distribution of kinetic energy at stations N and E
of the "BOSEX 77" area.

Station	depth (m)	$\bar{u}$ (cm/sec)	$\bar{v}$ (cm/sec)	K (cm^2/sec^2)	K_E (cm^2/sec^2)
N	20	-0.34	-0.71	248	35
	30	-0.52	0.47	231	29
	105	-0.09	-0.15	63	10
	118	0.61	1.44	80	23
E	80	0.50	1.71	138	35
	40	1.71	2.69	64	12
	108	2.45	6.12	52	39
	121	2.29	4.82	50	22

given. The quantity K_E will be described later. We can see that the kinetic energy K increases with depth at station N. At station E, where the bottom is flat, the kinetic energy does not increase with depth. The latter observation suggests that the kinetic energy increase is related to the bottom topography. We believe that the increase of kinetic energy agrees well with the theory of bottom-trapped topographic waves developed by Rhines (1970) for an infinite basin. The governing equations for the horizontal stream function P are as follows:

$$\frac{d}{dz}\left(\frac{f^2}{N^2}\frac{dP}{dz}\right) = \eta^2 P,$$

$$\frac{dP}{dz} = 0 \text{ at } z = 0,$$

$$\frac{dP}{dz} = \frac{\alpha k N^2}{f\omega} P \text{ at } z = -H, \quad \eta^2 = k^2 + \ell^2,$$

where a linear wave of the form $\exp(i(kx + \ell y - \omega t))$ is assumed, α denotes the bottom slope, f the Coriolis parameter, N^2 the Väisälä frequency, and z the vertical coordinate, directed upwards with its origin at the sea surface.

For the case N = constant, this equation yields the following solution: $P = P_0 \cosh(\eta Nz/f)$; the dispersion relation is $\omega = -\alpha N \sin\theta \coth(\eta NH/f)$, where $\sin\theta = k/\eta$; for relatively short waves and strong stratification, this relation becomes $\omega = \alpha N \sin\theta$. The assumption of constant N is based on the stratification characteristic of this region during September 1977 (Fig. 3). The horizontal stream function P indicates an increase in the velocity components with depth. Thus, on the basis of Table 2, the theoret-

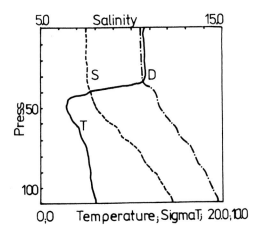

Figure 3. Characteristic vertical profiles of temperature (T), salinity (S), and relative density (D) during BOSEX at station N of the 1977 experiment.

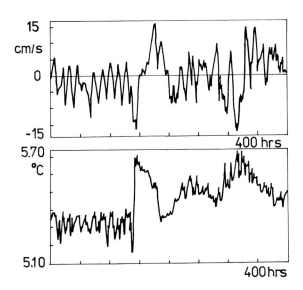

Figure 4. Time series of the eastern velocity component and of the temperature at a depth of 118 m at station N.

ical results are supported by the observed kinetic energy distribution, as in the study of Thompson and Luyten (1977).

We think that, although the vertical distribution of the total kinetic energy demonstrates the presence of bottom-trapped waves, stronger evidence is provided by the distribution of the quantity K_E which characterizes the energy of oscillations with periods from one to six days. We can see that the kinetic energy increases with depth due to K_E. The preceding theoretical calculations show that the periods of the topographic waves fall within this interval. As mentioned above, station E is situated at a distance of about 35 km from the region of rough bottom slope. Since the kinetic energy K does not increase with depth at station E and there is no other evidence for low frequency oscillations, it seems likely that oscillations observed at station N do not propagate that far. The absence of low frequency oscillations at station E seems to support the idea of bottom-induced waves. Only results of station N will be discussed hereafter.

Figure 4 shows the variation of the eastern component of the velocity and that of the temperature during the first 400 hours. The same data after removal of the high frequency oscillations are shown in Figure 5, where the dominant periods are much more visible. These periods are also apparent in the temperature series as the current directed upslope upwells warmer water. The highest temperature occurs at the time when the upslope current changes its sign. The same series at the 105 m level are shown in Figure 6. It should also be noted that the coherence between temperature and upslope current is strongest at frequencies corresponding to topographic waves. Using a least squares method, the dominant periods are found to be equal to 68 and 44 hours.

Using the kinetic energy distribution obtained from spectral calculations and the Rhines model of topographic waves, theoretical wavelengths are found equal to 12-14 km at those frequencies. We have no experimental data to check this theoretical result. In order to determine the wave orientation, we have to find the angle ψ of coordinate system rotation such that the coherence between components in the new system is minimal. Minimizing the coherence we obtain the formula

$$\tan 2\psi = \frac{2\,P_{uv}}{S_{uu} - S_{vv}} \tag{1}$$

where S_{uu} and S_{vv} are the spectral densities of the velocity components, and P_{uv} is the cospectrum. The orientation and energy of waves are characterized by energy ellipses, where the angle ψ is obtained from (1), and the axes of the ellipses are the eigenvalues of the matrix

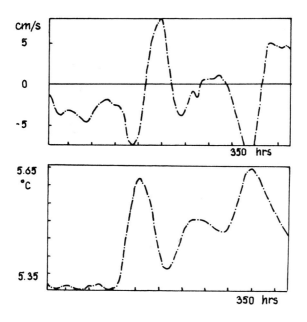

Figure 5.   Same as Fig. 4 after removal of the high frequency oscillations.

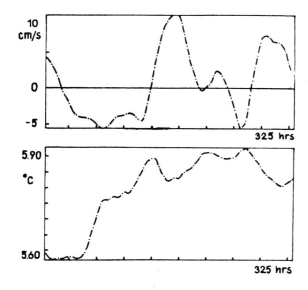

Figure 6.   Same as Fig. 5 as the 105 m level of station N.

$$\begin{vmatrix} S_{uu} & P_{uv} \\ P_{uv} & S_{vv} \end{vmatrix} \quad .$$

The length of the axes of the ellipses gauges the spectral density of the velocity components in the new coordinate system. In Figure 7 we see that the waves propagate along the slope, and that there is more energy at the aforementioned dominant periods.

DESCRIPTION OF THE DATA OBTAINED DURING THE 1979 AND 1980 EXPERIMENTS

In the May-June 1979 data, we find no evidence of the presence of bottom-trapped topographic waves in the same region. For instance, there is no increase of the kinetic energy of the fluctuations in the bottom layer. The spectral analysis shows that there is considerably less energy in the synoptic interval as compared to the data of the 1977 or 1980 experiments. Figure 8 shows a series of maps of daily mean currents at a depth of 15 meters above the bottom. Daily mean velocities are of the order of 2-5 cm/s. On the whole the picture is not simple, although eddy like currents can be observed at the end of the experiment period. The vector diagrams (Fig. 9) for the surface layer at stations SW, NW are similar to the diagrams obtained after a 30 km eddy has extended to the north at the rate of 2-3 cm/s. It should be mentioned that inertial oscillations with periods of about 13.8 hours dominate the water motion, having amplitudes of up to 15 cm/sec which vary in space and in time.

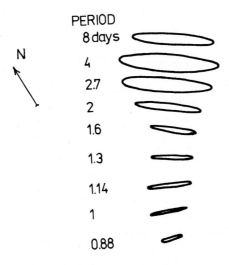

Figure 7. Energy ellipses at the 118 m level of station N.

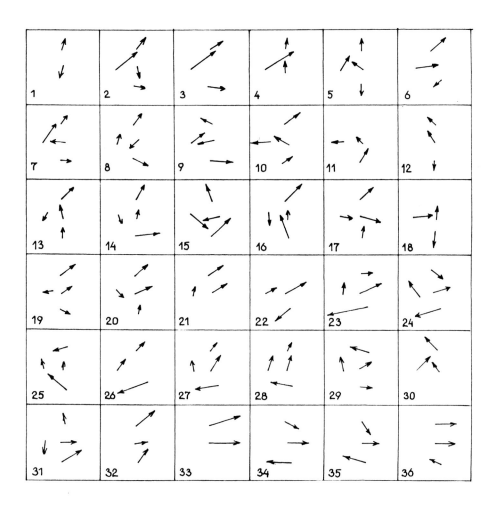

Figure 8. Maps of daily mean currents in the bottom layer in 1979.

478

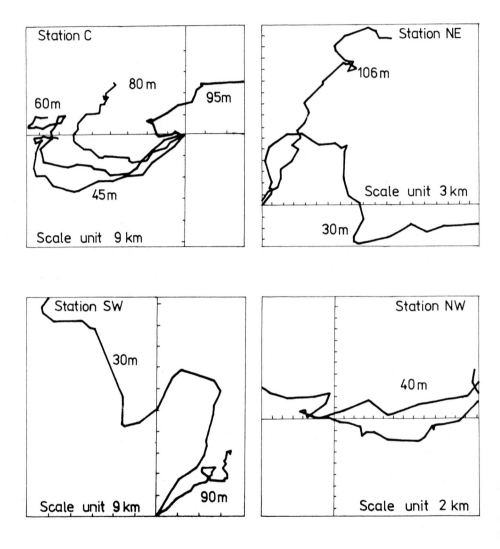

Figure 9.   Vector diagrams of daily mean currents at the site of the 1979 experiment.

At that time (May-June 1979), still weather was prevailing over the Baltic Sea. It has been more than once hypothesized that the atmosphere may be the source of energy for topographic waves. Thus, the low level of energy of the synoptic scale variability for that year can be explained by the absence of the energy transfer from the atmosphere. Also, the bottom topography of the experimental site is quite complicated, thus demanding a complicated model.

The results of the 1980 experiment show a slightly different situation in the area. There are large fluctuations with periods of six to nine days in the velocity components. Figures 10 and 11 show the variation of daily mean velocities at stations B and C, respectively, during 102 days. Low frequency oscillations can be noticed in those time series. Figure 12 shows that such periods also exist in temperature records. Note that the temperature fluctuations are slighly damped at the end of the experiment.

The spectra of the velocity components have peaks approximately within the range of 6-8 days. Figures 13 and 14 show the spectral function $\omega \cdot S(\omega)$ of the velocity components at stations E and C. There are peaks at the inertial frequency and at 6-7 days. In these plots, the total energy is proportional to the area under the curve. Peaks at 6-8 days are apparent in all the measurements.

Figure 15 shows the vectors of daily mean currents obtained with Aanderaa RCM-4 current meters. Low frequency variability of the currents can be observed. Figure 16 displays the time sequence of daily mean currents in the bottom layer of the experiment area. Eddylike currents can be seen at various times.

During the 1980 experiment, the mean velocity at stations B and C (Figure 17) is directed along the channel. The velocity is directed to the south-south-east during the first 70 days and in the opposite direction during the last month. The stratification shown in Figure 18 is representative of the whole data set.

MODEL OF BAROCLINIC INSTABILITY

In this section, we consider the question of whether baroclinic instability can be the reason for the observed variability. In view of the observed stratification, stability will be investigated using a two-layer model. Let us consider a channel extending in the y-direction with bottom sloping in the x-direction, and let us assume that mean currents are present in both layers. Using the subscript i = 1,2 to identify the upper and lower layer respectively, and denoting by

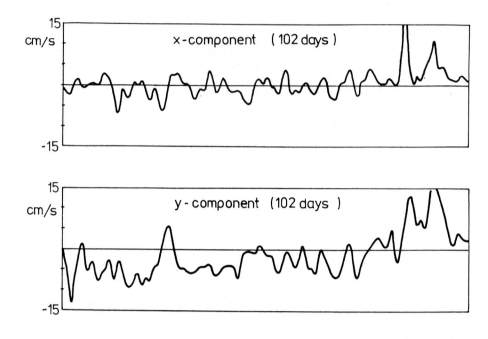

Figure 10.   Time series of the velocity components at station B of the 1980 experiment.

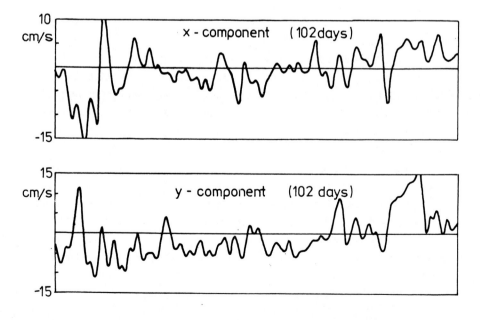

Figure 11.   Time series of the velocity components at station C.

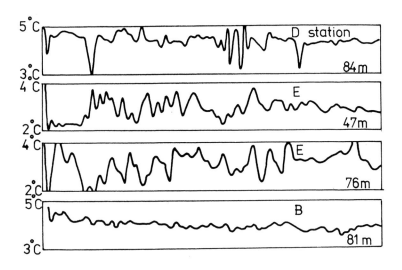

Figure 12. Daily mean temperatures at various stations of the 1980 experiment.

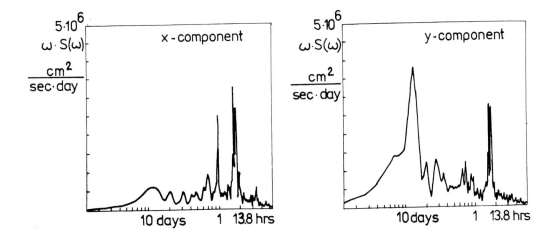

Figure 13. The spectral function ω · S(ω) of the eastern and northern velocity components at station E in 1980.

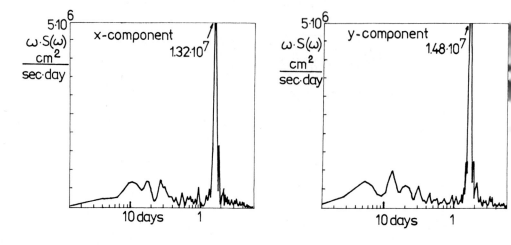

Figure 14.   The spectral function ω · S(ω) of the eastern and northern velocity components at station C in 1980.

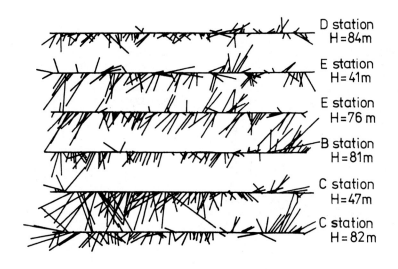

Figure 15.   Velocity vectors at various stations of the 1980 experiment.

V_i the mean nondimensional velocities along the channel,

H_i the mean layer thicknesses,

ρ_i the densities,

ϕ_i the wavelike perturbations propagating in the y-direction (ϕ_i include the multiplicator $e^{i(ly-\omega t)}$),

U   a characteristic velocity in the upper layer,

g   the acceleration due to gravity,

α the bottom slope,

f   the Coriolis parameter, and

L   a length scale characteristic of the perturbation,

the equations of the model are:

$$(\partial_t + V_1\partial_y)[\Delta\phi_1 + F_1(\phi_2 - \phi_1)] + F_1(V_1 - V_2)\phi_{1y} = 0,$$

$$(\partial_t + V_2\partial_y)[\Delta\phi_2 + F_2(\phi_1 - \phi_2)] - F_2(V_1 - V_2)\phi_{2y} - T\phi_{2y} = 0,$$

where

$$F_1 = f^2 L^2 / g' H_1, \quad F_2 = f^2 L^2 / g' H_2,$$
$$T = \alpha f L / H_2 U, \quad \Delta = \partial_{xx} + \partial_{yy},$$
$$g' = g(\rho_2 - \rho_1)/\rho_2.$$

This model is derived from an ordinary quasi-geostrophic system, where the stream functions ψ_1, ψ_2 are assumed of the form

$$\psi_1 = V_1 x + \phi_1,$$
$$\psi_2 = V_2 x + \phi_2.$$

Let us now consider the dispersion curves obtained from the model. Two solutions for the first mode are presented in Figure 19 (for seven groups of parameters). In this figure, the wavelength (in km) is measured along the abscissa, and the period (in days) along the ordinate. At wavelengths where two solutions coincide, the waves become unstable. The doubling time D of the amplitudes of the unstable waves is shown in the same figure. Thus, in Figure 19a (the parameter values are given in the figure caption, where $\Delta\rho = \rho_2 - \rho_1$ denotes the density jump) unstable waves appear at wavelengths of about 30-35 km and they have periods of 7-8 days. We can also study the dependence of instability on parameter changes. In Figure 19b the density jump has been changed. It appears that when the density jump is increased, waves become unstable at shorter wavelengths and the doubling time of their amplitude is increased.

484

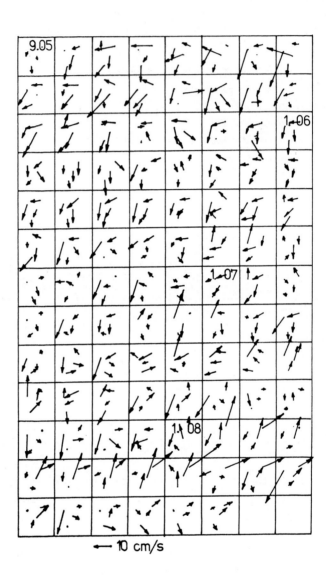

Figure 16. Maps of daily mean currents in the bottom layer in 1980.

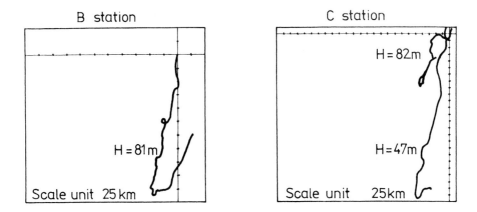

Figure 17. Vector diagrams of daily mean currents at stations B and C in 1980.

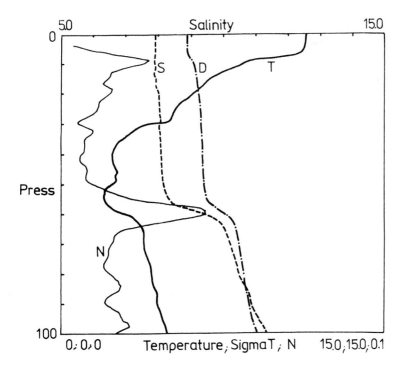

Figure 18. Characteristic vertical profiles of temperature (T), salinity (S), relative density (D), and Väisälä frequency (N) during the 1980 experiment.

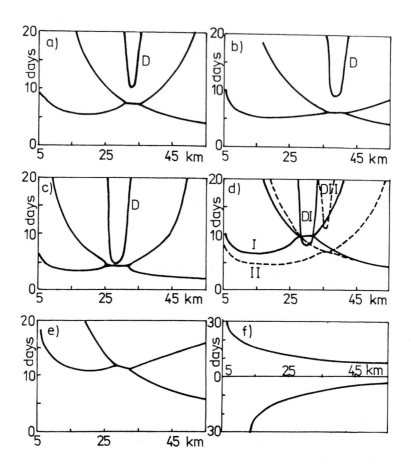

Figure 19. Dispersion curves and doubling time (D) of the amplitudes of unstable waves in the two-layer model for the following values of the parameters: (a) $V_1 = -5$ cm/sec^{-1}, $V_2 = 2.5$ cm/sec^{-1}, $H_1 = 70$ m, $H_2 = 30$ m, $\Delta\rho = 0.003$, $\alpha = 0.001$; (b) $\Delta\rho = 0.002$; (c) $\alpha = 0.0015$, $V_1 = -10$ cm/sec^{-1}, $V_2 = 5$ cm/sec^{-1}; (d) continuous line : $\alpha = 0.0015$, $H_1 = 60$ m, $H_2 = 40$ m; dashed line : $\alpha = 0.0015$, $H_1 = 40$ m, $H_2 = 60$ m; (e) $\alpha = 0.0005$, $V_1 = -3.5$ cm/sec^{-1}, $V_2 = 0$, $H_1 = 60$ m, $H_2 = 40$ m; (f) $\alpha = 0.0015$, $V_1 = 5$ cm/sec^{-1}, $V_2 = -3.5$ cm/sec^{-1}. Note: parameters not explicitly given for cases (b)-(f) are as in case (a).

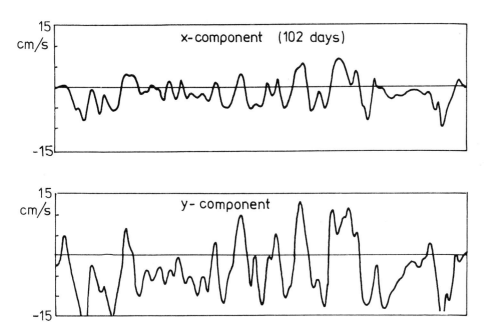

Figure 20. Time series of the northern velocity component at station E in 1980.

If the bottom slope is decreased, the amplitude of unstable waves doubles more rapidly, their wavelengths become shorter and their periods longer. On the contrary, an increase in the mean velocities shortens both the lengths and the periods of unstable waves, and the amplitudes of unstable waves double much more rapidly (Fig. 19c).

Figure 19d shows how a change in the thickness of the upper and lower layers alters the parameters of unstable waves. Figure 19e demonstrates that baroclinic instability may occur when there is no mean current in the bottom layer. In all the cases discussed so far, the mean current is directed so that the shallower water is to the right of the downstream direction. We find that baroclinic instability is very sensitive to the direction of the current in the upper layer. Indeed, if the mean current is directed so that the shallower water is to the left of the downstream direction, no baroclinic instability occurs. Dispersion curves for that case are shown in Figure 19f. As pointed out earlier, the temperature fluctuations displayed in Figure 12 dampen during the last third of the experiment. The same can be said of the variation of the velocity components at station E shown in Fig. 20. Here the amplitude of the fluctuations increases at first, but during the last month of the experiment, a change in sign of the mean velocity is followed by an abrupt termination of a fairly uniform increase (as in the temperature series). The latter circumstance can be explained using the model of baroclinic instability.

CONCLUSIONS

The results presented here demonstrate the existence of synoptic variability in the Baltic Sea. We have shown that stratification, bottom topography, and the character of the mean flow affect the temporal and spatial scales of synoptic variability. Although it is not theoretically shown here, it seems possible that atmospheric conditions are also very important. This possibility, and the mechanism by which such a coupling might operate, deserve further investigation.

REFERENCES

Aitsam, A., Elken, J., Pavelson and L. Talpsepp, 1981. Preliminary results of the study of spatial and temporal characteristics of the synoptic variability in the Baltic. In: The Investigation and Modelling of Processes in the Baltic Sea, Part I, pp. 70-98.
Rhines, P., 1970. Edge-, bottom-, and Rossby waves in a rotating stratified fluid, Geophysical Fluid Dynamics, 1: 273-302.
Thompson, R.O.R.Y. and J. Luyten, 1976. Evidence for bottom-trapped topographic Rossby waves from single current moorings, Deep-Sea Research, 23: 625-635.

THE VARIABILITY OF THE TEMPERATURE, SALINITY AND DENSITY FIELDS IN THE UPPER LAYERS OF THE BALTIC SEA

A. Aitsam, J. Pavelson

Institute of Thermophysics and Electrophysics,
Academy of Sciences of the Estonian S.S.R.

INTRODUCTION

In recent years, the use of a towed CTD has proved successful in determining the structure of the temperature, salinity and density fields. The spatial distributions of fields obtained by this method in a comparatively short time have an essentially higher resolution than those obtained from observations at discrete points. Depending on the aims of the investigation, three towing regimes are possible:

1. the CTD moves at a fixed depth (Gargett, 1978),
2. the CTD performs wavelike motion between two levels (Allen et al. 1980),
3. the CTD moves along a fixed isotherm or isopycnal (Katz, 1973, 1975).

In most of the studies just mentioned, the spatial structure of the temperature and salinity fields was obtained without separating the "background" of internal waves. However, when studying the variability of these variables, the relative part due to internal waves should be determined. This is important for a correct evaluation of the characteristics of the non-wave perturbations. As a first approximation, an isopycnal analysis might be used as in recent studies by Woods and Minnett (1979), and Cairns (1980). Despite its shortcomings, this method is the best one at present.

The aim of the present study is to determine the main characteristics of the temperature, salinity and density fields on horizontal scales larger than 1 km in the upper layers of the open part of the Baltic Sea. First, we shall describe the experiments and the processing of the data. Then, the most typical results will be presented and discussed. Finally, some hypotheses about the origin of the observed structure will be formulated.

EXPERIMENTS AND DATA PROCESSING

All the experimental data were obtained using the towed measuring device constructed at the Institute of Thermophysics and Electrophysics of the Academy of Sciences of the Estonian S.S.R. (Pavelson and Portsmuth, 1981). The instrument consists of an underwater unit, the "FISH", and an onboard system (Figure 1). The "FISH" is equipped with a CTD MARK III

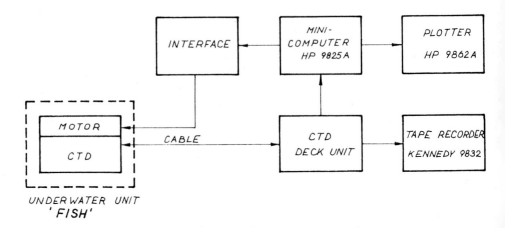

Figure 1. Block diagram of the towed measuring device.

(NBIS) and guided by means of small wings activated by a miniature electric motor. The data are transmitted to the onboard terminal and stored on a tape recorder KENNEDY-9832 with the help of special interfaces. The control of the "FISH" motion and the preliminary plotting of temperature sections are performed by an HP-9825-A computer.

For the experiments reported in this paper, the computer was programmed to give the "FISH" a wavelike motion. The towing speed was between 5 and 7 knots, the CTD was lowered to a depth of 40 m, and the length of the horizontal cycle varied from 370 to 500 m. Using a measuring frequency of 30 hertz, the vertical resolution was better than 5 cm, since the vertical velocity did not exceed 1.5 m s^{-1}.

Experiments using the towed CTD were performed during the 9th and 15th cruises of the R/V "Ayu-Dag" in the central and southern parts of the Baltic Sea. The locations of the CTD sections are shown in Figure 2. During the 9th cruise (1978), we worked in the extended BOSEX area and obtained sections 1, 2 and 3; the lengths of these sections were 90, 85 and 120 km respectively. During the 15th cruise (1979), measurements were made along section 4 (200 km), extending from the BOSEX area to the Island of Bornholm. Hydrometeorological conditions during these two cruises were various. The measurements of the 9th cruise took place at the beginning of August, i.e., at a time of weak winds and strong thermal stratification. During the 15th cruise (at the end of September), strong variable winds and a negative heat flux prevailed and combined to destroy the stratification of the upper layers.

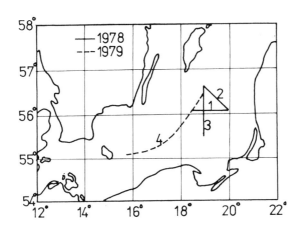

Figure 2. Locations of the "FISH" tow sections.

A characteristic feature of measurements made with a towed high frequency device, when studying synoptic scale phenomena, is the accumulation of a great amount of information. For example, some of our series have up to 16×10^6 data points. It is evident that subsampling the series results in essential losses in the determination of isolines. Therefore, this method is not used here. The data processing cycle includes a preliminary processing and the determination of characteristic perturbations of the temperature and salinity fields. First, syncroerrors are eliminated from the CTD data; there are about 300 syncroerrors per hour. At the same stage, incorrect values of pressure P, temperature T and conductivity C are removed, using the following criteria: Those P_i, T_i and C_i which do not meet the conditions

$$P_i - P_{i-1} < 1 \text{ dbar}, \quad T_i - T_{i-1} < 1°C, \quad C_i - C_{i-1} < 1 \text{ mmho cm}^{-1}$$

are considered incorrect.

In the second step, all the series are smoothed, to lessen the influence of the vertical microstructure and the noise level. Taking a running average of the data with a 1 m filter appears to be the best way to eliminate the microstructure, although it results in a certain deformation of the synoptic scale thermohaline structure. From the smoothed series, salinity and specific density, σ_t, are calculated based on known formulae for the Baltic Sea (Perkin and Walker, 1971; Millero and Kremling, 1976).

In the final step, all possible spatial isolines are determined. Time isolines are transformed into spatial isolines with the help of the corresponding navigation data. This is followed by the plotting of sections of the T, S, and σ_t fields in space P; finally, sections of the T and S fields are plotted in space σ_t, in order to eliminate the kinematic effect of internal waves. The comparison of the sections of both types allows us to divide the fields into components, to separate the various perturbations and to evaluate their characteristics.

ERRORS

The estimation of errors is also important in data processing and interpretation. The main sources of errors are:

1. the thermal inertia of the pressure sensor, particularly in case of high temperature gradients;

2. the accuracy with which P,T,C are measured, and S and σ_t calculated;

3. the use of T and σ_t instead of the potential temperature, θ, and the potential density σ_θ.

The analysis of our calculations leads to the following conclusion. When the stratification is strong (e.g. summer of 1978), the recording of a change in the vertical direction of the CTD motion is significantly delayed due to the thermal inertia of the pressure sensor. This causes apparent shifts in the depths of the various isolines within the following ranges: up to 1, 5 and 2 m for isotherms, isohalines and isopycnals, respectively. Therefore, we chose to use only CTD data collected during the upward motion of the FISH. In doing so, the horizontal resolution is decreased by a factor two but this is not critical in view of the scales of the phenomena under study.

The second source of errors is the absolute accuracy of the instruments. In view of the long term stability of the probe's operation and partial calibration, $\Delta T = \pm 0.005°C$, $\Delta C = \pm 0.005$ mmho cm^{-1} and $\Delta P = \pm 3$ m may be taken as error bounds. The latter reflects mainly the thermal inertia of the pressure sensor. Since we are mainly interested in relative isoline changes and data are collected in one vertical direction only, the pressure error may be considered systematic. Based on the formulae used in the calculations, it can be determined that $\Delta S = \pm 0.010$ °/oo and $\Delta \sigma_t = \pm 0.0085$ σ_t units.

Finally, let us consider the problem of the deformation of the isolines, which is related to the nonconservative nature of the temperature and density. Indeed, under the influence of internal waves, a given water parcel moves up and down. At certain depths, because of compression, the same water parcel has different temperature and density. According to Cairns (1980), the use of density instead of potential density leads to the following errors in temperature and salinity:

$$\Delta T = \frac{dT}{dz} \left(\kappa / \frac{d\rho}{dz} \right) \zeta \quad , \tag{1}$$

$$\Delta S = \frac{dS}{dz} \left(\kappa / \frac{d\rho}{dz} \right) \zeta \quad , \tag{2}$$

where κ = coefficient of adiabatic compression,

ζ = displacement of water parcel due to internal waves.

It can be seen that the smaller the vertical density gradient and the larger the amplitude of the internal waves, the greater are the errors in the iso-pycnal analysis. Taking values typical of the upper layer of the Baltic Sea for the gradients ($dT/dz = 10^{-1}$ °C m^{-1}, $dS/dz = 5 \times 10^{-3}$ °/oo m^{-1}, and $d\sigma_t/dz = 2 \times 10^{-2}$ σ_t units m^{-1}) and for the amplitude of the internal waves, we get $\Delta T \cong 2 \times 10^{-2}$ °C and $\Delta S \cong 10^{-3}$ °/oo. We shall add the errors made in the determination of isotherms and isopycnals in space P without considering compressibility $\Delta T \cong 2 \times 10^{-3}$ °C and $\Delta\sigma_t \cong 5 \times 10^{-3}$ σ_t units. The latter are smaller than the corresponding absolute accuracies. Consequently, it is necessary to use the potential temperature and density in isopycnal analysis only in the presence of extremely small density gradients.

RESULTS

In this section, we present and discuss the results obtained along the sections described earlier. The difference between the 1978 and the 1979 experiments is striking. During the summer experiment (1978), the structure of the isolines of the temperature and salinity fields is rather smooth. In the thermocline region, long wavelike perturbations with lengths of 30-40 km and amplitudes of up to 3 m can be distinguished. The results of the section made along the axis of the Baltic Sea in autumn (1979) are quite different in character. We find large fluctuations (up to 10 m) of the iso-lines at all depths where measurements were made. The length scale of these perturbations is 20-25 km, i.e. smaller than in summer. Wavelike perturbations of small scales were not studied, since they are distorted because of the Doppler effect during field measurements. Typical examples of sections obtained during these experiments are presented in Figures 3 and 4.

494

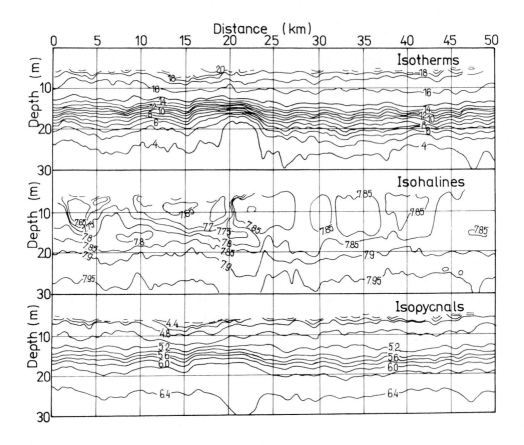

Figure 3. Temperature, salinity and density fields from tow section 1 (summer 1978). Contour intervals: temperature: 1°C; salinity: 0.05 °/oo; density: 0.2 σ_t units.

Figure 4 (facing page). Temperature, salinity and density fields from tow section 4 (autumn 1979). Contour intervals: temperature: 1°C; salinity: 0.05 °/oo; density: 0.1 σ_t units.

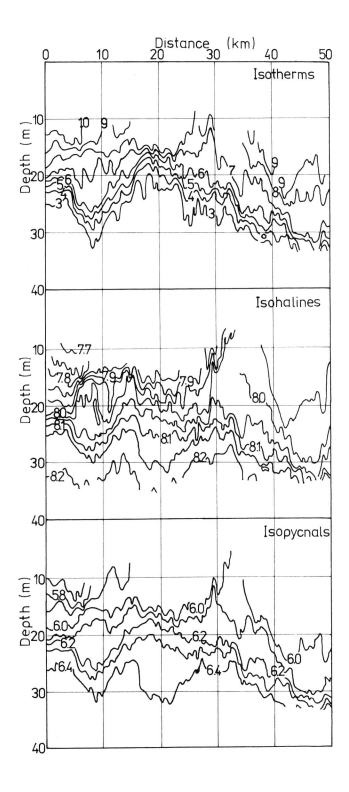

On the basis of temperature sections, it is practically impossible to identify perturbations of non-wave origin. However, on sections of the salinity field, such perturbations can be distinguished, but qualitatively only. Therefore, we shall use the isopycnal analysis hereafter. This method, however, has a grave shortcoming. If non-wave perturbations of temperature and salinity do not fully compensate each other, density sections will not reflect a "purely" wavelike picture. When this is the case, the study of the temperature and salinity fields in σ_t-space may not yield reliable estimates of the dimensions and amplitudes of the perturbations.

As a first approximation, let us assume that the observed perturbations of temperature and salinity are density compensated. Then, we may identify perturbations with the following statistics for the 1978 summer experiment (Table 1).

Table 1

Characteristics of the temperature field perturbations, summer 1978

	No.	Mean length (km)	Maximum length (km)	Mean distance (km)	Mean temperature change (°C)
Upper layer (16°C)	8	10	19	28	0.6
Intermediate layer (4°C)	13	4	8	21	0.8

The following conclusions can be drawn from these results. Relatively rare and long perturbations dominate in the upper layer. In the intermediate layer, below the thermocline, there are more perturbations, but their dimensions are considerably smaller. Note that the mean temperature change is larger in the intermediate layer than in the upper layer.

We were unable to calculate analogous statistics for the 1979 autumn experiment because the isotherms varied greatly (the thermocline is at the bottom of the layer under study over part of the section). In spite of that, temperature perturbations with length scales of 4 to 12 km and average amplitudes of 1°C may be identified against a background of small-scale "noise" (perturbations shorter than 4 km with amplitudes of 0.3°C).

A considerable non-wave variability of salinity is observed mainly in the upper layer. In most cases, the perturbations are similar to those of temperature. For example in Figure 3, we see a salinity perturbation which is about 18 km long. There is a sharp salinity gradient on both sides of the perturbation. A similar perturbation can also be seen in the temperature field in σ_t-space (Fig. 5), i.e. after removal of the variability due to internal waves.

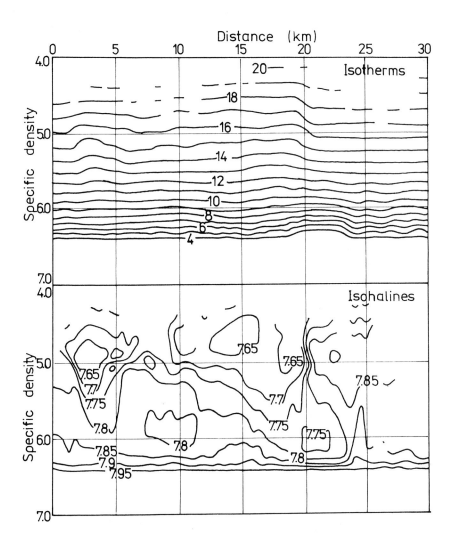

Figure 5. Temperature and salinity fields in σ_t-space (first half of the section presented in Fig. 3).

Thus, in the present case, the temperature and the salinity of the water mass are different from those of the neighboring environment. To study the density characteristics of these water masses, we shall use the T-S presentation (Gargett, 1978). The essence of the method is as follows. Moving at a fixed depth within the core of a given water mass corresponds to moving up and down on a T-S curve on account of internal waves. Crossing the borderline between two different water masses corresponds to switching to another T-S curve. If the translation from one T-S curve to another takes place along an isopycnal, we may consider that the temperature and salinity perturbations are density compensated. If the translation takes place at an angle to the isopycnals, we may draw the conclusion that the perturbations are not compensated by density. Figure 7 shows the T-S plot at a depth of 10 m for the example just discussed. Despite a considerable sparseness of the data points in the first half of the perturbation, two types of translations or "crossings" may be distinguished. In the left-hand part of the perturbation, the passage over the 4 km subperturbation is not isopycnal (dotted lines 1 and 2). However, on the right-hand edge of the perturbation (dotted line 3) the crossing of the water mass boundary is isopycnal, i.e. without any density jump. Thermohaline perturbations along the relatively more variable section of the 1979 experiment are even harder to detect. The filtering of the internal waves gives a picture with irregular variability (Fig. 6). Nevertheless, an 11 km long perturbation (the amplitude of the temperature change is 1.3°C, and that of the salinity change 0.1 $^{o}/oo$) can be distinguished; 10 km further, a considerably larger perturbation begins. Two problems in studying this type of variability are the facts that points on the T-S plane are greatly scattered, and that the density relations of the perturbations are difficult to elucidate.

CONCLUSION

Finally, we would like to say a few words about the origin of the thermohaline perturbations. We have observed only two types of perturbations: "cold-fresh" and "warm-salty". Those types indicate with high probability that density compensation is achieved. Since the observed patches of water masses with different T and S characteristics are density compensated, we may call these patches "macro-intrusions". We believe that the observed "cold-fresh" intrusion was advected from neighboring areas of the northern Baltic, and that the "warm-salty" intrusion was probably of southern Baltic origin. We note that the first type of perturbations prevailed in the summer of 1978 and the second type in the autumn of 1979.

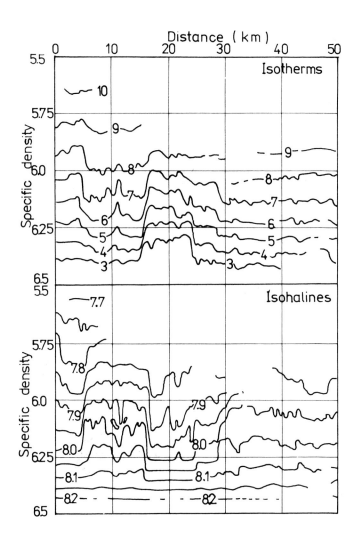

Figure 6. Temperature and salinity fields in σ_t-space (same section as in Fig. 4).

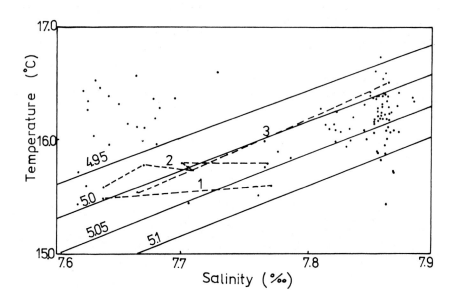

Figure 7. T-S plot of section 1 at a depth of 10 m.

Unfortunately, our data are still insufficient to answer some key questions about the thermohaline variablity in the upper layers of the Baltic. Nevertheless, the data presented in this paper demonstrate that the CTD towing method is useful for the study of the spatial structure of the temperature and salinity fields on meso- and synoptic scales.

REFERENCES

Allen, C.M., Simpson, J.H., Carson, R.M., 1980. The structure and variability of shelf sea fronts as observed by an undulating CTD system. Oceanologica Acta, 3(1): 59-68.
Cairns, J.L., 1980. Variability in the Gulf of Cadiz: Internal waves and globs. J. Phys. Oceanogr., 10(4): 579-595.

Gargett, A.E., 1978. Microstructure and finestructure in an upper ocean frontal regime. J. Geophys. Res., 83(C10): 5123-5134.

Katz, E.J., 1973. Profile of an isopycnal surface in the main thermocline of the Sargasso Sea. J. Pys. Oceanogr., 3: 448-457.

Katz, E.J., 1975. Tow spectra from MODE. J. Geophys. Res., 80(9): 1163-1167.

Millero, F.J., Kremling, K., 1976. The densities of Baltic Sea waters. Deep-Sea Res., 23: 1129-1138.

Pavelson, J., Portsmuth, R., 1981. A towed system for thermohaline fields measurements. The Investigation and Modelling of the Processes in the Baltic Sea., Tallinn, pp. 16-25.

Perkin, R.G., Walker, E.R., 1972. Salinity calculations from "in situ" measurements. J. Geophys. Res., 77(33).

Woods, J.D., Minnett, P.J., 1979. Analysis of mesoscale thermoclinicity with an example from the tropical thermocline during GATE. Deep-Sea Res., 26A: 85-96.

MODELING OF THE CLIMATIC SCALE VARIABILITY OF THE HYDRODYNAMICS OF THE BALTIC SEA

T. Kullas, V. Kraav

Institute of Thermophysics and Electrophysics

Academy of Sciences of the Estonian S.S.R.

ABSTRACT

A numerical model is used to describe the characteristics of the hydro-dynamical regime and the distributions of temperature, salinity and density in the Baltic Sea. The model equations are the linearized equations of motion (without horizontal diffusion), the continuity equation, the equations of conservation of heat and salt, and a nonlinear equation of state. The system of equations is integrated numerically using a finite difference method. Some results of numerical experiments on the seasonal changes of the hydrological characteristics of the Baltic Sea are presented. Although the modeling of such seasonal changes gives satisfactory results, several difficulties are obvious. One of the possible ways of saving computer time is the parametrization of the vertical profiles of velocity, temperature and salinity.

INTRODUCTION

Oceanic processes can be described by a set of dynamic and thermodynamic equations together with an equation of state and the law of conservation of mass. There are, obviously, very many processes to be described: transport of heat, salt and momentum by advection, convection and turbulence, evaporation and precipitation, radiation, etc.

In order to model hydrodynamic processes of climatological scale, we must make physical and numerical approximations because our possibilities of observing the system or calculating its behavior are limited. In models of the climatological variability of hydrophysical fields, several physical processes must be parameterized because they are impossible to describe explicitly. Such processes include the transport of heat by radiation, the turbulent fluxes of heat, salt and momentum, convection, mesoscale eddies, bottom stress and so on.

BAROCLINIC MODEL OF THE BALTIC SEA

For several years, we have used a time-dependent, baroclinic, three-dimensional numerical model to calculate the seasonal variability of the hydrological characteristics of the Baltic Sea (Kullas and Tamsalu, 1979). The basic equations of the model are:

$$\frac{\partial u}{\partial t} - fv = g \frac{\partial \xi}{\partial x} - \frac{g}{\rho_0} \int_0^z \frac{\partial \rho}{\partial x} \, dz + \frac{\partial}{\partial z} \left(K \frac{\partial u}{\partial z} \right) \tag{1}$$

$$\frac{\partial v}{\partial t} + fu = g \frac{\partial \xi}{\partial y} - \frac{g}{\rho_0} \int_0^z \frac{\partial \rho}{\partial y} \, dz + \frac{\partial}{\partial z} \left(K \frac{\partial v}{\partial z} \right) \tag{2}$$

$$\frac{\partial u}{\partial x} + \frac{\partial v}{\partial y} + \frac{\partial w}{\partial z} = 0 \tag{3}$$

$$\frac{\partial T}{\partial t} + u \frac{\partial T}{\partial x} + v \frac{\partial T}{\partial y} + w \frac{\partial T}{\partial z} = \frac{1}{c_p \rho_0} \left[\frac{\partial}{\partial z} \left(K_T \frac{\partial T}{\partial z} \right) + \mu \Delta T \right] \tag{4}$$

$$\frac{\partial S}{\partial t} + u \frac{\partial S}{\partial x} + v \frac{\partial S}{\partial y} + w \frac{\partial S}{\partial z} = \frac{\partial}{\partial z} \left(K_s \frac{\partial S}{\partial z} \right) + \mu \Delta S \tag{5}$$

$$\rho = f(T, S, z) \tag{6}$$

where the various symbols are defined as follows:

x, y, z:	Cartesian coordinates
u, v, w:	components of the velocity vector
f :	Coriolis parameter
t :	time
ξ :	deviation of the free surface elevation from its average value
c_p :	specific heat for constant pressure
ρ :	density of sea water
ρ_0 :	mean density
g :	acceleration of gravity
K, K_T, K_s:	coefficients of vertical turbulent exchange of momentum and vertical turbulent diffusion of heat and salt, respectivey
μ :	coefficient of horizontal turbulent diffusion
T :	temperature
S :	salinity.

The system of equations (1)-(6) requires the following boundary conditions:

- at the surface, the shear stress (due to wind) and the fluxes of heat and salt are specified;
- at the bottom, we use the no-slip condition and we assume that there is no flux of heat and salt;
- along closed boundaries, the normal velocity component and the normal gradients of temperature and salinity are set equal to zero;
- along open boundaries, the mass transport, temperature and salinity are specified.

As initial conditions, we use observed distributions of temperature and salinity and we assume that the water is at rest. The coefficients of vertical turbulent exchange are functions of the Richardson number, and the coefficient of horizontal turbulent diffusion is a function of the velocity gradient and of the character of the horizontal scale of turbulence (grid size). In order to improve the approximation of the topography, we use the method of "bottom straightening", i.e. we transform z into the curvilinear coordinate η = z/H(x,y), where H(x,y) is the local depth of the water.

The system of equations (1)-(6) is solved by an implicit finite difference method that is stable for arbitrary time step.

We now present some results of numerical experiments aimed at modeling seasonal changes of hydrological characteristics in the open part of the Baltic Sea. These changes are caused by variations in the air temperature and the wind stress at the sea surface. The central part of the Baltic basin was covered with a uniform grid, with $\Delta x = \Delta y$ = 25 miles. The vertical grid size was taken equal to 0.125 H, i.e. the calculations were made at 9 levels. The time step was taken equal to 5 days. The shear stress due to wind and the heat flux were obtained from the empirical relations

$$\tau_{xz} = \rho_a \, \gamma \, (U^2 + V^2)^{\frac{1}{2}} \cdot U \tag{7}$$

$$\tau_{yz} = \rho_a \, \gamma \, (U^2 + V^2)^{\frac{1}{2}} \cdot V \tag{8}$$

$$Q = \rho_0 \, c_p \, c_D \cdot (T_0 - T_a) \cdot (U^2 + V^2)^{\frac{1}{2}} \, , \tag{9}$$

where we denote by

τ_{xz}, τ_{yz}	the components of wind stress,
Q	the heat flux,
ρ_a	the air density,
γ	a constant,
U,V	the horizontal components of the wind velocity at the level of an anemometer,
c_D	the Stenton number, and by
T_a	the air temperature at the measuring level.

The temperature field of the Baltic Sea is extremely variable. Figure 1 shows the vertical distribution of temperature in the Gotland Deep at different times of the year, and Figure 2 shows the vertical distribution of temperature along a longitudinal section in the Baltic after 225 days of calculation. The comparison of observational data and theoretical results shows good agreement in the formation and deepening of the thermocline. However, the comparison also indicates that heat from the surface layers is transferred too quickly to the deeper layers of the basin in the model results. The reason for the rapid transfer of heat in the vertical direction is that the coefficient of vertical turbulent diffusion and the vertical grid spacing are too large. The calculations show that zones of upwelling and downwelling exist in the Baltic Sea. The area where the most intensive upwelling occurs is the northern part of the Gotland Deep, as indicated by a noticeable rising of the isotherms.

Although the modeling of seasonal changes using a three-dimensional baroclinic model gives satisfactory results, several difficulties are evident.

1. When using mean meteorological data (wind, cloudiness, air temperature) as boundary conditions, it is questionable whether the conventional parametrization of momentum, heat and salt fluxes at the sea surface is appropriate. Indeed, the existing equations for calculationg these fluxes describe only small-scale exchanges between the ocean and the atmosphere.

2. When using large time steps (many days), it is difficult to parametrize the turbulent exchanges in the upper boundary layer, since the heat flux may change its sign during the averaging interval, and there exist two different regimes of turbulence (advective and convective).

3. The methods of parametrizing bottom friction when calculating integral circulation are incorrect. Bottom friction does not depend on the

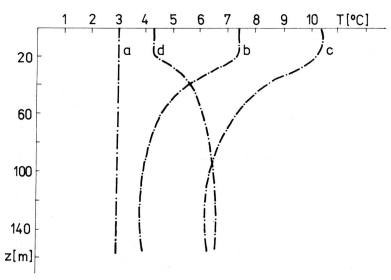

Fig. 1. Vertical distribution of temperature in the Gotland Deep (a: beginning of the calculation, b: spring, c: summer, d: autumn).

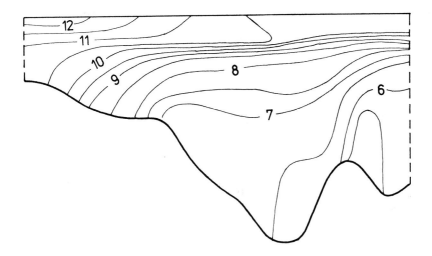

Fig. 2. Vertical distribution of temperature along a longitudinal section in the Baltic after 225 days of calculation.

velocity profile, nor on the bottom topography.

　　　4.　The calculated vertical profiles of temperature and salinity do not agree well with the observations because it is impossible to describe more precisely the zones of large shears in the model.

　　　5.　There is no reliable method for smoothing the bottom topography. The roughness of the bottom of the Baltic Sea causes mistakes in the averaging process.

PARAMETRIZATION OF THE VERTICAL PROFILES

　　　The numerical modeling approach described in the previous section enables us to model real processes only in a limited range of spatial and temporal scales. An alternative approach, which can lead to a substantial saving of computer time, is to parametrize the vertical profiles of velocity, temperature and salinity. In doing so, we must take into account the fact that the vertical structure of the Baltic Sea can be divided into 3 layers:

1)　the surface boundary layer, of thickness h;

2)　the intermediate layer, of thickness $h_M = H - h - h_B$, where H is the total depth of the water;

3)　the bottom layer, of thickness h_B.

　　　In the determination of the vertical structure of the upper layer, we use the hypothesis of self-similarity of the boundary layer (Zilitinkevich

and Monin, 1974). According to that hypothesis, nonstationarity and horizontal inhomogeneity depend only on the thickness of the boundary layer h,
the time t, and the horizontal coordinates x and y. Hence, if the height z
is scaled by h, the structure of the velocity, temperature and salinity
profiles is "universal," i.e. it is determined at every time and position by
the instantaneous and local values of the following internal parameters:

$$u_* = (\tau/\rho)^{\frac{1}{2}}; \quad Q = R(c_p\rho)^{-1}; \quad S'; \quad g/\rho; \ f; \ h \tag{10}$$

where we denote by

u_*	the shear velocity,
τ	the frictional stress,
ρ	the density of the water,
Q	the normalized heat flux at the surface,
R	the heat flux at the surface,
S'	the normalized salinity flux in the surface layer.

Combining these parameters, we can form the following quantities with
dimensions of velocity, temperature, salinity and length respectively:

$$u_* = (\tau/\rho)^{\frac{1}{2}}; \quad T_* = -Q/\kappa u_*; \quad S_* = S'/\kappa\, u_*; \tag{11}$$

$$L = \frac{u_*^3}{\kappa(g\alpha_T\, Q - g\,\alpha_s\, S')} = -\frac{u_*^3}{\kappa\,\frac{g}{\rho}\,M}\ ;$$

where

α_T	denotes the coefficient of thermal expansion,
α_s	an analogous coefficient for salinity,
κ	the von Karman's constant, and
M	the mass flux.

Using these parameters we can form one more combination, λ, whose
dimension is length, and two dimensionless parameters, μ_0 and μ, given by:

$$\lambda = \kappa\, u_*/f; \quad \mu_0 = \lambda/L; \quad \mu = h/L\ . \tag{12}$$

The values of velocity, temperature and salinity, scaled by u_*, T_*, and S_*,
respectively, depend on the nondimensional height z/h and on the parameters
μ_0 and μ. The profiles of velocity, temperature and salinity are given by:

$$\phi(z) - \phi(h) = \Phi \cdot f_\phi (z/h, \mu_o, \mu), \tag{13}$$

where

$\phi = \{u, v, T, S\}$,

$\Phi = \{u_*/\kappa; u_*/\kappa; T_*, S_*\}$,   and where

$f_\phi = \{f_u, f_v, f_T, f_S\}$, the universal functions determined from observational data or from numerical experiments using models of boundary layers.

Thus, the determination of the vertical structure of the surface layer is reduced to a two-dimensional equation for the thickness of the boundary layer.

On the basis of his analysis of temperature distributions in the intermediate layer of the Baltic Sea, Tamsalu (1979) discovered that the nondimensional combination $(T_S - T)/(T_S - T_H)$ is approximately a universal function of the nondimensional depth $\zeta = (H - z)/(H - h)$ (T_S is the temperature of the upper quasi-homogeneous layer, T_H the temperature at the lower boundary of the intermediate layer, i.e. at $z \cong H$). An analogous expression for the salinity, in terms of $S_h = S|_{z=h}$ and $S_H = S|_{z=H}$, proved to be also universal. Thus, in the intermediate layer the following approximations are justified:

$$T = T_S - (T_S - T_H) \cdot k_T(\zeta) \tag{14}$$
$$S = S_S - (S_S - S_H) \cdot k_S(\zeta), \tag{15}$$

where $k_T(\zeta)$, $k_S(\zeta)$ are the nondimensional functions for temperature and salinity, respectively.

The velocities in the intermediate layer can be assumed to satisfy the geostrophic equations, i.e.

$$u = \frac{1}{f} (g \frac{\partial \xi}{\partial y} - \frac{g}{\rho_o} \int_o^z \frac{\partial \rho}{\partial y} dz); \tag{16}$$

$$v = - \frac{1}{f} (g \frac{\partial \xi}{\partial x} - \frac{g}{\rho_o} \int_o^z \frac{\partial \rho}{\partial x} dz). \tag{17}$$

In the parametrization of the vertical structure of the bottom boundary layer, the mass flux is excluded from the parameters determining the structure (at $z = H$, $\partial M/\partial z = \partial T/\partial z = \partial S/\partial z$ 0). Hence the vertical structure is determined by the parameters $u_*^!, f$ and h_B.

The thickness of the bottom boundary layer is determined by the following formula (Weatherly and Martin, 1978):

$$h_B = \frac{A \cdot u_*^!}{f \ (1 + N_o^2/f^2)^{1/4}} \quad , \tag{18}$$

where

A is a constant (A = 1.3), and

N_o is the Väisälä frequency outside the boundary layer.

The shear velocity at the bottom is determined from the law of drag friction as a function of the geostrophic velocity in the upper part of the boundary layer and of the bottom roughness.

CONCLUSION

In conclusion we can say that the modeling of the climatic variability of the thermohaline fields in the Baltic Sea leads to the solution of two-dimensional equations for the thicknesses of the boundary layers and for the free surface elevation.

REFERENCES

Kullas, T.E. and Tamsalu, R.E., 1979. A predictive model of the Baltic Sea and its numerical realization (in Russian). In: Water Resources, 1: 144-154.

Tamsalu, R.E., 1979. Modeling of the dynamics and structure of the Baltic Sea Waters (in Russian). In: Zvaigzne, Riga, 152 pp.

Wheatherly, G.L. and Martin, P.J., 1978. On the structure and dynamics of the oceanic bottom boundary layer. J. of Physical Oceanography, 8: 557-570.

Zilitinkevich, S.S. and Monin, A.S., 1974. Similarity theory for the atmospheric planetary boundary layer (in Russian). In: Izv. Akad. Nauk S.S.S.R. Fiz.atmos.okeana, 10(6): 587-599 .

MODELING OF SOME HYDRODYNAMICAL PROCESSES
BY A MODEL OF ROTATIONALLY ANISOTROPIC TURBULENT FLOW

J. Heinloo

Institute of Thermophysics and Electrophysics

Academy of Sciences of the Estonian S.S.R.

ABSTRACT

An original method for describing geophysical turbulence is presented. The method takes into account rotationally anisotropic eddylike patterns of the turbulent flow field. The general equations are illustrated by various special cases which may be of relevance to some oceanographic phenomena.

INTRODUCTION

A growing interest in eddylike patterns is one of the characteristic features of the recent evolution of turbulence theory. The concept of eddy is discussed more and more often in the scientific literature about turbulence, including the oceanographic literature. The concept of eddies as specific carriers of the turbulent nature of a flow is being pieced together step by step but more and more definitely. This development influences the makeup of the problem of turbulent flows in general, as well as the premises of specific models of turbulent flows. The difficulty of defining more or less strictly a "turbulent eddy" is one of the main restrictions to the further evolution of the theory in that direction.

Nemirovsky and Heinloo (1980) have proposed an original method that takes into account eddylike patterns of the turbulent flow field and at least partially avoids this uncertainty. The essence of the method lies in taking into account the eddylike pattern of the flow field by introducing a correlation between a kinematic and some geometric characteristics of the flow field. This allows the inclusion of many important characteristics of turbulence in the averaged description of "eddying" turbulent flows. For example we can take into account the orientation and the rotational velocity of eddies in the environment, some aspects of their cascadelike scattering, etc., without determining exactly the meaning of "the" turbulent eddy.

GENERAL EQUATIONS

As the main characteristic of the turbulent flow pattern, we introduce the quantity $\vec{\Omega}$, defined by

$$\vec{\Omega} = \overline{\vec{v}' \times \frac{\partial}{\partial s} \left(\frac{\vec{v}'}{v'}\right)} \tag{1}$$

where $\vec{v}'$ is the pulsation of the velocity field and s is the length of the arc of the velocity pulsation streamline; the overbar over the expression denotes averaging.

The condition $\vec{\Omega} \neq 0$ determines the class of turbulent environments called "rotationally anisotropic" by Nemirovsky and Heinloo (1980).

The equations of motion for turbulent flows with rotationally anisotropic eddy patterns have the form

$$\rho \frac{D}{Dt} \vec{v} = -\nabla p + (\mu + \gamma)\Delta\vec{v} + 2\gamma \nabla \times \vec{\Omega} + \rho\vec{f}$$

$$\rho J \frac{D}{Dt} \vec{\Omega} = \theta J(\Delta\vec{\Omega} + \frac{1}{3} \nabla \nabla \cdot \vec{\Omega}) - 4 (\gamma + \kappa) \vec{\Omega} \tag{2}$$

$$+ 2 \gamma\nabla \times \vec{v} + \rho J (\nabla\vec{v}) \cdot \vec{\Omega} + \rho \vec{m} \quad ,$$

where

$$\vec{f} = \frac{\rho^*}{\rho} \vec{g} + 2 \vec{w}^\circ \times \vec{v}$$

$$\vec{m} = \vec{g} \times (k^{(1)} \nabla \frac{\rho^*}{\rho} + k^{(2)} (\nabla \frac{\rho^*}{\rho}) \times \vec{\Omega}) + J\vec{\Omega} \times \vec{w}^\circ \quad , \tag{3}$$

and where the various symbols are defined as follows:

ρ	:	some characteristic density of the region
ρ^*	:	the real density of the environment
p	:	the pressure
$\vec{g}$	:	the gravitational acceleration
$\vec{w}^\circ$	:	the angular velocity of the Earth's rotation
$\mu, \gamma, \kappa, \theta$	:	coefficients of environmental viscosity
J	:	the effective moment of eddy inertia
$k^{(1)}, k^{(2)}$	:	constants .

Equations (2) are to be integrated together with the equation of conservation of mass

$$\frac{D}{Dt} \rho^* = k \Delta\rho^* + \nabla \cdot [(k^{(1)} \nabla\rho^* + k^{(2)} \nabla\rho^* \times \vec{\Omega}) \times \vec{\Omega}] \quad . \tag{4}$$

Equation (4) can be written in the form

$$\frac{D}{Dt} \rho^* = \nabla \cdot [K \cdot \nabla\rho^*] , \tag{5}$$

with

$$K = k \cdot I + k^{(1)} E \cdot \vec{\Omega} + k^{(2)} (\Omega^2 I - \vec{\Omega} \vec{\Omega}) \tag{6}$$

where

      I is the unit tensor, and

      E is the Levy-Chiwitt tensor .

If we decompose K into its symmetric and antisymmetric parts

$$K^{(s)} = k I + k^{(2)} (\Omega^2 I - \vec{\Omega} \vec{\Omega}) \tag{7}$$

$$K^{(as)} = k^{(1)} E \cdot \vec{\Omega} , \tag{8}$$

we can write as follows the term on the right-hand side of equation (5) which contains the antisymmetric part of K:

$$\nabla \cdot [K^{(as)} \cdot \nabla\rho^*] = - \vec{c} \cdot \nabla\rho^* , \tag{9}$$

where

$$\vec{c} = k^{(1)} \nabla \times \vec{\Omega} . \tag{10}$$

Now we can rewrite equation (5) in the form

$$\frac{\partial}{\partial t} \rho^* + (\vec{v} + \vec{c}) \cdot \nabla\rho^* = \nabla \cdot [K^{(s)} \cdot \nabla\rho^*] . \tag{11}$$

This shows that the antisymmetric part of K influences the density field as some additional mean velocity.

SPECIAL CASES

    In this section, we discuss three special cases that are described by equations (2) and (4).

    1.   Let

$$\vec{v} = 0, \vec{\Omega} = \vec{\Omega}(t), \nabla\rho^* = (0, 0, \frac{\partial\rho^*}{\partial z} = \text{const}) . \tag{12}$$

In this case, equations (2) and (4) reduce to

$$\frac{\partial \vec{\Omega}}{\partial t} = - \frac{1}{\rho J} \left[(4(\gamma + \kappa) + k^{(2)} \vec{g} \cdot \nabla\rho^*) I - k^{(2)} \nabla\rho^* \vec{g} \right] \cdot \vec{\Omega} + \vec{\Omega} \times \vec{w}^\circ \quad (13)$$

Equation (13) can describe two interesting effects: the precession of the vector $\vec{\Omega}$ around the vector $\vec{w}^\circ$, and the different rates of attenuation (decay) of different components of $\vec{\Omega}$ caused by the stratification of the environment.

In the special case where the last term of (13) can be neglected (this term represents the moment of pulsations of the Coriolis force), the differences in the attenuation rate of the components of $\vec{\Omega}$ results in the turning of the vector $\vec{\Omega}$ in the direction of the vector $\nabla\rho^*$. When such a situation is achieved, the environmental stratification ceases to influence the attenuation of $\vec{\Omega}$.

Another situation occurs when we do not neglect the moment of pulsations of the Coriolis force. Then $\vec{\Omega}$, which at some time is directed along $\nabla\rho^*$, will be rotated with respect to $\nabla\rho^*$ by the moment of pulsations of the Coriolis force at the next instant; in other words, $\vec{\Omega}$ acquires a component perpendicular to $\nabla\rho^*$ and becomes affected again by the damping influence of the environmental stratification. This discussion shows the importance of the Coriolis force and of the stratification in the process of eddy decay in the environment.

2. Let

$$\vec{v} = 0, \ \vec{\Omega} = \vec{\Omega}(z), \ \rho^* = \text{const.} \quad (14)$$

We can then derive the following equation for $\vec{\Omega}$

$$\theta J(\Delta\vec{\Omega} + \frac{1}{3} \nabla \nabla \cdot \vec{\Omega}) - 4(\gamma + \kappa)\vec{\Omega} + \rho J \vec{\Omega} \times \vec{w}^\circ = 0. \quad (15)$$

Equation (15) describes the diffusion of $\vec{\Omega}$, with simultaneous decay of $\vec{\Omega}$ as a result of friction and eddy scattering, and with rotation of $\vec{\Omega}$ around $\vec{w}^\circ$.

3. Let

$$\vec{v} = 0, \ \vec{g} = (0,0,g), \ \vec{\Omega} = \vec{\Omega}(z,t), \ \Omega_z = 0, \ \rho^* = \rho^*(z,t) \ , \quad (16)$$

and assume that the moment of pulsations of the Coriolis force can be neglected.

Equations (2) and (4) become

$$\frac{\partial}{\partial t} \vec{\Omega} = \frac{\theta}{\rho} \frac{\partial^2 \vec{\Omega}}{\partial z^2} - \frac{1}{\rho J} [4(\gamma + \kappa) + k^{(2)} g \frac{\partial \rho^*}{\partial z}] \vec{\Omega}$$

$$\frac{\partial}{\partial t} \rho^* = \frac{\partial}{\partial z} [k + k^{(2)} \Omega^2) \frac{\partial}{\partial z} \rho^*] \qquad (17)$$

Let $\vec{\Omega}$ be caused by the breaking of surface waves. As long as $\vec{\Omega}$ decreases with depth, the characteristic diffusion time of ρ^* also decreases with depth. Consequently, the surface layer will be mixed over a shorter period of time than the layer below it, and both layers become separated by a "jump" layer, i.e. a region with relatively rapid change of ρ^*.

REFERENCE

Nemirovsky, Y.V. and Heinloo, J.L., 1980. The local vortex theory of turbulent flows. Novosibirsk. (In Russian).

A CASCADE MODEL OF TURBULENT DIFFUSION

J. Heinloo, A. Toompuu

Institute of Thermophysics and Electrophysics

Academy of Sciences of the Estonian S.S.R.

ABSTRACT

Some formal aspects of the construction of models describing phenomena involving a variety of physical processes are developed. By introducing a certain hierarchy of filtration operators, we derive a system of equations that represent the turbulent diffusion of a scalar substance at the level of the second-order moment (variance of concentration). The result is illustrated by a theory of turbulent diffusion in a turbulent flow with rotationally anisotropic eddy pattern.

INTRODUCTION

The simultaneous presence of a variety of physical processes which have different space and time scales, different sources of energy, and different properties of space-time structure is a typical feature of oceanic hydrodynamics. It is useful to take this state of affairs into account when constructing special models of hydrodynamic processes in the sea. In this paper we examine some formal aspects of one of the possible ways of constructing such models. In order to describe the process of turbulent diffusion, we introduce a certain hierarchy of filtration (averaging) operators each of which is assumed to filter one of the physical processes present.

GENERAL TREATMENT

Consider a sequence of N operators of filtration, for instance, in some special case, averaging operators (in the sense proposed in Heinloo and Toompuu, 1981, and Toompuu and Heinloo, 1981). Let q denote the quantity to be filtrated, q_k the result of the filtration of q by the filtration operator of index $k (k = 1, \ldots, N)$, and $q_{(k)}$ the result of the successive filtration of q by the operators of indices 1 to k. For an arbitrary quantity q, setting $q'_{(n)} = q_{(n-1)} - q_{(n)}$, the expansion

$$q = q_{(k)} + \sum_{n=1}^{k} q'_{(n)} \tag{1}$$

is always valid. The quantity $q'_{(n)}$ represents the pulsation of the quantity $q_{(n-1)}$ at the n-th level of description.

Now let q denote the concentration of a passive substance that satisfies the equation of mass conservation

$$(\frac{\partial}{\partial t} + \vec{v} \cdot \nabla) \, q = \nabla \cdot \vec{j}(0) \,, \tag{2}$$

where the vector $\vec{j}(0)$ is the flux of q at the zero-th level of description. Substitute expansion (1) for q and an analogous expansion for $\vec{v}$ into (2), and apply the filtration operators from the first to the k-th to the resulting equation. In doing so, take into account the following rule

$$\begin{aligned} (q_{(k)} \, P_{(m)})_m &= q_{(m)} \, P_{(m)} \quad \text{for} \quad k \leq m \\ (q_{(k)} \, P_{(m)})_m &= q_{(k)} \, P_{(m)} \quad \text{for} \quad k \geq m \,, \end{aligned}$$

which follows from the definition of a filtration operator (Toompuu and Heinloo, 1980). The result of these operations is the equation

$$(\frac{\partial}{\partial t} + \vec{v}_{(k)} \cdot \nabla) \, q_{(k)} = \nabla \cdot \vec{j}_{(k)}(n) \,, \tag{3}$$

where the vector $\vec{j}(n) = -(\vec{v}'_{(n)} \, q'_{(n)})_n$ (n = 1,...,k) is the flux of $q_{(n)}$ that is determined by the velocity pulsations at the n-th level of description.

Let $c(k) = (q'^2_{(k)})_k$ be the variance of the substance concentration at the k-th level of description and $C(k) = c(k)_{k+1,...,N}$. According to (1), we have

$$(q^2)_{(N)} = (q_{(N)})^2 + \sum_{k=1}^{N} C(k) \,.$$

The equations for $q^2_{(N)}$ and $C(k)$ follow from equation (3). After some simple but laborious transformations, these equations can be written

$$(\frac{\partial}{\partial t} + \vec{v}_{(N)} \cdot \nabla) \, q^2_{(N)} = \nabla \cdot \vec{h}(N+1) - \sum_{n=0}^{N} (N+1,n)$$

$$(\frac{\partial}{\partial t} + \vec{v}_N \cdot \nabla) \, C_{(k)} = \nabla \cdot \vec{h}(k) - \sum_{n=0}^{k-1} (k,n) + \sum_{n=k+1}^{N+1} (n,k) \tag{4}$$

where

$$(N+1,n) = 2 \, \vec{j}_{(N)}(n) \cdot \nabla \, q_{(N)}$$

$$(k,n) = 2 \, (\vec{j}'_{(k)}(n) \cdot \nabla \, q'_{(k)})_{(N)}$$

are the terms that describe the interaction of the variables $q^2_{(N)}$ and $C(k)$, and $C(k)$ and $C(n)$, respectively, and where

$$\vec{h}(N+1) = \sum_{n=0}^{N} 2 \, q_{(N)} \, \vec{j}_N(n)$$

$$\vec{h}(k) = \sum_{n=0}^{k-1} (\vec{j}'_{(k)}(n) \, q'_{(k)})_{(N)} - \sum_{n=k}^{N} (\vec{v}'_{(n)}(q'^2_{(k)})'_{(n)})_{(N)}$$

are the flux vectors of $q^2_{(N)}$ and $C(k)$, respectively.

If the problem is set in general, for instance before the precise meaning of the filtration operations is established, the quantities $(N+1, n)$ and (k,n) can take positive as well as negative values. However, if the preceding mathematics is used to describe the transfer of some substance in a turbulent flow, and if the filtration operators are chosen in such a way that the scales of the motion to be described increase with k, it can be shown that

$$(N+1, n) \geq 0$$
$$(k, n) \geq 0 \qquad . \tag{5}$$

The inequalities (5) applied to equations (4) are the mathematical expression of the cascade process of redistribution of inhomogeneities in a turbulent flow (Fig. 1).

SPECIAL CASE

In order to describe the process of turbulent diffusion, it is advantageous to introduce several filtration operators simultaneously. This allows us to apply different closure assumptions to processes of different scales that may have various physical origin or differ in some important characteristics.

Let is illustrate the proposed formalism by a model of diffusion in a turbulent flow with rotationally anisotropic eddy pattern. The concept of rotationally anisotropic turbulent flow was introduced by Nemirovsky and Heinloo, 1977, to describe a turbulent field which can be characterized by the relative orientation of eddy motion in the environment. In a detailed discussion of the theory, Nemirovsky and Heinloo (1980) pointed out that

520

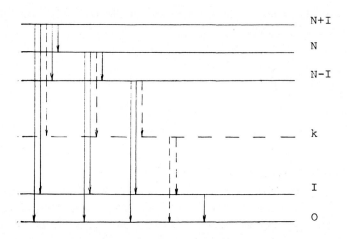

Fig. 1. Schematic representation of the cascade process of redistribution of inhomogenities between different levels of description in a turbulent flow (transitions to or from all intermediate levels, 2 to N-2, are denoted by dashed arrows).

the existence of oriented eddy motion in the environment leads to certain correlation between kinematic and geometric characteristics of the field of motion. Based on the existence of such a correlation, a new kinematic characteristic of environment, denoted $\vec{\Omega}$, is introduced (a definition of $\vec{\Omega}$ can be found in another paper by Heinloo appearing in this volume). It must be obvious that the case $\vec{\Omega} \neq 0$ corresponds to some specific features of the process of turbulent diffusion. Since the contributions to the quantity $\vec{\Omega}$ originate only in large-scale eddies (i.e. the eddies responsible for the orientation of the eddy motion in the environment), the quantity $\vec{\Omega}$ influences only that part of the diffusion that is affected by large-scale eddies.

Let us choose the "black-and-white" diffusion of the molecules of a substance as the zero-th level of description (note that $\vec{j}(0) = 0$ in this case). As the first filtration operator we choose the averaging operation over the so-called "elementary volume", i.e. a volume large enough for the molecular pulsations to be filtered out, or smoothed, and small enough for the fields of $\vec{v}_1$ and q_1 to be considered continuous functions of space and time. The second operator of filtration (averaging) is chosen in order to filter the pulsations of $\vec{v}_1$ and q_1, which are caused by motion of small-scale eddies. The third operator of filtration (averaging) filters the inhomogeneities of $\vec{v}_{(2)}$ and $q_{(2)}$, which are caused by the motion of large-scale eddies. As for the diffusion terms in (3) and (4), it is assumed that

$$
\begin{aligned}
-(\vec{v}_1' \, Q')_1 &= k_M \, \nabla \, Q \\
-(v_2' \, Q')_{(2)} &= k_T \, \nabla \, Q \\
-(v_3' \, Q')_{(3)} &= K_T \, \nabla \, Q \quad ,
\end{aligned}
\tag{6}
$$

where Q denotes an arbitrary scalar quantity, k_M and k_T the coefficients of molecular and turbulent diffusion (the last one being determined by the motion of the small-scale eddies), and where $K_T = K_T(\Omega)$ is the tensor of diffusion coefficients determined by the motion of large-scale eddies.

Expanding K_T into a series in $\vec{\Omega}$ (keeping in mind that $K_T(\vec{0}) = 0$), and limiting the expansion to terms of first and second order, we have

$$
K_T = -k_T^{(1)} \, E \cdot \vec{\Omega} + k_T^{(2)} \, (\vec{\Omega} \, I - \vec{\Omega} \, \vec{\Omega}) \, ,
\tag{7}
$$

where E is the Levy-Chiwitt tensor, I is the unit tensor, and $k_T^{(1)}$ and $k_T^{(2)}$ are constant. Taking into account the assumptions (5) and (6), we can derive from equations (3) and (4) the following system, henceforth referred to as equations (8):

$$
\frac{D}{Dt} q_{(3)} = \nabla \cdot \vec{h} \, (q_{(3)})
$$

$$
\frac{D}{Dt} q_{(3)}^2 = \nabla \cdot \vec{h}(4) - 2k_M (\nabla \, q_{(3)})^2 - 2k_T (\nabla q_{(3)})^2 - 2k_T^{(2)} (\nabla q_{(3)} \times \vec{\Omega})^2
$$

$$
\frac{D}{Dt} C(3) = \nabla \cdot \vec{h}(3) + 2k_T^{(2)} (\nabla \, q_{(3)} \times \vec{\Omega} \,)^2 - 2k_T (\nabla \, q_{(3)}')_{(3)}^2 - 2k_M (\nabla \, q_{(3)}')_3^2
$$

$$
\frac{D}{Dt} C(2) = \nabla \cdot \vec{h}(2) + 2k_T (\nabla \, q_{(3)})^2 + 2k_T (\nabla \, q_{(3)}')_3^2 - 2k_M (\nabla \, q_{(2)}')_{2,3}^2
$$

$$
\frac{D}{Dt} C(1) = \nabla \cdot \vec{h}(1) + 2k_M (\nabla \, q_{(3)})^2 + 2k_M (\nabla \, q_{(3)}')_3^2 + 2k_M (\nabla \, q_{(2)}')_{2,3}^2
$$

where $\quad \dfrac{D}{Dt} = \dfrac{\partial}{\partial t} + \vec{v}_{(3)} \cdot \nabla \quad$, and

$$\vec{h} \begin{bmatrix} q_{(3)} \\ 4 \\ k \end{bmatrix} = [(k_M + k_T)\, I + K_T] \cdot \nabla \begin{bmatrix} q_{(3)} \\ q_{(3)}^2 \\ C(k) \end{bmatrix} .$$

Following the physical ideas of the cascade character of turbulent diffusion, we can retain on the right-hand side of equations (8) the terms that correspond to interactions between neighboring levels and neglect the terms that describe "dissipation" of the fields $q_{(3)}^2$ and $C(3)$ into subsequent levels. Also, some assumptions are needed concerning the terms $2k_T (\nabla\, q_{(3)}')_3^2$ and $2k_M (\nabla\, q_{(2)}')_{2,3}^2$ in order to close the system of equations (8). These assumptions could be

$$2k_T\, (\nabla\, q_{(3)}')_3^2 = \frac{1}{\tau_T}\, C(3)$$

$$2k_M\, (\nabla\, q_{(2)}')_{2,3}^2 = \frac{1}{\tau_M}\, C(2)\ , \qquad\qquad (9)$$

where τ_T and τ_M are characteristic time scales of decay of $C(3)$ and $C(2)$.

REFERENCES

Heinloo, J. and Toompuu, A., 1981. Applications of averaging (filtration) operators to hydrodynamical problems and to experimental data. The Investigation and Modelling of the Processes of the Baltic Sea, Part II, Tallinn, pp. 78-81.
Nemirovsky, Y.V. and Heinloo, J.L., 1977. A new approach to the description of turbulent flows (in Russian).
Nemirovsky, Y.V. and Heinloo, J.L., 1980. The local vortex theory of turbulent flows. Novosibirsk (in Russian).
Toompuu, A. and Heinloo, J., 1980. The generalized representation of a state of a physical situation and its application to problems of hydrodynamics (in Russian).

WATER QUALITY STUDY OF THE BALTIC SEA
BY OPTICAL REMOTE SENSING METHODS

J. Lokk, A. Purga

Institute of Thermophysics and Electrophysics

Academy of Sciences of the Estonian S.S.R.

INTRODUCTION

Optical remote sensing methods enable us to save time in studying the spatial and temporal variability of oceanic properties, and to collect simultaneous data for large area.

In this paper, we discuss the possibility of using measurements of the upward spectral radiance to study the distribution of suspended and dissolved matter in the sea. The experiments were performed during cruises of the research vessel R/V "Ayu-Dag" in the Baltic Proper, and from aboard a helicopter in coastal areas.

DISCUSSION

The study of the spatial distributions of various constituents in the sea by remote sensing methods is somewhat limited by the fact that we can only measure directly the optically active matter in the water, such as phytoplankton pigments, suspended matter, and yellow substance. The quantity of other substances can only be estimated in an indirect way, using known relationships between these substances and the optically active matter. Many authors simply use the correlations between the concentration of a given substance and sea brightness in one or two spectral bands. This method can only be used under certain conditions, for we know that brightness is not only a function of water quality but it is also strongly correlated with the downward spectral irradiance. The downward spectral irradiance varies greatly in the Baltic area. For a direct study of the characteristics of water masses, we use the spectral radiance index, $\rho(\lambda)$, defined by the expression:

$$\rho(\lambda) = \frac{B\!\uparrow\!(\lambda)}{B_o(\lambda)} \tag{1}$$

where $B\!\uparrow\!(\lambda)$ is the sea radiance toward the nadir point and $B_o(\lambda)$ is the diffuse radiance.

When measurements are made to study suspended and dissolved matter in the sea, reflections from the sea surface contaminate the data. However, in studies of the conditions of the sea surface (oil slicks, waves, etc.), the sun glitters constitute the main signal. Experiments show that, on a cloud-less day and with a high sun, about 40% of the sea surface is covered with sun glitters in the Baltic Sea. In order to obtain reliable information on subsurface layers in the presence of sun glitters, we have to make measure-ments when the height of the sun is less than 50° or to incline the radio-meter at some angle from the nadir point in the direction facing the sun. Assuming that all radiation registered in near infrared is reflected only from the water surface, we can then estimate corrections for reflected light in the other spectral bands.

An alternative method is to use, as a first approximation, the fol-lowing expression (Lokk and Pelevin, 1978; Pelevin, Pelevina and Kelbalikhanov, 1979):

$$R(\lambda) = \frac{B\uparrow(\lambda) - 0.02\ B\downarrow(\lambda)}{B_o(\lambda)} \ , \tag{2}$$

where $R(\lambda)$ denotes the diffuse spectral radiance index, $B\downarrow(\lambda)$ the zenith point spectral radiance and 0.02 is the value of the Fresnel coefficient for orthogonally falling light beam radiance. The underlying assumption is that the zenith point and a 20° area around it have equal brightness. We will have the best results if the surface is smooth.

The two beam approximation discussed by Morel and Prieur (1977) des-cribes the diffuse spectral radiance index by the expression:

$$R(\lambda) = k\ \frac{\beta(\lambda)}{\beta(\lambda) + \kappa(\lambda)} \ , \tag{3}$$

where k is a nondimensional coefficient, $\beta(\lambda)$ the backward scattering co-efficient and $\kappa(\lambda)$ the light absorption coefficient (absorbance).

The absorbance can be calculated in the following way

$$\kappa(\lambda) = \kappa_w(\lambda) + \kappa_p(\lambda) + \kappa_y(\lambda) + \kappa_M \ , \tag{4}$$

where $\kappa_w(\lambda)$ denotes the absorbance by pure water, $\kappa_p(\lambda)$ the absorbance caused by phytoplankton pigments (mainly chlorophyll a), $\kappa_y(\lambda)$ the absorbance caused by dissolved organic matter (yellow substance) and κ_M the absorbance caused by nonselective particles or "grey" suspended matter. Using (4), equation (3) can be written as

$$R(\lambda) = k\ \frac{\beta(\lambda)}{\beta(\lambda) + \kappa_w(\lambda) + \kappa_p(\lambda) + \kappa_y(\lambda) + \kappa_M} \ . \tag{5}$$

For water, the function $\beta(\lambda)$ varies slowly. Qualitative spectral distribution curves of other quantities are known. The influence of the different components on the spectral curve $R(\lambda)$ varies with the wavelength. The dominant factors in various spectral bands can be categorized as follows:

550-600 nm $\quad\quad\quad\quad \kappa_M,\ \beta_M \quad$ (β_M denotes the backward scattering from suspended matter)

500-550 and 600-680 nm $\quad \kappa_M,\ \beta_M,\ \kappa_p(\lambda)$

400-500 nm $\quad\quad\quad\quad\quad \kappa_M,\ \beta_M,\ \kappa_p(\lambda),\ \kappa_y(\lambda)$

350-400 nm $\quad\quad\quad\quad\quad \kappa_M,\ \beta_M,\ \kappa_p(\lambda),\ \kappa_y(\lambda),\ \beta(\lambda)$.

In the case of clear oceanic water, where the influence of some components is small, the system of equations based on (5) gives satisfactory results. However, when the water consists of a complicated mixture of optically active matter (like the Baltic Sea and the estuaries of large rivers), the results are found wanting. Accuracy in such conditions is determined by the simplifications that have been made on a case by case basis. Choosing these simplifications gives us the possibility of finding more sensitive spectral ranges and relations for calculating the quantitative distribution of some substances. As an example, Figure 1 shows a map based on measurements from the helicopter after a strong storm in the Gulf of Riga (Pelevin, Gruzevich and Lokk, 1980). The map shows the distribution (in relative units) of yellow substance in the sea. The ratio ρ_{369}/ρ_{560} is used to describe the yellow substance content of the water. The measurements were confirmed by analyzing water samples collected at various sites from the helicopter for calibration and determination of the optical characteristics of the main optically active substances in laboratory.

A more precise method is one which utilizes the whole spectrum of light backscattered from the sea. Knowing the optical characteristics of the most important substances obtained in laboratory experiments for the study area, we can estimate the universal spectral curves for different concentrations, given by

$$N(\lambda) = \frac{R(\lambda)}{R(\lambda_0)} = \frac{\beta'(\lambda)}{\beta'(\lambda_0)} \frac{\beta(\lambda_0) + \kappa_w(\lambda_0) + c\kappa_p(\lambda_0) + S\kappa_y(\lambda_0)}{\beta(\lambda) + \kappa_w(\lambda) + c\kappa_p(\lambda) + S\kappa_y(\lambda)} \quad , \quad (6)$$

where

$$\beta\lambda) = \beta'(\lambda) + \kappa_p,$$

and where we denote by

526

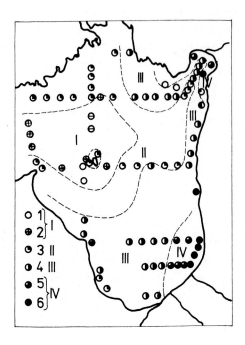

Fig. 1. Distribution of the ratio ρ_{369}/ρ_{560} for the Riga Gulf area on the basis of the data of 18 and 19 September 1977. The numerical scale is defined as follows:

(1) $1.35 < \rho_{369}/\rho_{560}$;

(2) $0.90 < \rho_{369}/\rho_{560} \leq 1.35$;

(3) $0.60 < \rho_{369}/\rho_{560} \leq 0.90$;

(4) $0.40 < \rho_{369}/\rho_{560} \leq 0.60$;

(5) $0.33 < \rho_{369}/\rho_{560} \leq 0.40$;

(6) $\rho_{369}/\rho_{560} \leq 0.33$.

κ_p the nonselective absorbance by particles,

$\beta'(\lambda)$ the backward scattering coefficient for water with suspended matter,

κ_w the pure water absorbance,

κ_p, κ_y the relative absorbances by chlorophyll and yellow substance, respectively, and by

c, S   the concentrations of chlorophyll and yellow substance.

The concentrations of optically active substances can then be obtained by comparing the measured spectral distribution curves with the calculated curves. The "measured" concentrations are the set of values for which the calculated spectrum is most similar to the observed spectral curve. Figure 2 shows actual measured spectral curves and Figures 3, 4 and 5 show various estimated model curves.

Finally, it may be that measurements of chlorophyll concentration by the UNESCO method and by the remote method are inherently different. In one case the analysis applies to samples from discrete depths which may all be outside the maximum concentration layers, whereas in the other case the variable we measure accounts for all the chlorophyll in the active layer (really up to Secchy disc visibility depth) with different influence at different depths.

CONCLUSIONS

We have shown that information about the full spectrum of upwelling light is needed for water quality studies by optical remote sensing methods. In waters with a complicated composition of optically active matter (e.g. estuaries, closed seas) information is needed about the optical properties of the main components present in the area (chlorophyll, yellow substance, etc.).

528

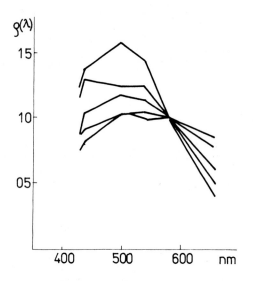

Fig. 2. Measured spectral radiance.

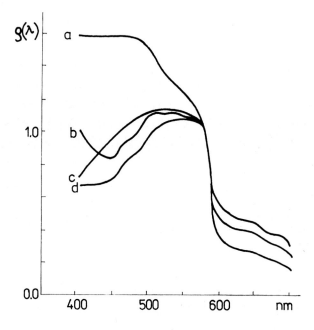

Fig. 3. Computed spectral radiance with a) c=0.1, y=0.0, B=0.0020; b) c=0.01, y=1.0, B=0.0018; c) c=2.0, y=0.0, B=0.0020; d) c=2.0, y=1.0, B=0.0020.

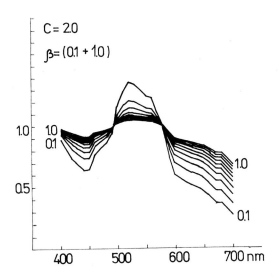

Fig. 4. Dependence of the spectral radiance, $\rho(\lambda)$, on the parameter β for fixed chlorophyll concentration ($c=2mg.m^{-3}$).

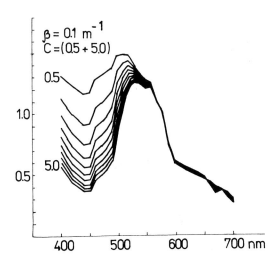

Fig. 5. Dependence of the spectral radiance, $\rho(\lambda)$, on the chlorophyll concentration for $\beta = 0.1 \ m^{-1}$.

REFERENCES

Eerme, K. and J. Lokk, 1980. On the Baltic Sea water brightness and colour measurements by the research vessel "Ayu-Dag" in August 1977. Proc. of the 11th Conf. of Baltic Oceanographers, Vol. 2, Rostock.

Lokk, J. and V. Pelevin, 1977. The interpretation of the spectrum of the upwelling radiation based on the Baltic Sea. Proc. of the 11th Conf. of Baltic Oceanographers, Vol. 2, Rostock.

Morel, A. and Prieur, L., 1977. Analysis of variations in ocean color. Limnol. Oceanogr., 22: 709-722.

Pelevin, V.N., M.A. Pelevina and B.F. Kelbalikhanov, 1979. Upwelling spectrum studies from aboard a helicopter (in Russian) Opticheskie metody izuchenija okeanov i vnutrennih vodojemov, Novosibirsk.

Pelevin, V., A. Gruzevich and J. Lokk, 1980. On the possibility of evaluating the distribution of yellow substance in the sea water by the outcoming radiation spectra (in Russian), Svetovye polja v okeane., Moskva.

Schmidt, D. and K.A. Ulbricht, 1978. Mass occurrence of blue-green algae in the Western Baltic evaluation of satellite imagery and implications on marine chemistry and pollution. Proc. of the 11th Conf. of Baltic Oceanographers, Vol. 1, Rostock.

THE INFLUENCE OF HYDRODYNAMICS ON THE CHLOROPHYLL
FIELD IN THE OPEN BALTIC

MATI KAHRU

Department of the Baltic Sea, Institute of Thermophysics and
Electrophysics, Paldiski St. 1, Tallinn 200031, USSR

INTRODUCTION

The concentration of chlorophyll $\underline{a}$ - more correctly, its $\underline{in}$ $\underline{vivo}$ fluorescence - is unique among the many biological parameters characterizing a pelagic ecosystem, because it is amenable to measurement by $\underline{in}$ $\underline{situ}$ and remote sensors. The chlorophyll $\underline{a}$ concentration is important as an index of the phytoplankton abundance. Moreover, it may be a useful indicator of hydrodynamic processes, as discussed in this paper.

The spatio-temporal dynamics of chlorophyll is much more complicated than that of the common hydrographic variables, e.g. salinity, due to its intense vertical fine structure and its essentially nonconservative nature. The time scales of the spatially heterogeneous nonconservative processes, the phytoplankton reproduction and the grazing by zooplankton, are of the order of 1 day. Hydrodynamics controls the chlorophyll field by 1) advection and diffusion, and 2) by changing the local rates, e.g., of reproduction and grazing. A delicate balance between these processes determines which one of them dominates on some particular space and time scales.

Skellam (1951), Kierstead and Slobodkin (1953), and a number of their followers (Okubo, 1978) have examined the balance between diffusion and reproduction. Their analysis leads to a critical patch size, below which a phytoplankton patch is erased by diffusion. However, the concept is only of limited cognitive value to a field ecologist because all the relevant processes are spatially heterogeneous.

The relative importance of advection versus reproduction may be assessed by the nondimensional number, S, introduced by O'Brien and Wroblewski (1973). For a geostrophic flow;

$$S = \frac{U}{r} \left(\frac{f}{A_H}\right)^{\frac{1}{2}} \tag{1}$$

where U is the characteristic speed of the organized flow, r is the maximum growth rate of the plankton, f is the Coriolis parameter, and A_H is the eddy diffusivity for momentum. When S exceeds unity, advection becomes dominant over biological turnover in determining the horizontal chlorophyll distribution. For parameter values typical of the Baltic ($r = 2 \times 10^{-5}$ s^{-1}; $f = 10^{-4}$ s^{-1}; $A_H = 10^6$ cm^2 s^{-1}) it appears that advection dominates if $U > 2$ cm s^{-1}. Despite the uncertainty in the estimate of A_H, the gross validity of this result will be demonstrated later.

METHODS

The chlorophyll field and its interaction with the hydrodynamic processes in the south-eastern Gotland Basin were studied by means of recurrent quasi-synoptic surveys at stations covering various rectangular grids, with a spacing of 5 nautical miles (9.3 km) between grid points. A typical grid area was 20x25 nautical miles. At each grid point, vertical profiles were obtained using a Variosens in situ fluorometer, measuring chlorophyll a fluorescence, and a Neil Brown Mark III CTD probe. The fluorometer calibration and other details may be found in Kahru (1981a) and Kahru et al. (1981). The duration of a survey was about 1 day. As the chlorophyll concentrations at fixed depths are readily contaminated by internal waves and the variable vertical fine structure (Kahru et al., 1981), only vertically integrated concentrations are considered in this paper. The CTD data of the same surveys are interpreted in detail by Aitsam and Elken (this volume).

OBSERVATIONS AND DISCUSSION

The ecology of the Baltic Sea has been recently reviewed by Jansson (1978). A characteristic feature of the Baltic Sea hydrography is the distinct layering of the water column into 3 layers in summer: the upper layer, which coincides approximately with the photic layer; the intermediate layer, or the winter convection layer; and the deep, saline layer (Fig. 1). The 2 peaks in the Brunt-Väisälä frequency, separating the layers, are associated with the seasonal thermocline (depth of 15 to 30 m) and the permanent halocline (50-70 m). After the spring phytoplankton bloom, lasting for a few weeks, the upper 2 layers are almost depleted of inorganic nitrogen, and the phytoplankton growth is limited by biological destruction and by the rate of upward mixing of nitrates from the deep layer (where the nitrate concentration remains about 100 times higher than in the higher layers). Consequently, the influence of the hydrodynamics on the phytoplankton growth is manifested mainly through the transfer of nutrients into the upper layer. A number of mixing patterns is revealed by the chlorophyll surveys.

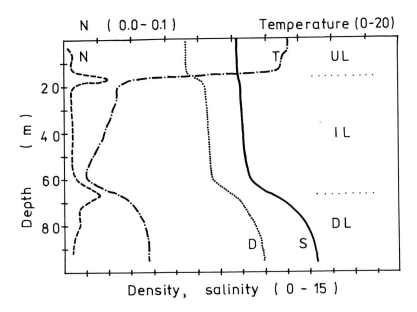

Fig. 1. Typical thermohaline layering of the Baltic Proper into 3 layers: upper (UL), intermediate (IL), and deep layer (DL), with plots of temperature (T, °C), salinity (S, °/oo), density (D, sigma-t), and the Brunt-Väisälä frequency (N, rad s^{-1}) (from Kahru et al., 1981).

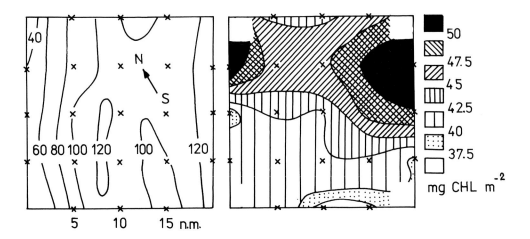

Fig. 2. Chlorophyll distribution (mg m^{-2}, integrated between 2.5 and 32.5 m) in relation to the bottom topography (m). July 15-16, 1979. The upper left patch was observed repeatedly and is ascribed to bottom mixing on the shallow bank. The upper right patch remains unexplained.

The bathymetry of the Baltic is very irregular so that the currents (Kielman et al., 1973) and, hence, the intensity of vertical mixing are subject to a strong topographical influence. When a stratified fluid flows over a shallow submarine bank, and if the flow is subcritical with respect to the internal Froude number, the isopycnals are compressed (Turner, 1973), and the bottom turbulence may cause an upward transport of nutrients. This can be recognized on some of the chlorophyll maps (Fig. 2). Although little is known about bottom mixing in the Baltic, this kind of boundary mixing can be important for the overall ecology due to the frequent occurrence of shallow banks.

Geostrophic currents, significantly guided by the topography, are asso-ciated with the sloping of isopycnals. The resulting vertical displacement of the thermocline and/or of the halocline modifies the thicknesses of the basic layers. We have established significant relationships between the water stratification and the chlorophyll level, suggesting intensified mixing under certain conditions. In particular, both the rising of the top of the deep layer (Fig. 3) and the narrowing of the intermediate layer (Fig. 4) are clearly associated with an increase in chlorophyll concentration in several surveys. I suggest that the rising of the halocline and the com-pression of

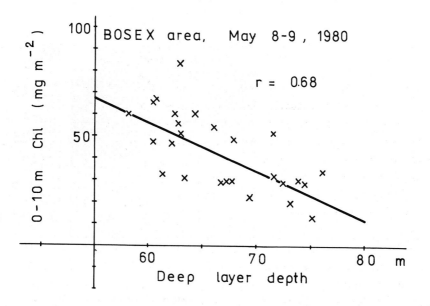

Fig. 3. Dependence of chlorophyll _a_ in the upper 10-m layer (mg m^{-2}) on the halocline depth.

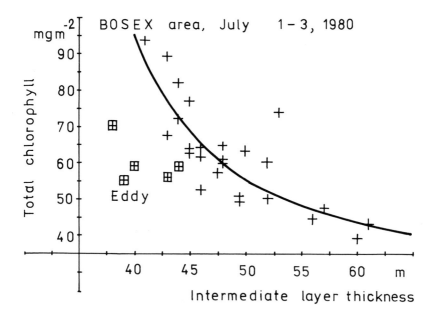

Fig. 4. Dependence of the total chlorophyll a̲ in the upper 60 m layer on the intermediate layer thickness. The circled points, originating from a cyclonic eddy center, suggest suppressed mixing in the eddy center. They have been excluded when fitting the curve by least squares (from Kahru et al., 1981).

the intermediate layer, both favorable to the development of vertical shears, can give rise to instabilities, e.g. internal wave breaking, causing intense mixing and, hence, increased chlorophyll biomass. Figure 5 presents a typical section across a topographically guided baroclinic jet, showing the bottom contour and the corresponding integrated chlorophyll concentrations. Here, contrary to the case of bottom mixing, the chlorophyll concentration is inversely proportional to the depth: the shallowest area with the thickest intermediate layer supports the lowest chlorophyll level and vice versa.

The chlorophyll field shows striking mesoscale ($\cong$ 10 km) patterns even if the concentration is integrated vertically over the upper 60 m layer. The correlations with the stratification suggest that most of the variability is caused by uneven nutrient fluxes from the deep layer rather than by lateral mixing of different water masses. It is tempting to try to estimate the vertical diffusivities that might be responsible for the generation of such heterogeneities. Using a ratio of nitrogen/chlorophyll = 16, appropri-

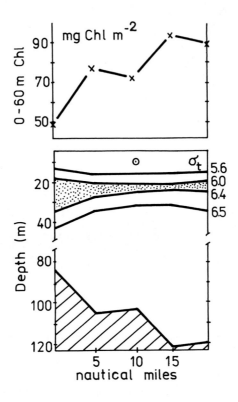

Fig. 5. Section across a baroclinic jet along the isobaths showing the bathymetry, the isopycnals in the intermediate layer, and the corresponding total chlorophyll levels. BOSEX area, July 1-3, 1980.

ate for nitrogen-deficient phytoplankton (Strickland, 1965), the chlorophyll concentrations may be crudely expressed in terms of nitrogen. For the surveys shown in Figures 3 and 4, the differences between maximum and minimum concentrations in the upper 60 m layer are 2220 and 875 mg N m^{-2}, respectively. These amounts correspond to about 18% and 8%, respectively, of the mean total nitrogen above the halocline. As a first approximation, the nitrate flux across the halocline may be estimated as

$$\Omega = - K_z \frac{\partial NO_3}{\partial z} \qquad (2)$$

where K_z is the vertical diffusivity and $\frac{\partial NO_3}{\partial z}$ is the vertical gradient of nitrate. The latter is approximately equal to 3 mg N m^{-3}/m for the 50-70 m
layer. By means of dye diffusion experiments, Kullenberg (1977) obtained a
value of $K_z = 2.2 \times 10^{-6}$ m^2 s^{-1} for the mean vertical diffusivity in the halocline of the Bornholm Basin. Substituting these numerical values into equation (2), we obtain an upward nitrogen flux of 0.57 mg N m^{-2}/day. This flux
is extremely small in view of the observed variability. Indeed, at this
rate, more than 1000 days would be needed to accumulate an amount of nitrate
similar to the typical observed variations (more than 500 mg N m^{-2}). As the
time scale of the phytoplankton patches is probably of the order of 10 days,
the observed chlorophyll variability cannot be explained with the above
value of the vertical diffusivity. Consequently, processes with diffusivities higher by at least 2 orders of magnitude ($> 10^{-4}$ m^2 s^{-1}) should exist
at least locally and temporarily. In the Baltic thermocline, vigorous
short-term mixing caused by internal wave breaking in the intense shear
zones, created by inertial waves, was shown by Krauss (1978). The possibility of nutrient transfer across the thermocline, e.g. during storms, is
further substantiated by the very low nitrate values below the thermo- and
above the halocline. The intermittency and dramatic variability of the
vertical mixing in stratified waters has been stressed by Woods (1977).
Hence, the vertical diffusivities $> 10^{-4}$ m^2 s^{-1}, required to explain my
observations, are not necessarily in contradiction with the 2 orders of
magnitude lower values measured by Kullenberg (1977) in quieter conditions.
However, the evidence presented here for the existence of intense mixing
events in the halocline of the open Baltic is indirect and no well-documen-
ted observations are available.

Satellite images (Ulbricht and Horstmann, 1979) as well as our CTD
surveys (Aitsam and Elken, this volume) show a frequent occurrence of mesoscale eddies: on every survey eddylike disturbances of the relative dynamic
topography can be discerned. The analysis of the interaction between energetic mesoscale eddies and the chlorophyll field is complicated by the
advection and stirring action during the phytoplankton growth phase (1-3
days): taking into account the effect of advection, we have to relate the
chlorophyll biomass to mixing conditions several days earlier. This has
hardly been feasible in practice, and the apparent effect of advection is a
reduction in the correlation between the stratification (i.e. mixing conditions) and the chlorophyll level.

Two surveys made 10 days apart during comparatively even phytoplankton
growth showed that the chlorophyll field was distorted by a passing eddy as
a passive scalar field (Kahru, 1981b).

Another survey (Fig. 4) seems to indicate that the mixing activity in a cyclonic eddy is remarkably suppressed. It seems that the hypothesis of a reduction of mixing energy in the eddy center is supported by observations suggesting a decrease in wave energy in the center of oceanic eddies (Frankignoul, 1974; Dykman et al., 1981).

Three surveys made during the decaying phase of a particularly energetic mesoscale eddy show unusually weak correlations between the stratification and the chlorophyll level. This is probably the result of the vigorous advection, stirring, and current shears, associated with the eddy. The observational evidence for this conclusion is as follows. The eddy has a translational velocity of about 2 cm s^{-1} and the rotational velocities are estimated at 20 cm s^{-1}. The isopycnal elevations in the center are 22 m at the top of the deep layer. Although the nutrient concentrations were not measured, a significant increase in the near-surface salinity provides evidence of intense vertical mixing and nutrient input. This evidence is based on a close relationship between the nutrients and salinity (Nehring, 1979) as both are mixed upwards from the deep, saline layer. The correlation between the upper and deep layer salinities is maximal during the most active phase of the eddy (Fig. 6A), also suggesting vertical mixing, and it decreases later to zero as a result of strong vertical shears. At the same time the near-surface salinity reaches its maximum. The occurrence of vigorous stirring is also substantiated by a decrease in the spatial scales of variability

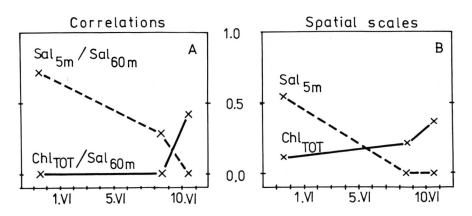

Fig. 6. Trends in several parameters on 3 consecutive surveys during the breakdown of an energetic mesoscale eddy: correlations between the total chlorophyll and the salinity at 60 m, and between the salinities at 5 m and 60 m (A); spatial autocorrelations over 5 nautical miles of the total chlorophyll and the salinity at 5 m (B).

of the near-surface salinity, i.e. by a shift from a coarse-grained to a fine-grained pattern (Fig. 6B). The chlorophyll field also shows an unusually fine-grained pattern. Although substantial amounts of nutrients were probably mixed into the upper layer by the cyclonic eddy, this is not apparent in the chlorophyll/salinity correlation due to the vigorous advection, stirring, and shears. The O'Brien-Wroblewski parameter, equation (1), calculated for the rotational velocity of the eddy, surely exceeds unity, which confirms the dominance of advection over the phytoplankton reproduction. In accordance with this concept, the weakening of the eddy coincides with a slight increase in both the chlorophyll/ salinity correlation and the spatial scales of the chlorophyll field (Fig. 6).

It should be stressed that our ability to interpret the biological dynamics and its complicated interaction with vigorous hydrodynamic processes is by no means unambiguous. More detailed synoptic surveys of several representative biological and hydrographic parameters are needed. A routine use of biological sensors mounted on a vertically undulating 'Batfish' (Denman and Herman, 1978) would represent a substantial progress.

CONCLUSIONS

The chlorophyll field in the open Baltic Sea is closely related to various hydrodynamic processes. The spatial and temporal scales considered in this paper are the so-called mesoscales (10-100 km and 1-10 days), where the biological turnover rate of the phytoplankton becomes comparable to the processes of advection and diffusion. An increase in chlorophyll biomass may be ascribed to the phytoplankton growth in response to a nutrient input from the deep layer as a result of vertical mixing. Several mixing regimes are discerned from the chlorophyll patterns: bottom mixing on shallow banks, shear induced mixing in a thin intermediate layer, and a suppression of mixing in the center of a cyclonic eddy. High vertical diffusivities in the halocline ($> 10^{-4}$ m^2 s^{-1}), at least locally and temporarily, are needed to explain the observed chlorophyll variability by uneven nutrient fluxes. This eddy diffusivity is 2 orders of magnitude higher than that measured by dye experiments in "quiet" conditions (Kullenberg, 1977). In accordance with the O'Brien-Wroblewski criterion, vigorous advection and stirring dominate over the biological turnover for some periods. For these periods the apparent correlations between the chlorophyll levels and the hydrography are decreased.

ACKNOWLEDGEMENTS

I am indebted to Prof. A. Aitsam for his support and guidance. Without the help of many members of the Department of the Baltic Sea this work would have been impossible; the technical assistance of R. Portsmuth and discussions with J. Elken were most helpful. I thank Prof. J.C.J. Nihoul for supporting my participation in the Colloquium and Dr. B.M. Jamart for help in processing the manuscript.

REFERENCES

Denman, K.L. and Herman, A.W., 1978. Space-time structure of a continental ecosystem measured by a towed porpoising vehicle. J. Mar. Res., 36: 693-714.

Dykman, V.Z., Kiselev, O.A. and Efremov, O.I., 1981. Studies of internal wave energy in synoptic eddies based on the temperature field structure. Oceanology, 21: 441-446.

Frankignoul, C.J., 1974. Preliminary observations of internal wave energy flux in frequency, depth-space. Deep-Sea Res., 21: 895-909.

Jansson, B.-O, 1978. The Baltic - A system analysis of a semi-enclosed sea. In: H. Charnock and G. Deacon (editors), Advances in Oceanography, Plenum Press, New York, pp. 131-183.

Kahru, M., 1981a. Variability in the chlorophyll field in the Baltic Sea. In: A. Atisam (editor), The investigation and modelling of processes in the Baltic, Academy of Sciences of the USSR, Tallinn, pp. 165-171.

Kahru, M., 1981b. Variability in the three-dimensional structure of the chlorophyll field in the open Baltic Sea. Oceanology, 21: 685-690.

Kahru, M., Aitsam, A. and Elken, J., 1981. Coarse-scale spatial structure of phytoplankton standing crop in relation to hydrography in the open Baltic Sea. Mar. Ecol. Prog. Ser., in press.

Kielman, J., Krauss, W. and Keunecke, K.-H., 1973. Currents and stratification in the Belt Sea and Arkona Basin during 1962-1968. Kieler Meeresforsch., 29: 90-111.

Kierstead, H. and Slobodkin, L.B., 1953. The size of water masses containing plankton blooms. J. Mar. Res., 12: 141-147.

Krauss, W., 1978. Inertial waves and mixing in the thermocline (BOSEX-Results). Proc. 11 Conf. Baltic Oceanogr., Rostock, pp. 709-728.

Kullenberg, G.E.B., 1977. Observations of the mixing in the Baltic thermo- and halocline layers. Tellus, 29: 572-587.

Nehring, D., 1979. Relationships between salinity and increasing nutrient concentrations in the mixed winter surface layer of the Baltic from 1969 to 1978. ICES C.M. C: 24, 8 pp.

O'Brien, J.J. and Wroblewski, J.S., 1973. On advection in phytoplankton models. J. Theor. Biol., 38: 197-202.

Okubo, A., 1978. Horizontal dispersion and critical scales for phytoplankton patches. In: J.H. Steele (editor), Spatial patterns in plankton communities, Plenum Press, New York, pp. 21-42.

Skellam, J.G., 1951. Random dispersal in theoretical populations. Biometrika, 38: 196-218.

Strickland, L.D.H., 1965. Production of organic matter in the primary stages of the marine food chain. In: J.P. Riley and G. Skirrow (editors), Chemical Oceanography, Academic Press, London, Vol. 1, pp. 447-610.

Turner, J.S., 1973. Buoyancy effects in fluids. Cambridge University Press, New York, 367 pp.

Ulbricht, K.A. and Horstmann, U., 1979. Blue green algae in the south-western Baltic; detection from satellite. Int. Symp. on Remote Sensing, July 2-8, 1978, Freiberg, FRG, 9 pp.

Woods, J.D., 1977. Parameterization of unresolved motions. In: E.B. Kraus (editor), Modelling and prediction of the upper layers of the ocean, Pergamon Press, Oxford, pp. 118-140.

CHARACTERISTIC PROPERTIES OF TURBULENT TRANSPORT
IN THE BLACK SEA

V.I. Zats and R.V. Ozmidov

P.P. Shirshov Institute of Oceanology

Academy of Sciences, USSR

The properties of turbulent transport in the Black Sea are peculiar because the Black Sea is a closed basin with no significant tidal currents and a somewhat unusual hydrometeorological regime. For example, the well-known contamination of the main body of the Black Sea by hydrogen sulphide is indicative of rather weak vertical mixing in the deep layers of the basin. In this study of the characteristic properties of turbulent exchange in the Black Sea, we use the data of long-term current observations obtained with buoy stations as well as the results of experiments on the diffusion of dye artificially introduced in the water.

We have calculated the horizontal turbulent transfer coefficients, K_1, using measurements of the fluctuations of the horizontal velocity components obtained with propeller-type current meters. The instruments were mounted on buoy stations located in deep coastal waters off the Crimea and the Caucasus. The stations were located at different distances from the shore and the depth of the lowest instrument ranged from 100 to 200 meters. The sampling rate of the velocity observations was 5 to 30 minutes. The series so obtained were filtered with a cosine filter with the parameter ranging from 20 minutes to a few tens of hours. The calculation of K_1 was performed by Ertel's method. The results show that the values of K_1 are critically dependent on the averaging time scale, T_0. For small T_0, the values of K_1 are 10^2 to 10^3 cm^2/s for coastal regions; for the core of near-coastal currents (about 5 miles from the coastline), the values of K_1 are larger, up to 10^4 cm^2/s. The values of K_1 increase with T_0 by about one order of magnitude, and they reach some "saturation" value for $T_0 \cong 20$ hours. The dependence of K_1 on T_0 can be approximated by a power law with an exponent n that depends on the sampling rate of the observations and on the hydrometeorological conditions. The value of n is in the range 0 to 2, but in most cases we find that $0 < n < 1$.

The values of K_1 usually decrease with depth. However, we have sometimes noted an increase of K_1 in the intermediate layers (in the depth range 27-75 m or 50-100 m, for example). In the bottom layers the horizontal transport coefficients are usually smaller than in the main water body by 1 to 3 orders of magnitude. During periods of calm weather or unsteady breeze, K_1 is usually almost constant in the upper layer; it is maximum in the intermediate layer below which it decreases down to the bottom. At high wind velocities, turbulent mixing is most intense in the upper layer. In this case, K_1 either decreases monotonically with depth or it decreases down to the intermediate layer and remains almost constant thereunder. As a rule, the horizontal turbulent transport in coastal regions is anisotropic. The elongation of the ellipses of transport is variable and depends on the distance from the shoreline.

A number of statistical characteristics of the current velocity variability was calculated using the long-term current observations. As expected, the variance of the current velocity fluctuations increases with the averaging scale T_0. The variance of the current fluctuations usually decreases with depth, but now and again maxima of variance are observed in the intermediate layers. The contribution of the fluctuations with periods ranging from 40 min to 3 hours to the total energy is usually 45 to 60% for the surface layer (10-20 m), about 10% for the thin bottom layer and 10 to 30% for the intermediate layers. But these estimates may vary from one season to another and they depend on the weather conditions and the hydrological situation.

The shape of the autocorrelation functions of the velocity components for deep shelf regions of the Black Sea turned out to be rather diverse. The observed functions can be approximated either by exponential functions or by a combination of exponential and harmonic functions with different values of the parameters. The periodic components in the correlation functions are usually more obvious for large smoothing periods (exceeding the inertial period). The decrease of the autocorrelation function values for a one point shift of the argument (10 min) reaches 60 to 90% for the upper layer, 30 to 90% for the intermediate layer (depending on the character of the current), and 10 to 30% for the bottom layer. The periodic component extracted using the correlation function does not always correspond exactly to the theoretical value of the inertial oscillations at the point of observation. This phenomenon may be explained by the nonhomogeneity of the current velocity field and of the overlying wind field as well as by the influence of the bottom topography and the shoreline geometry.

In most cases, the spectral functions of the current velocity components, $S(\omega)$, are maximum over a whole frequency band in the upper layer and minimum near the bottom. In general, the inertial frequency peaks also decrease with depth. Sometimes, however, ususally for weak unstable currents, the maximum value of $S(\omega)$ can be observed in the intermediate layers. For storm winds, the functions $S(\omega)$ generally increase with distance from the shoreline. Approximations of $S(\omega)$ by power expressions for frequencies higher than the inertial frequency give values of the exponent in the range

1 to 4. The nonuniversality of the spectra illustrates the great variety of factors influencing coastal hydrodynamics.

Estimates of the rate of turbulent energy dissipation, ε, range from 10^{-3} to 1.8×10^{-5} $cm^2 \cdot s^{-3}$, and the maximum values of ε are usually found in the upper layer. The lifetimes of turbulent eddies, estimated using the values of ε and the velocity variances, range from 20 to 102 hours; during that time, the eddies can be advected over distances from 5 to 31 km.

Some unusual properties of the horizontal turbulence were revealed by current observations in a shallow shelf region near the western coast of the Black Sea. At these stations, the maximum of the function $S(\omega)$ shifts from the inertial frequency to the high frequency region as the depth of the observations increases. The spectral maximum is less pronounced at the shallow water stations than at stations where the depth is 70 to 90 m. The spectra also show maxima corresponding to periods of synoptic variability (2 to 4 days). The rate of energy dissipation at stations located on shallow water shelves reaches values of 1.5×10^{-3} to 1.4×10^{-2} $cm^2 \cdot s^{-3}$. On the average, these values are about one order of magnitude higher than those obtained at stations located on the deep water shelves. The vertical structure of the horizontal turbulence is essentially dependent on season and weather conditions at stations located on both the deep and shallow water shelves.

The calculation of the vertical turbulent transfer coefficient, K_z, was performed using wind waves parameters and the data of dye diffusion experiments. The values of K_z range from 45 to 79 cm^2/s for waves due to wind of force III - IV on the Beaufort scale, and from 150 to 350 cm^2/s for waves due to wind of force V - VI. The wind waves produce turbulence penetrating to depths of 10 to 30 m during storms. The values of K_z determined using the data from the dye diffusion experiments in the surface layer are about 20 to 30 cm^2/s for waves of III - IV Beaufort numbers. From experiments on submerged jets of dye at depths of 30 to 50 m during the period of winter convection, we calculated values of K_z equal to 100 to 200 cm^2/s. For high vertical density gradients, the values of K_z decrease to 0.1 to 2.0 cm^2/s. Because K_z depends on the density stratification and weather conditions as well as on the dynamical regime of each particular region, one can observe two-, three-, and four-layer structures in the vertical distribution of the coefficient K_z.

Acknowledgments

The editor is endebted to his research student Ph. Ngendakumana for his help in preparing the index.